P9-CFI-353
3 2109 00098 8353

The Civil War and New Jersey

A Bibliography

THE CIVIL WAR
and
NEW JERSEY

BY

DONALD A. SINCLAIR

Curator of Special Collections · Rutgers University Library

New Brunswick: Published by the

FRIENDS OF THE RUTGERS UNIVERSITY LIBRARY

FOR THE NEW JERSEY

CIVIL WAR CENTENNIAL COMMISSION

•

Manufactured in the United States of America

by MacCrellish & Quigley Company

Trenton, New Jersey

•

Library of Congress Catalog Card

Number 67-29297

For
JEAN and JOHN

The Civil War and New Jersey

NOTWITHSTANDING tinges of local apathy, and of dissidence which shaded outward to the pro-Southern fringe, New Jersey in 1861 placed her weight firmly on the Union side of the scale. In the war years following, she contributed freely and solidly to the Union cause (albeit not in the purest sense of sacrifice) the output of her farms and factories, the vital service of her transportation system. Moved by patriotism, bounties, and the draft, thousands of her men engaged in armed duty.

The people of New Jersey were affected by the war in differing ways and in differing degree (in some cases seemingly not at all). While friends and relatives served on distant fields, renewed calls for troops stirred the home front intermittently. Throughout the state, funds and supplies were raised to ease the deprivations of army life, the sufferings of the wounded, the destitution of families left behind. News of the war filled the press, orators belabored the issues in assorted tones of righteousness, and politicians fought their noisy battles in the shadow of national crisis.

The record of New Jersey's wartime history is preserved in many written forms, both manuscript and printed. It is with the latter, the printed literature, that this bibliography deals. On the following pages are described, so far as the compiler has been able to discover and identify them, the various books, pamphlets, official publications (documents),* magazine articles, and broadsides which pertain to the subject: the Civil War and New Jersey. These are essentially on three levels—contemporary, retrospective, and historical.

The contemporary material (i.e., dating from the war years) includes numerous addresses, tracts, etc., reflecting the activity and views of political, church, and lay figures, societies and other groups. There are also reports of

* Reports of public agencies and officials are known in the language of librarians as "documents." The New Jersey state reports commonly were published in separate pamphlet or book form, and also collectively in annual volumes entitled *Legislative Documents*. For certain years, the latter were made up of actual pamphlets bound together, each with its own title-page and pagination; in such case, the component items have been recorded individually in this bibliography. More often the *Legislative Documents* were independent publications (continuously paged) containing reprints of the separately-published reports, also additional reports which appear in no other form—and which are *not* covered in the bibliography. An over-all approach to the material of both kinds can be had through Adelaide B. Hasse's prodigious *Index of Economic Material in Documents of the States of the United States: New Jersey, 1789-1904* (Washington, D.C., 1914), in which the term "economic" is applied with considerable latitude.

government agencies and officials, military orders and registers, propaganda, legal documents, recruiting literature, some negligible poetry, wartime letters and journals (these largely printed after the war), together with the usual unclassifiable miscellany.

Retrospective writing began during the war, but most of it dates from subsequent years. This takes the form chiefly of reminiscences, military and otherwise, covering either extended periods or isolated experiences. Among them are several accounts of battles, etc., which contain few personal allusions, but written nevertheless by Jerseymen who were participants.

The publication of history and its companion biography (including funeral and memorial addresses) likewise began during the war, and continues to the present. There are two works which assume something of a comprehensive character: Foster's official, military-slanted *New Jersey and the Rebellion* (1868) and Knapp's valuable *New Jersey Politics During the . . . Civil War and Reconstruction* (1924), a doctoral dissertation. Otherwise the histories, whether books or articles, are of limited scope, concerned chiefly with individual military units, specific events and localities.

The 1,227 entries in this volume, covering 1,359 separate items (of which the compiler has handled personally all but a very few), are the product of an extended winnowing operation. In the search for pertinent material—a process requiring knowledge of New Jersey names, places, and special relationships—great quantities of Civil War literature have been surveyed. The available bibliographies have been used profitably, of course, but a much larger amount of time has been invested in the wholesale checking of library collections—usually piece-by-piece, cross-checked by card catalog (to the extent that cataloging has been done).

Admission to the bibliography has been limited to items having a specific relationship to the war and New Jersey—if not total, at least in reasonable proportion or of reasonable significance.* Many wartime publications, while useful in background research, do not meet this requirement.

At the risk of stating the obvious, the reader must be reminded that, besides the publications of lesser content noted above, there are additional sources not within the scope of this bibliography. Most useful of these, perhaps, are the contemporary newspapers, still preserved in libraries of all kinds. Much pertinent manuscript material also survives—letters, diaries, etc.

* This definition covers also certain prewar and postwar material, which has been grouped in two appendixes. Recorded in Appendix I are a number of political items, sermons, etc., which reflect the imminence of war. Appendix II deals similarly with postwar reflections, including (selectively) veterans' affairs and the like.

—located similarly in libraries; often, too, in private hands. Lastly, the archives and public records—national, state, and local—contain voluminous documentation of New Jersey's role in the Civil War.

Immediately following this preface is a list of fifty libraries whose holdings are variously recorded in the bibliography. Sixteen of these—chiefly the largest and best-equipped—have been searched as fully as reasonably possible. The others are represented only selectively. In all cases, the utmost cooperation has been received from those in charge. Indeed, whatever degree of completeness has been achieved here is related measurably to the interest and helpfulness of librarians. The compiler is greatly indebted to all these libraries, and most particularly to the New-York Historical Society (Shirley Beresford, head of the reading room), New Jersey Historical Society (Mrs. Edith O. May, librarian), Princeton University Library, New Jersey State Library, Newark Public Library (Miriam V. Studley, principal New Jersey librarian), and Jersey City Free Public Library (William J. Roehrenbeck, librarian).

To this must be added, of course, that the largest body of material combining New Jersey and Civil War interest is in the Rutgers University Library, with which the compiler is associated, and where he has enjoyed every possible facility, freedom, and aid. Notable among the helpers are those of the Photoduplication Department staff who vastly lightened the burden of endless revision in the preparation of final copy. The writer's gratitude is due, most of all, to the three colleagues of his own Special Collections Department, who have given encouragement and support at every hand: Kay Lionikis, Anthony S. Nicolosi, and Ruth M. Perrine (the order is alphabetical). Their ultimate benefaction is the excellent index, prepared by Miss Lionikis and Mr. Nicolosi, which accompanies this bibliography.

No one undertaking a research project can fail to benefit from association and discussion with individuals of similar interests. The present compiler, widely involved both professionally and personally with such people, has been singularly fortunate in this respect. Much useful information or advice has been received from knowledgeable friends and well-wishers. Chief among these is the military bibliographer, Charles E. Dornbusch.

Three others shared parts of the checking. The entire galley proof was read thoroughly by Consolacion B. Rebadavia, an experienced bibliographer and esteemed associate. Another friend, Norman C. Wittwer, scanned about half of the finished typescript, chiefly for editorial defects. The portions dealing with politics were read by Maurice Tandler, a specialist in that area.

The compiler's wife Kathryn contributed much, both of toleration and encouragement, during the long period of preparation. Without her willing help finally, the proofreading—some two hundred hours of it scattered over five months—would have been nearly unmanageable.

The New Jersey Civil War Centennial Commission has played an indirect, although significant, part in this project. Most important, its underwriting the expense of printing has given meaning and incentive to the labor of compilation. The Commission is no longer in existence, but it has left behind a record of solid achievement—the work of dedicated membership and a versatile director, Everett J. Landers.

This bibliography is offered to the community of scholars, professional and amateur, in modest confidence that it will prove useful. While any thought of a second edition—unless perhaps in the year 2061—would be stark fantasy, readers are invited to inform the compiler of defects or omissions which may be noted. A supplement in some form is not beyond possibility.

Library Location Symbols

CSMH	Henry E. Huntington Library, San Marino, Cal.
CST	Stanford College Libraries, Stanford, Cal.
CT	Connecticut State Library, Hartford, Conn.
CTY	Yale University, New Haven, Conn.
DBRE	Bureau of Railway Economics, Washington, D. C.
DLC	Library of Congress, Washington, D. C.
DNW	U. S. National War College Library, Ft. McNair
ICN	Newberry Library, Chicago, Ill.
IHI	Illinois State Historical Library, Springfield, Ill.
IN	Indiana State Library, Indianapolis, Ind.
MB	Boston Public Library, Boston, Mass.
MH	Harvard University Library, Cambridge, Mass.
MWA	American Antiquarian Society, Worcester, Mass.
NH	New Hampshire State Library, Concord, N. H.
NJ	New Jersey State Library, Trenton, N. J.
NJFLHI	Hunterdon County Historical Society, Flemington, N. J.
NJFHI	Monmouth County Historical Association, Freehold, N. J.
NJHI	New Jersey Historical Society, Newark, N. J.
NJJ	Jersey City Free Public Library, Jersey City, N. J.
NJNBS	Gardner A. Sage Library, New Brunswick Theological Seminary, New Brunswick, N. J.

NJN	Newark Public Library, Newark, N. J.
NJNETD	Dennis Memorial Library, Newton, N. J.
NJPAT	Paterson Free Library, Paterson, N. J.
NJPATPHI	Passaic County Historical Society, Paterson, N. J.
NJPLAHI	Plainfield Historical Society, Plainfield, N. J.
NJP	Princeton University Library, Princeton, N. J.
NJPT	Princeton Theological Seminary, Princeton, N. J.
NJR	Rutgers University Library, New Brunswick, N. J.
NJT	Free Public Library, Trenton, N. J.
NJWDHI	Gloucester County Historical Society, Woodbury, N. J.
NHI	New-York Historical Society, New York City
NIC	Cornell University Library, Ithaca, N. Y.
NN	New York Public Library, New York City
NN-SC	Schomburg Collection, New York Public Library
NNC	Columbia University Library, New York City
NRAB	American Baptist Historical Society, Rochester, N. Y.
NCU	University of North Carolina, Chapel Hill, N. C.
OCLFC	Fenn College, Cleveland, Ohio
OCLWHI	Western Reserve Historical Society, Cleveland, Ohio
PCC	Crozer Theological Seminary, Chester, Pa.
PHC	Haverford College, Haverford, Pa.
PHI	Historical Society of Pennsylvania, Philadelphia
PP	Free Library of Philadelphia
PPL	Library Company of Philadelphia
PPLL	Military Order of the Loyal Legion of the United States, Philadelphia
PPPRHI	Presbyterian Historical Society, Philadelphia
PU	University of Pennsylvania, Philadelphia
RP	Providence Public Library, Providence, R. I.
RPB	Brown University Library, Providence, R. I.
WHI	State Historical Society of Wisconsin, Madison, Wis.

Contents

The Civil War

The Civil War

HISTORY AND BIBLIOGRAPHY

DORNBUSCH, CHARLES EMIL, 1907-

Regimental publications & personal narratives of the Civil War, a checklist. Compiled by C. E. Dornbusch. Volume one: Northern states. Part IV: New Jersey and Pennsylvania. New York: The New York Public Library, 1962. 71p. CSMH DLC NJ NJHI NJJ NJN NJP NJR NJT NHI NN PHI PP 1

"New Jersey": p.[15]-26. Record of 107 unit histories, publications of unit veterans' associations, biographies, diaries, wartime letters, etc., of participants, classified by regiment or battery. All New Jersey items described in this checklist are covered in the present volume.

DYER, FREDERICK HENRY, 1849-

A compendium of the War of the Rebellion . . . By Frederick H. Dyer . . . Including . . . a complete record of the battles, engagements, combats, actions, skirmishes and important operations . . . showing the Union troops engaged in each event [and] a concise history of each and every regiment, battery, battalion and other organizations mustered by the several states for service in the Union army . . . Des Moines, Iowa: The Dyer Publishing Company, 1908. 1796p. CSMH DLC DNW MWA NJN NJP NJR NJT NHI NN OCLWHI PPL 1a

A valuable standard reference tool. Available also in 1959 facsimile reprint (3v.). Copies in DLC, NJJ, NJN, NJR, etc.

"A complete record of the campaigns, battles [etc.] . . .": p.[579]-991. Chronological lists with names of regiments and batteries engaged.

"Regimental histories": p.[993]-1747 ("New Jersey volunteers," p.1353-1366). Concise, detailed sketches of all units, listing the various actions and campaigns in which each participated. "Regimental index" (p.113-253) gives briefer sketches recording particularly brigade and other duty assignments (New Jersey: p.177-179).

FOSTER, JOHN YOUNG, 1831-1896.

New Jersey and the Rebellion: a history of the services of the troops and people of New Jersey in aid of the Union cause. By John Y. Foster. Published by authority of the state. Newark, N.J.: Martin R. Dennis & Co., 1868. viii, 872p. front. (port.) CSMH DLC DNW MB MWA NJ NJHI NJJ NJNBS NJN NJP NJR NJT NHI NN OCLWHI PHI PP PPL PPLL PU 2

Largely (p.63-726) histories of individual New Jersey military units.

"Jerseymen in other organizations": p.[727]-765.

"Distinguished general officers": p.[804]-855. Biographies of Philip Kearny ("Kearney"), Gershom Mott, A. T. A. Torbert, Robert McAllister, John Ramsey, William J. Sewell, Hugh Judson Kilpatrick, Charles A. Heckman, George W. Mindil, George W. Taylor, William S. Truex, Caldwell K. Hall, E. L. Campbell, Charles G. Harker.

Other chapters include: legislation of the war period; popular sympathy with the cause; attitude of the church.

See no. 1022 for Foster's preliminary report.

FRANK, WILLIAM P.

The story of Fort Delaware. [Wilmington, Del.: Wilmington Printing Co., 1955?] [15]p. illus. DLC NJR NN 3

Caption title.

"The story of Fort Delaware is based on material collected by W. Emerson Wilson, president of the Fort Delaware Society. The booklet was prepared by William P. Frank, historian for the society . . . The pictures were taken by Harry A. Lemmon."

Fort Delaware, located on Pea Patch Island between New Jersey and Delaware, was used from 1863 as a prison for Confederates. The conditions and treatment there have been compared with those at Andersonville, Libby, etc.

Pea Patch Island is not officially part of New Jersey; however, a number of Fort Delaware items have been included in this bibliography. Further material can be found in H. C. Reed, *Bibliography of Delaware* (1966), nos. 3217-3233.

FURMAN, DAVID DICKSON, 1917-

An address by David D. Furman, attorney general, state of New Jersey, at the rededication of the Salem Church battle monument by the New Jersey Civil War Centennial Commission, May 6, 1961, Salem Church, Va. Trenton, N. J.: New Jersey Civil War Centennial Commission [1961] [2], 2-3, [1] leaves. NJR 4

Mimeographed.

An account of the battle in May 1863, especially the participation of the 23rd N.J. Vols.

———————

[*Same: second edition*] Ordeal by fire; an address by David D. Furman, attorney general, state of New Jersey, at the rededication of the Salem Church battle monument by the New Jersey Civil War Centennial Commission, May 6, 1961, Spotsylvania, Va. Trenton, N.J.: New Jersey Civil War Centennial Commission [1961] [2], 2-5 leaves. NJ NJN NJR 4a

Mimeographed.

———————

The call to arms: New Jersey in 1861. An address by David D. Furman, attorney general, state of New Jersey before the Haddonfield Historical Society, May 23, 1961 . . . Trenton, N.J.: New Jersey Civil War Centennial Commission [1961] [1], 11, [1] leaves. NJ NJN NJR

Mimeographed.

GILBERT, HAROLD N.

"The Office of Dependency Benefits. Address by Brig. Gen. H. N. Gilbert, U.S.A." *Proceedings of the New Jersey Historical Society.* v.63, 1945. p.15-23. 5

Describes the work of Marcus L. Ward of Newark, in arranging pay allotments for dependents of New Jersey Civil War soldiers.

GOLDSMITH, BERTHOLD HENRY, 1882-

"Military history of the Civil War. By B. H. Goldsmith, historian and author." Kull, I. S., *New Jersey, a history.* New York, 1930. v.3, p.[856]-867. 6

Bibliography: p.867.

HALL, FLORENCE.

"Fort Delaware." *Almanac and year book, First National Bank, Woodstown, N.J.* 1921. p.10-12. 7

"Copy of paper . . . read before the Woman's Club, of Wilmington, Del. . . ." Gives earlier historical background, but largely relates to the Civil War period.

KNAPP, CHARLES MERRIAM, 1892-

"Contest over United States senatorship, 1865-66." Kull, I. S., *New Jersey, a history.* New York, 1930. v.3, p.[868]-882. 8

Disputed election of John P. Stockton.

———————

"New Jersey and states' rights during Civil War." *Ibid.*, p.[810]-816. 9

———————

New Jersey politics during the period of the Civil War and Reconstruction. By Charles Merriam Knapp . . . Geneva, N.Y.: W. F. Humphrey, 1924. ivp., 1 leaf, 212p. front. (map) DLC NJ NJHI NJN NJP NJR NJT NN PHC PU 10

Bibliography: p.186-188.

Ph.D. dissertation, Columbia University, 1924.

"The materials for this study have been gathered largely from newspaper files . . ." (p. iv).

———————

"The peace Democracy gains control of the state." Kull, I. S., *New Jersey, a history.* New York, 1930. v.3, p.[830]-855. 11

———————

"The presidential campaign of 1864 in New Jersey." *Ibid.*, p.[801]-809. 12

———————

"The rise of copperheadism." *Ibid.*, p.[770]-786. 13

———————

"The Union-Republican movement in New Jersey." *Ibid.*, p.[817]-829. 14

McNALLY, BERNARD.

Soldiers and sailors of New Jersey in the Spanish-American War, embracing a chronological account of the Army and Navy. Newark, N.J.: Publisher, B. McNally, c1898. 46p. DLC MB NJ NJHI NJJ NJN NJR OCLWHI 15

Relates in considerable degree to the First Regiment (raised in 1898), New Jersey Volunteers, and includes (p.44-46) a list of the First Regiment soldiers whose fathers had served in the Civil War, with names of the latter, and the units in which they had served (many being New Jersey regiments).

MEYERS, WILSON S.

"Southern New Jersey during the Civil War. By Wilson S. Meyers." *Electric meter.* v.15, no. 3. Jan. 1961. p.6-7. illus. 15a

A publication of the Atlantic City Electric Company.

MIERS, EARL SCHENCK, 1910-

"New Jersey goes to war. By Earl Schenck Miers." *Journal of the Rutgers University Library.* v.24, 1960/61. p.[33]-39. 16

———————

New Jersey in the year of the [Emancipation] Proclamation; an address by Earl Schenck Miers, New Brunswick Historical Club, April 18, 1963. Trenton, N.J.: Civil War Centennial Commission [1963] [1], 6, [1] leaves. NJ NJJ NJR 17

Mimeographed.

NEW JERSEY. CIVIL WAR CENTENNIAL COMMISSION.

New Jersey in the Civil War, and Civil War facts. Compiled by N.J. Civil War Centennial Commission. [Trenton, N.J., 1962] [3], 9, [1] leaves. NJ NJJ NJR 18

Mimeographed.

"Selected sources on New Jersey and the Civil War, by Donald A. Sinclair": unnumbered last leaf.

———————

Proceedings, third annual American History Workshop, presented by New Jersey Civil War Centennial Commission . . . December 14, 1963, Rutgers, the State University, New Brunswick, New Jersey . . . [Trenton, N.J.: The Commission, 1964] 2p.l., 3-80, [2]p. incl. ports. NJ NJN NJP NJR NJT 19

Covers two seminars: "Unanswered questions posed by the Civil War" and "New Jersey: northernmost border state."

"New Jersey discovers a general [Robert McAllister]": 2p. at end.

———————

[*Same*: 4th, 1964] Proceedings, fourth annual American History Workshop, presented by New Jersey Civil War Centennial Commission . . . December 19, 1964, Rutgers, the State University, New Brunswick, New Jersey . . . [Trenton, N.J.: The Commission, 1965] 100p. incl. ports., facsim. NJ NJN NJP NJR 20

First seminar ("New Jersey in the Civil War: three fronts"): "The home front," by Willie Lee Rose; "The battle front," by James J. Flynn; "The political front," by Maurice Tandler.

Second seminar ("Final triumph: the Thirteenth Amendment"): "Last best hope," by Roy P. Basler; "Law and morality meet: the Thirteenth Amendment," by David D. Furman; "The freedom amendments: impact on New Jersey," by Herbert H. Tate.

Dinner address: "The Reconstruction amendments: the end of the beginning," by John Hope Franklin.

———————

Special joint session of the New Jersey Senate and the General Assembly commemorating the 100th anniversary of Abraham Lincoln's historic appearance before the Legislature February 21, 1861. Presented by New Jersey Civil War Centennial Commission . . . February 21, 1961, state house, Trenton. [Trenton, N.J., 1961] cover-title, 28p. incl. ports., facsims. NJ NJN NJR 21

Partial contents: "Who in triumph advances, [by] David C. Mearns" (reprint of no. 779), p.7-23; "New Jersey in the Civil War, by Everett J. Landers," p.26-27; "Selected sources on New Jersey and the Civil War, by Donald A. Sinclair," p.28.

———————

Views on the Emancipation Proclamation. Selected papers presented at the second annual American History Workshop of the N.J. Civil War Centennial Commission . . . December 8, 1962, Rutgers, the State University, New Brunswick, N.J. . . . [Trenton, N.J., 1963?] cover-title, [1], 11, [1] leaves. NJ NJJ NJN NJR NJT 22

Mimeographed.

Contents: "The Emancipation Proclamation: a centenary appraisal," by Benjamin Quarles (leaves 1-6); "The Emancipation Proclamation: New Jersey's reaction," by Richard P. McCormick (leaves 7-11, [1]).

REDMOND, ROBERT A.

"The revenue steamer E. A. Stevens in the Civil War. By R. A. Redmond." *American Neptune*. v.20, 1960. p.155-166. 23

An undocumented history of the *Naugatuck* (also called the *E. A. Stevens*), used in naval service during the war. It was an iron-hulled coastal steamer purchased by Edwin A. Stevens and presented to the U.S. Treasury Department after refitting to incorporate principles developed by the Stevens family, of Hoboken, N.J., for armored vessels.

SINCLAIR, DONALD ARLEIGH, 1916-

"New Jersey and the Civil War: notes toward a bibliography. By Donald A. Sinclair." *Journal of the Rutgers University Library*. v.24, 1960/61. p.[73]-77. 24

STEINMETZ, SAMUEL, 1916-

"New Jersey, state of conflict, 1861-1865. [By] The Venerable Canon Samuel Steinmetz, Jr." *Proceedings of the New Jersey Historical Society*. v.80, 1962. p.[236]-244. 25

TANDLER, MAURICE, 1937-

"The political front in Civil War New Jersey. [By] Maurice Tandler." *Proceedings of the New*

Jersey Historical Society. v.83, 1965. p.[223]-233. 25a

"Mr. Tandler's Article, with minor revisions, was presented originally as a seminar paper at the Fourth Annual American History Workshop of the New Jersey Civil War Centennial Commission, held at Rutgers University on December 19, 1964."

TOOMBS, SAMUEL, 1844-1889.

New Jersey troops in the Gettysburg campaign, from June 5 to July 31, 1863. By Samuel Toombs, author of "Reminiscences of the war," and historian of the Veteran Association, Thirteenth New Jersey Volunteers. Illustrated by specially drawn maps of the battle-field, the monuments erected by the state of New Jersey, and portraits of brigade and regimental commanders. Orange, N.J.: The Evening Mail publishing house, 1888. xvi, 460p. incl. ports., plans. front. (port.) illus., fold. plan. CSMH DLC NJ NJHI NJJ NJN NJR NJT NHI NN PHI PP PPLL PU 26

"Biographical sketches": p.[359]-406. Outstanding officers.

TRASK, DAVID FREDERIC.

"Charles Sumner and the New Jersey railroad monopoly during the Civil War. [By] David F. Trask." *Proceedings of the New Jersey Historical Society*. v.75, 1957. p.259-275. 27

THE UNION ARMY; A HISTORY OF MILITARY affairs in the loyal states 1861-65—records of the regiments in the Union army—cyclopedia of battles—memoirs of commanders and soldiers . . . Madison, Wis.: Federal Publishing Company, 1908. 8v. front., ports. DLC NN 27a

"James Stewart, Jr.": v.3, p.17-18. Biography and portrait. Stewart was "associate-editor of this work for the state of New Jersey."

"Military affairs in New Jersey, 1861-65": *ibid.*, p.18-31.

"Record of New Jersey regiments": *ibid.*, p.32-71.

WILSON, W. EMERSON.

Fort Delaware. By W. Emerson Wilson. Newark, Delaware: University of Delaware Press, 1957. 32p. illus. (Delaware. University. Institute of Delaware History and Culture pamphlet series. no. 4) DLC NJR NJT NN PP 28

"For further reading": p.32.

H. C. Reed's *Bibliography of Delaware*, no. 3217, notes also an undated 5-page mimeographed publication of the same author and title.

———

"Fort Delaware—Northern Andersonville. By W. Emerson Wilson." *Civil War times*. v.2, no. 7. Nov. 1960. p.14-15. illus. 29

Cf. also reader's response and author's reply in *ibid.*, v.2, no. 9, Jan. 1961, p.3.

WRITERS PROJECT. NEW JERSEY.

A Confederate shrine in New Jersey. Newark, N.J., 1937. [4]p. illus. (Stories of New Jersey. 1936/37 series. School bulletin no. 22) NJN NJR 30

Finn's Point National Cemetery, near Salem, N.J., burial place of Confederate prisoners who died at Fort Delaware.

Printed also in Writers Project, New Jersey, *Stories of New Jersey* (New York, 1938), p.79-83.

LOCAL PARTICIPATION: HISTORY, ROSTERS, ETC.

BERGEN COUNTY

CLAYTON, W. WOODFORD.

History of Bergen and Passaic counties, New Jersey, with biographical sketches of many of its pioneers and prominent men. Compiled under the supervision of W. Woodford Clayton, assisted by William Nelson . . . Philadelphia: Everts & Peck; press of J. B. Lippincott & Co., 1882. 577p. illus., plates, ports., maps. DLC NJ NJHI NJJ NJN NJP NJR NJT NN OCLWHI PHI 31

"Bergen and Passaic counties in the War of the Rebellion": p.126-152. Included are accounts and rosters of the 9th, 23rd, and 25th N.J. regiments, brief sketches of other units.

"Record [i.e., lists] of Passaic County men in the War of the Rebellion": p.152-160. Out-of-state units included.

BERGENFIELD

LEIBY, ADRIAN COULTER.

The Huguenot settlement of Schraalenburgh: the history of Bergenfield, New Jersey. [By] Adrian C. Leiby in collaboration with Albert T. Klyberg, Jr., and Emorie A. Leiby. Bergenfield, N.J.: Bergenfield Free Public Library, 1964. xip., 2 leaves, 3-188p. illus. (incl. facsims., maps) plates, ports. DLC NJ NJHI NJR 31a

Bibliography: p.177-179.

"The Civil War, 1860-1865": p.73-99. A good chapter, effectively relating the local to county and state history; a picture of reluctant participation (including service of the 22nd N.J. Regiment) and copperheadism.

BURLINGTON

GRUBB, EDWARD BURD, 1841-1913.

The volunteer soldiers of Burlington. A Memorial Day oration delivered by General E. Burd Grubb. At Birch's Opera House, Burlington, N.J., May 30th, 1889. Burlington, N.J.: The Enterprise book and job print, 1889. 18p. CSMH NJR OCLWHI 32

"The patriot dead. The heroes of Burlington who gave up their lives in the rebellion": p.[16]-18. A list, with rank, unit, date and place of death.

Includes some details on soldiers of earlier wars.

BURLINGTON COUNTY

WOODWARD, EVAN MORRISON.

History of Burlington and Mercer counties, New Jersey, with biographical sketches of many of their pioneers and prominent men. By Major E. M. Woodward and John F. Hageman . . . Philadelphia: Everts & Peck; press of J. B. Lippincott & Co., 1883. viii, 888p. front., illus., plates, ports., maps. DLC NJ NJHI NJJ NJN NJP NJR NJT OCLWHI PHI 33

"War for the Union" (Burlington County): p.35-53. Included are sketches and lists of officers of the 1st N.J. Cavalry, 6th N.J. Vols., shorter accounts of the 23rd and other regiments.

"The late Civil War" (Mercer County): p.594-595.

CAMDEN COUNTY

PROWELL, GEORGE REESER, 1849-1928.

The history of Camden County, New Jersey. By Geo. R. Prowell . . . Philadelphia: L. J. Richards & Co., 1886. x, 769p. illus., ports., maps, plan. DLC MWA NJ NJHI NJJ NJN NJP NJR NJT OCLWHI PHC PHI PP PU 34

"The war for the Union": p.89-179. Includes accounts and rosters of various companies raised in the county; history of the soldiers' monument in Camden; lists of veterans buried in Camden County cemeteries; accounts of veterans' organizations.

CAPE MAY COUNTY

STEVENS, LEWIS TOWNSEND, 1868-1948.

The history of Cape May County, New Jersey, from aboriginal times to the present day . . . By Lewis Townsend Stevens . . . Cape May City, N.J.: Lewis T. Stevens, publisher, 1897. 479, [1]p. front., illus. (incl. ports., map) port. DLC MB MWA NJ NJHI NJJ NJN NJP NJR NJT NIC OCLWHI PHI PP PPL 35

Civil War period: p.[301]-354. Four chapters, including chapter 23 (p.[316]-327), "First New Jersey Cavalry."

CUMBERLAND COUNTY (*see also* GLOUCESTER COUNTY)

NICHOLS, ISAAC T. 1848-

Historic days in Cumberland County, New Jersey, 1855-1865. Political and war time reminiscences. By Isaac T. Nichols. [Bridgeton, N.J., 1907] 257p. front., illus. (incl. ports.) DLC MWA NJ NJHI NJJ NJN NJP NJR NJT NN OCLWHI PHI 36

Deals chiefly with local activities in relation to the war, including accounts of military units raised in the county, lists of soldiers, political events, etc.

ESSEX COUNTY

SHAW, WILLIAM H.

History of Essex and Hudson counties, New Jersey. Compiled by William H. Shaw . . . Philadelphia: Everts & Peck, 1884. 2v. illus., plates, ports., maps. DLC MB NJHI NJJ NJN NJP NJR NJT NN OCLWHI PHI 37

Paged continuously.

"Essex County in the war of 1861-65": v.1, p.51-184. Includes histories and rosters of the 2nd, 8th, 13th, 26th, and 33rd N.J. Vols.

"Hudson County in the Rebellion": v.2, p.988-1037. Included are histories and rosters of the 2nd Regt. (militia, serving May-July 1861) and 23rd N.J. Vols.; also selected companies or elements of the 1st, 5th, 6th, 7th, 9th, 10th, 11th, 13th, 33rd regiments, and Hexamer's Battery (Batt. A, 1st N.J. Artillery), the last made up largely of Germans.

GLOUCESTER COUNTY

CUSHING, THOMAS, 1821-

History of the counties of Gloucester, Salem, and Cumberland, New Jersey, with biographical sketches of their prominent citizens. By Thos. Cushing, M.D., and Charles E. Sheppard, Esq. Philadelphia: Everts & Peck; press of J. B. Lippincott & Co., 1883. xiv, 728p. illus. (incl. ports.) plates, ports., fold. map. DLC NJ NJHI NJR NJT PHI 38

"Gloucester, Salem, and Cumberland counties in the War of the Rebellion": p.53-97. Includes accounts and partial rosters of the 12th and 24th N.J. Vols., briefer sketches of the 9th, 32nd (2nd Cavalry), 34th, and other regiments. No breakdown by county.

In the local sections are further short war sketches: Gloucester County, p.152-155; Woolwich Township, p.299-300; Salem County, p.358-360; Cumberland County, p.542-546.

STEWART, FRANK H., 1873-1948.

Gloucester County in the Civil War . . . Compiled and edited by Frank H. Stewart . . . assisted by Raymond Archut . . . Woodbury, N.J.: Printed by the Constitution Company [c1939-c1943 and n.d.] 3v. DLC NJ NJHI NJR 39

Copies of contemporary articles, soldiers' letters, etc., relating to the war (especially local participation) printed originally in the Woodbury *Constitution,* May 1860-September 1864. The present three volumes, each consisting of three sections issued in pamphlet form (v.1-2, 1939-1944; v.3, undated), with text in two columns, are reprints of the 1860-1864 articles as republished serially, 1938-1944 and subsequent issues (not identified for v.3), in the same Woodbury *Constitution.*

Volume 3, compiled solely by Raymond Archut and bearing imprint of the Gloucester County Historical Society as publisher, includes a surname index (covering v.3 only).

HUDSON COUNTY (*see* ESSEX COUNTY)

HUNTERDON COUNTY

SNELL, JAMES P.

History of Hunterdon and Somerset counties, New Jersey, with illustrations and biographical sketches of its prominent men and pioneers. Compiled by James P. Snell, assisted by Franklin Ellis and a numerous corps of writers. Philadelphia: Everts & Peck; press of J. B. Lippincott & Co., 1881. 864p. illus., plates, ports., maps, plan. DLC MWA NJ NJHI NJNBS NJN NJP NJR NJT NN PHI 40

Civil War period: p.116-153. Included are sketches and rosters of the 3rd, 5th, 6th, 15th, 30th, and 31st N.J. regiments.

JERSEY CITY

RICHARDSON, WILLIAM H. 1864-1937.

The "makings" of the Lincoln Association of Jersey City. A souvenir of the dinner at the Carteret Club commemorating the one hundred and tenth anniversary of the birth of Abraham Lincoln. By William H. Richardson. [Jersey City, N.J.] The Jersey City Printing Company, 1919. 3p.l., 5-54p. front. (ports.) illus. (incl. ports.) facsims. DLC NJJ NJR 40a

Largely a history of Jersey City and the Civil War, covering also pertinent events immediately preceding and following.

MIDDLESEX COUNTY (*see* UNION COUNTY)

MONMOUTH COUNTY

ELLIS, FRANKLIN, 1828-1885.

History of Monmouth County, New Jersey . . . By Franklin Ellis. Philadelphia: R. T. Peck & Co., 1885. x, 902p. illus., ports., map. DLC NJ NJHI NJJ NJN NJR NJT NN OCLWHI PHI 41

Civil War period: p.242-270. Includes sketch and rosters of the 29th N.J. Vols.; briefer treatment of selected companies from other units.

MONTCLAIR

DOREMUS, PHILIP, 1825-1910.

Reminiscences of Montclair, with some account of Montclair's part in the Civil War. By Philip Doremus. Montclair, N.J., 1908. 2p.l., 111p. front. (port.) plates, ports. DLC MWA NJ NJHI NJJ NJN NJR NN PHI 42

"The Civil War": p.84-111.

MORRIS COUNTY

[HALSEY, EDMUND DRAKE] 1840-1896.

. . . History of Morris County, New Jersey, with illustrations, and biographical sketches of prominent citizens and pioneers. New York: W. W. Munsell & Co., 1882. 407p. incl. plates. front., illus., plates, ports., map. DLC NJ NJHI NJJ NJN NJR NJT PHI 43

At head of title: 1739.

Civil War period: p.80-102. Including sketches and rosters of selected companies of the 7th, 11th, 15th, 27th, 33rd, and 39th regiments.

NEW BRUNSWICK

LAWRENCE, JOHN, 1839-1912.

History of the Grand Army of the Republic and New Brunswick's representation in the Civil War. By John Lawrence, past Department commander. Read at a meeting of the New Brunswick Historical Club, March 18, 1909. [New Brunswick, N.J., 1909] cover-title, [8]p. illus. (ports.) NJ NJJ NJR NHI 44

Text in two columns.

About half deals with the national G.A.R.

NEWARK

ATKINSON, JOSEPH.

The history of Newark, New Jersey . . . By Joseph Atkinson . . . Newark, N.J.: Published by William B. Guild, 1878. xiv, [2], [5]-334p.

front., plates, ports., map, plan, facsims. DLC NJ NJHI NJJ NJN NJR NJT PHI 45

Civil War period: p.[238]-295.

CUNNINGHAM, JOHN THOMAS.

. . . Newark. By John T. Cunningham. Designed by Homer Hill. Newark, N.J.: Published by the New Jersey Historical Society [c1966] 320p. illus. (incl. ports., maps, facsims.) DLC NJ NJHI NJN NJR (etc.) 45a

"Newark in print" (bibliographical note): p.316. "Torn by blue and gray": p.150-165.

OCEAN COUNTY

SALTER, EDWIN, 1824-1888.

A history of Monmouth and Ocean counties, embracing a genealogical record of earliest settlers in Monmouth and Ocean counties and their descendants. The Indians: their language, manners and customs. Important historical events. The Revolutionary War, Battle of Monmouth, the War of the Rebellion. Names of officers and men of Monmouth and Ocean counties engaged in it, etc., etc. By Edwin Salter. Bayonne, N.J.: E. Gardner & Son, publishers, 1890. 4p.1., [iii]-xiiip., 1 leaf, 442, lxxxp. front. (port.) illus. (incl. ports.) plate, ports. DLC NJ NJHI NJN NJR NJT 46

Has been reprinted recently in facsimile.
"Ocean County soldiers in the late War of the Rebellion": p.329-347. Lists of names, with service dates, for Co. D, 9th Regt., Co. F, 14th Regt., and Co. H, 29th Regt.
Nothing about Monmouth County in the Civil War.
"Joel Parker": p.[431]-437. Abstract of the memorial read by James S. Yard before the New Jersey Historical Society, May 17, 1888 (see no. 161).

PASSAIC COUNTY (*see* BERGEN COUNTY)

PATERSON

SHAW, CHARLES DANNELLY, 1834-1909.

An oration delivered at the Wigwam, Paterson, N.J., on July 4th, 1865, by Rev. Chas. D. Shaw, with a "roll of honor," comprising the names of Paterson soldiers, who have given their lives to their country. Paterson, N.J.: Printed by Chiswell & Wurts, "Press" office, 1865. 24p. NJPAT NJR (photo) 47

The "roll of honor" (p.[21]-24) includes name of unit, service and death dates, age and place of birth.

PILESGROVE TOWNSHIP

BORTON, BENJAMIN, 1841-1912.

"Local war history." *Almanac and year book, First National Bank, Woodstown, N.J.* 1912. p.31, 33. 48

"The chief purpose of preparing this paper . . . is to detail the casualties among the one hundred and seventy-two volunteers who represented Pilesgrove Township" (Salem County) in the Civil War. Signed: B. Borton. Woodstown, Oct., 1911.

PRINCETON

HAGEMAN, JOHN FRELINGHUYSEN, 1816-1892.

History of Princeton and its institutions . . . By John Frelinghuysen Hageman . . . Philadelphia: J. B. Lippincott & Co., 1879. 2v. illus., plate, ports., maps. DLC NJ NJHI NJN NJP NJR NJT 49

"Princeton in the late Civil War.—1860-1866": v.1, p.[284]-309. Covers all aspects of the local war history, including names of volunteers, white and Negro, and short service records of officers.

PRINCETON UNIVERSITY

DURYEA, JOSEPH TUTHILL, 1832-1898.

An oration commemorative of the restoration of the Union, with a tribute to the alumni and under-graduates of the College of New Jersey, who fell in the national struggle. Delivered . . . June 26th, 1866, at the request of the trustees of the College, by the Rev. Joseph T. Duryea. Philadelphia: McCalla & Stavely, printers, 1866. 101p., 1 leaf. CSMH DLC NJ NJHI NJJ NJN NJP NJPT NJR NJT NHI NN PP PU 50

Includes individual biographies of the students and alumni who lost their lives (p.45-52; "In memoriam, by Prof. Henry C. Cameron," p.[55]-70); also "Roll of the alumni and former students . . . who served . . . in the war for the Union" (individual service records), with separate 1867 imprint (p.[71]-101).

[SMITH, DATUS CLIFFORD] 1907-

"Martyrs of the pump. A dramatic tale of the Civil War in which a secessionist is given the water cure, his punishers in turn disciplined by the faculty, and the whole affair concluded with a p-rade." *Princeton alumni weekly.* v.34, 1933/34. p.[103]-104. facsim. 51

A widely-reported event of September 1861 involving mistreatment of an alleged Southern sympathizer (Francis DuBois, Jr.) by fellow-students at Princeton.

RANDOLPH TOWNSHIP

IRON ERA, *Dover, N.J.*

Randolph's roll of honor. Decoration Day, in Dover, N.J. . . . May 30th, 1876. Dover, N.J.: Benj. H. Vogt, steam book and job printer, 1876. cover-title, 12p. NJJ NJNBS NJP NHI 52

Caption title: Decoration Day. Its observance in Dover—from the Iron Era of June 3, 1876.

"John S. Gibson, Reporter."—p.12.

Apparently a reprint (text in two columns) of the newspaper article, including editorial comment, an account of the ceremonies, and individual sketches of the dead ("Assisted by . . . Alonzo B. Searing . . . we have been enabled to collect a brief history of the soldiers of Randolph townehip [*sic*] who have passed beyond the reach of mortal roll call") .

ROCKAWAY TOWNSHIP

HALSEY, EDMUND DRAKE, 1840-1896.

Rockaway Township in the War of the Rebellion. An address delivered by Edmund D. Halsey at the dedication of the soldiers' monument at Rockaway, N.J., May 30, 1892. Dover, N.J.: The Iron Era print, 1892. 16p. CSMH CTY DNW MB NJ NJHI NJR NN OCLWHI PHI 53

Contains lists of the local men in service.

[HALSEY, EDMUND DRAKE] 1840-1896.

Roll of honor of Rockaway Township, Morris County, N.J. May 30, 1890. Printed for Edmund D. Halsey. [Trenton, N.J.: Albert Brandt, Jr., printer, 1890] 15p. NJ NJHI NJN NJP NJR NN

"Soldiers from Rockaway Township who lost their lives during the War of the Rebellion." Individual sketches with service details and some other biographical matter.

"Soldiers buried at Rockaway Cemetery": p.15.

RUTGERS UNIVERSITY

MCCORMICK, RICHARD PATRICK, 1916-

"Rutgers and the Civil War. By Richard P. McCormick." *Journal of the Rutgers University Library*. v.24, 1960/61. p.[40]-45. 55

Reprinted in George J. Lukac, ed., *Aloud to Alma Mater* (New Brunswick, N.J., 1966), p.55-61.

SALEM COUNTY (*see* GLOUCESTER COUNTY)

SOMERSET COUNTY (*see also* HUNTERDON COUNTY)

[HONEYMAN, ABRAHAM VAN DOREN] 1849-1936.

"Somerset County Union League, 1863-'65." *Somerset County historical quarterly*. v.7, 1918. p.41-46. 55a

An account of meetings and other activities, based on the surviving minutes of Somerset Council No. 61, Union League. Included is a list of the 220 members, in large part Somerville residents.

Doubtless by the *Quarterly's* editor, Honeyman, a prolific local historian and genealogist.

SUSSEX COUNTY

SNELL, JAMES P.

History of Sussex and Warren counties, New Jersey, with illustrations and biographical sketches of its prominent men and pioneers. Compiled by James P. Snell . . . assisted by Prof. W. W. Clayton and a numerous corps of writers. Philadelphia: Everts & Peck; press of J. B. Lippincott & Co., 1881. xi, 9-748p. illus., plates, ports., maps. DLC MWA NJ NJHI NJJ NJN NJP NJR NJT NN OCLWHI PHI 56

"Sussex and Warren counties in the War of the Rebellion": p.80-148. Includes accounts of the Harris Light Cavalry (2nd N.Y. Cavalry), 15th N.J. Regt., 1st N.J. Cavalry, and other units; rosters of Sussex and Warren county soldiers.

UNION COUNTY

CLAYTON, W. WOODFORD.

History of Union and Middlesex counties, New Jersey, with biographical sketches of many of their pioneers and prominent men. Edited by W. Woodford Clayton . . . Philadelphia: Everts & Peck; press of J. B. Lippincott & Co., 1882. viii, 13-885p. illus., plates, ports., maps. DLC NJ NJHI NJJ NJN NJP NJR NJT NN OCLWHI PHI PPL 57

"Union County in the War of the Rebellion": p.142-157 (lists of soldiers, p.157-173). Includes short accounts of the 9th, 11th, and 14th N.J. regiments.

"Middlesex County in the War of the Rebellion": p.537-539 (lists of soldiers, p.539-552). With a short sketch of the 29th N.J. Regt.

VINELAND

[ANDREWS, FRANK DEWITTE?] 1847-1937.

"Vineland's Civil War record." *Vineland historical magazine*. v.7, 1922. p.24-25. 58

WARREN COUNTY (*see* SUSSEX COUNTY)

BIOGRAPHY

ACKLEY, WILLIAM SCATTERGOOD (1841-1965)

PURVIS, WILSON J. 1846-1924.

"One of the heroic Blackwater boys. By Wilson J. Purvis." *Vineland historical magazine.* v.6, 1921. p.203. 59

Lieut. Ackley, Co. K, 4th N.J. Vols., was killed in 1865, near Petersburg. In the article he is called William F. Ackley.

ANDREWS, SOLOMON (1806-1872)

KINGSLEY, MARY.

"The flying Jerseyman: Dr. Solomon Andrews of Perth Amboy. [By] Mary Kingsley." *Proceedings of the New Jersey Historical Society.* v.72, 1954. p.[163]-183. illus., plate. 60

Includes an account of Andrews' wartime efforts to interest the federal government in military application of his airship, or "aereon." He was a noted inventor, manufacturer, and promoter.

ARROWSMITH, GEORGE (1839-1863)

APPLEGATE, JOHN STILWELL, 1837-1916.

Reminiscences and letters of George Arrowsmith of New Jersey, late lieutenant-colonel of the One Hundred and Fifty-Seventh Regiment, New York State volunteers. By John S. Applegate. Red Bank, N.J.: John H. Cook, publisher, 1893. 3p.l., [xiii]-xiv, [2], 254p. front. (port.) CSMH DLC MWA NJ NJJ NJR OCLWHI 61

Native of present Holmdel Township, a young lawyer in Hamilton, N.Y., at the time of enlistment, Arrowsmith was killed at Gettysburg.

Included are copies of Arrowsmith's wartime letters to the Utica (N.Y.) *Morning Herald,* which had been published under the pseudonym "Aliquis."

BABCOCK, PAUL (1841-1903)

MITCHELL, CHARLES BAYARD, 1857-1942.

Paul Babcock: a memorial. Sermon preached in Cedar Street Chapel, Montclair, N.J. . . . October 30, 1904, by Rev. Chas. B. Mitchell . . . [n.p.: Herald print, 1904] 18p. NJP 62

Babcock was a Jersey City resident (removed 1883 to Montclair) with New York City business interests. He was a member of a uniformed company raised by his brother Edwin, which became Co. H, 2nd N.J. Regt. (three-month militia), serving May-July 1861. Upon expiration of his enlistment, he joined the 7th N.J. Vols., September 1861, serving as sergeant-major and lieutenant. From March 1862 he was an officer of the U.S. Signal Corps, from January 1864 chief signal officer on the staff of Gen. George H. Thomas, and resigned in April 1864.

BRADLEY, JOSEPH P. (1813-1892)

IN MEMORIAM. Joseph P. Bradley. [Philadelphia: The press of Allen, Lane & Scott, 1892?] 118p. front. (port.) DLC NJN NJR 63

Various memorial addresses and proceedings. Bradley (of Newark) was a distinguished New Jersey attorney and jurist, justice of the U.S. Supreme Court. In 1862 he ran for Congress on the Union ticket.

PARKER, CORTLANDT, 1818-1907.

"Mr. Justice Bradley, of the United States Supreme Court. By Cortlandt Parker. Read before the Historical Society of New Jersey, January 24, 1893." *Proceedings of the New Jersey Historical Society.* 2nd series. v.12, 1892/93. p.[143]-177. 64

———————

Mr. Justice Bradley, of the United States Supreme Court. By Cortlandt Parker. Read before the Historical Society of New Jersey, January 24, 1893. [Newark, N.J.: Advertiser printing house, 1893] 35p. front. (port.) DLC NJHI NJP NJR PHI 65

Reprint of no. 64.

WEART, JACOB, 1829-1905.

". . . Justice Joseph P. Bradley." *New Jersey law journal.* v.20, 1897. p.259-269. 65a

Part of a series, "Reminiscences of Some Former Noted Members of the New Jersey Bar."

BRAISTED, JAMES E. (1842?-1863)

JAMES E. BRAISTED, of the 21st Regiment New Jersey volunteers, who fell at the battle of Fredericksburg, May 4, 1863. [New York: American Tract Society, 1863?] 16p. NJP 66

Caption title.

Braisted lived about two miles from Saltersville (now part of Bayonne). He enlisted August 1862 in Co. C, 21st N.J. Vols., and was killed shortly before the regiment's nine-month term of service expired. This tract may have been written by the pastor of his church at Saltersville.

BURR, CHARLES CHAUNCEY (1817-1883)

ROGERS, WILLIAM WARREN.

"C. Chauncey Burr and *The Old guard.* [By] William Warren Rogers." *Proceedings of the New Jersey Historical Society.* v.73, 1955. p.[168]-181. 67

Editor of the copperhead *Old Guard* (Hackensack and New York), 1862-1869, and briefly in 1861 of the *Bergen County Democrat* (Hackensack), Burr lived in New Jersey during the war.

COCHRAN, WILLIAM HENRY (1844-1864)

TAYLOR, BENJAMIN COOK, 1801-1881.

A sermon, delivered in the Reformed Dutch Church at Bergen, N.J., July 10, 1864, on the death of Capt. Wm. H. Cochran, who was killed in battle, June 16, 1864, at Pine Knoll, near Marietta, Ga. By Benjamin C. Taylor, D.D. . . . New York: C. S. Westcott & Co., printers, 1864. 21p. DLC NJJ NJNBT NJP NJR 68

Cochran served with the 33rd N.J. Vols., a member of Co. K but commanding Co. G at the time of his death.

COOPER, SAMUEL (1798-1876)

LEE, FITZHUGH, 1835-1905.

"Sketch of the late General S. Cooper. By General Fitz. Lee." *Southern Historical Society papers.* v.3, 1877. p.269-276. 69

Samuel Cooper was a native of Hackensack, N.J., and graduate of West Point. After serving forty-six years in the U.S. Army, during which time he married a Virginia woman, he resigned his commission in March 1861 and soon became head of the Confederate Adjutant and Inspector-General's Department.

CRAVEN, JOHN JOSEPH (1822-1893)

BARBEE, DAVID RANKIN, 1874-

"Dr. Craven's 'Prison life of Jefferson Davis'—an exposé. By David Rankin Barbee." *Tyler's quarterly historical and genealogical magazine.* v.32, 1950/51. p.[282]-295. 70

Craven, a Newark physician, attended Jefferson Davis during the latter's imprisonment at Fortress Monroe in 1865. This article is part of the authorship controversy involving reminiscences published in 1866 under Craven's name (see no. 202).

BRADLEY, CHESTER D.

"Craven and O'Meara: medical Boswells to Jefferson Davis and Napoleon Bonaparte. [By] Chester D. Bradley and Miriam D. Bradley." *Bulletin of the history of medicine.* v.26, 1952. p.141-152. ports. 71

———

"Dr. Craven and The prison life of Jefferson Davis. By Chester D. Bradley." *Virginia magazine of history and biography.* v.62, 1954. p.50-94. 72

A detailed, carefully documented account of Craven and his *Prison Life of Jefferson Davis.* Particular attention is given to charges by R. B. Rhett and others, that the book was actually written by General C. G. Halpine.

———

"Dr. John J. Craven, physician to Jefferson Davis. [By] Chester D. Bradley." *Virginia medical monthly.* v.78, 1951. p.433-437. 73

———

Dr. John J. Craven, physician to Jefferson Davis. [By] Chester D. Bradley . . . [n.p., 1951] 5p. illus. (incl. port.) NJN NJR 74

Caption title.
Bibliography: p.5.
Reprint of no. 73.
"Read before the medical staff of Riverside Hospital, Newport News, Virginia, October 13, 1950."

W. , C. C.

"The Prison life of Jefferson Davis." *Current literature.* v.38, 1905. p.500-502. 75

Supports the argument that the book was really authored by General Halpine.

DAYTON, WILLIAM LEWIS (1807-1864)

BRADLEY, JOSEPH P., 1813-1892.

"A memorial of the life and character of Hon. William L. Dayton . . . By Joseph P. Bradley . . ." *Proceedings of the New Jersey Historical Society.* 2nd series. v.4, 1875/77. p.69-118. 76

Dayton was a New Jersey lawyer, jurist, politician (1856 vice-presidential candidate, etc.), minister to France, 1861-1864.

———

A memorial of the life and character of Hon. William L. Dayton, late U.S. minister to France. By Joseph P. Bradley, Esq. Prepared in conformity with a resolution of the New Jersey Historical Society. Newark: Daily Advertiser printing house, 1875. 50p. DLC NJHI NJN NJP NJR NJT NHI NN PHI 77

"THE LATE Hon. William L. Dayton." *Harper's weekly.* v.9, 1865. p.28-29. port. 77a

[SCOVEL, JAMES MATLACK] 1833-1904.

"William L. Dayton." *Northern monthly magazine.* v.1, 1867. p.[495]-503. port. 78

Author's name from volume table-of-contents.

WEART, JACOB, 1829-1905.

". . . Judge William L. Dayton." *New Jersey law journal.* v.23, 1900, p.354-359, continued serially through v.24, 1901, p.453-460. 78a

Part of a series, "Reminiscences of Some Former Noted Members of the New Jersey Bar."

DEMAREST, ABRAHAM GARRISON (1830-1900)

IN MEMORY. [N.Y.: Patteson Press, 1900?] [15]p. NJJ NJR 78b

Demarest was a Cresskill (N.J.) merchant who served September 1862-June 1863 as an officer of the 22nd N.J. Vols., from January 1863 as colonel commanding the regiment. From 1867, he lived at Tenafly, N.J.

Contents: biography; funeral address by Rev. Fisher Howe Booth and memorial tribute by Frederic L. Colver, both at Tenafly Presbyterian Church; obituary by family physician and friend, J. J. Haring, from the Tenafly *Record.*

DOD, CHARLES HODGE (1841-1864)

MACDONALD, JAMES MADISON, 1812-1876.

Charles Hodge Dod. A memorial: containing in substance the address delivered at his funeral in the First Presbyterian Church, Princeton, N.J., August 31st, 1864. By his pastor James M. Macdonald. New York: Robert Carter & Brothers, 1864. 36p. NJP NJPT 79

An 1862 Princeton College graduate, son of Albert B. Dod, Presbyterian clergyman and Princeton professor, Dod was first lieutenant, Co. F, 2nd N.J. Cavalry, Sept. 1863-June 1864; captain and assistant adjutant-general, U.S. vols., until his death at City Point, Va.

The publication contains biographical data and excerpts from his wartime letters, etc.

DUDLEY, THOMAS HAINES (1819-1893)

DYER, BRAINERD, 1901-

"Thomas H. Dudley. [By] Brainerd Dyer." *Civil war history.* v.1, 1955. p.401-413. 80

Camden attorney and politician, Whig and Republican. At the 1860 Republican national convention, he and fellow New Jersey delegates had a significant part in Lincoln's nomination. While U.S. consul at Liverpool (from 1861), he did much to counter British aid to the Confederates.

POTTS, WILLIAM JOHN, 1842-1895.

Biographical sketch of the late Hon. Thomas H. Dudley. By William John Potts, Camden, N.J. A paper read before the American Philosophical Society, April 19, 1895. Reprinted from the Proc. Amer. Philos. Soc., vol. xxxiv, June 4, 1895. Philadelphia: Press of MacCalla & Company, inc., 1895. 36p. front. (port.) DLC MB MH NJ NJR NHI NN PHI PPL 81

Bibliography: p.28-30.

———————

"Biographical sketch of the Hon. Thomas H. Dudley, of Camden, N.J., who died April 15, 1893. By William John Potts." *Proceedings of the American Philosophical Society.* v.34, 1895. p.101-128. port. 82

Read before the Society, April 19, 1895.

Bibliography: p.126-128.

FIELD, RICHARD STOCKTON (1803-1870)

HART, CHARLES HENRY, 1847-1918.

A necrological notice of the Hon. Richard Stockton Field, LL.D., of Princeton, New Jersey. Read before the Numismatic and Antiquarian Society of Philadelphia . . . October 6, 1870. By Charles Henry Hart . . . Philadelphia: [C. B. Collins, printer] 1870. 10p. DLC MWA NJHI NN

Princeton attorney, jurist, Republican, and U.S. senator for one month, Dec. 12, 1862-Jan. 13, 1863.

KEASBEY, ANTHONY QUINTON, 1824-1895.

"Memoir of the Hon. Richard S. Field. By Anthony Q. Keasbey. Read before the Society, Jan. 19th, 1871." *Proceedings of the New Jersey Historical Society.* 2nd series. v.2, 1870/72. p.[111]-132. 84

———————

Memoir of the Hon. Richard S. Field, late president of the New Jersey Historical Society. By Anthony Q. Keasbey. Read before the Society, Jan. 19th, 1871. [Newark, N.J.: Printed at the Daily Advertiser office, 1871?] 23p. NJP 85

Reprint of no. 84.

FOGG, JOHN M. (1842-1864)

"LIEUTENANT John M. Fogg, of Woodstown, N.J." *Almanac and year book, First National Bank, Woodstown, N.J.* 1918. p.9. port. 86

Member of Co. H, 12th N.J. Vols., killed during the Wilderness campaign.

FOWLER, JOHN (1825-1863)

[WASHBURNE, MARY ESTELLE (FOWLER)] 1819-1878.

Dr. Samuel Fowler. [n.p., 186–?] 10p. NJR 87

Caption title.

Consists of two biographical sketches: p.1-5, Dr. Samuel Fowler (1779-1844) of Franklin, N.J., written by "M.E.W.," doubtless his daughter Mary E. Washburne; p.6-10, Lieut. John Fowler (1825-1863), written by "C.F.," probably his sister Clarinda Fowler. Lieut. Fowler served in the 1st N.J. Cavalry (Co. K, Aug.-Nov. 1861; regimental quartermaster, Nov. 1861-Feb. 1862) and 15th N.J. Vols. (July 1862-May 1863, part of the time in Co. K); was killed at Salem Heights.

FRANCINE, LOUIS RAYMOND (1837-1863)

[FRANCINE, ALBERT PHILIP] 1873-1924.

Louis Raymond Francine, brevet brigadier-general U.S. volunteers, 1837-1863. [Philadelphia? 1910?] 2p.l., 7-29p. front. CSMH DLC MB NJ NJJ NHI NN OCLWHI PHI PU 88

Francine, Philadelphia-born and French-educated, entered service 1861 as captain of Co. A, 7th N.J. Vols., and at the time of his death was serving as colonel of the same regiment. He was mortally wounded at Gettysburg.

"100 copies printed."—Nicholson, *Catalogue* (1914), p.294.

FRELINGHUYSEN, FREDERICK THEODORE (1817-1885)

HAGEMAN, JOHN FRELINGHUYSEN, 1816-1892.

"The life, character and services of Frederick T. Frelinghuysen, LL.D., of New Jersey, late secretary of state in President Arthur's cabinet. By John F. Hageman. Read, by request, before the New Jersey Historical Society, at Newark, May 20, 1886." *Proceedings of the New Jersey Historical Society.* 2nd series. v.9, 1886/87. p.[45]-75. port. 89

A Newark attorney, member of the Peace Conference in 1861, attorney-general of New Jersey, 1861-1866, member (Republican) of the U.S. Senate, 1866-1869, 1871-1877, etc.

———————

The life, character and services of Frederick T. Frelinghuysen, LL.D., of New Jersey, late secretary of state in President Arthur's cabinet. By John F. Hageman, read, by request, before the New Jersey Historical Society, at Newark, May 20, 1886. Newark, N.J.: Advertiser printing house, 1886. 31p. front. (port.) NJN NJP NJR 90

Reprint of no. 89.

GRIGGS, GEORGE V. (1839-1863)

[MATTISON, WILLIAM R.] 1840-

"A New-Jersey cavalryman. The late Captain George V. Griggs, of the Harris Light Cavalry." *Northern monthly magazine.* v.1, 1867. p.548-559. 91

Griggs was born near Newton, N.J., attended the Collegiate Institute and the State Normal School, and was a district school teacher at Hamburg in 1861. He joined Lt. Col. Kilpatrick in recruiting for the Harris Light Cavalry, later becoming captain of Co. K. He was killed in October 1863 near Culpeper Court House, Va.

The Harris Light Cavalry (2nd N.Y. Cavalry) included two companies largely recruited in Sussex County, N.J. Most of Co. A was raised by Griggs.

The writer (named erroneously in the volume table-of-contents as "M. R. Mattison") was a lieutenant of Co. K, serving under Griggs and also in Co. B of the same regiment.

MOTT, GEORGE SCUDDER, 1829-1901.

Discourse delivered at the funeral of George V. Griggs, capt. Co. K, "Harris Light," 2d N.Y. Cavalry, in the Presbyterian Church, Newton, N.J., by the pastor, Rev. George S. Mott, on the fifth of February, 1864. New York: Pratt & Grinton, book and job printers, 1864. 14,[1]p. CSMH NJR (photo) 92

GRISCOM, ELWOOD (1840?-)

KENDERDINE, THADDEUS S.

"A friendly enemy. Experience in the Civil War of Lieutenant Elwood Griscom, a young Quaker of Gloucester Co., N.J." *Almanac and year book, First National Bank, Woodstown, N.J.* 1918. p.[14]-21. 93

Included is a copy of Griscom's letter, "5 mo 17, 1863," written after the battle of Chancellorsville to Gideon Peaslee, of Clarksboro, N.J.

Griscom, who served successively as sergeant, second and first lieutenant in Co.'s F, E, and A, 12th N.J. Vols., lived for several years at Petersburg, Va., to which his family had removed from South Jersey. He returned to New Jersey two years before the war, in which he did pioneer duty. The article tells considerable about his pro-Southern family at Petersburg.

GUSTIN, JAMES S. (1840?-1862)

LLOYD, GEORGE WILLIAM, 1821-1906.

The patriot's death—its bloody lessons. A funeral discourse on the death of Corp'l James S. Gustin, who fell in the advanced guard before Williamsburg, Va. Preached in the Presbyterian Church of Branchville, N.J., by Rev. G. W. Lloyd. New York: John F. Trow, printer, 1862. 24p. DLC NJR NHI 94

A soldier of Co. I, 7th N.J. Vols.

Inside the back cover are words of a song "Composed by Mr. Lloyd and sung on the occasion."

HALSEY, EDMUND DRAKE (1840-1896)

CHAMBERS, THEODORE FRELINGHUYSEN, 1849-1916.

"Edmund Drake Halsey. By Theodore Frelinghuysen Chambers." *Proceedings of the New Jersey Historical Society.* 3rd series. v.3, 1898/1900. p.62-85. port. 95

Halsey, a Morristown attorney, served Aug. 1862-Dec. 1864 in the 15th N.J. Vols., variously as private (Co. K), regimental sergeant-major, first licutenant (Co. D), adjutant, etc. He was the author of an article, "The Gallant Fifteenth," published in the Boonton (N.J.) *Morris County Chronicle,* Sept. 4, 1896.

———

A sketch of the life and character of Edmund Drake Halsey, by the Rev. Theodore Frelinghuysen Chambers. Read by request before the Historical Society of New Jersey, at Newark, May 19, 1898. [Morristown, N.J.: Pierson & Rowell, printers] 1898. 36p. front. (port.) DLC NJR NHI 96

HALSTED, WILLIAM (1794-1878)

WEART, JACOB, 1829-1905.

". . . Col. William Halsted." *New Jersey law journal.* v.20, 1897. p.133-140. 96a

A leading Trenton lawyer and political figure (Whig and Republican), member of Congress, etc., Halsted—although in his late sixties—in 1861 raised the First N.J. Cavalry Regiment, commonly called "Halsted's Horse," but was removed from command and mustered out a few months later.

Part of a series, "Reminiscences of Some Former Noted Members of the New Jersey Bar."

HANCOCK, CORNELIA (1840-1926)

MCCONNELL, JANE (TOMKINS) 1898-

Cornelia; the story of a Civil War nurse. By Jane T. McConnell. Illustrated by Dorothy Bayley Morse. New York: Thomas Y. Crowell Company [1959] 3p.l., 184p., 1 leaf incl. front. illus. DLC NJN NJR NJT 97

Biography of Cornelia Hancock, of Salem County, N.J., based on her published letters (see nos. 237 and 238).

HODGE, CHARLES (1797-1878)

MARCH, WALLACE EUGENE.

"Charles Hodge on schism and civil strife." *Journal of the Presbyterian Historical Society.* v.39, 1961. p.88-97. 98

A graduate of Princeton College and the Princeton Theological Seminary, Hodge spent most of his life as a member of the Seminary faculty and editor of the *Biblical Repertory and Princeton Review.* In the *Review,* during the war, he wrote and published articles strongly backing the Northern cause.

HOLSMAN, DANIEL

[BURR, CHARLES CHAUNCEY?] 1817-1883.

"Hon. Daniel Holsman." *The Old guard.* v.2, 1864. p.282-283. port. (facing p.[265]) 99

Senator from Bergen County, 1863-1865, vocal copperhead.

JACKSON, HUNTINGTON WOLCOTT (1841-1901)

CHICAGO LITERARY CLUB, *Chicago, Ill.*

In memoriam: Huntington Wolcott Jackson, born January 28, 1841, died January 3, 1901. [Chicago, Ill.: Printed by R. R. Donnelley and Sons Company at the Lakeside Press] 1901. 23, [1]p. front. (port.) NJP NN 100

Jackson was a Newark man and Princeton alumnus, who practiced law in Chicago after the war. In September 1862 he joined the 4th N.J. Vols. as second lieutenant and served with it until the regiment was mustered out.

MILITARY ORDER OF THE LOYAL LEGION OF THE UNITED STATES. ILLINOIS COMMANDERY.

"Huntington Wolcott Jackson. First lieutenant Fourth New Jersey Infantry and brevet lieutenant colonel, United States volunteers. Died at Newark, New Jersey, January 3, 1901." Military Order of the Loyal Legion of the United States. Illinois commandery. *Memorials of deceased companions of the Commandery of the state of Illinois . . . from May 8, 1879 . . . to July 1, 1901.* Chicago, Ill., 1901. p.566-573. illus. (port.) NJP NHI 101

———————

. . . In memoriam: Companion First Lieutenant and Brevet Lieutenant Colonel Huntington Wolcott Jackson, died at Newark, New Jersey, January 3, 1901. [Chicago? 1901] [7]p. NJP 102

Reprinted in no. 101.

JONES, JOHN BEAUCHAMP (1810-1866)

BRADFORD, GAMALIEL, 1863-1932.

"A Confederate Pepys. By Gamaliel Bradford." *American Mercury.* v.6, 1925. p.470-478 (Dec. 1925) 103

John B. Jones, author of the *Rebel War Clerk's Diary* (no. 250), was a resident of Burlington, N.J., 1857-1861 and after the war, following his service (1861-1865) in the Confederate War Department.

Reprinted in Bradford's *Biography and the Human Heart* (Boston, 1932): chapter 6, "An American Pepys," p.[153]-[184].

KARGE, JOSEPH (1823-1892)

[AMERICAN POLISH CIVIL WAR CENTENNIAL COMMITTEE OF NEWARK, N.J.]

A Civil War centennial tribute to Brig. General Joseph Karge, organizer of the Second Regiment New Jersey Cavalry, September 21, 1963 at the New Jersey Historical Society, Newark, N.J. [n.p., 1963] cover-title, [20]p. illus. (incl. ports.) NJHI NJP NJR 104

Contains biographical and historical material, program of the occasion, advertising matter.

Kargé, commander of the 1st N.J. Cavalry, 1862, and 2nd N.J. Cavalry from 1863, was a native of Posen, professor of continental languages and literature at Princeton, 1870-1892.

[HOPKINS, EDWIN MORTIMER] 1862-1946.

"An evening with our professor [Joseph Kargé] . . ." *Nassau literary magazine.* v.43, 1887/88. p.195-201, 289-295, 341-349. 105

"Copyright 1888, by E. M. Hopkins." Author also identified in volume table-of-contents.

PACKARD, WILLIAM ALFRED, 1830-1909.

Joseph Kargé. A memorial sketch, by William A. Packard. New York: Anson D. F. Randolph and Co. [c1893] 1p.l., [5]-32p. CSMH DLC NJ NJR NN 106

"Reprinted from the Princeton College Bulletin of April, 1893, for private circulation."

———————

"Professor Joseph Kargé, Ph.D." *Princeton College bulletin.* v.5, no. 2. April 1893. p.[25]-34. 107

Anonymous.

[POLISH AMERICAN NEW JERSEY TERCENTENARY COMMITTEE]

Polish American Day, New Jersey pavilion, September 12, 1964. [n.p., 1964] cover-title, [40]p. incl. ports. illus. NJR 108

"Gen. Joseph Kargé, by Ann Sidwa. Reprinted from Proceedings of the New Jersey Historical Society, October 1963 issue . . .": p.[12]-[15].

[SIDWA, ANNE (HANKOWSKI)]

"Joseph Kargé, 1823-1892." *Proceedings of the New Jersey Historical Society.* v.81, 1963. p.[247]-255. plate. 109

KEARNY, PHILIP (1815-1862)

CAMPBELL, EDWARD LIVINGSTON, 1833-

"Kearny. By Gen. E. L. Campbell." *Beecher's magazine.* v.4, 1871. p.[379]-391. port. 110

Kearny was a career soldier, member of the Perth Amboy Kearny family. After serving in the Mexican War, he lived for several years near Newark. In 1861, at outbreak of the Civil War, he was placed in command of the 1st N.J. Brigade. After distinguishing himself repeatedly, he was killed at Chantilly in September 1862.

CUNNINGHAM, JOHN THOMAS.

"Phil Kearny: greater than legend. [By] John T. Cunningham." *Proceedings of the New Jersey Historical Society.* v.79, 1961. p.[149]-160. 111

DEPEYSTER, JOHN WATTS, 1821-1907.

"A character of Phil Kearny." *The Volunteer.* v.1, 1869. p.3-16. 112

Signed (p.16): Maj.-Gen. DePeyster.

———————

"Kearny's death and burial." *Ibid.*, p.97-110. 113

———————

Personal and military history of Philip Kearny, major-general United States volunteers . . . By John Watts DePeyster. New York: Rice and Gage, publishers; Newark, N.J.: Bliss & Co.,

1869. 2p.l., xii, 13-512p. front. (port.) plates, ports., map. DLC NJ NJHI NJJ NJN NJR NJT PPLL 114

Pictorial fore-title.

———————

[*Same*] 516p. DLC MWA NJP PHI 115

Extended by an added "Appendix" (p.513-516) giving texts of four documents relating to Kearny, received "After this work had gone to press."

———————

[*Same: "second edition"*] Personal and military history of Philip Kearny, major-general United States volunteers . . . Second edition. By John Watts De Peyster. Elizabeth, N.J.: Palmer & Co.; New York: James Miller, 1870. 2p.l., xii, [13]-512p. front., plates, ports., map. CSMH DLC NJ NJP NJT 116

Pictorial fore-title.

———————

"Philip Kearny, major general, U.S.V., by his cousin, John Watts de Peyster . . ." [Kearny, Philip] *Service with the French troops in Africa.* [n.p., 1888?] p.61-81. 117

FLYNN, DAVID M.

"Philip Kearny. Read by Col. David M. Flynn, vice-president of the American Irish Historical Society for New Jersey at the seventeenth annual meeting of the Society." *Journal of the American Irish Historical Society.* v.14, 1914/15. p.127-139. plate. 118

Ends with President Wilson's address at the dedication of a Kearny monument in Arlington National Cemetery, Nov. 11, 1914 (p.138-139).

GOLDSMITH, W. L.

"Death of General Phil Kearney [*sic*]. [By] Colonel W. L. Goldsmith." *Blue and gray.* v.2, 1893. p.388. 119

HUNT, VIRGINIA.

"Saluting our ancestors: the Kearny patch. By Virginia Hunt." *Fashion digest.* Fall/winter 1956/57. p.40, 80. illus. (incl. port.) 119a

The red, diamond-shaped insignia, worn originally by French volunteers of Kearny's brigade, later identified with the brigade itself (1st N.J. Brigade).

"Miss Hunt, the author, is a granddaughter of General Kearny."

[KEARNY, PHILIP] 1815-1862.

Service with the French troops in Africa. By an officer in the United States Army. New York: 1844. [n.p., 1888?] iii, 100p. front. (port.) DLC NJ NJJ NJN NJP NJR NJT 120

Contents include: "Philip Kearny, major general, U.S.V., by his cousin, John Watts de Peyster . . ." (p.61-81); "Kearny at Seven Pines [poem]. By Edmund Clarence Stedman" (p.83-86); "A dashing dragoon. The Murat of the American Army. <From 'Onward,' January, 1869, vol. I., p.25.>" (p.87-95), signed "Mayne Reid."

The copy in NJJ contains a presentation inscription signed by John Watts Kearny, "Belgrove, Kearny, N.J. July 6th 1889."

KEARNY, THOMAS, 1878-1942.

General Philip Kearny, battle soldier of five wars, including the conquest of the West by General Stephen Watts Kearny. By Thomas Kearny. With a preface by Frank Monaghan . . . New York: G. P. Putnam's Sons, 1937. xvp., 1 leaf, 19-496p. plates, ports. (incl. front.) DLC MB NJ NJHI NJN NJP NJR NJT NHI NN PHC PP 121

"Bibliography and memoranda": p.459-478.

A disorganized work, but based partially on unpublished sources.

For a brief article derived from this book, see *Journal of the American Irish Historical Society,* v.32, 1941, p.105-110.

"THE LATE Gen. Phil Kearney [*sic*]." *Harper's weekly.* v.6, 1862. p.603 (Sept. 20, 1862) port. (p.604) 121a

[LEIGH, ETHEL (TRAPHAGEN)] 1884-

"Agnes Maxwell . . . the General's lady." *Fashion digest.* Fall/winter 1956/57. p.41, 84. illus. (ports.) 121b

Hugh Maxwell's daughter, whom Philip Kearny met in France and eventually married as his second wife, after an elopement and period of adulterous relationship which scandalized society. Following his death, she became the wife of Admiral J. H. Upshur. Ethel Traphagen Leigh was a granddaughter of Agnes Maxwell's brother.

MCPHERSON, JOHN RHODERIC, 1833-1897.

Remarks of Senator John R. McPherson and Senator Rufus Blodgett, of New Jersey, on presenting to Congress the statues of Richard Stockton and Philip Kearny, delivered in the United

States Senate, August 21, 1888. Washington, 1888. 14p. NJ 122

Pages [5]-12 by McPherson.
Largely biographical (Kearny: p.7-12).

————————

Remarks of Senator John R. McPherson, of New Jersey, on presenting to Congress the statues of Richard Stockton and Philip Kearny, delivered in the United States Senate, August 21, 1888. Washington, 1889. 12p. CSMH NJHI NJR 123

Kearny biography: p.7-12.

MAHONY, WILLIAM H.

"General Phil. Kearny. By W. H. Mahony." *Journal of the American Irish Historical Society.* v.26, 1927. p.240-241. 124

Account of ceremonies in 1926 in connection with removal of the Kearny statue in Newark to another location.

"MAJOR-GENERAL Philip Kearny." *Frank Leslie's illustrated newspaper.* v.14, 1862. p.408 (Sept. 20, 1862) port. 124a

In same issue (p.407): "Death of Gens. Kearny and [Isaac I.] Stevens," copy of an article by the New York *Tribune* correspondent.

NYE, WILBUR STURTEVANT, 1898-

"Kearny's death grieved both sides." *Civil War times.* v.2, no. 9. Jan. 1961. p.24. illus. (incl. port.) 125

O'BRIEN, MICHAEL J.

"The ancestry of Major-General Philip Kearny. By Michael J. O'Brien." *Journal of the American Irish Historical Society.* v.11, 1911/12. p.160-168. 126

PARKER, CORTLANDT, 1818-1907.

"Major-General Philip Kearny." *Northern monthly magazine.* v.2, 1867/68. p.21-33, 97-112, 365-382. 127

Text of an address before the New Jersey Historical Society in January 1867.
Anonymous, but author is identified in volume table-of-contents.

————————

Philip Kearny: soldier and patriot. An address delivered before the New-Jersey Historical Society, January 17, 1867, by Cortlandt Parker . . . Newark: From the "Northern monthly," 1868. 49p. front. (port.) DLC MWA NJ NJHI NJJ NJP NJR NHI NN OCLWHI PHI PPL 128

Cover-title has imprint: . . . From the Northern monthly for March, 1868.
"Presented by the author to Phil Kearny Post No. 2, Grand Army of the Republic, Department of New Jersey, Newark, N.J."—p.[2].

REID, MAYNE, 1818-1883.

"A dashing dragoon [Philip Kearny]. The Murat of the American Army." *Onward.* v.1, 1869. p.[25]-29. 129

Anonymous, but reprinted under Reid's name in nos. 120 and 130.

————————

"A dashing dragoon, the Murat of the American Army; by Captain Mayne Reid." *Magazine of history.* Extra number 22, 1913. p.[57]-65. 130

Reprint of no. 129, preceding.

WERSTEIN, IRVING.

Kearny, the magnificent; the story of General Philip Kearny, 1815-1862. New York: John Day Co. [1962] 248p. illus. DLC NJ NJN NJR NJT

Includes bibliography.
Reviewed in *Civil War History,* v.9, 1963, p.224.

KILPATRICK, HUGH JUDSON (1836-1881)

"BRIG.-GEN. Judson Kilpatrick." *Frank Leslie's illustrated newspaper.* v.16, 1863. p.331 (Aug. 15, 1863) port. (p.337) 131a

A native of Sussex County, N.J., graduate of West Point (1861), Kilpatrick served with distinction throughout the war. He resigned from the Army in 1865 to enter political life (Republican except in the 1872 presidential campaign).
Kilpatrick dropped the use of his first name, Hugh, upon entering West Point.

[BROCKETT, LINUS PIERPONT] 1820-1893.

"Brevet Major-General Hugh Judson Kilpatrick." *United States service magazine.* v.4, 1865. p.419-430. 132

"GENERAL Kilpatrick's operations [March 1865]." *Harper's weekly.* v.9, 1865. p.204 (April 1, 1865) illus. 132a

"GENERALS Kilpatrick and Custer." *Ibid.* v.8, 1864. p.187 (March 19, 1864) port. (p.180) 132b

JONES, JOHN WILLIAM, 1836-1909.

"The Kilpatrick-Dahlgren raid against Richmond. Compiled by J. Wm. Jones." *Southern Historical Society papers.* v.13, 1885. p.515-560. 133

JONES, VIRGIL CARRINGTON, 1906-

. . . Eight hours before Richmond. Introduction by Colonel Robert Selph Henry . . . New York: Henry Holt and Company [1957] xp., 2 leaves, 3-180p. plates (incl. ports., facsims.) DLC NJR 133a

The Kilpatrick-Dahlgren raid.

———————

"The Kilpatrick-Dahlgren raid: poorly planned . . . timidly executed. By V. C. Jones." *Civil War times illustrated.* v.4, no. 1. April 1965. p.[12]-21. illus. (incl. ports., facsim., map) 134

"KILPATRICK'S RAID." *Frank Leslie's illustrated newspaper.* v.18, 1864. p.7 (March 26, 1864) illus. (p.8-9) 134a

MOORE, JAMES.

Kilpatrick and our cavalry: comprising a sketch of the life of General Kilpatrick, with an account of the cavalry raids, engagements, and operations under his command, from the beginning of the Rebellion to the surrender of Johnston. By James Moore, M.D., surgeon Ninth Pennsylvania Cavalry. With twelve illustrations, from original designs by Waud. New York: W. J. Widdleton, publisher, 1865. 4p.l., [11]-14, [25]-245, [4]p. incl. plates. front. (port.) CSMH DLC MB MWA NJHI NJP NJR NJT NHI PHI PP PPLL 135

"M'Crea and Miller, stereotypers. C. A. Alvord, printer."

Publisher's advertisements on unnumbered final leaves.

———————

[*Same: reprint*] New York: Hurst & Co., publishers [188–?] 4p.l., [11]-14, [25]-245, [4]p. incl. plates. 136

Printed from plates of the 1865 edition, with changed imprint, omitting frontispiece and identification of printer and stereotyper on verso of title-page. Preliminary matter has been changed. Quality of paper is poor.

On cover: "Arlington Edition."

Publisher's advertisements on unnumbered final leaves.

Only copy seen is in private hands.

———————

[*Same: reprint*] New York: International Book Co. [n.d.] 4p.l., [11]-14, [25]-245, [4]p. incl. plates. NCU 136a

Not seen. Probably another reprint from plates of the 1865 edition.

[MUNFORD, GEORGE WYTHE] 1803-1882.

"The cavalry raid by Custer, Kilpatrick and Dahlgren." *Transactions of the Southern Historical Society.* v.1, 1874. p.155-175. 137

Signed (p.175): G.W.M.

Preceded (p.150-154) by excerpts from Gen. Wade Hampton's report concerning the attempt of Kilpatrick and Dahlgren to capture Richmond.

NYE, WILBUR STURTEVANT, 1898-

"Lesser-known actions: Kilpatrick caught in his underwear at battle of Monroe's Crossroads. By Wilbur S. Nye." *Civil War times.* v.3, no. 1. April 1961. p.17-18. ports., map. 138

Cf. reader's comment in *ibid.*, July 1961, p.3.

"OUR CAVALRY OFFICERS." *Harper's weekly.* v.7, 1863. p.541-542. ports. 138a

Four short biographies, one of Kilpatrick.

"REVIEW of Kilpatrick's cavalry, and enthusiastic reception of Secretary Stanton, at Savannah, Ga." *Frank Leslie's illustrated newspaper.* v.19, 1864/65. p.331 (Feb. 11, 1865) illus. (p.329)

Very short article but good illustration.

[THROCKMORTON, A. B.]

"Major-General Kilpatrick." *Northern monthly magazine.* v.2, 1867/68. p.590-605. 139

Author's name from volume table-of-contents.

LAMBERT, WILLIAM HARRISON (1842-1912)

GERMANTOWN, PA. SECOND PRESBYTERIAN CHURCH.

Memorial service in the Second Presbyterian Church, Germantown, Philadelphia . . . June the sixteenth . . . nineteen hundred and twelve. [Philadelphia, 1912?] 30p. front. (port.) CSMH NHI NN PHI PP PPLL 140

Cover-title: In memoriam. William H. Lambert.
Lambert, later a prominent Philadelphia insurance underwriter, served briefly in the 15th Penn. Cavalry, then as adjutant of the 27th N.J. Vols. (Nov. 1862-July 1863) and the 33rd N.J. Vols. (July-Dec. 1863), captain of Co. A in the 33rd (Dec. 1863-July 1865), brevetted major (March 1865).

IN MEMORIAM. Major William Harrison Lambert, 1842-1912. [Philadelphia, 1912] cover-title, 4 leaves. NHI 141

Portrait on cover.
Program of the funeral service only.

LINCOLN FELLOWSHIP, *New York.*
... In memoriam: William Harrison Lambert, May, 1842-June, 1912, first president of the Lincoln Fellowship ... Edited by the first vice-president [James Grant Wilson] New York: The Lincoln Fellowship, 1912. 36, [3]p. front. (port.) (Publications of the Lincoln Fellowship of New York. no. 4) CSMH DLC NHI NN PPLL 142

"Major Lambert's bibliography": p.[33]-35.
"250 copies printed ..."

MILITARY ORDER OF THE LOYAL LEGION OF THE UNITED STATES. PENNSYLVANIA COMMANDERY.
... In memoriam. William Harrison Lambert, brevet major U.S. volunteers. Died at Philadelphia, Pa. June 1 1912. [Philadelphia, 1912] [4]p. (The Commandery's *Circular.* Series of 1912. no. 14. whole no. 750) CSMH NJR (photo) 143

McALLISTER, ROBERT (1813-1891)

DEPEYSTER, JOHN WATTS, 1821-1907.
Sketch of Gen. Robert McAllister, by Gen. John Watts DePeyster, from Representative men, (third edition,) a biographical work ... New York: Atlantic Publishing Co. [1875?] cover-title, 10p. front. (port.) CSMH DLC MWA NJP NJR 144

At the outbreak of war, McAllister raised a company at Oxford Furnace, N.J., and was made lieutenant-colonel of the 1st N.J. Regt. He served June 1862-June 1865 as colonel of the 11th N.J. Regt.

MILLIGAN, JOHN DUNHAM (-1864)

ADAMS, JOSEPH R. 1824-1889.
Synopsis of a funeral discourse, delivered by Rev. J. R. Adams, pastor of the New Providence M.E. Church, May 1st, 1864, in connection with the death of the late John Dunham Milligan, of the 2d N.J. Vols., who died at Washington, March 25th, 1864. New York: Isaac J. Oliver, steam book and job printer, 1864. 8p. NJP

MOTT, GERSHOM (1822-1884)

BRUCE, WILLIAM J. -1894.
Memorial address: read before the Society of the Officers of the New Jersey Battalion at Yorktown, upon its third anniversary at Edgewater [near Burlington] ... October 20, 1885, by William J. Bruce, historian. [Camden, N.J.: C. S. Magrath, Democrat printing house, 1885] 40p. illus. (col.) ports. CSMH NJ NJR PP 146

Half-title: Memorial address: Mott-Chambers.
"One hundred copies printed."
Contains a biographical sketch and eulogy of Gen. Gershom Mott, of Lamberton, N.J., who had served in the Mexican War and Civil War (lieut. col., 5th N.J. Vols., Aug. 1861-May 1862; colonel commanding 6th N.J. Vols., May-Sept. 1862; brig.-general commanding 2nd N.J. Brigade from Sept. 1862, and later commanded a division of the Army of the Potomac), and after the war was state treasurer, state prison keeper, a National Guard division commander, etc.
The rest of the address concerns Col. Benjamin F. Chambers (1850-1885), a National Guard officer.

DEPEYSTER, JOHN WATTS, 1821-1907.
"Major-General Gershom Mott, U.S.V., and the Third Corps, Army of the Potomac." *United service.* v.13, 1885. p.152-167. 147

Signed (p.167): J. Watts de Peyster, Brevet Major-General S.N.Y.

"MAJOR-GENERAL MOTT." *Harper's weekly.* v.8, 1864. p.764 (Nov. 26, 1864) port. 147a

STRATTON, JAMES NEWBOLD, 1845-1886.
A sketch of the life of Major General Gershom Mott, by Lieutenant Colonel James Newbold Stratton ... Read before the Society of the Cincinnati in the State of New Jersey, at Princeton, July 4, 1885. [n.p., 1885] [4]p. CSMH NJR (photo) 148

NAAR, DAVID (1800-1880)

KOHN, SOLOMON JOSHUA, 1899-
"David Naar, 1800-1880, editor and public servant, by S. Joshua Kohn." *Kelsey review.* v.2, no. 2. Spring 1964. p.9-22. port. (p.8) 148a

A Sephardic Jew and native of the West Indies, Naar lived in Elizabeth and (from 1853) Trenton. He was an active Democrat, holder of various political offices, editor and owner of the Trenton *True American,* a spokesman for the pro-Southern, anti-abolition element of his party in New Jersey during the war.

———————

"David Naar of Trenton, New Jersey. By S. Joshua Kohn." *American Jewish historical quarterly.* v.53, 1963/64. p.373-395. port. 148b

———————

David Naar of Trenton, New Jersey. By S. Joshua Kohn. Reprinted from American Jewish historical quarterly, vol. liii, no. 4 (June, 1964) [New York, N.Y.: Printed by Marstin Press, inc., 1964] cover-title, p.373-395. port. NJ NJR NJT

NIXON, JOHN THOMPSON (1820-1889)

KEASBEY, ANTHONY QUINTON, 1824-1895.

"John T. Nixon. Memoir prepared and read by A. Q. Keasbey, before the New Jersey Historical Society . . . January 28th, 1890." *Proceedings of the New Jersey Historical Society.* 2nd series. v.11, 1890/91. p.39-51. 150

Nixon, a Bridgeton attorney, was a Republican member of Congress, 1859-1863.

———————

John T. Nixon. Memoir prepared and read by A. Q. Keasbey, before the New Jersey Historical Society at its annual meeting in Trenton, January 28th, 1890. [Newark? 1890?] 13p. NJP NN 151

Reprint of no. 150.

OLDEN, CHARLES SMITH (1799-1876)

"CHARLES S. OLDEN." *Beecher's magazine.* v.3, 1871. p.162-166. port. 152

A Princeton Quaker, Olden prospered as a business man there, and in Philadelphia and New Orleans, retiring in 1832 to the family homestead for the life of a gentleman farmer. He served in the New Jersey Legislature and held various state offices. Elected governor in 1859 on a fusion ticket opposing the Democratic candidate, he proved a strong Union supporter during the early years of the war.

PARKER, CORTLANDT (1818-1907)

COLIE, EDWARD MARTIN, 1852-1931.

"Cortlandt Parker, 1818-1907. By Edward M. Colie . . ." *Proceedings of the New Jersey Historical Society.* new series. v.5, 1920. p.73-106. port. 153

Civil War period: p.81-89.

"Partial list of public addresses delivered by Cortlandt Parker": p.105-106.

Parker was a prominent Newark attorney, Whig and Republican politician, holder of various public offices (e.g., Essex County prosecutor, 1857-1867).

Printed also in no. 154, following.

CORTLANDT PARKER, citizen, lawyer and churchman. A memorial volume. Consisting of Address by Mr. Edward M. Colie before the New Jersey Historical Society, January 5, 1920. Addresses delivered at a complimentary dinner by the bench and bar of New Jersey, December 8, 1905. Addresses delivered at a memorial service in Trinity Church, Newark, November 17, 1907. [n.p.] Printed for private circulation [1920?] 91p. front. (port.) NJN NJR 154

PARKER, JOEL (1816-1887)

[BURR, CHARLES CHAUNCEY] 1817-1883.

"Governor Parker." *The Old guard.* v.1, 1863. p.68. port. (opp. p.49) 155

Very brief (favorable) comments.

Parker, a Freehold attorney and Democrat, served as wartime governor, 1863-1866, and again in 1872-1875.

[DEMOCRATIC PARTY. NEW JERSEY]

Candid men read! Gov. Parker's record. True to his country. [n.p., 1871] 8p. NJR 156

Caption title.

"It having been asserted that Gov. Parker was tardy in his support of the General Government in the war, the following conclusively contradicts this slander . . ."—p.[1].

Campaign literature. The wartime governor ran for the same office again in 1871.

———————

The presidency. Sketch of the Democratic candidate, Joel Parker. [n.p., 1876] [4]p. NJ

Caption title.

A review of Parker's life and political career, issued soon after the state Democratic convention had passed a resolution proposing him to the forthcoming national convention as the party's presidential candidate.

———————

The war record of Hon. Joel Parker, ex-governor of New Jersey. Being some extracts from the official records of New Jersey relating to the connection of Governor Parker with the late war. [n.p., 1871] cover-title, [3]-14p. CSMH NJP NJR NHI 158

Campaign literature.

MEMORIAL of Joel Parker. [Freehold, N.J.: Monmouth Democrat print, 1889] 130p. ports. (incl. front.) DLC NJ NJJ NJN NJP NJR NHI NN OCLWHI PHI 159

Biographical sketch of Parker by James S. Yard (p.[5]-39) was published also in *Proceedings of the New Jersey Historical Society* and elsewhere (see no. 161). Remainder of the volume is devoted to a description of the funeral, memorial resolutions, newspaper articles, etc.

PERSONAL and political sketch of Hon. Joel Parker. Freehold: Printed at the Democrat office, 1871. 8p. NJ NJR 160

Engraved portrait on title-page.
Campaign literature.
"The following sketch . . . is re-printed from *The Four Quarters,* a weekly newspaper published in Philadelphia, by J. Trainor King, and forms No. 21 of the series of 'Sketches of Prominent Democrats,' now publishing in that paper."—p.[3].

STRYKER, WILLIAM SCUDDER, 1838-1900.

An address on the life and character of Joel Parker, by Brevet Major-General William Scudder Stryker, adjutant-general of New Jersey. Read before the Society of the Cincinnati in the State of New Jersey, at Princeton, July 4, 1888. [n.p., 1888] 4p. NJJ 160a

Caption title.
More eulogy than biography.

WEART, JACOB, 1829-1905.

". . . Governor Joel Parker." *New Jersey law journal.* v.23, 1900. p.323-330. 160b

One article of a series, "Reminiscences of Some Former Noted Members of the New Jersey Bar."

YARD, JAMES STERLING, 1826-1900.

"Joel Parker, 'the war governor of New Jersey.' A memorial prepared at the request of the New Jersey Historical Society, by James S. Yard. Read at the regular meeting of the Society, at Newark, May 17th, 1888." *Proceedings of the New Jersey Historical Society.* 2nd series. v.10, 1888/89. p.[57]-92. 161

Published also in nos. 159, 162-163; abstract in no. 46.

——————

Joel Parker: "The war governor of New Jersey." A biographical sketch. By James S. Yard. Freehold, N.J.: Printed at the Monmouth Democrat office, 1889. 43p. front. (port.) port. DLC NJ OCLWHI 162

Printed for private circulation.

——————

[*Same: facsimile reprint*] [Houston, Texas: Printed for private circulation, 1962] NJR 163

"Compliments of Frederick Parker."

PRICE, RODMAN McCAMLEY (1816-1894)

[BURR, CHARLES CHAUNCEY?] 1817-1883.

"Ex-Governor Price." *The Old guard.* v.2, 1864. p.212. port. (facing p.[193]) 164

Democratic leader, one-time congressman and governor, 1854-1857, delegate to the 1861 Peace Convention, and copperhead. For a fuller, general biography, see W. W. Clayton, *History of Bergen and Passaic Counties* (1882), p.339-343.

PRUDEN, OCTAVIUS LONGWORTH (1842-1902)

UNION SOLDIERS' ALLIANCE, *Washington, D.C.*

Octavius Longworth Pruden. In memoriam . . . The following brief sketch of the military services of Comrade Pruden was prepared by the committee appointed for that purpose . . . [Washington, 1902] [8]p. front. (port.) DLC NJR (photo) 165

Served 1862-1863 in Co. E, 11th N.J. Vols.

ROEBLING, WASHINGTON AUGUSTUS (1837-1926)

[CLEAVES, FREEMAN]

"Col. Washington Augustus Roebling (1837-1926)" *Crossed flags.* v.6, no. 2, Oct. 1965, p.1-3; no. 3, Nov. 1965, p.4-5. 165a

Trenton engineer and bridge-builder, Roebling served as artilleryman and military engineer.

RUNYON, THEODORE (1822-1896)

WEART, JACOB, 1829-1905.

". . . Chancellor Theodore Runyon." *New Jersey law journal.* v.23, 1900. p.292-298. 165b

Newark attorney and jurist, Democratic gubernatorial candidate in 1865, militia brigadier-general, commander of the three-month brigade in 1861.

Part of a series of articles, "Reminiscences of Some Former Noted Members of the New Jersey Bar."

SAWYER, HENRY WASHINGTON (1829-1893)

GODFREY, CARLOS EMMOR, 1864?-1941.

Sketch of Major Henry Washington Sawyer, First Regiment, Cavalry, New Jersey volunteers, a Union soldier and prisoner of war in Libby Prison under sentence of death. By Dr. C. E. Godfrey . . . Trenton, N.J.: MacCrellish & Quigley, printers, 1907. 11p. front. (port.) CSMH DLC NJ NJHI NJJ NJP NJR NJT NHI NN PHI PP 166

Sawyer, captured June 9, 1863, at Brandy Station, Va., was one of two Libby prisoners chosen to be shot in reprisal for two Confederates previously executed. They were exchanged in March 1864. He lived from 1848 largely in Cape May, N.J., built in 1876 and managed for some years the Chalfonte Hotel.

LIPPINCOTT, GEORGE E.

"Lee-Sawyer exchange. When the Confederates planned to hang two Union officers, the Federals threatened to execute two Southerners in return. One was the son of Robert E. Lee. By George E. Lippincott." *Civil War times illustrated.* v.1, no. 3. June 1962. p.39-40. port. 167

MCMAHON, WILLIAM.

"The decision; a tale of the War between the States, by William McMahon." *Kelsey review.* v.2, no. 2. Spring 1964. p.61-66. 167a

The ordeal of Henry W. Sawyer.

STRADLING, JAMES M.

"The lottery of death; two death prizes drawn by Major Henry W. Sawyer, of New Jersey and Captain John M. Flinn, of Indiana. By Lieutenant James M. Stradling." *McClure's magazine.* v.26, 1905. p.94-101. illus. (ports.) 168

Stradling, like Sawyer, had served in the 1st N.J. Cavalry.

SEWELL, WILLIAM JOYCE (1835-1901)

STOKES, EDWARD CASPER, 1860-1942.

Memorial address upon William J. Sewell, United States senator of New Jersey, by Hon. Edward C. Stokes, delivered before the Legislature of New Jersey, March 24, 1902. Trenton, N.J.: The John L. Murphy Publishing Co., printers, 1902. 32p. front. (port.) DLC NJN NJR NJT PHI 169

Sewell (of Camden) was an officer of the 5th N.J. Vols., later commander of the 38th N.J. Vols., brevet brigadier-general and major-general.

U.S. CONGRESS.

Memorial addresses on the life and character of William J. Sewell (late a Senator from New Jersey), delivered in the Senate and House of Representatives, fifty-seventh Congress, second session. Washington: Government Printing Office, 1903. 96p. front. (port.) DLC NJR NJT 169a

SHALER, ALEXANDER (1827-1911)

[WALKER, J. B. F.]

"Major-General Alexander Shaler." *Northern monthly magazine.* v.1, 1867. p.13-23 (May 1867) 170

Shaler was a businessman who lived five or six years at Hoboken, during that time serving also as colonel of the 1st Regt., Hudson (County) Brigade (militia), later an officer of the 7th N.Y. Regt. Soon after outbreak of the war he was assigned to the 1st U.S. Chasseurs (later 65th N.Y. Vols.) of which he eventually became commanding officer.

The author is identified in the volume table-of-contents as "F. B. C. Walker, M.D.," in an editorial note (p.175) as Dr. J. B. F. Walker of New York.

SMITH, MYRON WINSLOW (1838-1864)

[SMITH, LYNDON ARNOLD] 1795-1865.

Memorial of Adjt. M. W. Smith. [Newark, N.J., 1865?] cover-title, 47p. ports. CSMH DLC NJ NJR NHI 171

Half-title: A tribute to a beloved son and brother.

Funeral sermon by Rev. J. F. Stearns, First Presbyterian Church, Newark; newspaper obituaries; extracts from letters by and concerning Smith, a young Newark attorney who served as first lieutenant and adjutant, 1st Regt., U.S. Colored Troops, and was killed in Virginia.

F. P. Hill, *Books, Pamphlets and Newspapers Printed at Newark* (1902), lists this publication as no. 445. Cf. also Hill no. 537: Stearns, Jonathan French, *Funeral Sermon on Myron W. Smith* (1869), believed to be an erroneous entry for the same item; no pagination, imprint, or other details given.

"'A Memorial of Adjutant Myron W. Smith,' son of Dr. L. A. Smith, of this city—who died on the 5th of October last, from a wound . . . has just been published."—*Newark Daily Advertiser,* Jan. 24, 1865.

STRYKER, WILLIAM SCUDDER (1838-1900)

MILITARY ORDER OF THE LOYAL LEGION OF THE UNITED STATES. PENNSYLVANIA COMMANDERY.

. . . In memoriam. William Scudder Stryker, brevet lieutenant-colonel U.S. volunteers. Died at Trenton N.J. October 29, 1900. [Philadelphia, 1900] [4]p. (The Commandery's *Circular.* Series of 1900. no. 19. whole no. 406) NJR (photo) PPPRHI 171a

Stryker, a law student from Trenton, served in a New Jersey militia regiment in 1861; 1862-1863 as an officer of the 14th N.J. Vols.; later in staff positions. For many years, following the war, he was adjutant-general of New Jersey.

NELSON, WILLIAM, 1847-1914.

Gen. William Scudder Stryker, adjutant-general of New Jersey, 1867-1900; president of the New Jersey Historical Society; president of the Society of the Cincinnati in New Jersey; author of "The battles of Trenton and Princeton," etc. A memorial tribute. By William Nelson. Paterson, N.J.: The Paterson History Club, 1901. 8p. front. (port.) DLC MWA NJR NJT 172

"One Hundred Copies Printed. Reprinted (with some additions) from The New York Genealogical and Biographical Record, for January, 1901."

———

"Gen. William Scudder Stryker. By William Nelson." *New York genealogical and biographical record.* v.32, 1901. p.[65]-67. port. 173

SOCIETY OF THE CINCINNATI. NEW JERSEY.

Proceedings of the Society of the Cincinnati in the State of New Jersey at the meeting held at Trenton, New Jersey, February 22nd, 1901, as a memorial of William Scudder Stryker. [n.p., 1901] 52p. port. DLC NJ NJT 174

Cover-title: The Stryker memorial.

TODD, HENRY HUGH (1838-1908)

MILITARY ORDER OF THE LOYAL LEGION OF THE UNITED STATES. CALIFORNIA COMMANDERY.

... In memoriam: Henry Hugh Todd, captain 8th New Jersey Volunteer Infantry. Died at Almeda, Cal., Sunday, January 5, 1908. [San Francisco, Cal., 1908] 3p. (The Commandery's *Circular*. Series of 1908. no. 2. whole no. 889) NJR 175

Sketch of his life and military service. Todd served April-July 1861 in Co. K, 2nd N.J. Regt. (militia), Sept. 1861-July 1865 in various ranks with companies K, D, and I, 8th N.J. Vols.

TORBERT, ALFRED THOMAS ARCHIMEDES (1833-1880)

"MAJOR-GENERALS Crook and Torbert." *Harper's weekly.* v.8, 1864. p.661-662 (Oct. 15, 1864) ports. 175a

Torbert, a West Point graduate, commanded the 1st N.J. Regt., 1861-1862, and the 1st N.J. Brigade, 1862-1864.

MILITARY ORDER OF THE LOYAL LEGION OF THE UNITED STATES. PENNSYLVANIA COMMANDERY.

. . . In memoriam. Companion Alfred T. A. Torbert, brevet major-general U.S. Army. [Died] At sea, October 29, 1880, aged 47 years. [Philadelphia? 1880?] [3]p. PPLL 176

Caption title.

STOCKTON, ROBERT FIELD, 1832-1898.

Memorial address delivered by Gen. R. F. Stockton, at the service held in memory of Brevet Maj. Gen. A. T. A. Torbert, at Milford, Delaware, September 30th, 1880. Trenton, N.J.: William S. Sharp, printer, publisher and stereotyper, 1880. cover-title, 19p. CSMH NJHI NJR PPLL 177

Chiefly an account of his Civil War career.

TOWNSEND, GEORGE ALFRED, 1841-1914.

. . . General Alfred T. A. Torbert memorial, by George Alfred Townsend, taken from the Army and Navy journal, November 13th, 1880. [Wilmington, Del.] Published by the Historical Society of Delaware, 1922. 122p. (Historical Society of Delaware. Papers. no. lxvii) DLC NJR NN 178

TUCKER, ISAAC MILLER (1832-1862)

CRAVEN, ELIJAH RICHARDSON, 1824-1908.

In memoriam. Sermon and oration: sermon preached by E. R. Craven, D.D., in the Third Presbyterian Church, Newark, N.J., July 20, 1862, on occasion of the death of Col. I. M. Tucker, 2d Reg't N.J. vols., who fell at the battle of Gaines' Mills, before Richmond, June 27, 1862. Oration delivered by Bro. John Y. Foster, on invitation of Protection Lodge no. 28, I.O.O.F., in 3d Pres. Church, Newark, N.J., July 29, 1862, in commemoration of the death of P.G. Representative Isaac M. Tucker, col. 2d Reg't N.J. vols., and a member of said lodge. Newark, N.J.: Published by Protection Lodge no. 28 I.O.O.F., 1862. 42p. CSMH DLC NJ NJHI NJP NHI PPL 179

VANATTA, JACOB (1824-1879)

IN MEMORY of Jacob Vanatta, late of the Morris County bar. Died . . . April 30th, 1879. Aet: fifty-four years, ten months, twenty-six days. [Morristown, N.J.: Banner steam printing establishment, 1879] 41p. front. (port.) NJ NJHI NJJ NJR NHI NN 180

Biographical sketch, funeral discourses, memorial proceedings and addresses, etc.

Vanatta was long a Morristown attorney, a Douglas Democrat, member of the New Jersey Assembly 1862-1863, defeated candidate for U.S. senatorial nomination in 1863.

VAN BRUNT, GERSHOM JAQUES (1798-1863)

SMITH, XANTHUS.

"The first engagement of ironclad vessels. Commodore Gresham [i.e., Gershom] Jaques Van Brunt, a Jerseyman, was a conspicuous figure in this momentous battle of the Civil War." *Almanac and year book, First National Bank, Woodstown, N.J.* 1921. p.14-18. 181

Dated: Phila., Oct., 1920.

Van Brunt, a Monmouth County native, served in the Navy from 1818 through April 1863. As commander of the U.S. frigate *Minnesota,* he participated in the action of March 1862, in which the Confederate ironclad *Merrimack* was engaged by the Union *Monitor.*

WAMSLEY, HENRY J., JOHN B., AND SOCRATES T.

WAMSLEY, JAMES A. 1851-

Memorial boulder to three Civil War soldiers, Henry Janvier Wamsley, John Burroughs Wamsley, Socrates Townsend Wamsley. Dedicated at Daretown, Salem County, New Jersey, May 24, 1912. Together with a brief family history of the descendants of Thomas Banks [and others] . . . By James A. Wamsley, M.D., Philadelphia, Penna. [Philadelphia? 1912] 15, [3]p. illus. (incl. ports.) NJ 182

"Supplement" on unnumbered last leaf.

Includes biographical sketches and portraits of the three soldiers, who served respectively in the 3rd and 12th N.J. infantry regiments, and the 2nd N.J. Cavalry.

WARD, MARCUS LAWRENCE (1812-1884)

"GOVERNOR WARD, of New Jersey." *Harper's weekly.* v.9, 1865. p.781 (Dec. 9, 1865) port.

Known as "the Soldiers' Friend," for his extensive work in aid of the soldiers and their families, Ward, a Newark businessman, was elected governor in 1865.

RICORD, FREDERICK WILLIAM, 1819-1897.

"Marcus Lawrence Ward, late governor of New Jersey, by F. W. Ricord. Read . . . before the New Jersey Historical Society, May 19, 1887." *Proceedings of the New Jersey Historical Society.* 2nd series. v.9, 1886/87. p.[137]-147. port. 183

———————

Marcus Lawrence Ward, late governor of New Jersey, by F. W. Ricord. Read, by request, before the New Jersey Historical Society, May 19th, 1887. Newark, N.J.: Advertiser steam printing house, 1887. 11p. front. (port.) NJJ NJN NJR

Reprint of no. 183.

YOUNGLOVE, JOHN, 1832?-1929.

Hon. Marcus L. Ward. "The Soldiers' Friend." A eulogy delivered before Marcus L. Ward Post and friends, in Music Hall, Newark, N.J., on December 18th, 1884. By John Younglove, M.D. . . . Newark, N.J.: Press of the Newark Daily Advertiser, 1885. 31p. MH NJ NJHI NJJ NJR OCLWHI 185

"Requested for publication, by Post 88, Department of New Jersey [G.A.R.]."

WINTON, EBEN (1823-)

CAPALDO, CHARLES F.

"Bergen County's copperhead. By Charles F. Capaldo." *Proceedings of the New Jersey Historical Society.* v.69, 1951. p.136-142. 186

Winton was editor of the *Bergen County Democrat* (Hackensack) and associate of C. Chauncey Burr.

WRIGHT, WILLIAM (1794-1866)

NEWELL, WILLIAM AUGUSTUS, 1819-1901.

Remarks of Hon. William A. Newell, of New Jersey, on the death of Senator Wright. House of Representatives, December 18, 1866. [Washington, D.C.: Printed at the Congressional Globe office, 1866] 4p. DLC NJR NN PHI 187

Wright was a Newark manufacturer and politician, originally a Whig, from 1851 a Democrat. He served in Congress, 1843-1847; the U.S. Senate, 1853-1859 and 1863-1866.

WYNDHAM, PERCY (1833?-1879)

"PLEASANTON, Bayard and Wyndham." *Frank Leslie's illustrated newspaper.* v.15, 1862/63. p.167. 187a

Short biographical sketches. Wyndham was a colorful English soldier of fortune, who commanded the 1st N.J. Cavalry, 1862-1864.

ZABRISKIE, ABRAM (1841-1864)

HUDSON COUNTY, N.J. BAR.

Memorial of Colonel Abram Zabriskie, by the bar of Hudson County, New Jersey. Jersey City: Printed by John H. Lyon, 1864. 34p. ports. CSMH DLC NJ NJJ NJP NJR 188

Contents: "Biographical sketch," p.[5]-13; "Address . . . by William H. Campbell, D.D., president of Rutgers College, N.J., at the funeral," p.[15]-22; "Memorials of public sentiment at the death of Col. Abram Zabriskie," p.[23]-34.

Zabriskie, commanding the 9th N.J. Vols., was mortally wounded in May 1864 at Drewry's Bluff.

PERSONAL NARRATIVES, JOURNALS, AND LETTERS

[ANONYMOUS]

"The 4th N.J. at Fredericksburg [Dec. 1862]. From a soldier's letter." *West Philadelphia Hospital register.* v.1, nos. 9-10. April 11, 18, 1863. p.[33]-34, [37] 189

The unidentified writer was apparently a private in the Regiment's 4th battalion.

———————

"Letter written during the Civil War to a relative in Vineland." *Vineland historical magazine.* v.9, 1924. p.163-164. 190

Dated May 4, 1864. Describes a recent visit to Washington and vicinity. Names of writer, recipient, and place of origin deleted.

———————

"Scenes and incidents at Gettysburg." *Harper's weekly.* v.8, 1864. p.38-39. 190a

A narrative of bravery and carnage. The unnamed author (evidently a junior company officer or noncommissioned officer), attached to the First N.J. Brigade, after participating in the battle was in charge of a burial squad.

ACTON, EDWARD A. 1829-1862.

" 'Dear Mollie': letters of Captain Edward A. Acton to his wife, [April-July] 1862." *Pennsylvania magazine of history and biography.* v.89, 1965. p.3-50 (final page misnumbered: "110")

Edited and abridged by Mary Acton Hammond. Acton, a Quaker from Salem, N.J., served at this time in Co. K, 5th N.J. Vols. He was killed in the second battle of Bull Run.

ALLEN, EDWARD LIVINGSTON, 1846-1920.

Descriptive lecture. Both sides of army life: the grave and the gay. By Rev. E. Livingston Allen, late sergeant Co. K, 13th N.J. Vols. . . . [Poughkeepsie, N.Y.: The Author, 1885] cover-title, 16p. CSMH DLC NJR (photo) 192

Reminiscences of the war.

BAYLOR, GEORGE, 1843-

Bull Run to Bull Run; or, Four years in the Army of Northern Virginia. Containing a detailed account of the career and adventures of the Baylor Light Horse, Company B, Twelfth Virginia Cavalry, C.S.A., with leaves from my scrap-book. By George Baylor . . . Richmond: B. F. Johnson Publishing Company, 1900. 412p. incl. front. (port.) ports. DLC DNW MB NJP NHI NN OCLWHI 193

Baylor was a Confederate imprisoned Feb. 23-April 2, 1863, at Fort Delaware, where his father also was held for a longer period. Cf. p.95-122.

BORTON, BENJAMIN, 1841-1912.

Awhile with the blue; or, Memories of war days. The true story of a private, by Benjamin Borton. Published by the author. Passaic, N.J.: Wm. Taylor, printer, 1898. 2p.l., [3]-168p. front., plates, ports. CSMH DLC DNW NJJ NHI NN OCLWHI PU 194

"Muster roll of the Twenty-Fourth Regiment, New Jersey volunteers": p.[153]-168. Borton served as a private in Co. A of the 24th.

———————

"An ex-soldier's reminiscence as a day scholar at Eldridge's Hill boarding school. By Benj. Borton." *Almanac and year book, First National Bank, Woodstown, N.J.* 1910. p.13, 15. 195

The school at Eldridge's Hill (a village near Woodstown) was run by Allen Flitcraft during the early 1850's. Borton's reminiscences of fellow students include details of their Civil War service, the students being part local, and part from New York, Pennsylvania, Ohio, etc.

———————

On the parallels; or, Chapters of inner history; a story of the Rappahannock, by Benjamin Borton . . . Woodstown, N.J.: Monitor-Register print, 1903. 333, [1]p. incl. front. (port.) plates.

DLC DNW MB MWA NJ NJP NJR NHI NN OCLWHI PHI 196

A revised, enlarged edition of no. 194.

BRAY, JOHN.

"My escape from Richmond." *Harper's monthly.* v.28, 1863/64. p.662-665 (April 1864)

The writer, identifying himself as a soldier of the 1st N.J. Cavalry, describes his capture in November 1863 at Warrenton, Va., and subsequent confinement in Pemberton Factory Prison (Richmond), finally Libby Prison, from which he escaped in January 1864.

The name of John Bray does not appear on the official lists of the 1st N.J. Cavalry.

———

[*Same*] "Escape from Richmond. It took more than a Rebel prison to hold this plucky Union cavalryman. A first-person account by John Bray, first published in Harper's magazine in April 1864." *Civil War times illustrated.* v.5, no. 2. May 1966. p.28-33. illus. 197

[BRODERICK, VIRGIL] -1863.

"Stealing a march." *Harper's weekly.* v.7, 1863. p.250 (April 18, 1863) 197a

Verbatim report of campfire reminiscences by the lieutenant-colonel ("B———") of the 1st N.J. Cavalry, dealing with a night raid in Virginia (April 1862). A description of the same event in H. R. Pyne, *History of the First New Jersey Cavalry* (p.32-37), identifies the narrator—who had commanded the small raiding party—as Virgil Broderick, at the time captain of Co. K, later major and lieutenant-colonel of the regiment. He was killed in June 1863 at Brandy Station.

BUCK, SAMUEL L. 1820-1892.

Recollections of army life, delivered in Woodside Presbyterian Church, April 3, 1879, by Col. Samuel L. Buck, Second N.J. Volunteer Infantry. [n.p., 1879] 9 leaves. NJHI 198

Caption title.

CARMAN, EZRA AYERS, 1834-1909.

. . . "General Hardee's escape from Savannah." Prepared by Companion Brevet Brigadier General E. A. Carman . . . and read . . . May 3, 1893. [Washington, 1893] 30p. illus. (map) (Military Order of the Loyal Legion of the United States. Commandery of the District of Columbia. War papers. 13) DLC NJHI NHI 199

An account of several days in Dec. 1864 in which Hardee's Confederate forces escaped Sherman's army. The author, a colonel commanding the 13th N.J. Vols., participated in these events.

CLEVELAND, EDMUND JANES, 1842-1902.

[Civil War diary, Aug. 24, 1862-Sept. 19, 1864] *Proceedings of the New Jersey Historical Society.* v.66, 1948, p.25-37, continued serially through v.71, 1953, p.[204]-209. 200

Extensive excerpts from Cleveland's diary kept during his service as a private in Co. K, 9th N.J. Vols., prepared for publication by his son, Rev. Edmund J. Cleveland, Jr., under various titles: "Early campaigns in North Carolina" (Aug. 24, 1862-March 16, 1864), v.68, p.119, serially through v.71, p.209; "Campaign of promise and disappointment" (March 17-May 27, 1864), v.67, p.218-240, 308-328; "Second battle of Cold Harbor" (June 1-15, 1864), v.66, p.25-37; "Siege of Petersburg" (June 15-Sept. 19, 1864), v.66, p.76-96, 176-196.

COLE, JACOB HENRY, 1847-

Under five commanders; or, A boy's experience with the Army of the Potomac, by Jacob H. Cole . . . Paterson, N.J.: News Printing Company, 1906. ixp., 1 leaf, 253p. illus., ports. DLC NHI NN 201

The author, of Paterson, N.J., served in the First N.Y. Fire Zouaves and the 57th N.Y. Regt.

Included are some anecdotes (and a picture) of the 25th N.J. Vols. (p.109, 117-119).

[CRAVEN, JOHN JOSEPH] 1822-1893.

Jefferson Davis in prison. Scenes and incidents of the life of the ex Confederate President in the casemate at Fortress Monroe. Extracts from the post-surgeon's diary . . . New Orleans: Printed at the Crescent office, 1866. 25p. ICN NJR (photo) 201a

Based on Craven's recently-published *Prison Life of Jefferson Davis* (see no. 202). "Without attempting to-day to review the work critically . . . we proceed to lay before our readers such copious extracts from its pages as will enable them to judge of its grave interest and value."

"From the New York World, June 16."

Text printed in two columns.

A Newark inventor and physician, Craven served as a surgeon, first with the 1st N.J. Regt. (militia), April-July 1861, later as 10th Corps medical director.

CRAVEN, JOHN JOSEPH, 1822-1893.

Prison life of Jefferson Davis. Embracing details and incidents in his captivity, particulars concerning his health and habits, together with many conversations on topics of great public interest. By Bvt. Lieut.-Col. John J. Craven, M.D., late surgeon U.S. vols., and physician of the prisoner during his confinement in Fortress Monroe, from May 25, 1865, up to December 25, 1865 . . . New York: Carleton, publisher; London: S. Low Son & Co., 1866. 2p.l., [vii]-x, [11]-377p. front. CTY DLC MH MWA NJN NJP NJR NHI NN OCLWHI PPL 202

In the *Historical Magazine* for March 1869 (2nd series, v.5, p.210-211), this work is erroneously attributed to Gen. Halpine.

———————

[*Same: reprint?*] New York, 1959. 203

Not seen. Cf. John Mebane, *Books Relating to the Civil War* (1963), no. 434a.

———————

[*Same: facsimile reprint*] Biloxi, Miss.: Souvenir shop, Jefferson Davis Shrine, 1960. 204

Not seen.

———————

[*Same: reprint*] Prison life of Jefferson Davis, embracing details and incidents in his captivity, particulars concerning his health and habits, together with many conversations on topics of great public interest. By Bvt. Lieut. Col. John J. Craven, M.D., late surgeon U.S. vols., and physician of the prisoner during his confinement in Fortress Monroe, from May 25, 1865, up to December 25, 1865 . . . New York: G. W. Dillingham Company, publishers [1905] 3p.l., 9-319, [1]p. front. (port.) DLC NHI NN OCLWHI PP PU 205

Essentially same text as in 1866 edition.

———————

[*Same: English edition*] Prison life of Jefferson Davis. Embracing details and incidents in his captivity, with conversations on topics of public interest. By Bvt. Lieut.-Col. John J. Craven, M.D., late surgeon U.S. vols. and physician of the prisoner during his confinement in Fortress Monroe, from May 25, 1865, up to December 25, 1865 . . . London: Sampson Low, Son, and Marston, 1866. viii, 310, [2], 16p. CTY NHI 206

"Published simultaneously in London and New York."

Publisher's advertisements on pages after 310.

———————

La vie de prison de Jefferson Davis . . . au Fort Monroe. Scénes tirées du journal rédigé par le Dr. Craven. Traduites de l'anglais par Wallace S. Jones. Paris: Faure, 1866. 32p. MB 206a

Not seen. Entry based on MB catalog card.

CRAWFORD, JOSEPH W.

"Hooker's division at Seven Pines." *United service.* new series. v.1, 1889. p.290-302. 207

By "Jos. U. Crawford, late captain Sixth New Jersey volunteers."—p.302. The *Record of Officers and Men of New Jersey* (v.1, p.269) records "Joseph W. Crawford" as captain of Co. A, 6th N.J. Vols.

A narrative of events in late May and early June 1862, in which the author took part.

CROWELL, JOSEPH EDGAR, 1844-1919.

The young volunteer. A record of the experiences of a private soldier. By Joseph E. Crowell, late private Co. K, 13th N.J. Volunteers and lieutenant Veteran Reserve Corps. London and New York: F. Tennyson Neely, publisher [1899] vi, [7]-490p. (Neely's universal library. no. 67) CSMH DLC NJ NHI 208

Interesting, well-written reminiscences, covering nearly two years of service to the time he was commissioned lieutenant, early in 1864.

———————

[*Same: second edition*] The young volunteer. The everyday experiences of a soldier boy in the Civil War. By Joseph E. Crowell, private Company K, 13th N.J. Volunteers and lieutenant Veteran Reserve Corps. Second edition—revised and illustrated. Paterson, N.J.: Published by Joseph E. Crowell, The Call [c1906] 5p.l., [iii]-vi, [7]-492p. front. (port.) plates, port. DLC MB MH NJHI NJR NHI OCLWHI PPLL PU 209

"The Antietam monument" (to the New Jersey troops): p.[479]-489. Dedicated 1903.

On the first four preliminary leaves are press and personal comments relating to the 1899 edition.

"This edition has been revised and brought up to date by disposing of some of the characters in the first edition who have passed away, and the correction of some historical details."

———————

[*Same*] The young volunteer. The everyday experiences of a soldier boy in the Civil War. By Joseph E. Crowell, private Company K, 13th

N.J. Volunteers and lieutenant Veteran Reserve Corps. Second edition—revised and illustrated. New York: G. W. Dillingham Company, publishers [c1906] 5p.l., [iii]-vi, [7]-492p. illus., plates, port. CSMH NHI NN PU 210

Except for the absent frontispiece, this appears identical with the Paterson issue of the same edition.

CURRIE, CHARLES F. 1842-1913.

"Army reminiscences.—The bugle call. [By] Charles F. Currie." *Blue and gray.* v.1, 1893. p.376. port. 211

The writer, of Millville, N.J., served 1861-1863 as a corporal in Co. H, 4th N.J. Vols., afterward in the U.S. Signal Service.

DODD, IRA SEYMOUR, 1842-1922.

"The household of the hundred thousand. Social life in the Army of the Union. By Ira Seymour [*pseud.*]." *McClure's magazine.* v.11, 1898. p.154-161. 212

Reprinted as a chapter in no. 215.

The writer was sergeant and first sergeant of Co. F, 26th N.J. Vols., Sept. 1862-June 1863.

———————

"The making of a regiment. What a service of seven months did for a troop of raw volunteers. By Ira Seymour [*pseud.*]." *Ibid.* v.9, 1897. p.1031-1044. illus. 213

Reprinted as a chapter in no. 215.

———————

One young soldier; formerly published as The song of the Rappahannock. By Ira Seymour Dodd. New York: Dodd, Mead and Company, 1918. 4p.l., 253p. DLC MB MH NJP NN 214

Reprinted from the plates of his *Song of the Rappahannock* (no. 215), but with preface and last paragraph omitted.

———————

The song of the Rappahannock. Sketches of the Civil War. By Ira Seymour Dodd. New York: Dodd, Mead and Company, 1898. viiip., 1 leaf, 254p. CSMH DLC MB NJHI NJP NJR NHI NN OCLWHI PPL PU 215

Contents: Song of the Rappahannock; Making of a regiment; Household of the hundred thousand; Little battle; One young soldier; Sacrifice.

Several of the sketches first appeared in *McClure's Magazine,* 1897-1898. (See nos. 212-213, 216.)

Reprinted 1918 under the title, *One Young Soldier* (no. 214).

———————

"The song of the Rappahannock. The real experience in battle of a young soldier of the Army of the Potomac. By Ira Seymour [*pseud.*]." *McClure's magazine.* v.8, 1896/97. p.314-320. illus. 216

Reprinted as a chapter in no. 215.

DRAKE, JAMES MADISON, 1837-1913.

"Adventurous escape from prison life; an incident of the late Civil War." *Magazine of American history.* v.14, 1885. p.404-406. 217

Signed (p.406): J. Madison Drake. Elizabeth, N.J., August 28, 1885.

Drake was an officer of the 9th N.J. Vols. He was captured at Drewry's Bluff in May 1864, escaped in October and made his way back to the Union lines. Besides the other narratives of this experience described below (nos. 218-221a), the *Newark Daily Advertiser* published, Dec. 1, 1864, "The Story of a Wonderful Escape. Experience of Lt. J. Madison Drake in the South His Escape—Unionism in North Carolina—Sufferings of the People—How They Live, &c." (a two-column piece, headed "For the Newark Daily Advertiser" and signed "Yours in suffering, J. Madison Drake").

———————

Fast and loose in Dixie. An unprejudiced narrative of personal experience as a prisoner of war at Libby, Macon, Savannah, and Charleston, with an account of a desperate leap from a moving train of cars, a weary tramp of forty-five days through swamps and mountains, places and people visited, etc., etc. By J. Madison Drake, captain Ninth New Jersey Veteran Vols. and brevet brig.-general N.G.N.J. New York: The Authors' Publishing Company, 1880. 1p.l., [v]-x, [11]-310p. front. (port.) plates (incl. ports.) CSMH DLC DNW MB NJ NJP NJR NHI NN OCLWHI PPL 218

Preface dated Elizabeth, N.J., 1880.

The greater part of the book is devoted to his adventures in reaching the Union lines.

Appendix contains excerpts from readers' comments, brief sketch of the 9th N.J. Regt., etc.

———————

Historical sketches of the Revolutionary and Civil wars. With an account of author's desperate leap from a swiftly moving train of cars, and a fatiguing tramp of 1,000 miles through three Confederate states, in making his escape from a prison-pen. By J. Madison Drake, captain Ninth

N.J. Volunteers and bt. brig.-general by special act of N.J. Legislature . . . New York: Printed for the author by the Webster Press, 1908. 272p. front. (port.) illus. NJ NJHI NJJ NJN NJP NJR NJT NHI NN OCLWHI PP PPL 219

"Part II.—The Civil War" (p.[125]-272). Includes "Fast and loose in Dixie; or General Drake's leap for liberty" (p.128-150), but consists chiefly of various anecdotes and reminiscences of the war.

———————

Narrative of the capture, imprisonment and escape of J. Madison Drake, captain Ninth New Jersey Veteran Volunteers . . . [n.p.] 1868. cover-title, 93p. DLC NJHI NJR NHI 220

Caption title: The battle, the capture, the prisons, and the escape. From the army diary of J. Madison Drake . . .

Text printed in double columns.

Illustration on cover shows four men escaping from a train.

———————

[*Same: variant*] cover-title, 94p. CSMH NJ NJHI NJJ NHI 221

Same text and printing but with three added "congratulatory letters" extending to 94p. Undated but presumably also 1868; no illustration on cover.

———————

"Out of bondage." *Harper's weekly.* v.9, 1865. p.30 (Jan. 14, 1865) 221a

Reminiscence of capture, prison life, escape from a moving train in South Carolina, and return to the Union lines.

Anonymous; however, the author is identified readily through a similar narrative of Captain H. H. Todd (see no. 288), one of his companions, and also through Drake's other writings on the same experience.

DUDLEY, THOMAS HAINES, 1819-1893.

"Three critical periods in our diplomatic relations with England during the late war. Personal recollections of Thomas H. Dudley, late United States consul at Liverpool." *Pennsylvania magazine of history and biography.* v.17, 1893. p.34-54. 222

Dudley, Camden attorney and Lincoln supporter, vigorously represented the Union cause in England, doing much to counter pro-Confederate activity there.

———————

Three critical periods in our diplomatic relations with England during the late war. Personal recollections of Thomas H. Dudley, late United States consul at Liverpool. Reprinted from "The Pennsylvania magazine of history and biography." April, 1893. [Philadelphia, 1893] cover-title, 22p. NHI 223

FERGUSON, JOSEPH, 1837?-

Life-struggles in Rebel prisons: a record of the sufferings, escapes, adventures and starvation of the Union prisoners. By Joseph Ferguson, late captain First New Jersey Vols. Containing an appendix with the names, regiments, and date of death of Pennsylvania soldiers who died at Andersonville. With an introduction by Rev. Joseph T. Cooper . . . Philadelphia, Pa.: James M. Ferguson, publisher, 1865. 2p.l., [7]-206, xxivp. front. (port.) plates. CTY DLC MB NJP NJR NHI NN OCLWHI PPL 224

The writer was captured in May 1864 in the vicinity of Spotsylvania Court House, imprisoned at Andersonville, Macon, Savannah, Charleston, Columbia, Charlotte, and was paroled at Knoxville.

———————

[*Same: "third edition"*] 225

Copy recorded in NJR but missing. From the catalog card describing it, this publication appears the same as the one put out in 1865, except that it bears imprint date 1866, and at head of title has been added the following: "<Third edition.>"

FORBES, EUGENE, 1833?-1865.

Diary of a soldier, and prisoner of war in the Rebel prisons. Written by Eugene Forbes, sergeant Company B, 4th Regiment New Jersey volunteers. Trenton: Murphy & Bechtel, printers, 1865. iv, 5-68p. CSMH DLC NJ NHI OCLWHI PPL WHI 226

The John P. Nicholson *Catalogue* (1914) reports a copy with different pagination (iv, 71p.). The Henry E. Huntington Library, which acquired the Nicholson collection, failed to receive the volume of this description.

FREESE, JACOB R. 1826-1885.

. . . Secrets of the late rebellion, now revealed for the first time. By Dr. Freese . . . Phila.: Crombarger & Co., 1882. 2p.l., ix-xvii, [19]-348, 3p. incl. front., plates. CSMH DLC MB MWA NJP NJR NHI NN OCLWHI PP PPLL PU 227

At head of title: Illustrated edition.—Price, $2.

Contains (p.159-278) an extended account (and defense) of the provost-court set up by Gen. William R. Montgomery, military governor of Alexandria, Va. Conducted by Freese as provost-judge, it dealt with both military and civilian cases (disorder, and various crimes), and was widely disliked, being attacked in the press as "Judge Freese's Bayonet Court."

Publisher's advertisements at end.

FRENCH, SAMUEL GIBBS, 1818-1910.

"Kennesaw Mountain. By General S. G. French." *Southern Historical Society papers.* v.9, 1881. p.505-511. 228

Chiefly extracts from his journal, June 14-27, 1864. Born in Gloucester County, N.J., of Quaker background, French graduated at West Point in 1843 (a classmate of U.S. Grant). He resigned a captaincy in the U.S. Army in 1856, moved to a Mississippi plantation with his Southern wife, and served in the Confederate Army as a brigadier-general and major-general.

See also Howard B. French, *Genealogy of the Descendants of Thomas French* (1913), v.2, p.292-304.

——————

"Movement against Allatoona [Oct. 1864]—letter from General S. G. French." *Ibid.* v.10, 1882. p.402-406. 229

Letter dated: Columbus, Georgia, May 30, 1881.

——————

Two wars: an autobiography of Gen. Samuel G. French . . . Mexican war; War between the states, a diary; Reconstruction period, his experience; incidents, reminiscences, etc. Nashville, Tenn.: Confederate Veteran, 1901. xv, [1], 404p. incl. ports. front. (port.) illus. CSMH DLC DNW MB NJHI NJP NJR NN PP 230

Besides telling of his military career, the book gives a substantial account of his New Jersey background and considerable defense of slavery.

GODDU, LOUIS, 1846?-

"The new recruit. [By] Louis Goddu." *Blue and gray.* v.2, 1893. p.[153]-159. port. 231

The writer was of Co. K, 14th N.J. Vols. The *Record of Officers and Men of New Jersey in the Civil War* shows Louis "Goddee," of the 2nd N.J. Vols., as a transfer from the 14th Regt., mustered in on March 25, 1865, deserted July 7, following.

Goddu describes himself as a French-speaking Canadian from Montreal, who came to New York in August 1864 and worked briefly as typesetter for a French newspaper there. According to the present narrative, he soon enlisted (for a promised bounty) and was sent as a replacement to Co. K, 14th N.J. Vols., at Petersburg, Va. The account of his inept soldiering and encounter with a Southern girl whom he later married is perhaps romanticized. After the war, he finally "re-entered journalism."

In Vol. 3 of the same periodical are two other articles by Goddu: "The Pretty Traitor" (p.[13]-18), ostensibly a true account of the capture and adventures of three soldiers from a New York regiment; the second, "A Young Massachusetts Cowboy" (p.63-64), relates alleged childhood experiences near Southbridge, Mass., where "my father owned a farm." Apparently Goddu was imaginative.

GRINER, JOSEPH ADDISON, 1837-1865.

"The Civil War of a Pennsylvania trooper." *Pennsylvania magazine of history and biography.* v.87, 1963. p.39-62. 232

Excerpts from letters, April 1861-March 1865, addressed to his mother and sister. Griner, apparently of South Jersey (Camden County?), served briefly in the Philadelphia Light Guards, and thereafter, from the summer of 1861 until his death at Dinwiddie Court House, in the 8th Pennsylvania Cavalry.

Edited, with extensive commentary, by Daniel H. Woodward.

GRUBB, EDWARD BURD, 1841-1913.

An account of the battle of Crampton's Pass, being an address delivered by Edward Burd Grubb, bvt. brig. genl., U.S. vols., at the re-union of Kearney's New Jersey Brigade, at Edgewater Park [near Burlington], Sept. 20, 1888. [n.p., 1888] cover-title, 21p. NJ NJR OCLWHI PHI 233

Includes copies of contemporary official reports relating to the battle (p.[7]-21).

——————

Notes of a staff officer of our First New Jersey Brigade on the Seven Day's Battle on the Peninsula in 1862, by E. Burd Grubb, brevet brigadier general U.S. volunteers. Moorestown, N.J.: Moorestown Printing Co., 1910. 1p.l., 5-32p. CSMH DLC NJ NJR NHI PHI 234

In the form of a letter to Camille Baquet, historian of the First New Jersey Brigade, and published first in the latter's *History of the First Brigade, New Jersey Volunteers* (no. 394). Grubb, during the battle described, was a lieutenant on the Brigade staff.

HAINES, WILLIAM PENN, 1840-1928.

"Surrender of General Lee at Appomattox." *Almanac and year book, First National Bank, Woodstown, N.J.* 1916. p.29-33. 235

An account of the last days of the war. Haines (the "fighting Quaker"), of Mickleton, N.J., was a soldier of Co. F, 12th N.J. Vols.

HAMILTON, EDWARD JOHN, 1834-1918.

"A Union chaplain's diary [March 25-July 7, 1865]. Edited by Chase C. Mooney." *Proceedings of the New Jersey Historical Society.* v.75, 1957. p.1-17. plate. 236

Service with the 7th N.J. Vols. in Virginia during the closing days of the war.

HANCOCK, CORNELIA, 1840-1926.

South after Gettysburg. Letters of Cornelia Hancock from the Army of the Potomac, 1863-1865. Edited by Henrietta Stratton Jaquette. Philadelphia: University of Pennsylvania Press, 1937. xiii, 173p. plates. DLC NJN NJP NJR PHI PP PU 237

A young Quaker lady from Hancock's Bridge (Salem County), N.J., who served in nursing and other hospital activities. Interesting and literate narrative, with occasional items about New Jersey (especially Salem County) soldiers. For biography, see no. 97.

———————

[*Same: second edition*] South after Gettysburg. Letters of Cornelia Hancock, 1863-1868. Edited by Henrietta Stratton Jaquette. Foreword by Bruce Catton. Drawings by Edward Shenton. New York: Thomas Y. Crowell Company [1956] xii, 288p. illus. DLC NJN NJR NHI PP PU 238

The 1866-1868 letters (not in 1937 edition) deal with her work as a teacher in a South Carolina school for Negro children.

HANDY, ISAAC WILLIAM KER, 1815-1878.

United States bonds; or Duress by federal authority: a journal of current events during an imprisonment of fifteen months, at Fort Delaware, by Isaac W. K. Handy, D.D., of Augusta County, Va. . . . Baltimore: Turnbull Brothers, 1874. 5, [vi]-xxviii, 670p. front. (port.) plates, ports. CSMH DLC DNW MB MWA NJP NJR NHI OCLWHI 239

Handy, a Presbyterian minister from Virginia, was arrested during a visit to Delaware in July 1863, finally released in October 1864. The narrative is detailed and bitter.

HARROLD, JOHN.

Libby, Andersonville, Florence. The capture, imprisonment, escape and rescue of John Harrold, a Union soldier in the War of the Rebellion. With a description of prison life among the Rebels—the treatment of Union prisoners—their privations and sufferings. Philadelphia: Wm. B. Selheimer, printer, 1870. 132p. CSMH DLC MB NJJ NJP NN OCLWHI PHI PP 240

Introduction signed by John Harrold, Atlantic City, N.J. The writer was a member of Co. A, 138th Penn. Vols.

Verso of title-page in NJJ copy bears a stamped notice of "John Harrold's Ladies' and Gents' First Class Boot and Shoe Store," Atlantic City.

———————

[*Same: second edition*] Atlantic City, N.J.: Daily Union book and job printing office, 1892. 117p. 240a

Not seen. Entry based on card in National Union Catalog.

HILLYER, WILLIAM R.

. . . Chancellorsville, May 2 and 3, 1863. Prepared by Companion Captain William R. Hillyer, U.S. volunteers, and read . . . November 2, 1904. [Washington, 1904] 40p. (Military Order of the Loyal Legion of the United States. Commandery of the District of Columbia. War papers. 55) DLC NHI OCLWHI 241

The writer, captain of Co. K, 7th N.J. Vols., served 1861-1864 with the regiment, from which he was discharged because of wounds received in action.

HONEYMAN, ROBERT RAYMOND, 1836-1873.

"Col. Honeyman and his war journal [Sept. 30, 1862-May 2, 1863]." *Our home.* v.1, 1873. p.347-353, continued serially through p.545-550. 242

Edited by A. Van Doren Honeyman.

The diarist was lieutenant-colonel of the 31st N.J. Vols., a nine-month regiment which served Sept. 1862-June 1863.

HOPKINS, CHARLES AUGUSTUS, 1841-1916.

The march to the sea. By Charles A. Hopkins, <late captain 13th Regiment, New Jersey Volunteers.> Providence: Published by the Society, 1885. 32p. (Added title-page: Personal narratives of events in the War of the Rebellion, being papers read before the Rhode Island Soldiers and Sailors Historical Society. Third series—no. 12) CSMH DLC MB NJP NJR NIC OCLWHI PPL 243

Read before the Society Feb. 17, 1885.

"Edition limited to two hundred and fifty copies."

The author at this time was captain of Co. K. His wartime letters, diaries, and other military papers are in the NJR manuscript collection.

HORNBLOWER, WILLIAM HENRY, 1820-1883.

"A Civil War letter [to his son Joseph C. Hornblower]. Introduction by Charles Bradley . . ." *Proceedings of the New Jersey Historical Society.* v.52, 1934. p.222-223. 244

Written about March 1865. Dr. Hornblower, pastor of the First Presbyterian Church, Paterson, N.J., describes a visit to the Army of the James by a party of fifteen ladies and gentlemen, including Judge Joseph P. Bradley.

HOWARD, McHENRY, 1838-1923.

Recollections of a Maryland Confederate soldier and staff officer under Johnston, Jackson and Lee. By McHenry Howard. Baltimore: Williams & Wilkins Company, 1914. 1p.l., 423p. front. (port.) illus., plates, ports., fold. map, facsim. DLC NJP NN OCLWHI 245

"Fort Delaware": p.305-334. Prisoner-of-war experiences.

HUNT, THEODORE WHITEFIELD, 1844-1930.

"College and Civil War reminiscences. By Professor Theodore W. Hunt '65." *Princeton alumni weekly.* v.17, 1916/17. p.759-760. illus. (incl. port.) 246

JACKSON, HUNTINGTON WOLCOTT, 1841-1901.

"The battle of Chancellorsville. By Huntington W. Jackson. (Read May 1, 1883.)" Military Order of the Loyal Legion of the United States. Illinois Commandery. *Military essays and recollections.* v.2 (Chicago, 1894) p.49-78. 247

Jackson was first lieutenant, Co. F, 4th N.J. Vols. Although he was present at the battle, the paper contains few personal references.

———————

"The battle of Gettysburg. By Huntington W. Jackson. (Read April 5, 1882.)" *Ibid.,* v.1 (Chicago, 1891) p.147-184. 248

———————

"Sedgwick at Fredericksburg and Salem Heights [April-May 1863]. By Huntington W. Jackson, brevet lieutenant-colonel, U.S.V." *Battles and leaders of the Civil War.* New York, 1887-1888. v.3. p.224-232. illus. 249

———————

"Sedgwick's assault at Fredericksburg [May 1863]." *Century.* v.32, 1886. p.770-777. illus. (incl. port.) 249a

Signed (p.777) : Huntington W. Jackson.

JONES, JOHN BEAUCHAMP, 1810-1866.

A Rebel war clerk's diary at the Confederate States capital. By J. B. Jones, clerk in the War Department of the Confederate States government . . . Philadelphia: J. B. Lippincott & Co., 1866. 2v. CSMH DLC MB MWA NJHI NJN NJP NHI NN PHI PP PPLL PU 250

The author, a native of Baltimore, lived during his youth in Kentucky and Missouri. He became a writer and editor, from 1857 running at Philadelphia the weekly *Southern Monitor,* a moderate publication devoted to Southern interests. He lived, in this period, at Burlington, N.J., and produced in 1859 a novel, *Wild Southern Scenes,* a prophetic story of an American civil war, republished in 1861 as *Secession, Coercion, and Civil War* (see nos. 340-342). Soon after the fall of Fort Sumter, concluding that his pro-Southern activities rendered his future in the North insecure, he left Burlington for Montgomery, Ala., and became a clerk in the Confederate War Department. His *Rebel War Clerk's Diary* is a classic among Civil War books. Jones died at Burlington while it was in the course of printing.

———————

[*Same: second edition*] A Rebel war clerk's diary at the Confederate States capital, by J. B. Jones . . . A new and enlarged edition, edited with an introduction and historical notes by Howard Swiggett . . . New York: Old Hickory Bookshop, 1935. 2v. DLC MB NJP NJR NN PU 251

———————

[*Same: third edition*] . . . A Rebel war clerk's diary. Condensed, edited, and annotated by Earl Schenck Miers . . . New York: Sagamore Press, inc., publishers [1958] xiv, 545p. NJR PP PU 252

At head of title: John B. Jones.

———————

[*Same*] New York: A. S. Barnes, 1961. 253

Paperback reprint of 1958 edition.
Not seen.

KEARNY, PHILIP, 1815-1862.

"Gen. Kearny's review of the campaign in the Peninsula." *Frank Leslie's illustrated newspaper.* v.15, 1862/63. p.86 (Nov. 1, 1862) 253a

A letter headed "Harrison's Landing, Aug. 4, 1862," addressed "To Mr. O. S. Halstead [i.e., Halsted], Jr., Newark, N.J.," with the curious salutation, "Dear Pet."

———————

Official reports of General Kearny and General Birney, of the battle of Seven Pines, May 31st, 1862. Philadelphia: U.S. Steampower Book and Job Printing Office, 1863. 16p. MB NHI PP PU 254

Kearny's report (p.[3]-9), dated "Head-Quarters, Third Div., Heintzelman's Corps, Entrenched Camp, near Savage's, June 2d, 1862," is addressed to "Capt. Chauncey McKeever, A. A. Gen." The report of Birney, "Head-Quarters Birney's Brigade, First Division, Third Corps. Harrison's Landing, July 8th, 1862," is addressed to "Capt. W. C. Sturges, A. A. A. G. Kearny's Division."

KEARNY, PHILIP J. 1841-1863.

"Letters from the field. Written to his relatives, by Major Philip J. Kearney [i.e., Kearny], Eleventh New Jersey Volunteers." *Historical magazine*. 2nd series. v.7, 1870. p.184-195. 255

Fifteen letters, Sept. 1862-June 1863, all but one written from Virginia. Kearny was captain of Co. A until May 1863, afterwards major on the regimental staff. He died July 2, 1863, of wounds received at Gettysburg.

See *ibid.,* 3rd series, v.1, 1872/73, p.122-123, for a communication from John Schoonover ("Late Lt. Col., 11th N.J. Vols.") of Oxford, N.J., defending the 11th Regt. and its commanding officer, Col. Robert McAllister, against expressions of unfavorable opinion in the Kearny letters; also rejoinder of the editor, Henry B. Dawson.

KILPATRICK, HUGH JUDSON, 1836-1881.

"Colonel Kilpatrick's raid into Secessia." *Harper's weekly*. v.7, 1863. p.343. illus. (p.348) 255a

Text of the report by Kilpatrick (commanding 1st Brigade, Third Division Cavalry) to the commander-in-chief, dated Yorktown, Va., May 8, 1863.

———————

"'Lee at Gettysburg.'" *Our magazine*. v.2, 1871. p.81-86. 255aa

Signed (p.86): Judson Kilpatrick.

A response to the article of this title by Confederate general John D. Imboden which appeared in the April *Galaxy*. Kilpatrick, who had commanded a cavalry division at Gettysburg, reviews the operations there, in part to correct Imboden's "manifest injustice to our cavalry."

Our Magazine (Newton, N.J.) was edited and published by William R. Mattison, from May 1871 jointly with Kilpatrick. Mattison had been an officer in Kilpatrick's former command, the Harris Light Cavalry (2nd New York).

[KITCHEN, MARCUS LAWRENCE WARD] 1826?-1896.

"How the First New Jersey fought at Brandy." *Harper's weekly*. v.7, 1863. p.606 (Sept. 19, 1863) 255b

The adjutant (not named), describing events of June 1863, is identified through a similar narrative in H. R. Pyne, *History of the First New Jersey Cavalry* (p.150, etc.). Kitchen served as First Cavalry adjutant, Oct. 1862-July 1863, subsequently transferred to the 2nd N.J. Cavalry.

———————

"The way Joe Allen buried Vandergrift." *Ibid.,* p.622 (Sept. 26, 1863) 255c

Reminiscences of the [former] adjutant, 1st N.J. Cavalry. The same events are described in H. R. Pyne's history of that regiment (p.160).

Lewis P. Vandergrift was a private of Co. D, killed at Aldie, Va., June 22, 1863. Joseph Allen was of Co. F.

KNOX, JAMES SUYDAM, 1840-1892.

"The assassination of President Lincoln. A contemporary letter by a Princeton graduate who witnessed the historic tragedy." *Princeton alumni weekly*. v.17, 1916/17. p.407-409 (Feb. 7, 1917) illus., facsim. 255d

Copy of the letter (April 16, 1865) with pertinent biographical and historical details. Knox, formerly a soldier, hospital steward, and War Department clerk, was a medical student at Georgetown University when the letter was written.

———————

"Lincoln's assassination viewed by young Princetonian. Details of tragedy outlined in contemporary letter written by eye-witness." *Ibid.* v.27, 1926/27. p.543-544 (Feb. 11, 1927) 255e

Essentially a reprint of the preceding (no. 255d).

LANDIS, CHARLES KLINE, 1833-1900.

"Washington in 1861. By Charles K. Landis." *Vineland historical magazine*. v.3, 1918. p.5-8.

Reminiscences of a visit soon after outbreak of the war. Landis, then of Hammonton, N.J., later was the developer of Vineland.

LOGAN, DORASTUS B. 1822?-1863.

[Letter of Capt. Logan, Co. H, 11th N.J. Vols., dated "Camp near Fredericksburgh, Dec. 2,

1862"] *Proceedings of the New Jersey Historical Society.* new series. v.8, 1923. p.58-59. 257

Logan was killed at Gettysburg.

McALLISTER, ROBERT, 1813-1891.

Address of Major-General Robert McAllister to the Eighth New Jersey Volunteers Veteran Association, at Newark, N.J., November 10th, 1881. [n.p.? 1881] cover-title, 11p. NJR 257a

The only copy seen has been cropped. At top and bottom, the cover is trimmed to the border inclosing the title—possibly eliminating an imprint below.

An account of the battle of Hatcher's Run (February 1865). McAllister, who commanded the brigade of which the 8th Regiment was a part, served with distinction and courage throughout the war: lieutenant colonel, 1st N.J. Regt., May 1861 June 1862; colonel commanding 11th N.J. Regt., June 1862-June 1865; brevet brigadier-general, October 1864. He was twice wounded.

"Letter of Lieut. [Uriel B.] Titus relative to the battle of Hatcher's Run": p.[9]-11. Dated Trenton, N.J., September 12, 1881, and signed: U. B. Titus. The writer had been an officer in Co. B, 11th N.J. Regt., at the time concerned.

———————

The Civil War letters of General Robert McAllister. Edited by James I. Robertson, Jr. New Brunswick, New Jersey: Published for the New Jersey Civil War Centennial Commission by Rutgers University Press [1965] xp., 3 leaves, [3]-638p. incl. map. front. (port.) plates, ports. DLC NJ NJHI NJP NJR NJT 258

From the McAllister papers in the NJR manuscript collection, which include over nine hundred wartime letters written to his wife (Oxford Furnace, N.J.) and two daughters (at home and in a Philadelphia school), together with letters which he received from them and others.

———————

"McAllister's brigade at the Bloody Angle [Spotsylvania, May 12, 1864]. By Robert McAllister, brevet major-general, U.S.V." *Battles and leaders of the Civil War.* New York, 1887-1888. v.4. p.176. illus. 259

The brigade included the 5th, 6th, 7th, 8th, and 11th N.J. Vols.

McCANN, THOMAS H.

The campaigns of the Civil War in the United States of America, 1861-1865, by Thomas H. M'Cann . . . [Hoboken, N.J.: Hudson Observer job print, 1915] 223, 9p. ports. DLC NJJ NJN NN OCLWHI 260

The author, "of Hoboken, N.J.," was "Sergeant of Company 'C,' Ninetieth Regiment, New York State Veteran Volunteers," 1861-1866.

"This story appeared originally in the Hudson Observer . . . June, July and August, 1915."—p.3.

A general treatment, with occasional accounts of personal experiences or of 90th Regt. participation.

MacCAULEY, CLAY, 1843-1925.

"Personal recollections of Princeton undergraduate life: the college during the Civil War. By Clay MacCauley '63 and '64." *Princeton alumni weekly.* v.17, 1916/17. p.84-87, 180-182. illus. (incl. ports.) 261

MINDIL, GEORGE WASHINGTON, 1843?-1907.

The battle of Fair Oaks [May 1862]. A reply to General Joseph E. Johnston. By George W. Mindil, late brevet major-general U.S. volunteers. Aide-de-camp to General Phil. Kearney [*sic*]. Philadelphia [New York: Printed by the American Church Press Company] 1874. 1p.l., 16p. map. CSMH DLC MB NJHI NJP NHI OCLWHI PPL 262

"250 copies printed for private distribution."

A response to Johnston's *Narrative of Military Operations* (1874).

Mindil was colonel commanding the 27th N.J. Vols., October 1862-July 1863, and the 33rd N.J. Vols., July 1863-July 1865, brevetted brigadier- and major-general, March 1865. He served first, July 1861-March 1862, in a Pennsylvania regiment; afterwards in various staff positions. He distinguished himself at Fair Oaks, then attached to Birney's brigade.

MORRIS, IRA K.

Recollections of old Camp Vredenburgh and An incident of the battle of Monmouth. Southern agents in Freehold and Margaret Rue. By Ira K. Morris. Freehold, N.J.: Monmouth Democrat print, 1905. cover-title, 23p. NJ NJFHI NJJ NJR (photo) NHI 263

Text printed in two columns.

"Southern agents in Freehold. How the Confederate Army was recruited in the North—recollections of old Camp Vredenburgh. By Ira K. Morris. From the Monmouth Democrat, March, 1905": p.1-14.

"Margaret Rue. An incident of the battle of Monmouth. By Ira K. Morris. From the Monmouth Democrat, June, 1905": p.[15]-23.

The first section, derived in part from boyhood memories of the camp, relates to the period of occupancy by the 14th N.J. Regt. and others later, discussion of the bounty system, and particularly an account of activity in the camp by Confederate agents.

PIERSON, STEPHEN, 1844-1911.

"From Chattanooga to Atlanta in 1864—a personal reminiscence. By the late Major Stephen Pierson, Morristown, N.J." *Proceedings of the New Jersey Historical Society.* new series. v.16, 1931. p.324-356. 264

See *ibid.*, p.506-507, for biographical details.

Pierson served first with the 27th N.J. Vols., and 1863-1865 as an officer of the 33rd N.J. Vols. After the war, he was a physician at Boonton and Morristown.

[PROUDFIT, ROBERT RALSTON] 1836-1897.

"The slaves in Virginia." *Friends' review.* v.15, 1861/62. p.714-715. 264a

"The following are extracts of a letter from the chaplain of one of the New Jersey regiments in the army before Richmond"; dated "Macon's Farm on the Chickahominy River, Virginia, May 26, 1862."

Observations of slave life and character, and a plea for emancipation.

"Brought up in the hot-bed of conservatism at New Brunswick and Princeton," the writer is not identified by name. The eight chaplains of New Jersey regiments in Virginia at this time, however, include only one to whom these words apply—Proudfit, son of a Rutgers College professor, graduate of Rutgers, who studied at New Brunswick Theological Seminary and Princeton Theological Seminary, chaplain of the 2nd N.J. Vols.

REID, WARREN D.

". . . Escaped from Fort Delaware. A Mississippi Confederate tells how he and a comrade escaped—afloat on a ladder, then a tramp. A story told by Sergeant Warren D. Reid, of Mississippi . . ." *Southern Historical Society papers.* v.36, 1908. p.271-279. 265

"From the Richmond *Dispatch,* August 19, 1900."

REVERE, JOSEPH WARREN, 1812-1880.

Keel and saddle: a retrospect of forty years of military and naval service. By Joseph W. Revere. Boston: James R. Osgood and Company, 1872. xiii, 360p. CSMH DLC MB NJR NHI NN PP PPL 266

Adventurer, world traveler, Revere commanded the 7th N.J. Vols. from its organization in August 1861 until October 1862 when he was promoted brigadier-general. Following the battle of Chancellorsville, he was court-martialed and dismissed from the service.

Chapter 35 deals briefly with the Civil War service, followed by several anecdotes relating to the war.

———————

[*Same*] 1873. NJP 267

RILEY, FRANK M. 1842-1923.

"Libby Prison experience of Frank M. Riley. Captain Co. F, Twelfth New Jersey Volunteers." *Almanac and year book, First National Bank, Woodstown, N.J.* 1917. p.[32]-40. port.

Previously published in William P. Haines, *History of the Men of Co. F* (no. 413).

RIVENBARK, CHARLES W.

"Two years at Fort Delaware. By Sergeant Chas. W. Rivenbark, Company C, First Regiment N.C.T." Clark, Walter, ed. *Histories of the several regiments and battalions from North Carolina in the great war 1861-'65.* Goldsboro, N.C., 1901. v.4. p.[725]-732. DLC PP PPLL 269

Dated Charlotte, N.C., 9 April, 1901. Originally written in 1874 "and published in our 'Living and Dead.' It has now been revised by its author for this work."

Rivenbark, a Confederate captured at Gettysburg, was imprisoned until a month before the war's end, when he managed to escape.

ROBBINS, WALTER RALEIGH, 1843-1923.

War record and personal experiences of Walter Raleigh Robbins from April 22, 1861, to August 4, 1865. Edited by Lilian Rea. [Chicago?] Privately printed, 1923. vii, 220p. front. (port.) ports. DLC MB NJHI NJP NJR NHI NN 270

Robbins served briefly in a New York regiment. In February 1862 he joined Co. G, 1st N.J. Cavalry, as a second lieutenant, and ended the war as lieutenant-colonel, brevetted brigadier-general. After the war he lived in Chicago, president of the Chicago Lumbermen's Association.

ROEBLING, WASHINGTON AUGUSTUS, 1837-1926.

Wash Roebling's war; being a selection from the unpublished Civil War letters of Washington Augustus Roebling. Edited and with an introduction by Earl Schenck Miers. With drawings by Abe Birnbaum. Newark, Delaware: Printed at the Spiral Press, and published . . . for the friends of the Curtis Paper Company, 1961. 33p., 1 leaf. illus. NJ NJR NJT 271

"This is the eighth title in a series of publications in Americana which have been commissioned annually by the Curtis Paper Company . . ."—unnumbered leaf at end.

"Of this booklet, five hundred copies have been printed for the friends of the Rutgers University Library."—p.[2].

Extracts (1861-1864) from wartime letters and postwar reminiscences which form part of the Roebling papers in the NJR manuscript collection. The writer (from Trenton), a noted engineer and bridge builder, served first in the 9th N.Y. Regt. and as an officer in the 6th N.Y. Artillery, then from January 1863 with the Army of the Potomac's Engineer Brigade and finally on the staff of Major-General G. K. Warren. His observations were literate, informative, sometimes critical.

ROUNSAVILLE, ISAAC W. -1862

" 'What bully times we have.' Letters from the 6th New Jersey, [edited] by Donald Crane." *Civil War times.* v.1, no. 9. Jan. 1960. p.8. 272

Reprinted from the *Hunterdon County Democrat* (Flemington, N.J.).

Rounsaville, of Hunterdon County, was a soldier of Co. H, 6th N.J. Vols.; he died of disease in May 1862, at Yorktown, Va. The three letters (Nov. 1861-Feb. 1862), addressed to William E. Haver, are owned by the Hunterdon County Historical Society.

RUNYAN, MORRIS C. 1837-

Eight days with the Confederates and capture of their archives, flags, &c. by Company "G" Ninth New Jersey Vol. Written by Captain Morris C. Runyan. Princeton, N.J.: Wm. C. C. Zapf, printer, 1896. 44p. front. (port.) CSMH DLC NJHI NJJ NJN NJP NJR NJT NHI NN PHI PPLL

Unit roster: p.[43]-44.

RUSLING, JAMES FOWLER, 1834-1918.

"General McClellan's baggage-destroying order . . . By James F. Rusling, late brevet brigadier-general, U.S.V." *Century.* v.38, 1889. p.157-158. 274

After the battle of Gaines' Mill, June 1862.

Rusling, a Trenton attorney, served from August 1861, first as a lieutenant in the 5th N.J. Vols., in quartermaster duty at regimental and higher levels through the end of the war.

———————

Men and things I saw in Civil War days. By James F. Rusling, A.M., LL.D., brigadier general (by brevet) United States volunteers. New York: Eaton & Mains; Cincinnati: Curts & Jennings, 1899. 411p. front. (port.) ports. CSMH DLC MB NJHI NJN NJP NJR NJT NHI NN PHI PP PPL 275

Nearly half devoted to individual sketches of major war leaders (e.g., Lincoln, McClellan), based on personal observation and contacts.

Two chapters deal entirely with Rusling's military career: "Campaigning and soldiering" (Chapter 12, p.159-173); "Some army letters" (Chapter 15, p.195-353), abridged copies of the author's letters to his father, brother, and friends, September 1861-July 1865.

Some of the chapters are revisions of sketches published previously in the *Christian Advocate* (New York). Cf. p.3.

———————

[*Same: second edition*] Men and things I saw in Civil War days. New edition. By James Fowler Rusling, A.M., LL.D., brigadier general (by brevet) United States volunteers . . . New York and Cincinnati: The Methodist Book Concern, 1914. 2p.l., 3-420p. front. (port.) ports. DLC NJ NJT NIC 276

"New appendix": p.412-419.

———————

"The victory at Nashville. By Captain James F. Rusling, A.Q.M." *United States service magazine.* v.3, 1865. p.[113]-123. 277

Dated Nashville, Tenn., December 20th, 1864.

Although Rusling speaks of himself as an eyewitness, there are virtually no personal references.

SANDER, HARRIET (SOUDER) 1874-1964.

"Civil War memories of a little girl with an uncle in each army." *Atlantic County Historical Society year book.* v.4, 1960/63. no. 2, 1961. p.49-53. 278

Signed (p.53): Harriet S. Sander.

Impressions of a childhood visit to her grandparents at Port Republic, N.J., especially of Memorial Day ceremonies at the town hall, and of her uncle Isaac Smallwood, a veteran of the 3rd N.J. Cavalry. The writer's home was in the South, her paternal relatives being Confederate sympathizers.

Notwithstanding the title, these are obviously recollections of *postwar* observations, conversations, etc. (relating to the war, veterans, and the like).

SCHMITT, FREDERICK EMIL, 1837-1923.

"Prisoner of war: experiences in Southern prisons, by Frederick Emil Schmitt." *Wisconsin magazine of history.* v.42, 1958/59. p.83-93. illus. 279

Edited by John P. Hunter.

A reminiscence written 1919 in Wisconsin. Schmitt, a native of Bavaria and resident of Elizabeth, N.J., served as a private in Co. D, 3rd N.J. Cavalry, and was captured near Richmond in June 1864.

SCHUYLER, COLFAX, 1835-

"A day with Mosby's men. [By] Colfax Schuyler." *Blue and gray.* v.3, 1894. p.[334]-339. illus. (incl. port.) 279a

The author served from 1861 in the 1st N.J. Cavalry, from November 1863 as a captain. The present narrative describes events in the Shenandoah Valley, apparently in early 1864.

SCOVEL, JAMES MATLACK, 1833-1904.

"Recollections of Lincoln and Seward. [By] James Matlack Scovel." *Overland monthly.* 2nd series. v.38, 1901. p.[265]-271. 279b

———————

"Side-lights on Lincoln. By James Matlack Scovel." *Ibid.*, p.[204]-207. 280

"I was a member of the State Senate for three years, and President of that body for one year, during the war, in one of the middle States [New Jersey], and saw much of Mr. Lincoln from 1862 to 1865."

SHOTWELL, RANDOLPH ABBOTT, 1844-1885.

The papers of Randolph Abbott Shotwell . . . Raleigh [N.C.] The North Carolina Historical Commission, 1929-1936. 3v. front. (port.) facsims., fold. table. DLC NJP NJR 280a

Includes (v.2, p.131-202) a detailed narrative and journal covering his imprisonment at Fort Delaware, from the summer of 1864 until the middle of June 1865. Following the war, Shotwell was a journalist and editor in North Carolina.

SLATER, THOMAS OGDEN, 1842-

Incidents of personal experience, given by Capt. T. O. Slater at the forty-third reunion of the Twelfth Regiment, New Jersey volunteers, held at Elmer, Salem County, N.J., Sept. 4, 1916. [New York: The Knickerbocker Press, 1916] 24p. NJR 281

SMITH, CHARLES PERRIN, 1819-1883.

Charles Perrin Smith New Jersey political reminiscences, 1828-1882. Edited by Hermann K. Platt. New Brunswick, New Jersey: Rutgers University Press [1965] viip., 2 leaves, 3-278p. front. (port.) DLC NJ NJHI NJP NJR NJT 282

"Critical bibliography": p.258-259.

An important source. Smith was long active and influential in the Republican (and "Opposition" or Union) Party, a member of the state executive committee 1859-1869. He began as a Whig, editing the Salem (N.J.) *National Standard* 1840-1851, serving in the state Senate 1855-1857. Appointed in 1857 to the lucrative New Jersey Supreme Court clerkship, he moved to Trenton, holding the position until 1872. The original manuscript of Smith's reminiscences—actually three volumes of overlapping reminiscences, written over a period of years—is owned by the New Jersey State Library (microfilm copy in NJR).

The present volume is a revision of Dr. Platt's 1963 Ph.D. dissertation (Rutgers University).

SMITH, JAMES O. 1844-

"A brave old Southern woman. [By] J. O. Smith." *Blue and gray.* v.2, 1893. p.[70]-72. illus. 283

Narrative of experiences (1864) at Big Shanty, in Georgia; the writer at that time had been detailed as receiving clerk of the Commissary Department, First Division, 20th Army Corps. Smith was a private of Co. A, 13th N.J. Vols., serving 1862-1865.

———————

"My first campaign and battle. A Jersey boy at Antietam [Sept. 1862]—seventeen days from home. [By] J. O. Smith." *Ibid.* v.1, 1893. p.280-290. illus. (incl. ports., map) 284

The writer, then an apprentice in a (Newark?) newspaper office, enlisted during August 1862.

SPRINGER, SAMUEL, 1800?-1877.

"A prisoner in Dixie." Tomlin, Charles. *Cape May spray.* Philadelphia, c1913. p.[93]-110. 285

A narrative written 1867. The writer, a Cape May County man, in February 1865 was appointed at Newbern, N.C., to take charge of a detail engaged in raising sunken vessels in that area. He was captured April 3, 1865, on the Neuse River, almost immediately after beginning operations, and was released on April 30, after various travels and prison adventures in North Carolina.

Appears also in the later editions of Tomlin.

TAYLOR, JOHN, 1836-1909.

. . . The story of a battle, by ex-Senator John Taylor, recited before the Young Men's Catholic Club, at Trenton . . . Dec. 11, 1893. Trenton, N.J.: From the press of J. A. Cresse & Co. [1893] 15p. NJR 286

Caption title.

Eye-witness account of the battle of Bull Run, as seen by a civilian. A few references to the 1st N.J. Vols., but the account largely concerns the action generally. Taylor was state senator from Mercer County, 1881-1883.

THOMPSON, RICHARD S. 1837-

"A scrap of Gettysburg. By Richard S. Thompson. (Read February 11, 1897.)" Military Order of the Loyal Legion of the United States. Illinois Commandery. *Military essays and recollections.* v.3 (Chicago, 1899) p.97-109. 287

At this time, Thompson was captain of Co. K, 12th N.J. Vols., and acting as major. Later he became regimental commander.

TODD, HENRY HUGH, 1838-1908.

The narrative of a prisoner of war. [A paper read before the] California Commandery of the Military Order of the Loyal Legion of the United States, March 25, 1893. By Companion Henry Hugh Todd, late captain 8th New Jersey Vol. Infantry. [n.p., 1893] 20p. (The Commandery's *War papers.* no. 11) DLC NJHI NJR (photo) NHI NN PPLL 288

The writer was captured at Spotsylvania in May 1864, was held in several Confederate prisons, escaped from a train en route from Charleston, along with J. Madison Drake (see nos. 217-221a), and finally reached Washington in December 1864. Todd joined the regiment in 1861 and was captain of Co. D at the time of his capture.

[TRELEASE, EDGAR H.] 1840?-1884.

"Letter from a soldier." *Harper's weekly.* v.9, 1865. p.93-94 (Feb. 11, 1865) 288a

Prison narrative. The writer was at Andersonville, July 7-Oct. 22, 1864, and after four weeks at Millen was removed to Savannah for exchange.

Signed: E.H.T. Newark, January, 1865.

"Among the released Union prisoners now at Annapolis, Md., are several from this city and vicinity . . . Corp. Edgar H. Trelease, of this city, and a member of the 11th N.J. Regiment [Company B], has . . . been exchanged, and has reached Annapolis."—*Newark Daily Advertiser,* Dec. 3, 1864. Cf. also an earlier item in *ibid.,* Nov. 22, 1864: A letter of October 8th from a former prisoner at Florence, S.C., states that "Edgar Trelease, of the 11th Regiment, was at Andersonville, when the other Newarkers left there in September."

VREDENBURGH, PETER, 1837-1864.

. . . Letters of Major Peter Vredenburgh . . . [relating to] the battles and marches of the old Fourteenth Regiment, N.J. vols. . . . [n.p.: Printed for private circulation, 187—?] 37, [1]p. DLC NJR NN 289

Vredenburgh, an Eatontown attorney, was killed at the battle of Winchester, Va.

WAR TALKS BY MORRISTOWN VETERANS, given in the Y.M.C.A. rooms before the G.A.R. and S. of V. Stenographically reported for and originally published in the True Democratic Banner. Morristown, N.J.: Vogt Bros., publishers, 1887. 42, [2]p. CSMH MB NJHI NJJ NJP NJR NHI OCLWHI PPL 290

Eight talks presented 1886: The Signal Service, by Fred. Wooster Owen; Reminiscences of Life on the U.S.S. "Nantasket," 1869-1870, by Rev. John Crawford; The Army of the Potomac—Its Heroic Dead and Living, by Captain A. H. Condict; Campaigns in the West in '61 and '62, by Gen. M. S. Littlefield; A Year of Service in North Carolina, by Rev. Addison Parker; Fragments from the History of a Quaker Regiment, by Lieut. E. L. Dobbins; Capture of Fort Pulaski, by Major H. M. Dalrymple; A Chaplain's Experience, by Rev. A. Erdman.

Edward L. Dobbins was a sergeant and lieutenant of the 23rd N.J. Vols., 1862-1863. Alfred H. Condict was captain of Co. I, 27th N.J. Vols., 1862-1863.

"A.T.A. Torbert Post, no. 24, Morristown, N.J.": p.[43]-[44]. Signed A. H. Condict. A history of the Post and its activities.

WATTS, CHARLES, 1845?-

A war friendship. "Bill and me." [Library, Pa.: Springbrook Printery, 1906] 23p. front. (ports.) CSMH NJR (photo) 291

Caption title.

Reminiscences of wartime experiences shared by two friends in Co. C, 1st N.J. Cavalry. Watts served 1863-1865 in various ranks from corporal to captain in three companies of the regiment. "Bill" was William W. Branson (1844-1906).

WEISER, GEORGE.

Nine months in Rebel prisons, by George Weiser, Company A, 10th Regiment, New Jersey volunteers. Philadelphia: John N. Reeve & Co., 1890. 2p.l., [9]-53, [1]p. front. (port.) ports. DLC IN NJR (photo) NHI OCLWHI 292

The author (then of Elizabeth, N.J.) enlisted September 1861, was captured near Spotsylvania, Va., in May 1864, imprisoned at Andersonville and elsewhere.

WELLS, EDWARD LAIGHT, 1839-

"A morning call on General Kilpatrick. By E. L. Wells." *Southern Historical Society papers.* v.12, 1884. p.123-130. 293

An event during Sherman's march to the sea. "The principal agent to whom this devastation was entrusted, General Kilpatrick, commanded Sherman's cavalry. A brief interview with him is the *raison d'etre* of the present article." The author, a Confederate cavalryman, describes a surprise foray into Kilpatrick's camp in March 1865, near Fayetteville, N.C.

[WOODHULL, ALFRED ALEXANDER] 1837-1921.

"Snicker's Gap." *United States service magazine.* v.4, 1865. p.323-328. 294

Woodhull, a native of Princeton (also resident there in retirement) and graduate of Princeton University, was an army medical officer, retiring 1894 as brevet lieutenant-colonel.

MINOR ESSAYS, PROPAGANDA, ETC.

[ANONYMOUS]

"E pluribus unum." *Nassau literary magazine.* v.21, 1860/61. p.288-292. 295

A student patriotic effusion. The *Nassau Literary Magazine* was conducted by Princeton College undergraduates, most of the articles in this period being unsigned.

———

"The instability of nations." *Ibid.* v.23, 1862/63. p.126-128. 296

———

"Public opinion." *Ibid.*, p.267-272. 297

Signed (p.272) : K.

———

"Sumter. By 'Beta.'" *Nassau quarterly magazine.* v.1, 1864/65. p.39-44. 298

Undergraduate views on the meaning of Sumter.

———

"Virtue of patriotism." *Nassau literary magazine.* v.24, 1863/64. p.84-89. 299

Signed (p.89) : My.

BROWNSON, ORESTES AUGUSTUS, 1803-1876.

The American republic: its Constitution, tendencies, and destiny. By O. A. Brownson, LL.D. New York: P. O'Shea [c1865] xvi, 439p., 1 leaf. DLC 299a

Preface signed (p.xvi) : O. A. Brownson. Elizabeth, N.J., September 16, 1865.
Includes chapters on secession, reconstruction, political tendencies.

———

[*Same*] 1866. xvi, 439p. DLC NJR 299b

There are also later printings of this book.

———

Brownson on the Rebellion. St. Louis: Reprinted from Brownson's quarterly review for Oct. by order of Committee Union men [1861] cover-title, 30p. NJR (photo) NNC 299c

Caption title: Slavery and the war.
Includes comment on the Catholic position (Brownson being a convert to the faith).

BURR, CHARLES CHAUNCEY, 1817-1883.

The history of the Union, and of the Constitution. Being the substance of three lectures on the Saxon and the Norman principles of government, as traced in the colonial, Revolutionary, and constitutional periods of American history. By C. Chauncey Burr . . . Hackensack, N.J., 1862. iv, [5]-80p. DLC NJP PHI 300

"Electrotyped by T. R. Dawley."
Noted copperhead editor, lecturer, and writer, resident of Hackensack, explores the background of states' rights, the nature of the Union (from a Southern viewpoint), etc.

———

[*Same: second edition?*] The history of the Union, and of the Constitution. Being the substance of three lectures, on the colonial, Revolutionary, and constitutional periods of American history, with an appendix containing the Constitution of the United States. By C. Chauncey Burr . . . New York: Van Evrie, Horton & Co., 1862. iv, [5]-92p. NN OCLWHI PU 301

"Electrotyped by T. R. Dawley."

———

[*Same: third edition*] The history of the Union, and of the Constitution. Being the substance of three lectures on the colonial, Revolutionary and constitutional periods of American history, with an appendix containing the Constitution of the United States, and the Virginia and Kentucky Resolutions of '98. By C. Chauncey Burr . . . Third edition. New York: Van Evrie, Horton & Co., 1863. iv, [5]-92, 4p. DLC NJHI OCLWHI PPL 302

"Electrotyped by T. R. Dawley."

———————

[*Same*] 1866. DLC NHI 303

———————

[*Same*] 1868. OCLFC 303a

———————

Notes on the Constitution of the United States, with expositions of the most eminent statesmen and jurists. Historical and explanatory notes on every article. By C. Chauncey Burr . . . New York: Published by J. F. Feeks [1864] 1p.l., ii, [5]-95, [1], viii, [4]p. DLC NJP NJR NN PHI PPL 304

Text of the Constitution with interspersed notes.

CAPEN, NAHUM, 1804-1886.

The indissoluble nature of the American Union, considered in connection with the assumed right of secession. A letter to Hon. Peter Cooper, New York. By Nahum Capen. Boston: A. Williams and Company; New York: Ross and Tousey, 1862. 36p. CTY DLC MB MWA NJHI NHI NN OCLWHI PHI PP PPL 305

Dated Mount Ida, Dorchester, Nov. 1, 1861.
Cooper, a New Yorker, had extensive commercial interests in New Jersey.

COOPER, PETER, 1791-1883.

. . . The death of slavery. Letter from Peter Cooper to Governor Seymour. [New York, 1863?] 7, [1]p. (Loyal Publication Society. [Pamphlet] no. 28) DLC NN 306

Caption title.
Except for added text on verso of p.7, this is from the same plates as no. 307.
Although a New York man, Cooper operated a wire factory at Trenton, foundries at Ringwood, and iron mines in northern New Jersey.

———————

. . . The death of slavery. Letter from Peter Cooper to Governor Seymour. New York, Oct., 1863. New York: Wm. C. Bryant & Co., printers, 1863. cover-title, 7p. (Loyal Publication Society. [Pamphlet] no. 28) DLC NJJ NN PP PU 307

———————

. . . A letter from Peter Cooper. To his excellency Abraham Lincoln, President of the United States. [New York, 1863] 4p. (Loyal Publication Society. [Pamphlet] no. 28, pt. 2) DLC 308

Caption title.
Not seen; description from DLC printed catalog.

———————

. . . A letter from Peter Cooper. To his excellency Abraham Lincoln, President of the United States. [New York, 1863?] [9]-12p. (Loyal Publication Society. [Pamphlet] no. 28, pt. 2) DLC NN 309

Caption title.
Paged to follow his *Death of Slavery*, which is no. 28 (i.e., no. 28, pt. 1) of the Society's pamphlet series.

———————

. . . Letter of Peter Cooper, on slave emancipation. [New York, 1863] 8p. (Loyal Publication Society. [Pamphlet] no. 23) DLC PP 310

Caption title.
A letter to President Lincoln, dated New York, January, 1862.

———————

. . . Letter of Peter Cooper on slave emancipation. New York, July, 1863. New York: Wm. C. Bryant & Co., printers, 1863. cover-title, 8p. (Loyal Publication Society. [Pamphlet] no. 23) DLC NHI NN 311

———————

. . . Letter of Peter Cooper on slave emancipation. New York, Oct., 1863. New York: Wm. C. Bryant & Co., printers, 1863. cover-title, 8p. (Loyal Publication Society. [Pamphlet] no. 23) DLC NHI NN OCLWHI PU 312

CUTTER, MARY H.

The McElroy prize compositions. Our country; by Mary H. Cutter and Mary T. Reed. Woodbridge, July 4, 1863. New York: W. C. Bryant & Co., 1863. 16p. 313

Not seen. Title taken from J. R. Bartlett, *Literature of the Rebellion* (3120), and Joseph Sabin, *Dictionary of Books Relating to America* (43228).

HOLT, JOSEPH, 1807-1894.

Letters of the Hon. Joseph Holt, the Hon. Edward Everett, and Commodore Charles Stewart, on the present crisis. Philadelphia: William S. & Alfred Martien, 1861. 45, [2]p. DLC MB NJHI NJNBS NJP NJR NHI NN PP PU 314

"Letter from Commodore Stewart. Bordentown, May 4, 1861": p.[41]-45. Reminiscences of an 1812 conversation with John C. Calhoun reflecting sectional differences and forecasting disruption of the Union.

[HUNT, EZRA MUNDY] 1830-1894.

About the war. Plain words to plain people, by a plain man. Philadelphia, 1863. 16p. DLC NJP NJR NHI 315

"Printed for gratuitous distribution."—*cover*.

Author identified in Halkett & Laing, *Dictionary of Anonymous and Pseudonymous English Literature*. Hunt was a Metuchen physician, briefly assistant surgeon of the 29th N.J. Vols., for several months on detached service in charge of the Calvert Street Hospital, Baltimore.

————

About the war. Plain words to plain people, by a plain man. Philadelphia: Printed for gratuitous distribution, 1863. 16p. DLC NHI NN PP PU 316

————

About the war. Plain words to plain people, by a plain man. [Philadelphia] Union League in Philadelphia [Henry B. Ashmead, printer] 1863. 16p. DLC NJR NHI NN PP 317

"Furnished gratuitously by the Union League."—*cover*. Cover-title of at least one of the copies seen (NJR) instead of these words has imprint: "Union League in Philadelphia. 1863."

————

[*Same: German edition*] Vom Kriege. Einfache Worte an einfache Leute, von einem einfachen Manne. Philadelphia, 1863. 16p. NHI NN PP PU 318

Engraved title vignette is identical with that of the several English versions, nos. 315-317.

HUNT, EZRA MUNDY, 1830-1894.

The war and its lessons, by Ezra M. Hunt, author of "Words about the war," &c. New York: Printed by F. Somers, 1862. 35p. CSMH DLC MB MWA NJP NJPT NJR NHI OCLWHI 319

Possibly a 4th of July oration.

————

Words about the war: or, Plain facts for plain people. By Ezra M. Hunt . . . New York: Printed by F. Somers, 1861. 39p. DLC NJHI NJP NHI NN OCLWHI 320

POTTS, WILLIAM D.

Our country vindicated; and democracy sustained. Being a review of the fallacies, fanaticism and delusions of the abolition preachers, and the policy of the Republican abolition party. By Rev. William D. Potts, M.D., author of "Lectures on the true development of man," "Nature the great physician," "Honorable courtship and true marriage," etc. etc. etc. Newark, N.J. New York: Published by the author, 1864. 96p. CSMH NJP NHI 321

Letterpress on covers.

A particular attack on Rev. Henry C. Fish's 1863 thanksgiving discourse, *The Valley of Achor* (no. 690). Potts appears in the Newark directories, 1859-1864, as proprietor of a botanic store on Broad Street, and another in New York.

PUGH, JOHN HOWARD, 1827-1905.

Our Union and its defenders: an oration, delivered before the citizens of Burlington, N.J., on . . . July 4th, 1862. By J. Howard Pugh, M.D. Philadelphia: King & Baird, printers, 1862. 23p. DLC NJR NHI PHI 322

Many allusions to the war.

The speaker was a Burlington physician who served during the war, without compensation, at the U.S. General Hospital, Beverly, N.J. Was a Republican member of Congress 1877-1879.

[SCHWARTZ, ?]

What are the conditions of a candid and lasting reconciliation between the two sections of the country? New York: Bowne & Co., stationers and printers, 1861. 69, [1]p. MB MH NHI NN OCLWHI PHC PHI PP 323

Contemporary note (by George Bancroft) on the title-page of one NN copy: "By Dr. Schwartz of Jersey City." Also presentation inscription: "Yours respectfully / B. Westermann & Co."

A detailed and moderate (but pro-Northern) analysis of disputed issues on which the author suggests compromises or concessions by one side or the other: nature of the Union; slavery; tariff; foreign policy; constitutional revision. Apparently written soon after outbreak of the war.

STITES, TOWNSEND, 1819-1863.

"A relic of Civil War times." *Almanac and year book, First National Bank, Woodstown, N.J.* 1915. p.23-25. port. 324

Copy of a long letter to Dan Ware of Woodstown, April 27, 1861. The writer (of Beesley's Point, Cape May County, N.J.), having just arrived at Philadelphia from Wilmington, N.C., expresses at length his views of the conflict just begun. He died two years later while serving in the U.S. Navy.

POETRY, FICTION, AND DRAMA

[BAKER, SARAH SCHOONMAKER (TUTHILL)] 1824-1906.

Charlie the drummer-boy. [New York: American Tract Society, 186–] cover-title, 16p. NJP 325

Caption title: Charlie the drummer-boy. By the author of The boy patriot, etc.

Narrative poem about a wounded drummer-boy.

Mrs. Woods Baker lived in Princeton from about 1852, writing under the name of "Aunt Friendly" many stories for children ("high-toned religious literature"). Cf J. F. Hageman, *History of Princeton* (1879), v.2, p.403-404.

————————

The picket-guard. By Aunt Friendly, author of "Little Verbena," "Amy and her brothers," etc. . . . New-York: Published by the Protestant Episcopal Society for the Promotion of Evangelical Knowledge [1864] 60p. NJP 326

Fiction. A pious widow and her little boy Harry nurse an ailing soldier and inspire him to Christian charity.

Year of publication taken from James Kelly, *American Catalogue,* 1861/66, p.164.

"THE BATTLE OF GETTYSBURG." *Nassau literary magazine.* v.24, 1862/63. p.102-104. 327

Signed (p.104): Tartan.

Poem by a Princeton undergraduate.

THE BATTLE OF THE WILDERNESS, MAY 5th, 6th and 7th, 1864. Trenton: Hough & Yard, printers, 1864. [17]p. NJR RPB 327a

Poetry.

BLACKMAN, LEAH (MATHIS)

An address, by the ladies of Little Eggharbor, to the Irick Infantry, of Little Eggharbor. [Tuckerton, N.J., 1861] Broadside. 7¼ x 4¾ in. NJR (photo) PPL 328

Signed: Leah Blackman. Tuskerton [*sic*], June, 1861.

Seven stanzas of patriotic cheer for the volunteers from Little Egg Harbor. "Soldiers we think that you feel proud, That you're likely to win a shroud, And sleep in a warrier's grave, O'er which the Stars and Stripes may wave."

Little Egg Harbor Township, then part of Burlington County, is now in Ocean County.

BRICK, JOHN.

The Richmond raid. A novel by John Brick. Garden City, N.Y.: Doubleday & Company, inc., 1963. 5p.l., [3]-279p. DLC 328a

The Kilpatrick-Dahlgren raid.

[BURR, CHARLES CHAUNCEY] 1817-1883.

"What has the war done?" *The Old guard.* v.5, 1867. p.500. 329

Verse, signed "C.C.B." (doubtless Burr, copperhead editor of the *Old Guard*).

CARRIERS' ADDRESS TO THE PATRONS OF the New-Brunswick Fredonian, January 1, 1862. [New Brunswick, N.J., 1861] Broadside. 18¾ x 12 in. NJR 330

A review (in verse) of the past year (1861), about three-quarters dealing with the war.

Carriers' addresses were distributed by newspaper carriers (newsboys) about Christmas or New Year's Day as a means of eliciting gratuities from their customers.

COLES, EDWIN, 1833?-

The Jersey boys' rations. Air.—"Joe Bowers." [n.p., 1861] Broadside. 12 x 4½ in. NJHI 331

A verse describing a riot by New Jersey volunteers (quartered at Trenton) in protest against unfit rations provided by one Dan Lockwood of Newark.

Signed: Edwin Coles, Co. F 1st Regiment New Jersey Volunteers.

The author was a member of the First Regiment (militia), which served April 30-July 31, 1861, mustered into service at Trenton, May 1, and leaving the state two days later for Washington. The event described must have taken place in late April or very early May, 1861.

One Edwin Coles later (1861-1863) served in the 8th N.J. Vols.

CULLEN, CASSIUS C.

The American melodies, in three parts, and miscellaneous poems, by Cassius C. Cullen. Trenton, N.J.: Murphy & Bechtel, printers, 1864. 96p. CTY DLC MB MWA NJ NJN NJP NN OCLWHI 332

Verses only.

Dedicated (p.[3]) "to the gallant and patriotic soldiers of New Jersey, as a slight tribute to their heroic conduct, unflinching gallantry and invincible courage . . ." (etc.).

In four groupings: Part I (p.[7]-62), "composed behind the plow prior to the war for the Union"; Part II (p.[63]-69), "composed at sea . . . during my term of service in the United States Navy, in the years 1862 and 1863"; Part III (p.[71]-79), "composed during the war for the Union"; and "Miscellaneous poems" (p.[81]-93).

Many patriotic and wartime verses.

[CURTS, HENRY] 1822?-1895.

New-Year's address, of the watchmen of Camden city, for the season of 1862. [Camden, N.J.] Curts, printer [1861] Broadside. 12 x 9½ in. NHI 333

Ten stanzas of verse, several having war allusions.

Like carriers' addresses, the watchmen's addresses were distributed about Christmas or New Year in the hope of cadging gifts from persons served by the watchmen (i.e., policemen) on their beats.

Added to the copy seen (in NHI) is the printed name, "Simpson Force, Policeman"; also a 19th-century pencil note: "Composed by Henry Curts of Camden N.J. Presented to Burl[ingto]n Co Lyceum by HC."

DEWOLFE, GEORGE G. B.

Lines on the death of Mrs. Gen. J. Kilpatrick. [n.p., 1864?] Broadside. 11 x 5½ in. NJR (photo) PPL 333a

Fifteen stanzas in two columns, the first headed by a cut of an officer on horseback.

" 'Twas near the classic Rapidan . . ." The ballad pictures Kilpatrick, while poised to cross the river with his troops, learning that his young wife Alice [Nailer] had died.

Signed: Geo. G. B. DeWolfe.

DeWolfe apparently called himself "the Wandering Poet of New Hampshire."

There is a shorter poem in James Moore, *Kilpatrick and Our Cavalry* (p.135), "Lines Written by Miss Jennie Gray, upon the Death of Her Friend, Mrs. General Kilpatrick."

"A DREAM OF DUTY." *Nassau literary magazine.* v.23, 1862/63. p.16-18. 334

Poem by a Princeton student.

Signed (p.18): L.

ELLIS, EDWARD SYLVESTER, 1840-1916.

"Through the 'green sea.' A tale of the Dismal Swamp in 1865. By Edward S. Ellis . . ." *Blue and gray.* v.1, 1893. p.241-246, 329-338, 421-427. 335

A fictional narrative, whose hero, Dick Wilkes, from Trenton, N.J., was a drummer of Co. K, 23rd N.J. Regt. The Dismal Swamp lay partly in Virginia, partly in North Carolina.

ENGLISH, THOMAS DUNN, 1819-1902.

"The charge by the ford." *The Old guard.* v.5, 1867. p.89-90. 336

Verse dealing with a cavalry raid.

The author was a well-known writer, Democratic politician (wartime copperhead), and editor (in 1870 of the *Old Guard*). He lived at this time in Bergen County, later in Newark. For several years during the 1850's he practiced law and medicine in present West Virginia.

———————

"The letter to the dead." *Northern monthly magazine.* v.1, 1867. p.565-566. 337

Poetry concerning an event at the Wilderness.

Anonymous but author is identified in volume table-of-contents.

———————

"The lost cause." *The Old guard.* v.5, 1867. p.62-63. 338

Verse expressing sympathy for the defeated South.

EXTRACT FROM THE MINUTES OF A stated meeting of the "Burlington Reserve Guard," after their visit to Mount Holly, Nov. 26, 1861. [n.p., 1861] Broadside. 11¾ x 6⅛ in. NJR 339

A humorous verse concerning hap and mishap during a militia training day. No apparent concern with realities of war.

HAVEN, CHARLES CHAUNCEY, 1787?-1874.

National Thanksgiving ode. By C. C. Haven. Air—Old hundred. [Trenton, N.J., 1863] Broadside. 11 x 7 in. NJR (photo) PPL 339a

Song sheet (words only).
Dated: Trenton, N.J., November, 1863.
Concerned chiefly with the war.

———————

Thanksgiving song. By C. C. Haven. Air—Old hundred. [Trenton, N.J., 1864] Broadside. 10¾ x 5¼ in. NJR (photo) PPL 339b

Words only.
Dated: Trenton, N.J., November 24, 1864.
About the war.

JOHNSON, F. B.

The sons of New Jersey. Composed at Dividing Creek, by F. B. Johnson. Air—Wait for the wagon. [Philadelphia] Johnson, printer [1863] Broadside. 9¾ x 4 in. NJR (photo) PPL 339c

Song sheet (words only).
"There was a call for Volunteers sometime in last year, And there the Sons of New Jersey did quickly volunteer, . . . in Company K, to give the South a slamb [*sic*] . . . There is our gallant 24th we know wont' [*sic*] leave the ranks . . ."

JONES, JOHN BEAUCHAMP, 1810-1866.

Border war; a tale of disunion. By J. B. Jones . . . New York: Rudd & Carleton, 1859. x, [11]-502, [2], 6p. DLC MH MWA NJP -NN OCLWHI PU

Publisher's advertisements at end.
A prophetic novel. Its Southern-born author left his Burlington (N.J.) home for more congenial climes soon after the firing at Fort Sumter. Jones' later experiences are described in his *Rebel War Clerk's Diary* (no. 250).
Published also under the title, *Wild Southern Scenes,* and republished in 1861 as *Secession, Coercion, and Civil War* (nos. 341, 342). L. H. Wright, *American Fiction, 1851-1875,* no. 1370, gives locations of fifteen copies.

[JONES, JOHN BEAUCHAMP] 1810-1866.

Secession, coercion, and civil war. The story of 1861 . . . Philadelphia: T. B. Peterson and Brothers [c1861] 1p.l., [v]-x, [11]-502, [2]-8, [1]p. DLC NJP NJR 341

Publisher's advertisements at end.
Appeared originally in two 1859 editions (see nos. 340, 342) under different titles. L. H. Wright, *American Fiction, 1851-1875,* no. 1370, gives library locations of four copies.

JONES, JOHN BEAUCHAMP, 1810-1866.

Wild Southern scenes. A tale of disunion! and border war! By J. B. Jones . . . Philadelphia: T. B. Peterson & Brothers [c1859] iv, [2], [v]-x, [11]-502, [2]-8, [1]p. front. DLC NJP NJR NN OCLWHI 342

Publisher's advertisements at end. Pagination differs in some copies.
Also published under two other titles (see nos. 340, 341). L. H. Wright, *American Fiction, 1851-1875,* no. 1370, locates nine copies.

KILPATRICK, HUGH JUDSON, 1836-1881.

. . . Allatoona. An historical and military drama in five acts. By Maj.-Gen. Judson Kilpatrick, and J. Owen Moore . . . New York: Published by Samuel French & Son, c1875. 48p. (French's standard drama, no. 376) DLC NJR OCLWHI PPL PU 343

Jonathan Owen Moore (1838-1908?), of Orange County, N.Y., ultimately a New York City businessman, met Kilpatrick during the war, and continued as a friend, admirer, and whilom companion. He accompanied the General on a three-week New England lecture tour in December 1875 (in the course of which, incidentally, the latter wrote a series of articles published in the New York *Times*). After the General's death, Moore prepared a sketch of his friend ("General Kilpatrick. A Brief Biography by Maj. J. Owen Moore"), which appeared serially, Dec. 23, 1881-Jan. 27, 1882, in the Deckertown (now Sussex), N.J., *Sussex Independent.*

———————

The blue and the gray; or, War is hell. Revised and edified by Christopher Morley from an old script by Judson Kilpatrick and J. Owen Moore. Garden City, N.Y.; Doubleday, Doran & Company, inc., 1930. xvp., 4 leaves, 126p. DLC MB NJR PU 344

Four-act play, "an adaptation of the forgotten Allatoona, conceived by the dashing cavalry commander Judson Kilpatrick and based on his own experiences in the Georgia campaign."
"First edition after the printing of a limited edition of one hundred copies, signed by the author [i.e., Morley]."
Differs considerably from the 1875 original.

KING, CHARLES, 1844-1933.

Between the lines. A story of the war. By Captain Charles King, U.S.A. . . . New York: Harper & Brothers, 1889. iv, 312, [4]p. front., plates. DLC NJHI NJP NJR NHI NN 345

A novel about one Frank Kearny, lieutenant (ultimately colonel) of a New Jersey cavalry regiment (his horse named "Ramapo"), serving with the Army of the Potomac in Virginia, and his love for a Southern girl.

———————

Between the lines; a story of the war. By Captain Charles King, U.S.A. . . . New York [etc.]: "Brentano's" [n.d.] iv, 312, [2]p. front., plates. NN 346

"Copyright, 1888, by Harper & Brothers." (Unnumbered last two pages also bear advertisements of Harper & Brothers.)

Other issues or editions of this novel can be identified.

———————

"Between the lines. By Captain Charles King, U.S.A." *Harper's weekly*. v.32, p.909ff. (Dec. 1, 1888), continued serially through v.33, p.190-191 (March 9, 1889) illus. 347

[LLOYD, G. W.]

The devil in Dixie: a tale of the times. Serio-comical, semi-historical, and quasi-diabolical . . . New-York: American News Company, 1865. 76p. DLC NJHI NN 347a

"Entered . . . in the year 1865, by G. W. Lloyd, in the Clerk's Office of the District Court of the United States for the Southern District of New York."—p.[2].

American history in verse. The author is believed to be Rev. George W. Lloyd (1821-1906), Presbyterian pastor at Branchville, N.J., 1857-1866. He produced at least one other published poem in this period (see no. 94), and also *Lyrics of Lake and Stream* (Branchville, 1899).

LONG, JOHN D. 1817?-

9th New-Jersey Volunteer Regiment.—By J. D. Long, private of Company C. N.Y.: H. De Marsan, publisher, of songs, ballads, toy books, etc. [1862] Broadside. 10¼ x 6½ in. NJR (photo) PPL 347b

Twelve stanzas of verse, in part recording the regiment's initial adventures.

LOPER, HORACE E. 1840?-

The New Jersey Third! By H. E. Loper, Company F. Air—"Caroline of Edinborough town." [n.p., 1861?] Broadside. 9¼ x 5 in. NJR (photo) PPL 347c

Song sheet (words only).

Fourteen verses, recording the regiment's history during the first months of its service, etc.

Loper was a musician (fifer).

NEW-YEAR'S ADDRESS OF THE CARRIERS of the New-Brunswick Fredonian. 1865. [New Brunswick, N.J., 1864] Broadside. 18 x 8 in. NJR 348

In verse; a review of events during the past year (1864), especially the war.

"ON THE BRIDGE." *Nassau literary magazine*. v.24, 1863/64. p.79-80. 349

Signed (p.80): Quiggle.

Verse concerning the reveries of a sentry, written by a Princeton student.

PEERS, REBECCA F.

The national fast. [Camden, N.J., 1861] Broadside. 8 x 4½ in. NJR (photo) PPL 349a

Twelve stanzas of verse, largely concerned with the war.

Signed: Miss Rebecca F. Peers. For the National Fast, September 26th, 1861. Camden, N.J.

PETTICOAT JEFF. AS SUNG BY G. C. B. Holloway . . . Jersey City: From the "Times" publishing house [1865] Broadside. 9¾ x 5½ in. NJHI 350

Song sheet (verse only).

"Air: 'Tim Finnegan's Wake.' "

"Entered according to act of Congress, in the year 1865, by T. F. Holloway . . ."

The subject, of course, was Jefferson Davis, whose effort (in female disguise) to escape capture at the war's end was widely ridiculed in the North.

. . . PETTICOAT JEFF. AS SUNG BY G. C. B. Holloway . . . Philada.: A. W. Auner's printing office [1865] Broadside. 9½ x 6 in. NJHI 351

At head of title: A. W. Auner, song publisher, N.E. cor. 11th, & Market, Philada. Pa.

"Air: Tim Finnegan's Wake."

"Entered according to Act of Congress, in the year 1865, by T. F. Holloway, in the Clerk's Office of the U.S. District Court of New Jersey."

PRICE, THEOPHILUS TOWNSEND, 1828-1908.

The true Jersey Blue. By T. T. Price, M.D. Tune—The "Red, white and blue." [Philadelphia] Johnson, song publisher [1861] Broadside. 8½ x 5 in. NJR (photo) PPL 351a

Song sheet (words only).

Dated: June, 1861.

Dr. Price was a leading citizen of Tuckerton, N.J.

PYATT, ASA, 1800?-

A national song: by Asa Pyatt, New-Brunswick, N.J. Tune.—Auld lang syne. [New Brunswick? 1861?] Broadside. 15¼ x 12¼ in. NJR

Fifty-six stanzas reciting poetically the history of the United States from 1776 to the beginning of the Civil War. "Abraham Lincoln has now the chair . . . And what course he will now pursue, Is not for me to tell" (etc.). Perhaps written for the Fourth of July, 1861.

Pyatt was a New Brunswick school teacher.

———————

The last of Jeff. Davis. Composed by Asa Pyatt of New-Brunswick, N.J. [New Brunswick? 1865] Broadside. 10¼ x 5 in. NJR 353

Verse; concerning Davis' arrest, etc.

SMITH, ELIAS DARBY, 1840-

My rhymes. [By] Elias D. Smith . . . Elizabeth, N.J.: Journal print, 1902. 64p. NJR 353a

"Private print."

"A goodly portion are re-union odes, read at the annual gatherings of the regiment [14th N.J. Vols.] to which I am proud to have belonged during the civil war."

———————

On Hurley hills and other verse. By Elias D. Smith. Boston: Sherman, French & Company, 1911. 5p.l., 86p. DLC NJR 353b

"Drums and bugles: military verse": p.[41]-86. ("A goodly portion are re-union odes, read at the annual gatherings of the regiment to which I am proud to have belonged . . . the 14th Regt. N.J. Vols. 6th Corps.")

About half of the war poems were printed also in his *My Rhymes* (see preceding entry).

SOEMMER, R. S.

Fourth of July. (For S.S. celebrations.) Written for the Fourth of July, festival of St Stephen's Sunday School, Millburn, New Jersey. Words by a friend of the school. Music by R. S. Soemmer, org. of the church. New York: Published by Horace Waters, c1864. Broadside. 9 x 11½ in. NJR 354

"Warren, Music Stereotyper, Rear 43 Centre-st., New York."

Music and seven verses, largely concerned with the war.

STAATS, ABRAHAM DUBOIS, 1846-1897.

"Prize poem. Pro patria. [By] A. DuBois Staats." *Nassau quarterly magazine.* v.1, 1864/65. p.[73]-75. 355

The writer was a Princeton College student.

STEDMAN, EDMUND CLARENCE, 1833-1908.

"Kearny at Seven Pines." [Kearny, Philip] *Service with the French troops in Africa.* [n.p., 1888?] p.83-86. 356

Verse.

Original of this poem is in the NJR manuscript collection.

TERRILL, LEWIS HALSEY, 1807-1874.

Carrier's address. 1866. 1866. [*sic*] New-Year compliments to the patrons of the New-Brunswick Fredonian. Written by Rev. Lewis Halsey Terrill. [New Brunswick, N.J., 1865] Broadside. 19 x 12 in. NJR 356a

A review of the past year (1865) in verse, largely concerned with the war and its conclusion.

VINING, ELIZABETH JANET (GRAY) 1902-

Tilly-Tod, by Elizabeth Janet Gray; illustrated by Mary Hamilton Frye. Garden City, N.Y.: Doubleday, Doran & Company, inc., 1929. 5p.l., 3-173p. col. front., illus. DLC 357

Not seen. Entry based on DLC catalog card.

Juvenile fiction. "Story of a little Quaker girl and her family in Woodstown during the Civil War."—Horace G. Richards, *One Hundred South Jersey Novels* (1947), no. 36.

MISCELLANY

ALBION, ROBERT GREENHALGH, 1896-

"An unrivalled Civil War collection. Princeton profits from the untiring work of John Shaw Pierson '40. By Robert G. Albion . . ." *Princeton alumni weekly.* v.33, 1932/33. p.[401]-402. illus. (incl. port.) 358

Informal description of the Princeton University Library's valuable Pierson collection. (For titles, see the Library's *Classed List* [1920], v.6, p.2985-3077.)

CATTON, BRUCE, 1899-

. . . Text of speech delivered by Mr. Bruce Catton. [Trenton, N.J.: New Jersey Civil War Centennial Commission, 1962] 8 leaves. NJR 358a

Caption title.

At head of title: N.J. Civil War Centennial Commission second annual American History Workshop, Saturday, December 8, 1962.

The Union army and its reaction to the Emancipation Proclamation.
Mimeographed.

CROSSED FLAGS; a publication of the Civil War Round Table of Northern New Jersey, inc. v.1-*plus*. Sept. 1961 *to date*. East Orange, N.J., 1961-*date*. NJR 359

"Published ten times a year at Upsala College."
Numbering erratic (v.3 omitted).
Mimeographed.

ELLIS, LEWIS ETHAN, 1898-

Steps in a journey toward understanding: activities of the New Jersey Civil War Centennial Commission in 1961 at Trenton, Charleston and Salem Church. By L. Ethan Ellis, Voorhees professor of history, Rutgers University, New Brunswick, N.J. Trenton, N.J.: N.J. Civil War Centennial Commission, 1963. 1p.l., 29, [1]p. incl. port., facsims. illus. NJ NJHI NJN NJR NJT 360

GRAPE AND CANISTER from the Civil War Round Table of Northern New Jersey, inc. v.1, nos. 1-6. Jan.-June 1961. East Orange, N.J., 1961. NJR 361

A mimeographed newsletter published monthly at Upsala College.
Followed by a similar publication, *Crossed Flags*.

[HAMILTON, E. J.]

Uncle John in the army and among the freedmen. New York: Published by the American Tract Society [1867] 94p. illus. NJNBT NJP NN 362

"A sketch of 'Uncle John [Vassar],' prepared by Rev. E. J. Hamilton, chaplain in the army of the Potomac, was published in the Appendix of 'Toils and Triumphs of Union Missionary Colportage for Twenty-five Years.' Its vivid and accurate delineation of the characteristics of this remarkable man, awakened so much interest . . . that it has been thought advisable to issue it in the present form . . ." —Introductory note, dated July 1867 (p.[2]).

Exact identification of the author, who had observed Vassar's work personally for about a year, is not certain. He may be the Rev. Edward J. Hamilton (1834-1918) who served as chaplain of the 7th N.J. Vols.

"Among the freedmen" (p.49-84), evidently by a different author, describes Uncle John's postwar labors "on the field of the Richmond Agency" of the American Tract Society.

"IMPORTANT OPINION OF THE UNITED States Attorney General. 'Are colored men citizens of the United States?'" *Friends' review*. v.16, 1862/63. p.269. 362a

Comments (with excerpts) on an affirmative opinion which resulted from the detaining of schooner *Elizabeth and Margaret*, of New Brunswick, "because commanded by a colored man, and so by a person not a citizen of the United States." The article notes that "colored masters are numerous in our coasting trade."

Text of the opinion, Nov. 29, 1862, can be found in U.S. Dept. of Justice, *Official Opinions of the Attorneys General*, v.10 (1868), p.382-413. See entry 370a.

KEARNY, PHILIP, 1815-1862.

. . . In chancery of New Jersey. Between Edward Kearny, executor of General [*portion of line cut out;* "Philip Kearney" *written at side in contemporary hand*] deceased, complainant, and Agnes Kearny, John Watts Kearny, and als., defendants. Bill for direction and relief. Trenton, N.J.: Hough & Yard, (successors to Phillips & Boswell) printers [1864?] 31p. NJ

Caption title.

MERCEREAU & CO.

. . . The star-spangled banner . . . [n.p., 1861] Broadside. 8½ x 6½ in. NJHI 364

Words only.
In two columns, each headed by a patriotic vignette. The left column consists of an advertisement for dry goods.
Dated June 1st, 1861.
Interesting as an example of wartime advertising.
Locality not determined.

MIERS, EARL SCHENCK, 1910-

. . . New Jersey and the Civil War; an album of contemporary accounts. Edited with introductions by Earl Schenck Miers. Princeton, N.J.: D. Van Nostrand Company, inc., 1964. xii, 135p. plates, ports. (New Jersey historical series. v.2) DLC NJ NJHI NJJ NJN NJP NJR NJT 365

Some three dozen short excerpts, chiefly from newspapers and other contemporary printed sources —descriptive articles, editorials, military letters and journals, etc.

NEW JERSEY. CIVIL WAR CENTENNIAL COMMISSION.

American History Workshop, presented by New Jersey Civil War Centennial Commission.

[1st]-4th, 1961-1964. [Trenton, N.J., 1961-1964] 4 pieces. illus. (ports., facsim.) NJ NJJ (4th) NJN (2nd-3rd) NJR NJT 366

Program, with portraits of the speakers, etc.
Workshops held at Princeton (1961) and Rutgers (1962-64) universities.
"New Jersey discovers a general" (Robert McAllister) : 3rd, 1963, p.[4]-[5], with port.

———————

Commemorative program marking the centennial of the battle of Ox Hill (Chantilly) sponsored jointly by Fairfax County Civil War Centennial Commission, New Jersey Civil War Centennial Commission, New York Civil War Centennial Commission, Virginia Civil War Commission, at Fairfax County, Virginia . . . September 1, 1962. Followed by a ceremony at the equestrian statue of Maj. Gen. Philip Kearny . . . Arlington National Cemetery, Arlington, Va. [Trenton, N.J.: N.J. Civil War Centennial Commission, 1962] [4]p. illus. (incl. ports.) NJR 366a

"The battle of Ox Hill, by Lt. Col. Robert Ross Smith": p.[3]-[4].

———————

Proceedings of rededication program honoring the memory of the gallant New Jersey men who fought in the battles of Salem Church, the Wilderness and Spotsylvania Court House. Presented by New Jersey Civil War Centennial Commission at the Bloody Angle, Spotsylvania, Va. . . . May 16, 1964, Fredericksburg & Spotsylvania National Military Park, Fredericksburg, Va. [Trenton, N.J., 1964] [2], 2-10, [5] leaves. NJ NJR 367

Mimeographed.
Contains brief addresses.

———————

Rededication program honoring the memory of the gallant New Jersey men who fought in the battles of Salem Church, the Wilderness and Spotsylvania Court House, presented by New Jersey Civil War Centennial Commission at the Bloody Angle, Spotsylvania, Va. . . . May 16, 1964, Fredericksburg & Spotsylvania National Military Park, Fredericksburg, Va. [Trenton, N.J., 1964] [8]p. illus. (incl. port.) map. NJ NJR 368

"Jerseymen at Spotsylvania, by Ralph Happel—park historian": p.[5].

NEW JERSEY EDUCATION ASSOCIATION.

Common man in crisis. Proceedings of special meeting, annual convention New Jersey Educational Association, Atlantic City, N.J., November 8, 1962, featuring Dr. Bell I. Wiley, distinguished professor of history, Emory University, Atlanta, Ga. Co-sponsored by: N.J. Council for the Social Studies . . . [and] N.J. Civil War Centennial Commission . . . Trenton, N.J.: New Jersey Civil War Centennial Commission [1962] [1], 13, [1] leaves. NJR 368a

Mimeographed.
Address by Dr. Wiley: leaves 3-[14]. Some details about New Jersey military participation and the work of the state Civil War Centennial Commission, otherwise largely concerned with the everyday lives, etc., of soldiers on both sides.

QUARLES, BENJAMIN.

. . . Summary of remarks by Dr. Benjamin Quarles. [Trenton, N.J.: New Jersey Civil War Centennial Commission, 1962] 2 leaves. NJR

Caption title.
At head of title: N.J. Civil War Centennial Commission second annual American History Workshop, Saturday, December 8, 1962.
Mimeographed.
Brief comments on the Emancipation Proclamation. No New Jersey allusions.

RICHARDSON, GEORGE C. 1929-

Lincoln Day speech delivered by Assemblyman George C. Richardson before the N.J. General Assembly, February 11, 1963. [Trenton, N.J.: New Jersey Civil War Centennial Commission, 1963] cover-title, 3, [1] leaves. NJR 368c

Mimeographed.
Deals chiefly with the Emancipation Proclamation and present-day desegregation.

SEIBERT, GEORGE CARL, 1828-1902.

Die Zerstörung der Stadt Chambersburg durch die Rebellen am 30. Juli 1864. Nach persönlicher Erkundigung an Ort und Stelle, sowie nach den veröffentlichten Berichten des Augenzeugen Dr. B. S. Schneck. Historisch treu dargestellt von Dr. George Seibert, Pastor zu Newark, New Jersey. Philadelphia, Pa.: Zu haben bei J. Kohler, 1865. 49, 7p. front. (plan) DLC PU 369

Although in 1865 serving the Third German Presbyterian Church of Newark, Seibert had been pastor formerly of a church in Chambersburg.

Final seven pages devoted to publisher's advertisements.

———————

[*Same: second edition*] Die Zerstörung der Stadt Chambersburg durch die Rebellen am 30. Juli 1864. Nach persönlicher Erkundigung an Ort und Stelle, sowie nach den veröffentlichten Berichten des Augenzeugen Dr. B. S. Schneck. Historisch treu dargestellt von Dr. George Seibert . . . Zweite vermehrte Auflage, enthaltend: Ein Namensverzeichniss der Betroffenen. Philadelphia, Pa.: Zu haben bei J. Kohler [Gedruckt bei King & Baird, Philadelphia] 1865. 58, [1], 7p. front. (plan) DLC 370

Final eight pages devoted to publisher's advertisements.

U.S. DEPT. OF JUSTICE.

"Citizenship." *Official opinions of the Attorneys General of the United States.* v.10 (Washington, D.C., 1868) p.382-413. 370a

An opinion, dated Nov. 29, 1862, in response to a letter from the Secretary of the Treasury stating that "the schooner Elizabeth and Margaret, of New Brunswick, is detained by the revenue cutter Tiger, at South Amboy, New Jersey, because commanded by a 'colored man,' and so by a person not a citizen of the United States. As colored masters are numerous in our coasting trade, I submit, for your opinion, the question suggested by Captain Martin of the Tiger: Are *colored men citizens* of the United States, and therefore competent to command American vessels?"

The Attorney-General expresses his opinion affirmatively.

WHITE, MARGARET E.

". . . New Jersey mementos of the Civil War. [By] Margaret E. White." *Proceedings of the New Jersey Historical Society.* v.79, 1961. p.[134]-138. plate. 371

Informal description of museum and library objects owned by the New Jersey Historical Society.

RECRUITING AND THE DRAFT

ATTENTION VOLUNTEERS! THE 1ST REGIment of the new brigade just ordered by Gen. Wool, of New York, will leave for Washington on Wednesday. Able bodied volunteers from Newark, will be accepted immediately and mustered into service at once. Ample provision will be made for the support of the family of each volunteer. For particulars enquire at the recruiting office, in Broad Street . . . W. E. Buckingham, captain, &c., &c. Newark: Daily Advertiser print [1861] Broadside. $42\frac{1}{2}$ x 28 in. 372

Not seen. Description from F. P. Hill, *Books, Pamphlets and Newspapers Printed at Newark* (1902), no. 1451.

CAMDEN COUNTY, N.J. MILITARY COMMISSIONER.

Notice of drafting. The quotas of certain of the townships of the county of Camden for the nine months service not having been filled by volunteers, I shall proceed to make a draft to fill such deficiency, at the court house, in the city of Camden . . . for the townships of Newton, Gloucester, Washington and Waterford, on Friday, September 5. For the townships of Winslow, Centre, Delaware, and Stockton, on Saturday, September 6 . . . The city of Camden, and the townships of Union and Monroe, having furnished their quotas, will not be liable to a draft . . . William P. Tatem, commissioner. September 2, 1862. Camden, N.J.: S. Chew printer, "West Jersey Press" office [1862] Broadside. $18\frac{1}{4}$ x $12\frac{3}{4}$ in. NHI 373

FRIENDS, SOCIETY OF. PHILADELPHIA YEARLY MEETING. MEETING FOR SUFFERINGS.

"Memorial of the Meeting for Sufferings held in Philadelphia. To the Senate and House of Representatives of the United States of America, in Congress assembled." *Friends' review.* v.16, 1862/63. p.436-437. 373a

An expression of Quaker loyalty to the government, condemning the Southern rebellion, but affirming the Society's pacifist beliefs and entreating that the pending bill for enrolling and drafting the militia, or any other legislation, be made "to avoid whatever would press hardly upon the tender consciences of peaceable and loyal citizens" (i.e., Friends).

Signed: . . . Philadelphia, the 24th of the 2d month, 1863. Joseph Snowden, Clerk.

———————

Report of the committee of the Meeting for Sufferings, to advise and assist such Friends as might be drafted for military service. Also the report of the Committee for the Gradual Improvement and Civilization of the Indian Natives. 1865. Philadelphia: Printed by Thomas Sinex [1865] 16p. DLC PHC 373b

First report (p.[3]-7) dated "Philadelphia, 4th mo. 13th. 1865."

———————

To the President, Senate and House of Representatives of the United States. This memorial of the Representative Committee, or Meeting for Sufferings, of the Religious Society of Friends of Pennsylvania, New Jersey, Delaware, and adjacent parts of Maryland . . . Philadelphia, 1864. Broadside. 12½ x 8½ in. NJR 374

Signed: Samuel Parry, clerk. Philadelphia, 1st mo. 22d, 1864.

Petition for exemption from military obligation for men of the Quaker faith.

JERSEY CITY, N.J. COMMON COUNCIL. COMMITTEE ON ENLISTMENTS.

To the residents of the First Ward: Your Enlistment Committee present the following . . . [*Signed*] A. Barricklo, chairman. Jersey City, August 23, 1864. [Jersey City, N.J., 1864] Broadside. 10 x 7¾ in. NJP 375

Describes the Committee's plans: (1) lowering of the draft quotas by reducing the number of enrolled men subject to service; (2) raising of voluntary contributions to pay enlistment bounties, thus avoiding compulsory conscription. Those enrolled for the draft are urged to bring their contributions.

MANCHESTER TOWNSHIP (PASSAIC COUNTY) N.J.

6 men wanted to fill the quota of Manchester Township, to avoid the draft. Township bounty $500, gov. bounty $100, state bounty 6 dollars per month for married men, $2 per month for single men, besides government monthly pay, all bounties promptly paid. The following recruiting officers have been appointed, to whom application can be made. John B. Van Blarcom, Henry G. Ryerson. Recruiting officers. By order of the Township Committee. Dated, May 27, 1864. Paterson, N.J.: Daily "Register" print [1864] Broadside. 16½ x 13 in. NJPATPHI 375a

MEN WANTED FOR THE OLD REGIMENTS! N.J. volunteers. Bounty $615! All able-bodied men, between the ages of 18 and 45, who have served a period of not less than 9 months, by enlisting in any of the old New Jersey regiments or First New Jersey Cavalry, shall receive . . . advance pay and bounty of $615, as follows . . . [*Signed*] Samuel B. Jobes, captain, 12th N.J.V., recruiting officer . . . Mt. Holly, N.J. August 10th, 1863. Mount Holly, N.J.: Printed at the "Mirror office" [1863] Broadside. 24 x 18 in. NJR 376

MUTUAL PROTECTIVE UNION, JERSEY CITY, N.J.

The last call! To the citizens of the First Ward of Jersey City: . . . [*Signed*] O. W. Payne . . . [*and* 4 *others*], committee. C. W. Pudney, chairman. Geo. Stratford, treas. W. N. Haven, sec'y. Jersey City: John H. Lyon, steam printer [1864] Broadside. 12 x 9¾ in. NJP 377

With a draft impending several days hence [Sept. 19, 1864], the "committee of the Mutual Protective Union" calls upon citizens of the ward to subscribe funds for obtaining substitutes.

NEW JERSEY, PLAINTIFF.

. . . New Jersey Court of Errors and Appeals. The state of New Jersey, ex rel., Albertus K. Wagner, et al., prosecutors, vs. David Jackson, collector of taxes of the township of Delaware in the county of Hunterdon. Writ of error. Returnable to the March term, 1865. A. V. Van Fleet, attorney. Trenton: Hough & Yard, printers [1865?] 39p. table. NJ 378

Involves the protest of Wagner and other taxpayers against an 1864 assessment "to relieve the inhabitants of said township from the burthen of a draft."

NEW JERSEY. ADJUTANT-GENERAL'S OFFICE.

. . . General orders. no. 3. [Trenton, N.J., 1863] 8p. NJP NJR 379

Caption title.

At head of title: State of New Jersey. Adjutant General's Office, Trenton, June 29, 1863.

Includes tables (grouped by district and county) showing the number of recruits required of each municipality under the governor's proclamation of

June 25; also pertinent information concerning recruiting stations, transportation, term of service, bounty, pay, and other benefits for recruits and veteran volunteers.

NEW JERSEY. GOVERNOR, 1863-1866 (PARKER)

A proclamation by the governor. [Trenton, N.J., 1863] Broadside. 10 x 8 in. NJR 380

Dated Oct. 22, 1863.

A call for 9,441 volunteers, New Jersey's quota under the presidential call for 300,000 men. Parker reports that deficiencies will be supplied by draft, and urges every exertion to fill the requirement, with the use of bounties, etc.

NEW JERSEY. LEGISLATURE. GENERAL ASSEMBLY.

. . . An act to authorize the inhabitants of the township of Beverly in the county of Burlington to raise by tax an amount necessary to pay the bounties advanced to volunteers of the said township. [Trenton, N.J., 1864] Broadside. 12¾ x 8 in. NJR 381

At head of title: Assembly—no. 113. State of New Jersey.

———

. . . An act to authorize the inhabitants of the township of Willingborough, in the county of Burlington, to raise money by taxation to pay bounties to volunteers. [Trenton, N.J., 1864] 2p. 13 x 7½ in. NJR 382

Caption title.

At head of title: Assembly—no. 172. State of New Jersey.

———

[*Same*] Broadside. 13¼ x 8 in. NJR 383

Title identical with the preceding, except that "Burlington" has no comma following.

At head of title: <Reprint.> Assembly—no. 172. State of New Jersey.

Differs entirely from original bill 172.

———

. . . An act to extend the provisions of the act entitled "An act to authorize the inhabitants of the township of Burlington, in the county of Burlington, to raise money to pay bounties to volunteers["] [Trenton, N.J., 1864] Broadside. 12½ x 8 in. NJHI NJR 384

At head of title: Assembly—no. 340. State of New Jersey.

NEW JERSEY INFANTRY. 31ST REGT., 1862-1863. COMPANY A.

War meeting! A meeting will be held at Readington church, on Saturday evening the 23d inst. at 7 o'clock, for the purpose of raising volunteers, for Capt. Honeyman's company, to serve for nine months. Speakers will be in attendance. All who feel an interest in this war are requested to turn out and give their aid and influence in this very important matter. Drafting will not be necessary if there are enough volunteers. Aug. 21st 1862. Lieut. A. A. Thompson. Flemington, N.J.: Suydam, printer, "Gazette" printing office [1862] Broadside. 9½ x 12 in. NJFLHI 385

Andrew A. Thompson was a second lieutenant of Co. A, 31st N.J. Vols. Robert R. Honeyman, named here as captain of the company to be raised, became lieutenant-colonel of the regiment in February 1863.

NEW JERSEY INFANTRY. 35TH REGT., 1863-1865. COMPANY G.

Cladek Zouaves Co. G, 35th Reg't N.J. vols. Col. J. J. Cladek. Bounty, $615; government bounty, $415; city bounty, $200; state pay, $216; cash paid on muster, $240; city aid furnished those having families! Recruiting offices, 107 Market Street, and on the park, Lieut. Frank S. Taylor, recruiting officer. Newark: Mercury print [1863] Broadside. 43 x 33 in. 386

Not seen. Title from F. P. Hill, *Books, Pamphlets and Newspapers Printed at Newark* (1902), no. 1455.

NEW JERSEY INFANTRY. 39TH REGT., 1864-1865. COMPANY H.

39th Regiment! Only one year! Recruits wanted! For the new regiment lately authorized to be raised, to whom the highest bounties will be paid. Look at the following figures: Bounty and pay $864 . . . Cash paid on muster, $533.33. Capt. George W. Harrison, (late of the 26th Reg't) having received authority to recruit a company for the 39th Regiment, has established his head-quarters in Main St., near Centre, Orange, where recruits will be received. The pay for married men, in addition to rations and clothing, amounts to $16.60 per week. For single men, $15.60 per week. [Newark, N.J.] Newark Daily Advertiser print [1864] Broadside. About 42½ x 29 in. NJR (photo) 387

Harrison served as captain of Co. H from September 1864 until his death in April 1865.

Original owned by William H. Guthman.

RARITAN TOWNSHIP (HUNTERDON COUNTY) N.J.

Special town meeting! Notice is hereby given that a special town meeting of the legal voters of the township of Raritan, will be held at the court house, in Flemington, on Monday, August 8, 1864, at 2 o'clock, P.M., for the following objects and purposes, viz: To consider and determine whether any money shall be raised to relieve the inhabitants of said township from the burden of the approaching draft by offering bounties and otherwise. If it is determined to raise money, then to consider and determine how it shall be raised, there being no law authorizing the assessment of a tax. Also, to consider and determine how the money raised shall be appropriated. By order of the Town Committee. Reading Moore, town clerk. Dated, Flemington, July 30th, 1864. Flemington, New Jersey: Adam Bellis, printer, "Democrat" office [1864] Broadside. 13½ x 12 in. NJFLHI 388

SALEM, N.J.

War meeting in Salem, to-night, Saturday, May 28. I call on the patriotic citizens of Salem to meet in the court house in this city to-night, to take into consideration the best means for procuring volunteers for the 100 days service! The meeting will be addressed by Wm. N. Hancock and others. Ebenezer Dunn, mayor. Salem, N.J., May 28, 1864. Salem, N.J.: William S. Sharp, printer, "National Standard" office [1864] Broadside. 18½ x 12 in. NJHI 389

SCRANTON, CHARLES, 1822-1888.

Dear sir: Our state is raising a regiment of sharp-shooters, or riflemen, for the war, to which every two counties is expected to contribute a company. I am authorized to raise one company in this and the adjoining counties, and will feel under obligation to you for your earnest cooperation . . . The first squad of this company will probably leave Belvidere about the 24th inst. Respectfully and truly yours, Charles Scranton. Oxford Furnace, N.J., Sept. 17, 1861. [n.p., 1861] Broadside. 8¼ x 5 in. NJR 390

TRENTON MONITOR, TRENTON, N.J.

Monitor extra. Conscription! Mercer County!! [Trenton, N.J., 1864 or 1865] Broadside. 15¾ x 4½ in. NJR (photo) NJT 390a

Lists of men enrolled in the first and third wards, Trenton.

The weekly and daily *Monitor* were published 1864-1865.

UNION COUNTY, N.J. MILITARY COMMISSIONER.

Office military commissioner, Elizabeth, 5th Sept., 1862, 1 o'clock, P.M. By virtue of authority from the governor of this state, the draft for the deficiency in the quota of the city of Elizabeth, and the townships of Union, Westfield and Springfield, is hereby postponed to Tuesday, the 9th instant . . . Transportation for volunteers will be furnished until Monday P.M., the 8th instant. George W. Savage, commissioner. Elizabeth, N.J.: New Jersey Journal power-press print [1862] Broadside. 11½ x 9 in. NJHI 391

U.S. ARMY. 12TH INFANTRY. COMPANY G.

100 recruits wanted for . . . Capt. E. R. Pennington's company, 12th Infantry, U.S. Army, able-bodied, unmarried men, between the ages of 18 and 35 years, not less than 5 feet 3 inches high, and of good character. A minor will not be enlisted without the consent of his parents or guardian. The term of service is three years. By good conduct and attention to duty, a soldier will certainly rise to the position of a non-commissioned officer, in the company, and it is from this class that the law provides that meritorious men may be selected, as the wants of the service require it, for promotion to the rank of commissioned officers in the service. The pay is from $13 to $23 per month. . . . Quarters, food, clothing and medical attendance are always provided by the government without deduction from the soldier's pay, immediately upon his enlistment. At the end of the service a bounty of one hundred dollars is paid to the soldier, and at the next session of Congress it is expected that it will be ordered that a land warrant will also be given to the soldier on his discharge. Handsome uniforms are furnished to the men immediately on their enlistment. Head-quarters of regiment Fort Hamilton, New York harbor. For further information upon the subject, apply to the officer at the recruiting rendezvous, 113 Market Street, Newark, N.J. Capt. E. R. Pennington, U.S.A., commanding company, 12th Reg't Infantry. [Newark, N.J.? 1861] Broadside. NJPLAHI 391a

This enticing piece is illustrated in John T. Cunningham, *Newark* (1966), p.157.

Edward R. Pennington, who commanded Company G, 12th U.S. Infantry, was commissioned Oct. 4, 1861, resigned Dec. 20, 1862. See *Manual of the One Hundred and Sixth Session of the Legislature* (1882), p.102-103; F. R. Heitman, *Historical Register and Dictionary of the United States Army* (1903), v.1, p.782.

WAR! ! THERE WILL BE A MEETING OF THE citizens of Delaware Township, on Wednesday evening, April 24th., at the military hall, in Sergeantsville, for the purpose of volunteering with the Delaware Guards in the defence of our country. At the same time and place the Delaware Guards are hereby notified to meet. By order of Maj. G. H. Larison. April 23, 1861. Lambertville, N.J.: Printed at the "Beacon" power press office [1861] Broadside. 24 x 19 in. NJFLHI 392

WEST JERSEY PRESS, CAMDEN, N.J.

West Jersey Press.—Extra. List of the drafted men in Camden, Gloucester, Salem and Cumberland. [Camden, N.J.: West Jersey Press, 1865] Broadside. 24 x 12¾ in. NJR 393

According to information provided by William C. Wright, this particular draft took place on Feb. 4, 1865. The list of men drafted was also published in the *Salem Sunbeam* of March 3, 1865.

The names, grouped by locality, are printed in five columns.

MILITARY UNITS: HISTORY, ROSTERS, ETC.

1ST N.J. BRIGADE

BAQUET, CAMILLE, -1924.

History of the First Brigade, New Jersey volunteers, from 1861 to 1865. Compiled under the authorization of Kearny's First New Jersey Brigade Society by Camille Baquet, second lieutenant, Company A, First Regiment, New Jersey volunteers. Published by the state of New Jersey, 1910. Trenton, N.J.: MacCrellish & Quigley, state printers, 1910. 1p.l., iii, [3]-515p. front. (port.) plates (incl. ports.) DLC NJ NJHI NJJ NJN NJP NJR NJT NN PHI PP 394

The brigade was formed originally of the first three New Jersey regiments, with addition later of the 4th, 15th, 23rd, finally the 10th and 40th.

Contents include histories of the 10th, 15th, 23rd, and 40th N.J. Vols., and Battery A, 1st N.J. Artillery (p.196-293); also reminiscences, etc., among them "The Seven Days' Battle on the Peninsula as seen by a lieutenant on the [Brigade] staff," E. Burd Grubb (p.310-340), this also published separately in pamphlet form (see no. 234); extracts from the diary of Sergt. John P. Beach, Co. B, 4th Regt., June 27, 1862, Dec. 8, 1864-July 10, 1865 (p.361-386); extracts from letters of Maj. David Hatfield, 1st Regt., May 1861-June 1862 (p.411-436); list of the killed and wounded (p.437-455); muster-in rolls of the 1st through 4th Regts. (p.459-515).

1ST N.J. ARTILLERY. BATTERY B

HANIFEN, MICHAEL, 1841-

History of Battery B, First New Jersey Artillery. By Michael Hanifen . . . [Ottawa, Ill.: Republican-Times, printers, c1905] 4p., 1 leaf, [5]-174p. front. (port.) ports. CSMH DLC NJ NJJ NJN NJP NJT NHI NN 395

"Roster of officers and enlisted men": p.151-174.

1ST N.J. CAVALRY

NEW JERSEY CAVALRY. 1ST REGT., 1861-1865.

Report of the operations of the First New Jersey Cavalry, from the 28th of March to the 25th of May, 1865, with a portion of the number of engagements in which the regiment has participated, and a complete roster of the commissioned officers. Published for the officers and men. Trenton, N.J.: Printed at the True American office, 1865. 19p. NJ NHI 396

Transmitted to the adjutant-general of New Jersey.

Signed: Walter R. Robbins, major com'dg 1st N.J. Cavalry.

[PYNE, HENRY ROGERS] 1834-1892.

"A dash across the Rappahannock.—No. II. A chapter in the history of the First New Jersey Cavalry. By the chaplain." *Beecher's magazine*. v.2, 1870. p.330-337. 397

Published as Chapter 2 of no. 399, Pyne's *History of the First New Jersey Cavalry* (1871), p.26-39.

———————

"Turning Lee's right. A chapter in the history of the First New Jersey Cavalry. By the chaplain." *Ibid.*, p.281-285. 398

Incidents of May 1864 near Hawe's Shop, in Virginia.

Reprinted as part (p.249-257) of Chapter 15, in Pyne's *History of the First New Jersey Cavalry* (no. 399, following).

PYNE, HENRY ROGERS, 1834-1892.

The history of the First New Jersey Cavalry, (Sixteenth Regiment, New Jersey volunteers.) By Henry R. Pyne, chaplain. Trenton, N.J.: J. A. Beecher, publisher, 1871. 2p.l., [9]-350p. front. (port.) CSMH DLC NJ NJHI NJJ NJN NJP NJR NJT NHI NN PHI PP PPL PPLL 399

Author was regimental chaplain.

Two parts were published earlier in magazine articles (nos. 397-398).

Complete rosters: p.[321]-350.

———

[*Same: second edition*] Ride to war; the history of the First New Jersey Cavalry, by Henry R. Pyne. Edited, with an introduction and notes, by Earl Schenck Miers. New Brunswick: Rutgers University Press [1961] xxxiii, 340p. maps. DLC NJ NJHI NJJ NJN NJR NJT NN PP 400

Appendix (p.[293]-340) contains list of actions and list of members of the organization.

2ND N.J. CAVALRY. COMPANY C

ANDERSON, J. L.

Soldiers memorial. 2nd Regiment Company C. N.J. cavalry. Trenton, N.J.: Published by J. L. Anderson, 1863. Broadside. 20 x 16 in. NJR

Colored lithograph, part pictorial, with unit roster.

"Lith. by A. Hoen & Co. Baltimore."

"Entered according to act of Congress in the year 1863 by Whitney & Anderson in Dist. C. of Md."

"Published at Trenton, N.J., Sept. 28, 1863, by J. L. Anderson." (Less than three weeks after the unit was mustered in.)

3RD N.J. CAVALRY

"FIRST U.S. HUSSARS." *Frank Leslie's illustrated newspaper.* v.17, 1863/64. p.252, 254 (Jan. 9, 1864) illus. 401a

Brief article on the "1st Hussar regiment raised for real service in the country [i.e., 3rd N.J. Cavalry]. It is now organized in Trenton, N.J., under command of Col. A. J. Morrison, formerly of the New York cavalry, and subsequently of the 26th New Jersey volunteers." Most of the article is an account (taken from the Newark *Journal*) of Morrison's part in the battle of Fredericksburg, with the 26th Regiment.

RISLEY, CLYDE ALAN.

"3rd New Jersey Cavalry Regiment, 1864-1865 (1st Regiment, U.S. hussars)" *Military collector & historian.* v.9, 1957. p.44-46. illus. 402

Signed (p.46) : Clyde A. Risley, Frederick P. Todd.

1ST N.J. INFANTRY. COMPANY F

BAKER, WALRAD & CASE, *New York.*

Soldiers memorial. Company F, 1st Regiment New Jersey vols. [New York] Baker, Walrad & Case, 1863. Broadside. $22\frac{1}{2}$ x 19 in. NJR 403

Rosters of officers and men, with brief service records; list of engagements.

With pictorial decorations.

"Entered acc. to act of Congress in the year 1863 by Baker, Walrad & Case in the clerks office of the Dist. Ct. of the Sn. [i.e., Southern] Dist. of N.Y."

"Lith. of Sarony, Major & Knapp, 449 Broadway, New York."

2ND N.J. INFANTRY. COMPANY B

[THOMPSON, WILMOT H.] 1841?-

War record, Company B, 2d Regiment, N.J.V. A souvenir of 1861. [n.p., n.d.] 16 leaves. illus. NJNETD NJP 404

Loose sheets inclosed in wrapper bearing letterpress title: War record / Company / B / Second Regiment / of / N.J.V. / Souvenir of 1861.

A lithographic reproduction (part two-color) of various lists and other records of the Company's service, hand-lettered, decorated, and illustrated in pen-and-ink by W. H. Thompson.

The general appearance suggests a publication date about the 1880's.

Thompson, a member of this company, later served in Co. G of the same regiment.

3RD N.J. INFANTRY. COMPANY A

WAMSLEY, JAMES A. 1851-

Co. A, Third Regiment, New Jersey volunteers. By Dr. J. A. Wamsley. [n.p., 19—?] Broadside. 12 x 6 in. NJR 405

Verse. A sentimental review.

Dr. Wamsley was reared in Gloucester County, practiced medicine from 1877 in Gloucester City.

7TH N.J. INFANTRY. COMPANY K

MARTIN'S SOLDIERS RECORD. Morris County Pioneers. Company "K," Seventh Regiment New Jersey vols. Milwaukee: Lith. by L. Kurz & Co. [1863] Broadside. $20\frac{1}{2}$ x $16\frac{1}{8}$ in. DLC NJR (photo) 406

Colored, illustrated lithograph.

Roster and list of actions, etc.

9TH N.J. INFANTRY

DRAKE, JAMES MADISON, 1837-1913.

The history of the Ninth New Jersey Veteran Vols. A record of its service from Sept. 13th, 1861, to July 12th, 1865, with a complete official roster, and sketches of prominent members, with anecdotes, incidents and thrilling reminiscences, by Captain J. Madison Drake, bt. brig.-general N.J. . . . Elizabeth, N.J.: Journal printing house, 1889. 501p. front. (port.) illus., ports. CSMH DLC DNW MB MH MWA NJ NJHI NJJ NJN NJP NJR NJT NHI NIC NN OCLWHI PHI PPL PPLL 407

"Reunions" (1887-1888) : p.409-421.
Unit roster: p.422-501.

EVERTS, HERMANN, 1826?-

A complete and comprehensive history of the Ninth Regiment New Jersey vols. infantry. From its first organization to its final muster out. By Hermann Everts. Newark, N.J.: A. Stephen Holbrook, printer, 1865. 197p. CSMH DLC NJ NJHI NJJ NJN NJP NJR NHI NN PPL 408

Contains lists of officers and men (p.[5]-71) ; also (p.194-197) "Tabular list of diseases," 1863-1865.

9TH N.J. INFANTRY. COMPANY C.

FULLER, J. C., & Co., *New York.*

Soldiers memorial. 9th Regiment, New Jersey volunteers. Company C. [New York] 1863. Broadside. About 22 x 17 in. NJR (photo) NJWDHI 408a

Roster of officers and men, with brief service records; lists of engagements and skirmishes.
Pictorial decorations.
"Published Aug. 25, 1863."
"Entered according to act of Congress in the year 1863 by J. C. Fuller & Co. in the clerks office of the District Court of the Southern District of New York."
"Lith. of Sarony, Major & Knapp, 449 Broadway, N. York."
Not seen. Entry based partly on unclear photocopy in NJR, partly on information provided by NJWDHI.

11TH N.J. INFANTRY

MARBAKER, THOMAS D. 1846-

History of the Eleventh New Jersey Volunteers from its organization to Appomattox, to which is added experiences of prison life and sketches of individual members. By Thos. D. Marbaker, serg't Co. E . . . Trenton, N.J.: MacCrellish & Quigley, book and job printers, 1898. viii, 364p. front. (port.) illus. (incl. ports.) CSMH DLC NJ NJHI NJJ NJN NJR NJT NHI NN PP PPLL 409

Sketches of certain officers and men: p.346-364.
Text of an historical address by Marbaker, delivered at a reunion of the 11th Regt., can be found in the Dover (N.J.) *Iron Era* of May 9, 1885.

12TH N.J. INFANTRY

HAINES, WILLIAM PENN, 1840-1928.

Historique. A sketch of the Twelfth Regiment, New Jersey volunteers . . . by Wm. P. Haines, private, Co. F. Mickleton, New Jersey, Sept. 4, 1896. [n.p., 1896] folder ([8]p.) NJR

"Dedicated to Ellwood [*sic*] Griscom. 'He was my Pard.' "
Historical sketch in verse (4p.) , table of casualties, list of battles and skirmishes, etc.
Published also in nos. 412 and 413.

[REUNION SOCIETY OF THE TWELFTH REGIMENT NEW JERSEY VOLUNTEERS]

Roster of the Twelfth Regiment New Jersey volunteers. [Woodbury? 1875] 32p. CSMH DLC NJ NHI PPLL 411

Caption title.
"Oration by Colonel William E. Potter, delivered before the surviving members of the Twelfth Regiment New Jersey volunteers in the War of the Rebellion, at their first reunion, held at Woodbury, New Jersey, February 22, 1875": p.[29]-32.

SOUVENIR PAMPHLET of dedication of a marker in memory of the 12th N.J. Vols. at battle of Wilderness . . . near Fredericksburg, Va. . . . May 30th, 1942 . . . [n.p., 1942] [18]p. illus. (incl. port.) NJR 412

Contents include: "History of New Jersey marker"; "Organization of regiment"; "Battles and skirmishes in which the 12th N.J. participated"; "Description of battle of Wilderness, by William P. Haines, private Co. F"; "Historique; a sketch of the Twelfth Regiment, New Jersey volunteers" (poetry, 1896) , by Wm. P. Haines.
The "Historique" was published also separately in 1896 (no. 410) , and in W. P. Haines, *History of the Men of Co. F* (no. 413) .

12TH N.J. INFANTRY. COMPANY F

FULLER, J. C., & Co., *New York.*

Soldiers memorial. Company F, 12th Regiment, New Jersey volunteers. [New York, 1864] Broadside. About 22 x 17 in. NJR (photo) NJWDHI 412a

"Organized at Woodbury. Mustered into United States Service for Three Years Sept. 4, 1862." Company F was raised in Gloucester County.

Roster of officers and men, with brief service records and list of engagements. Dates as late as Feb. 1, 1864.

Pictorial decorations.

"Entered according to act of Congress in the year 1863 by J. C. Fuller & Co. in the clerks office of the District Court of the Southern District of New York."

"Lith. of Sarony, Major & Knapp, 449 Broadway, N. York."

Not seen. Entry based partly on unclear photocopy in NJR, partly on information provided by NJWDHI.

HAINES, WILLIAM PENN, 1840-1928.

History of the men of Co. F, with description of the marches and battles of the 12th New Jersey Vols. . . . By Wm. P. Haines, private, Co. F. Mickleton, N.J. [Camden, N.J.: C. S. Magrath, printer] 1897. 1p.l., [v]-vii, 293p. DLC NJ NJR NN OCLWHI PP 413

"Life sketches, men of Co. F": p.[97]-163.

"Other men" (regimental personnel and certain men from other companies; biographical sketches): p.[173]-237.

Reminiscences include "Libby prison experience of Frank M. Riley" (p.[241]-253), republished 1917 in *Almanac and Year Book, First National Bank, Woodstown, N.J.* (see no. 268).

"Historique. Dedicated to Elwood Griscom—'He was my pard'" (verse): p.[287]-291. Also published separately in 1896 (no. 410). See also *Souvenir Pamphlet of Dedication of a Marker in Memory of the 12th N.J. Vols.* (no. 412).

13TH N.J. INFANTRY

RITZMAN, DEAN FRANKLIN.

"The homecoming." *Crossed flags.* v.5, no. 10. June 1965. p.[1]-5. 413a

The 13th Regiment's last days and final muster (June 1865); also brief review of its war service.

TOOMBS, SAMUEL, 1844-1889.

Reminiscences of the war, comprising a detailed account of the experiences of the Thirteenth Regiment New Jersey volunteers in camp, on the march, and in battle. By Samuel Toombs. With the personal recollections of the author. Orange, N.J.: Printed at the Journal office, 1878. 4p.l., 232, 47p. CSMH DLC NJ NJHI NJJ NJN NJP NJR NHI NN PHI PPL PPLL 414

Contains roster of the officers and men.

13TH N.J. INFANTRY. COMPANY D

"D" SOCIETY.

Historical sketch of Co. "D," 13th Regiment, N.J. vols. . . . with the muster roll of the company. Compiled and printed for the use of its members by the authority of "D" Society. Newark, N.J., 1875. New York: D. H. Gildersleeve & Co., publishers and printers, 1875. 87, [1]p. DLC NJ NJHI NJJ NJN NJP NJR NHI NN PPL PPLL 415

"A brief record of the members of Company D": p.[47]-80. Individual biographies.

"'D' Society" (constitution, membership roll, etc.): p.[81]-87, [1].

14TH N.J. INFANTRY

TERRILL, JOHN NEWTON, 1842-1916.

Campaign of the Fourteenth Regiment, New Jersey volunteers, by Sergeant J. Newton Terrill, Co. K, Fourteenth Regiment, New Jersey volunteers. New Brunswick, N.J.: Terhune & Van Anglen's press, 1866. 132p. NJ NJR NHI 416

"Commenced Sept. 1st, 1865; Finished July 15th, 1866."—p.132.

———————

[*Same: second edition*] Campaign of the Fourteenth Regiment, New Jersey volunteers, by Sergeant J. Newton Terrill, Co. K, Fourteenth Regiment, New Jersey volunteers. Second edition. New Brunswick, N.J.: Daily Home News press, 1884. 132p. CSMH DLC NJ NJHI NJJ NJN NJP NJR NHI NN PPL PPLL 417

15TH N.J. INFANTRY

[CAMPBELL, EDWARD LIVINGSTON] 1833-

Historical sketch of the Fifteenth Regiment, New Jersey volunteers. First Brigade, First Division, Sixth Corps. Trenton, N.J.: Wm. S. Sharp, printer and stereotyper, 1880. 1p.l., [5]-25p. CSMH DNW NJ NJHI NJR NJT NHI OCLWHI PPL 418

Includes statistics and lists of casualties.

In the several copies examined, a second preliminary leaf (i.e., p.3-4) is found to have been torn out.

HAINES, ALANSON AUSTIN, 1830-1891.

History of the Fifteenth Regiment, New Jersey volunteers. By Alanson A. Haines, chaplain of the regiment. New York: Jenkins & Thomas, printers, 1883. 388p. front. (port.)

illus., maps, port. CSMH DLC NJ NJHI NJJ NJN NJP NJR NJT NHI NN PP PPL PPLL 419

Rolls of the officers and men: p.[321]-388.

A sketch of Haines, written by Edmund Drake Halsey, was published in the Dover (N.J.) *Iron Era,* Dec. 18, 1891. For a condensed version, see *Proceedings of the New Jersey Historical Society,* 2nd series, v.12, 1892/93, p.7-11.

23RD N.J. INFANTRY

CURRIE, CHARLES F. 1842-1913.

"New Jersey blue honors Alabama gray. [By] Charles F. Currie." *Blue and gray.* v.1, 1893. p.443-446. illus. (incl. port.) 420

Short account of the battle of Salem Church, near Fredericksburg, Va., May 3, 1863, and of the 23rd N.J. Regt. which served there under Col. Edward Burd Grubb (whose portrait accompanies the article). In May 1893, the regiment's survivors resolved to erect a memorial pulpit in the Salem church building.

The writer, of Millville, N.J., had served 1861-1863 as a corporal in the 4th N.J. Vols., later in the U.S. Signal Corps.

24TH N.J. INFANTRY

REEVES, JAMES JOHNSON, 1839-

History of the Twenty-Fourth Regiment, New Jersey volunteers. By James J. Reeves. Printed by direction of the Society at their reunion in Woodbury, N.J., December 13, 1888. Camden, N.J.: S. Chew, printer, 1889. 45p. CSMH DLC NJ NJHI NJJ NJN NJR NHI NN PPLL 421

"Constitution and by-laws of 'The Reunion Society of the Twenty-Fourth Regiment, New Jersey Volunteers.' (Adopted at Woodbury, N.J., December 13th, 1888.) ": p.[39]-45.

29TH N.J. INFANTRY

MORFORD, TYLEE CONOVER, 1840-

Fifty years ago. Address of T. C. Morford, secretary of the Veteran Association of the 29th Regiment New Jersey Volunteers, delivered at Eatontown, N.J., at the 23d annual veterans reunion and 50th anniversary of mustering in, September 11th, 1912. [n.p., 1912] 12p. NJHI 422

The author, assistant quartermaster at Camp Vredenburgh when the regiment was formed in September 1862, became acting adjutant in February 1863.

30TH N.J. INFANTRY

BOWMAN, JAMES, 1833-1913.

A record of the services of the Thirtieth Regiment, New Jersey volunteers, in the War of the Rebellion. Compiled by Captain James Bowman. Somerville, N.J.: Printed by Unionist-Gazette Association, 1912. 20p. NJR (photo)

Prepared for the Thirtieth Regiment, New Jersey Volunteer Association. The author had been captain of Co. A.

30TH N.J. INFANTRY. COMPANY F

JOHNSON, CHAUNCEY A.

Johnson's military company and regimental record. Company F, New Jersey volunteer infantry. 30th Regiment. [Milwaukee, Wis.?] Chauncey A. Johnson, c1862. Broadside. 27½ x 21 in. NJR 424

Lithograph with pictorial decorations in color, and company roster.

"Des[ign]. by C. A. Johnson . . . Lith. by L. Lipman, Milwaukee."

35TH N.J. INFANTRY. COMPANY F

ANDERSON, J.   L.

Soldier's record. Cladek Zouaves. 35th Regiment Company F. N.J. volunteers. Flemington, N.J.: Published by J. L. Anderson, 1863. Broadside. 22 x 17 in. NJR 425

Lithograph with pictorial decorations in color, and company roster.

"Entered according to Act of Congress in the year 1863 by J. L. Anderson in the Clerks Office of the . . ." (*piece torn off*).

"Lith. & print. by Chas. Shober Chicago."

"Published at Flemington, N.J., Oct. 13, 1863, by J. L. Anderson."

37TH N.J. INFANTRY

RODGERS, RICHARD N.

Epitome of the 37th Reg't, New Jersey volunteers. By R. N. Rodgers, Co. E. New-York: J. Craft, steam job printer [1864] Broadside. 22 x 16¼ in. CSMH DLC NJ NJHI NJP NJR NHI NN PPL PPLL 426

Brief service details, roster of dead and wounded, lists of officers, statistics, etc.

Some copies are folded and mounted in boards, with label on p.2 of cover: Epitome 37th Regiment, N.J. vols., by R. N. Rodgers, Co. E. Privately printed, October 25th, 1864.

39TH N.J. INFANTRY. COMPANY F

LANCKTON, GEORGE M.

Military register. Company F, 39th Regiment, New Jersey volunteers . . . Organized at Newark, N.J. 1864. Mustered into U.S. service at Newark,

N.J. September 25, 1864. Washington, D.C.: Published by Geo. M. Lanckton [1865] Broadside. 23¼ x 18½ in. NJN NJR (photo) 427

"Lithographed by A. Hoen & Co. Baltimore."

A roster; in three columns, with pictorial decorations.

48TH NEW YORK INFANTRY. COMPANY D

CARLTON, WILLIAM J.

Company D, ("the Die-No-Mores") of the Forty-Eighth Regiment, New York state volunteers, 1861-5. A paper read at the first reunion of the surviving members, at Trenton, N.J., July 24, 1891,—the thirtieth anniversary of the organization of the company. By William J. Carlton . . . [n.p.] 1892. 19, [1]p. incl. port. CSMH DLC NJR (photo) NHI 428

Privately printed.

The company, formed almost entirely of New Jersey men, was raised to become part of Col. (and Rev.) James H. Perry's "regiment of moral and religious men."

EXCELSIOR BRIGADE

STEVENSON, JAMES.

History of the Excelsior or Sickles' Brigade, by Jas. Stevenson. Paterson, N.J.: Van Derhoven & Holms, book and job printers, 1863. 40p. DLC NHI 429

Written "expressly at the request of a few members of the 1st Regiment Excelsior Brigade, in which I had the honor to serve."—p.[3]. ". . . I will insert nothing but what I know personally to be true . . ." —p.[5].

Contains personal allusions and some special details about the author's own regiment.

In part a defense of the brigade and its commander, politician-soldier Daniel E. Sickles, by whom its five regiments were raised in the spring of 1861. A New York State organization, it contained elements from Pennsylvania, New Jersey, Massachusetts, etc.

MILITARY REGISTERS

NEW JERSEY. ADJUTANT-GENERAL'S OFFICE.

. . . List of promotions, appointments and casualties in the New Jersey regiments, in the service of the United States . . . March 1863-Jan. 1866. [Trenton, N.J., 1863-1866] CSMH (April 1863-Jan. 1866) MB (March-May, July 1863-Sept., Nov. 1864-Jan., March 1865-Jan. 1866) NJHI (Oct. 1864) NJR (April 1863-Jan. 1866) PU (Nov. 1864) 430

Caption title.

Covers officers only.

Was published monthly (except Sept.-Dec. 1865, omitted) and dated first day of the month in each case. Intended to follow the 584-page *Register* (no. 432) dated Jan. 1, 1863.

Varies from 2p. to 14p. each.

Letter of Garret D. W. Vroom, Trenton, Jan. 4, 1866, to P. Vanderbilt Spader (NJR manuscript collection), forwarding a set of the *List* ("monthly slips"), describes it as "complete with one exception, the first number, March '63 . . . Their publication was not commenced until some time after the large Registers." He also states that the slip for January 1866 will be the last.

J. P. Nicholson *Catalogue*, p.606, lists April 1, 1863-Jan. 1, 1866, as complete. "There are three complete sets in existence."

Record of officers and men of New Jersey in the Civil War, 1861-1865 . . . Compiled in the office of the Adjutant General. Published by authority of the Legislature. William S. Stryker, adjutant general. Trenton, New Jersey: John L. Murphy, steam book and job printer, 1876. 1758, 176p. CSMH DLC DNW MH MWA NJ NJHI NJJ NJN NJP NJR NJT NHI NN PP PPL PPLL PU 431

In two volumes, paged continuously.

Rosters and brief service details for officers and men of all New Jersey units (infantry, cavalry, artillery, and some militia); New Jersey soldiers serving in units of other states (chiefly Pennsylvania and New York) and U.S. Army, Veteran Reserve Corps, U.S. Colored Troops, and Navy; also list of brevet commissions, and burial record of New Jersey soldiers in various national cemeteries. Includes brief history of each New Jersey regiment or battery.

Register of the commissioned officers and privates of the New Jersey volunteers, in the service of the United States. Printed by order of the Legislature. Jersey City: Printed by John H. Lyon, 1863. 584p. CSMH DLC DNW MB NJ NJHI NJJ NJN NJP NJR NJT NN PP PPL PPLL 432

Dated (p.[3]) Jan. 1, 1863.

Rolls of staff and regimental officers; list of casualties, resignations and dismissals of officers since Oct. 22, 1862; rolls of three-month and of three-year volunteers (officers and men), both roughly alphabetical, giving rank, age, unit, and date of enrollment, and "remarks."

"Register of commissioned officers . . . January 1, 1863": p.[3]-45. Corresponds to the separately-published *Register of Commissioned Officers of the New Jersey Volunteers* bearing same date (see no. 433).

Followed by no. 430, the monthly *List of Promotions* . . . (etc.), 1863-1866.

Register of commissioned officers of the New Jersey volunteers, in the service of the United States . . . Trenton, N.J., 1862-1865. 433

July 1, 1862. [Trenton, N.J.: Murphy & Bechtel, printers, 1862] 21p. DLC MB NJ NJR NHI
Oct. 22, 1862. [Trenton, N.J.: Murphy & Bechtel, printers, 1862] 42p. DLC MB NJ NJP NJR
Jan. 1, 1863. [Trenton, N.J.: Murphy & Bechtel, printers, 1863] 44p. MB NJ NJP NJR NHI. See no. 432, preceding.
July 1, 1863. [Trenton, N.J., 1863] 31p. MB NJ NJHI NJR
Jan. 1, 1864. [Trenton, N.J., 1864] 38p. DLC MB NJ NJP NJR PU
July 1, 1864. [Trenton, N.J., 1864] 38p. DLC MB NJ NJHI NJP NJR
Jan. 1, 1865. [Trenton, N.J., 1865] 40p. MB NJ NJR NHI PU
July 1, 1865. [Trenton, N.J., 1865] 36p. DLC MB NJ NJP NJR

All numbers except the first (July 1, 1862) contain lists of casualties, resignations, etc.

J. P. Nicholson *Catalogue,* p.606, lists incorrectly as complete in seven numbers, July 1, 1862-July 1, 1865, and notes a letter from Adjutant-General Stryker in regard to this publication.

U.S. ADJUTANT-GENERAL'S OFFICE.

Official Army register of the volunteer force of the United States Army for the years 1861, '62, '63, '64, '65. Part II. (New York and New Jersey.) [Washington: Government Printing Office, 1865] 5p.l., p.305-755, 164p. DLC NJHI NJP NJR NHI PP 434

New Jersey: p.696-749, 755.

Roster of officers by regiments.

Contains (164p. at end) index of organizations, index of battles, and a single alphabetical index of names for both states.

MILITARY MEDICINE

CALHOUN, JAMES THEODORE, 1838-1866.

A few practical observations upon camp diarrhoea; a paper read before the "Essex Medical Union," Jan. 13, 1865, by J. Theodore Calhoun, M.D., ass't surgeon U.S. Army, surgeon in charge, "Ward" U.S. General Hospital, Newark, N.J. Newark, N.J.: Hospital print, 1865. 8p. NJHI 435

The author, a Rahway physician, entered military service in 1861.

CULLEN, THOMAS FRANKFORD, 1822-1877.

"Essay by Thos. F. Cullen, M.D." Medical Society of New Jersey. *Transactions.* 98th annual meeting, 1864. p.[21]-44. 436

The annual essay for 1864, presented to the Society at its meeting—"more properly entitled, Observations on the Influence of the Present War upon American Medicine and Surgery" (cf. p.22).

Observations on the influence of the present war upon American medicine and surgery. An essay: read before the Medical Society of New-Jersey, at its ninety-eighth annual meeting. By Thomas F. Cullen, M.D., of Camden. New-York: John A. Gray & Green, printers, stereotypers, and binders, 1864. 26p. NJP 437

Reprint of no. 436.

HOSPITAL BULLETIN. Newark, N.J., 1865-(?) v.1, no. 7. Aug. 10, 1865. 18¼ x 12 in. NJR

Two inside columns headed "The 'Ward' Hospital Bulletin."

A four-page newspaper (in four columns), published by C. A. Mandeville, devoted substantially to items about the war and veterans' affairs, commonly with New Jersey connections; also notices, orders, etc., of "'Ward' U.S. General Hospital," at Newark.

The only issue found (Aug. 10, 1865) contains a "History of the 'Ward' U.S.A. General Hospital" in six columns, continued from an earlier number and in turn to be continued.

MEDICAL SOCIETY OF NEW JERSEY. COMMITTEE ON RECORDS OF NEW JERSEY MEDICAL MEN WHO SERVED IN THE WAR.

[Report] Medical Society of New Jersey. *Transactions.* 101st annual meeting, 1867. p.[14]-18. 439

Rosters of (1) surgeons and (2) assistant surgeons of the New Jersey volunteer units, with dates of commission, discharge, etc.

MUTUAL BENEFIT LIFE INSURANCE COMPANY, NEWARK, N.J.

. . . At a meeting of the directors, held August 26, 1862, it was resolved, that, until further ordered, term policies . . . with the war risk . . . be issued . . . to parties entering the military or naval service . . . with the understanding that if the party returns in sound health, a life policy will be issued, on application, at the same rate the party would have been entitled to when the first policy was issued . . . [Newark, N.J., 1862] Broadside. 8 x 5 in. NJR 440

Signed: B. C. Miller, Sec'y.

———————

. . . At a meeting of the directors, held October 8th, 1862, it was resolved, that medical examiners be directed to make special examinations in all cases where applicants expect to enter the Army . . . [Newark, N.J., 1862] Broadside. 8 x 5 in. NJR 441

Dated Oct. 10, 1862, and signed: B. C. Miller, Sec'y.

Printed covering letter bears same date.

———————

. . . Dear sir: We enclose herewith a circular to the medical examiner, connected with your agency, in relation to his examination of parties for war service . . . [Newark, N.J., 1862] Broadside. 8 x 5 in. NJR 442

Dated Oct. 10, 1862, and signed: B. C. Miller, Sec'y.

Covering letter for the printed notice bearing same date.

STEVENSON, JOHN RUDEROW, 1834-1917.

"Vital statistics. By Jno. R. Stevenson, M.D." Medical Society of New Jersey. *Transactions.* 98th annual meeting, 1864. p.145-153. 443

"It gives me pleasure to submit . . . a report of such statistics and facts, as have been obtained during an examination of applicants for exemption from the draft, on the grounds of physical disability, in the First Congressional District of New-Jersey."

Signed (p.153) : Jno. R. Stevenson, Surgeon of the Board of Enrollment First Congressional District of . . . New-Jersey. Camden, January 18, 1864.

The First District contained the southernmost counties.

WAGNER, CLINTON, 1837-1914.

Report of interesting surgical operations, performed at the U.S.A. General Hospital, Beverly, New Jersey. By C. Wagner, ass't surgeon U.S.A., commanding hospital. [n.p., 1865] 16p. plate. NHI 444

"The preceding Report includes nearly all the capital operations that were performed at this Hospital, from the latter part of August, 1864, to March 1st, 1865."—p.16.

Descriptions of the individual cases (p.4-13) are presented in tabular form.

"WARD" U.S. GENERAL HOSPITAL, NEWARK, N.J.

Circular. no. 3, Dec. 6, 1864. [Newark, N.J., 1864] Broadside. 8 x 4¾ in. NJR 445

Regulations concerning autopsy procedure.

[WOODHULL, ALFRED ALEXANDER] 1837-1921.

"Eligibility of medical officers of the Army as members of certain courts-martial." *United States service magazine.* v.1, 1864. p.258-263.

Contains no personal allusions.

The author, native of Princeton, graduate of Princeton University, was a career medical officer.

———————

"An inquiry into the military rights and duties of medical officers in the land forces." *Ibid.*, p.478-489. 447

No personal allusions.

MILITARY RELIEF

LADIES' RELIEF SOCIETY, PASSAIC, N.J.

Report of the Ladies' Relief Society. Passaic, N.J., 1865. cover-title, 8p. DLC NJR (photo)

Includes a summary of activities, 1861-1865, lists of donors, subscribers and honorary members, etc. The ladies "have been sewing for the past four years for the relief of our sick and wounded soldiers."

LADIES' SOLDIERS' AID SOCIETY OF LAMBERTVILLE, N.J.

Ladies' Soldiers' Aid Society of Lambertville, N.J. Third annual report. Lambertville, N.J.: Clark Pierson, printer, 1864. 25p. NHI 449

Contains a short review of the Society's activities since its organization in October 1861—raising cash and other contributions to provide clothing, food, and objects useful to soldiers in the field, in hospitals, and prisons.

THE MESSENGER OF THE UNITED STATES Sanitary Commission for New Jersey. v.1, no. 1. March 1864. Newark, N.J., 1864. 32, [2]p. NJHI NJPT NJR 450

Probably no more published.

Cover-title: The Messenger of the United States Sanitary Commission for New Jersey. Devoted to the welfare of the soldiers in the field and in the hospitals, with a necrological table, recording the names of those noble heroes from the state who have died on the field of honor during the war. Also giving the names of the committees and societies of the various cities and townships of the state, together with a statement of their labors and contributions . . . Newark, N.J.: Printed for the U.S. Sanitary Commission for New Jersey, by F. Starbuck, 1864.

"Necrological": p.27-28. Alphabetical list, A through B only ("To be continued"), giving rank, age, unit, death date. All but four of those listed died in 1862.

NEW JERSEY. BOARD OF COMMISSIONERS ON PROVISION FOR DISABLED NEW JERSEY SOLDIERS.

Report of the Board of Commissioners on Provision for Disabled New Jersey Soldiers. Presented in the House of Assembly, Feb. 1, 1865, and ordered to be printed. Trenton, N.J.: Printed by J. R. Freese, "State Gazette" office, 1865. 6p. DLC NJHI NJR (photo) NN 451

Statistics, discussion of the problem and possible measures to answer the need, including recommended construction of an asylum. The commissioners (Marcus L. Ward, Daniel Haines, William A. Newell, Charles S. Olden, Edwin A. Stevens) were appointed under a joint resolution of April 12, 1864.

———————

[*Same: German edition*] Bericht des Boards der Commissäre für Versorgung invalider New Jersey Soldaten. Dem Hause der Assembly am 1. Februar 1865 vorgelegt und zum Drucke beordert. Newark, N.J.: Gedruckt in der Office der New Jersey freie Zeitung, 1865. 7p. NHI

NEW JERSEY. LEGISLATURE. GENERAL ASSEMBLY.

. . . Supplement to the act entitled "An act for the relief of such portion of the militia of this state as may be called into service," approved May eleventh, eighteen hundred and sixty-one. [Trenton, N.J., 1865] 2p. 13¾ x 8¼ in. NJR 453

Caption title.

At head of title: <Re-printed in House of Assembly, with amendments.> Senate—no. 50. State of New Jersey.

Copy in NJR bears manuscript notations ("Approved March 31, 1865," etc.) .

"THE NEW JERSEY DEPARTMENT [of the Metropolitan Fair, New York City]." *Spirit of the Fair.* no. 7, April 12, 1864. p.75-76. 454

Description of New Jersey exhibits for the Sanitary Fair.

NEWARK DAILY MERCURY.

. . . The families of volunteers. [Newark, N.J., 1861] Broadside. 8½ x 6¼ in. NJR 455

At head of title: Newark Daily Mercury. Monday morning, July 15, 1861.

Reprint (in two columns) of an article on the destitute condition of families left behind by soldiers of Col. McLean's 2nd N.J. Regt., "now at Washington," with the text of a letter from Marcus L. Ward (on behalf of the Newark Public Aid Committee) to McLean urging a system for soldiers' pay remittances.

PUBLIC AID COMMITTEE OF THE CITY OF NEWARK, N.J.

Public Aid Committee of the City of Newark. [Newark, N.J., 1861] [2]p. 10½ x 8½ in. NJHI 456

Caption title.

Report of a public meeting (April 22, 1861), organization and objectives of a committee to aid the families of local men who enter military service. Includes names of subcommittees, their members, and a request for donations.

Signed: Marcus L. Ward, Chairman of the Committee.

———————

. . . Report of the Public Aid Committee, to the people of Newark. [Newark, N.J., 1861] Broadside. 14 x 11 in. NJR 457

At head of title: Public Aid Committee of the City of Newark. Marcus L. Ward, chairman, Beach Vanderpool, treasurer, Jacob Van Arsdale, secretary, James F. Bond, assistant secretary. Newark, N.J., Sept. 28th, 1861.

Announcement of the Committee's suspension, due to a conflict with the Newark Common Council as to the authority for disbursement of appropriated funds. Includes a review of the situation, of the Committee's work, and concluding financial statement.

Text in four columns.

———————

. . . To the mayor and Common Council of the city of Newark. [Newark, N.J., 1861] Broadside. 18¾ x 11¼ in. NJR 458

At head of title: Public Aid Committee of the City of Newark. Marcus L. Ward, chairman, Beach Vanderpool, treasurer, Jacob Van Arsdale, secretary, James F. Bond, assistant secretary. Newark, N.J., Sept. 6th, 1861.

A report on the Committee's operations and finances, with an account of its appointment by a citizens' meeting, after which the city Common Council appropriated $100,000 for aid to the families of Newark soldiers. Details of a dispute between the Public Aid Committee and a committee of the Common Council (on responsibility for administration of the fund) are given.

Signed: Marcus L. Ward, Chairman Public Aid Committee.

Text in four columns.

SOLDIER'S AID ASSOCIATION OF WOODSTOWN, N.J.

"Extracts from minutes of Soldier's Aid Association, Woodstown, N.J., 1862-64." *Almanac and year book, First National Bank, Woodstown, N.J.* 1919. p.10-[15] 459

Lists of officers and members, 1862-1864; minutes, Jan. 14, 1863-July 20, 1865. Taken from original records.

TABLEAUX FOR THE BENEFIT OF THE Sanitary Commission, at Greer's Hall, New-Brunswick, March 28, 1864. [New Brunswick, N.J., 1864] [3]p. NJR 460

"Programme."

Copy in NJR has names of performers added in pencil.

UNITED STATES SANITARY COMMISSION FOR NEW JERSEY.

Annual report of the United States Sanitary Commission for N.J., December 14th, 1864. Being a statement of the amount of money and goods contributed by the people of the state of New Jersey in aid of the Commission. [Newark, N.J., 1864?] Broadside. 14¼ x 8¼ in. NJR 460a

Includes a list of communities, with a statement of the cash and supplies provided from each.

Signed: Marcus L. Ward, Treas. U.S. Sanitary Commission of N.J.

———————

. . . Dear sir: The U.S. Sanitary Commission is in urgent want of funds . . . Newark [1864] [3]p. 7¾ x 5 in. NJR 460b

At head of title: U.S. Sanitary Commission for New Jersey, office, 255 Broad Street, Newark.

A call for gifts and the organization of fund-raising activities. "New Jersey, *as a State*, has, so far, not done justice to herself."

Signed (p.[2]): C. Walsh, President. S. G. Gould, Vice President. M. L. Ward, Treasurer. George Taylor, Secretary. George O. Glavis, Corres. Sec'y.

"Honorary members": p.[3].

———————

[*Same*] [4]p. 7¾ x 5 in. NJR 461

At head of title: (Circular no. 3.) . . .

Signed (p.[3]) essentially same as the preceding, of which it apparently is a revision. Some of the text is identical or similar. The list of honorary members includes six added names.

MILITARY MISCELLANY

ADDRESS OF WELCOME TO REAR ADMIRAL David D. Porter, on his temporary return to his home, Perth Amboy, New Jersey, July 27th, 1864. [n.p., 1864] Broadside. 11 x 8½ in.
NJR NHI 462

ANDREWS, EDWIN N.

The chaplain's address, to the soldiers of the First Brigade, Second Division, Cavalry Corps, composed of the Second New Jersey [and four other] . . . regiments. Memphis, Tenn., July, 1864. Written by Edwin N. Andrews, chaplain 2d N.J. Cavalry. [n.p., 1864] [2]p. 11 x 8¼ in.
IHI NJR 463

Caption title.
Poetry, in part an appeal to the soldiers against cursing and drunkenness.
On p.[2]: National songs.

[ANDREWS, SOLOMON] 1806-1872.

The aereon. [Washington, D.C., 1864] 8p.
DLC 463a

Caption title.
Signed: Solomon Andrews. Washington, D.C., January, 1864.
Addressed to the Senate and House of Representatives: a querulous recital of difficulties encountered by Andrews (Perth Amboy physician, inventor, etc.) since August 1862 in attempting to interest the government in his plan for an airship ("aereon"), to be used in military reconnaisance. Presses for open-minded consideration of the project.
Reprinted in no. 1015.

BURLINGTON ISLAND LAND ASSOCIATION.

Memorial of Burlington Island Association. [n.p., 1862?] cover-title, 4p. fold. map. DLC NJR (photo) 464

Sets forth the advantages for a national armory and foundry, of a 250-acre tract on Matiniconk (or Burlington) Island, located in the Delaware River between Burlington and Bristol, owned by the Burlington (or Matiniconk) Island Land Association.

Signed "Thomas E. Morris, president," and endorsed by the governor of New Jersey and several other political figures.

Included also (p.150-153) in the report of the House Select Committee on National Armories, submitted Feb. 28, 1862, *National Armory. <To Accompany H. Res. no. 42>* (U.S. House of Representatives. 37th Congress, 2d Session. Rept. no. 43), which likewise contains (p.145) the text of the New Jersey Legislature's Joint Resolution no. 3, May 10, 1861, recommending consideration of an armory for New Jersey.

"A CLEAR-HEADED SAILOR." *Harper's weekly.* v.9, 1865. p.435 (July 15, 1865) 464a

Capt. Charles S. Boggs [of New Brunswick, N.J.], commanding the U.S.S. *Connecticut,* in February 1865 defies a British governor's circular restricting anchorage rights of "all Federal or Confederate vessels of war" at St. George's, W.I.

DELAWARE. GENERAL ASSEMBLY.

. . . Resolutions of the Legislature of Delaware, in favor of an appropriation to erect a suitable fortification for the protection of the Delaware bay and river, and an appropriation for the completion of the railroad from Milford to the Delaware breakwater. February 10, 1862. —Referred to the Committee on Military Affairs and the Militia, and ordered to be printed. [Washington, D.C., 1862] [1]p. (U.S. Senate. 37th Congress, 2d session. Miscel. doc. no. 43)

EAGLESWOOD MILITARY ACADEMY, PERTH AMBOY, N.J.

Catalogue of the officers and students of the Eagleswood Military Academy, at Perth Amboy, New Jersey, embracing the students in the military department of the past year. Eagleswood, Perth Amboy, N.J., July 1st, 1862. Marcus Spring, proprietor. New York: Wm. C. Bryant & Co., printers, 1862. 26, [1]p. plate. NJP

Cover-title: Eagleswood Military Academy. 1861-62.
A private school located one mile west of Perth Amboy.
Contains lists of faculty and students for 1861/62, description of the school, its routines, etc.

———————

[*Same:* 1862/63] Catalogue of the officers and students of the Eagleswood Military Academy, at Perth Amboy, New Jersey. Eagleswood, Perth Amboy, N.J., July 1st, 1863. New York: Wm. C. Bryant & Co., printers, 1863. 23, [1]p. plate.
NJP NJR NHI 467

Cover-title: Eagleswood Military Academy. 1862-3.
Letterpress on back cover.

———————

[*Same:* 1863/64] Triennial catalogue of Eagleswood Military Academy, and prospectus for 1864-5. Eagleswood, Perth Amboy, N.J., July 1st, 1864. New York: Wm. C. Bryant & Co., printers, 1864. 22, [1]p. plate. NN OCLWHI

Cover-title: Eagleswood Military Academy. 1863-4. "Triennial catalogue of students [1861/62-1863/64] . . .": p.[8]-[15].

———————

[*Same:* 1864/65] 469

Not seen.

———————

[*Same:* 1865/66] Catalogue for five years of Eagleswood Military Academy, and prospectus for 1866-67. Eagleswood, Perth Amboy, N.J., July 1, 1866. New-York: John A. Gray & Green, printers, 1866. 24p. front. NJR 470

Letterpress on covers.
Includes lists of the alumni, 1861/62-1865/66.

FUNERAL OF GEN. KEARNEY [*sic*]. CITIZENS are requested to close their places of business from 12 to 3 P.M. Join the funeral procession at the bridge at 1 o'clock, to escort the remains down Broad Street, to the Market Street depot. Newark, N.J.: Printed at the Daily Advertiser office [1862] Broadside. 12¾ x 18¼ in. NJHI

GRAND ILLUMINATION AND PROCESSION!! This (Tuesday) evening, in honor of the fall of Richmond!! Fireworks! In college campus!!! Speeches from Seminary and College professors and others! Every body is invited to join. Please illuminate from 8 to 10 o'clock. By order of the Committee. [Princeton, N.J., 1865] Broadside. 9¼ x 6 in. NJP 472

HAVELOCK ASSOCIATION.

Havelock Association. Constitution and circular letter. Philadelphia: Henry B. Ashmead, book & job printer [1861] cover-title, 16p. PHI PPL 473

A society formed within the 1st N.J. Regt., for "the moral and religious improvement of its members and of their fellow soldiers of the regiment."

The "circular letter" (p.[8]-16) is signed: R. B. Yard, President, Havelock Association, 1st Reg. N.J.V. J. B. Woodward, Secretary. Camp Fairfax Seminary, Va., November 21, 1861.

LADIES OF TRENTON; YOU HAVE COME forward nobly to [————] in behalf of the defenders of our glorious Union. We do not propose to interfere with the arrangements of the proper authorities, but for fear there should be a deficiency of provision that might reflect upon the hospitality of the town, we are fitting up the riding school in Front Street, for the purpose of providing a soldier's lunch, and we ask you to send this day, and as long as necessary, to the above named place, cooked provisions, so that a cold collation shall be offered three times a day. Mr. William Bamford will take charge and attend to the matter in behalf of the ladies of Trenton. We would suggest roast and boiled meats, pickles, bread and butter, stewed fruit, coffee, &c. [Trenton, N.J., 186–] Broadside. 5¼ x 3¾ in. NJR (photo) NJT 473a

Entry based on an unclear copy of the somewhat damaged original.

MINSTRELS! GRAND VARIETY ENTERTAINment by the 9th Regt. New Jersey minstrels, on [*blank;* "Saturday Eveng" *supplied in pencil*] 1865. At [*supplied in pencil:* "Feb 25 at Hospital"] Jack Tully, the great eccentric Negro delineator . . . Herr Bruno Auerswald, the great German performer [will perform] . . . The gentlemen composing the minstrel troupe, are soldiers belonging to the 9th New Jersey Regiment, stationed at Carolina City . . . [n.p.] Printed at the office of the North Carolina Times [1865] Broadside. 16¾ x 5¾ in. NJHI

NEW JERSEY. ADJUTANT-GENERAL'S OFFICE.

Annual report of the Adjutant-General . . . for the year . . . 475

1861. Jersey City: Printed by John H. Lyon, 1862. 55p. NJ NJHI NJJ NJN NJP NJR NHI
Trenton, 1862. 58p. CSMH DLC DNW NJHI NJP NJR NHI
Trenton, N.J.: Printed at the "True American" office, 1862. 79p. NHI

1862. Trenton, 1863. 19p. NJR NHI
Trenton, N.J.: Printed by David Naar, "True American" office, 1863. 19p. CSMH DNW NJ NJHI NJN NJP NJR
[*Same: reprint,* 1904?] DLC NN

1863. Trenton, 1864. 27p. CSMH DNW NJHI NJP NJR NHI
Trenton, N.J.: Printed by David Naar, "True American" office, 1864. 31, [1]p. NJJ NJP NJR
[*Same*] 32p. NJN NJR NN

[*Same: reprint,* 1904?] 24p. DLC. Noted in Hasse, *Index of Economic Material in Documents of . . . New Jersey, 1789-1904.*
Includes tables showing local quotas and enlistments under calls of July and October 1863.

1864. Trenton, N.J.: The J. L. Murphy Publishing Co., printers, 1904. [3]p. NN
Text (p.[3]) consists of one sentence: "The report for 1864 is incorporated in the report for 1865."
Manuscript note in NJR 1865 report states that none was published for 1864.

1864 and 1865. Trenton, N.J.: Printed at the "State Gazette" office, 1866. 92p. NJP
Trenton, 1866. 38p. Not seen. Noted in Nicholson bibliography.

1865. Trenton, 1866. 42p. CSMH DNW NJHI NJP NJR NHI NN PPLL
Nicholson bibliography notes as privately printed.

Robert F. Stockton, Jr., was Adjutant-General 1858-1867.

NEW JERSEY. GOVERNOR, 1863-1866 (PARKER)

Document transmitted by the governor of New Jersey to the Legislature, in reference to the Gettysburg cemetery. [Trenton, N.J.: Printed by David Naar, "True American" office, 1864] 4p. NJP NJR 476

Caption title.
Concerns the appointment of a trustee from New Jersey to participate in management of the national cemetery at Gettysburg.

NEW JERSEY. LAWS, STATUTES, ETC.

Laws relating to the organization and regulation of the militia of the state of New Jersey, from 1846 to 1860. Trenton, N.J.: Printed at the "True American" office, 1861. 67p. NJR

Copy seen is complete, in original wrappers.

———————

[*Same*] 79p. DLC NJP 478

Pagination extended by addition of an index.

———————

[*Same*] 1863. DLC 479

NEW JERSEY. LEGISLATURE.

. . . Defence of the states of New Jersey, Pennsylvania and Delaware. Joint resolutions of the Legislature of New Jersey [March 20, 1862], relative to the defences of the states of New Jersey, Pennsylvania, and Delaware. March 24, 1862.—Referred to the Committee on Military Affairs, and ordered to be printed. [Washington, D.C., 1862] 2p. (U.S. House of Representatives. 37th Congress, 2d session. Miscel. doc. no. 61) 480

Request for immediate federal action to prepare the Delaware River and bay for defense, with an offer to join the other states concerned, in lending the required funds, "if necessary."

———————

. . . Resolutions of the Legislature of New Jersey, in favor of the employment of the Billinghurst and Requa battery in the public service. March 24, 1864.—Referred to the Committee on Military Affairs and the Militia and ordered to be printed. [Washington, D.C., 1864] 2p. (U.S. Senate. 38th Congress, 1st session. Miscel. doc. no. 85) 481

"Col. James R. Morgan, of South Amboy, in this State, has made a satisfactory exhibition to the legislature . . . of a most effective weapon, known as 'The Billinghurst and Requa battery . . .' "
See Francis A. Lord, "175 Shots per Minute—'Requa Rifle Battery,' " *Civil War Times Illustrated,* June 1962, p.29-30.

NEW JERSEY. MILITIA. HUNTERDON COUNTY BRIGADE. 1ST REGT.

. . . Regimental orders, no. 2. [n.p., 1861] Broadside. 10 x 8½ in. NJR 482

Headed "Head Quarters of the First Regiment of the Hunterdon Brigade, N.J.M., Lambertville, July 13, 1861."
"By order of G. H. Larison, Colonel . . ."
Call for a regimental court-martial on August 3.

NEW JERSEY. MILITIA. MONMOUTH AND OCEAN COUNTY BRIGADE. 4TH REGT. CO. A (GOVERNOR'S LIGHT GUARD)

By-laws of the Governor's Light Guard, Company A, Fourth Regiment of the Monmouth and Ocean Brigade, New Jersey. Organized 1861. Red Bank, N.J.: Printed at the Standard office, 1862. 40p. NJR 483

NEW JERSEY. QUARTERMASTER-GENERAL'S DEPT.

Annual report of the Quartermaster-General . . . for the year . . . 484

1861. Jersey City: Printed by John H. Lyon, 1862. 126p. DLC NJ NJHI NJJ NJN NJP NJR NN

1862. Trenton, N.J.: Printed by David Naar, "True American" office, 1863. 180p. DLC NJ NJN NJP NJR NN

Includes reports of superintendents of hospitals at Jersey City and Newark (p.[19]-23).

1863. Trenton, N.J.: Printed at the "True American" office, 1864. 154p. DLC NJ NJJ NJN NJP NJR NN

1864. Jersey City: Printed by John H. Lyon, 1865. 119p. NJ NJJ NJN NJP NJR

Trenton, N.J.: Printed by J. R. Freese, "State Gazette" office, 1865. 119p. DLC NJP

1865. Trenton, N.J.: Printed at the "State Gazette" office, 1866. 107p. fold. tables. NJHI NJP NN

Lewis Perrine served as Quartermaster-General 1855-1889.

NEW JERSEY. SUPREME COURT.

Opinions delivered by the Supreme Court of New Jersey, deciding and designating the classes of volunteers, who are entitled to state pay, provided by the act of May 11th, 1861. Trenton: Murphy & Bechtel, printers, 1861. 19p. NN 485

NEW JERSEY MILITARY ASSOCIATION.

Proceedings of the New Jersey Military Association, at the called meeting, December 20th, 1861, and annual meeting, January 28th, 1862. Freehold, N.J.: James S. Yard, printer, 1862. 14p. NJ NJR 486

Folding insert at end: List of members.

An organization of militia officers (not engaged in war service).

For earlier proceedings, see nos. 827h, 829.

———————

Proceedings of the New Jersey Military Association, at the annual meeting, January 27th, 1863, and adjourned meeting, February 11th, 1863. Freehold, N.J.: James S. Yard, printer, 1863. 15p. NJR 487

Folding insert at end: List of members.

———————

Proceedings of the New Jersey Military Association, at the annual meeting, January 26th, 1864, and special meeting, February 9th, 1864. Freehold, N.J.: James S. Yard, printer, 1865. 16p. DLC NJR 488

Folding insert at end: List of members.

PENNSYLVANIA. GENERAL ASSEMBLY.

. . . Resolution of the Legislature of Pennsylvania, in favor of the construction of one or more iron-clad gunboats, or other adequate means of defence, for the protection of the city of Philadelphia and all the important region of country bordering upon the Delaware. April 3, 1862.—Referred to the Committee on Naval Affairs, and ordered to be printed. [Washington, D.C., 1862] 2p. (U.S. Senate. 37th Congress, 2d session. Miscel. doc. no. 80) 489

POTTS, WILLIAM HENRY, 1815-1901, COMPLAINANT.

In chancery of New Jersey. Between William H. Potts, complainant, vs. Addison M. Burt, and als., defendants. Bill for injunction and relief. [n.p., 1865?] 102p. NJ 490

Caption title.

Potts, stockholder of the New Jersey Arms and Ordnance Company (successor to the bankrupt Trenton Arms Company), manufacturing Springfield muskets for the Army, charges Burt and other directors with fraud.

"PRISON PASTIMES. HOW OUR SOLDIER boys at Fort Delaware amused themselves while in confinement as prisoners of war—the publication of the 'Prison Times.' " *Southern Historical Society papers.* v.19, 1891. p.35-47. 491

Text of a handwritten newspaper of April 8, 1865 (v.1, no. 1), prepared by Confederate prisoners at Fort Delaware. Derived from a New Orleans *Picayune* article concerning a "manuscript" copy of the issue, presented to the Louisiana Historical Association by a former inmate of the camp. The *Times* apparently was circulated in a printed form which resembled manuscript (i.e., lithographic reproduction of handwritten text). Cf. next entry.

PRISON TIMES. v.1, no. 1. Fort Delaware, April 8, 1865. [4]p. 13¾ x 9¼ in. NJR 492

Probably no more published.

A newspaper produced by Confederate officers imprisoned at Fort Delaware. "Published in Div 27 by J W Hibbs / Capt 13th Va Inf / Proprietors / & / Editors / Geo S Thomas . . . / W H Bennett . . . / A Harris . . ."

Printed in lithographic reproduction of handwritten text.

In three-column newspaper format, with advertisements, camp news items, notices and lists concerned with various societies organized by the inmates; also verse, etc.

[REVERE, JOSEPH WARREN?] 1812-1880.

A review of the case of Brigadier-Gen. Joseph W. Revere, U.S. volunteers, tried by court-martial and dismissed from the service of the United States, August 10, 1863. Boston: J. H. Eastburn's press, 1864. 19p. CSMH DLC MB MH MWA NJP NHI 493

A defense, anonymous but containing copies of documents, etc., which could have come from Revere himself.

Revere commanded the 7th N.J. Vols. until October 1862 when he was promoted brigadier-general.

REVERE, JOSEPH WARREN, 1812-1880.

Sequel to the Statement. [Morristown, N.J., 1865] 11p. CSMH NHI 494

Caption title.

Includes copies of testimonials, both military and civilian, received since publication of his *Statement of the Case* (no. 495).

Dated (p.11): "The Willows," Morristown, N.J., January, 1865.

———————

A statement of the case of Brigadier-General Joseph W. Revere, United States volunteers, tried by court-martial, and dismissed from the service of the United States, August 10th, 1863. With a map, a copy of the record of the trial, and an appendix. New York: Printed by C. A. Alvord, 1863. 48p. front. (map) CSMH DLC DNW MB MWA NJP NJR NHI PPL 495

RUSLING, JAMES FOWLER, 1834-1918.

". . . The war for the Union." *Methodist quarterly review*. 4th series. v.16, 1864. p.307-316. 496

Volume contents-list identifies the author as Capt. James F. Rusling, Nashville, Tenn. Rusling was a Trenton man.

———————

"A word for the Quartermaster's Department." *United States service magazine*. v.3, 1865. p.57-67, 133-143, 255-259, 446-455. 497

Few personal references.

———————

"The Yankee as a fighter. By Colonel James F. Rusling, A.Q.M." *Ibid*. v.4, 1865. p.27-43.

[STEVENS, EDWIN AUGUSTUS] 1795-1868.

The Stevens Battery. Memorial to Congress. Merits of the battery as unanimously admitted by the Board of Examiners. Opinions of experts and results of experiments disproving the objections of the majority. [n.p., 1862] 71p. illus. DLC MWA NJP NN OCLWHI 499

Memorial signed (p.42) by E. A. Stevens, February, 1862.

"The Stevens Battery is a shot-proof vessel of war, capable of unusually great speed and manageableness, and of throwing a broadside of unusual weight."—p.46.

Construction of this 415-foot armored ship (intended for defensive use in the Hudson Bay) was begun at Hoboken in 1856, after long planning. It became a costly embarrassment to the Stevens family, and U.S. Navy Department support was sought during the war. Later the state of New Jersey accepted the battery and the sum of one million dollars (which proved insufficient) was provided to finish the construction. In 1874 the still-unfinished hulk was sold for scrap.

STEVENS, EDWIN AUGUSTUS, 1795-1868.

The Stevens Battery. Official note of experiments recently made. [n.p., 1862] Broadside. 10¼ x 6½ in. NJR 500

In the form of a letter to the editor of the New York *Times*, headed Hoboken, N.J., Thursday, Jan. 23, 1862. Probably reprinted from the *Times*.

[STEVENS, JOHN COX] 1785-1857.

Letter from Messrs. Stevens, on harbor defence. In 1841, to Colonels Totten, Thayer, and Talcott, of the Army, and Commodores Stewart, Perry, and Smith, of the Navy, who were appointed by the President to superintend the experiments of the Messrs. Stevens, on iron as a protection for war vessels, and on Stevens' elongated shells. [n.p., 1862?] [3]p. NJR 501

Caption title.

Letter headed "New York, August 13th, 1841"; signed (p.[3]): J. C. & E. A. Stevens.

Apparently printed to accompany a broadside dated Jan. 23, 1862 (no. 500, above).

"STEVENS'S BOMB-PROOF FLOATING BATtery." *Harper's weekly*. v.5, 1861. p.284-285 (May 4, 1861) illus. 501a

See also "A Bomb-Proof Battery." *Ibid.*, p.443 (July 13, 1861); illus.

TORBERT, ALFRED THOMAS ARCHIMEDES, 1833-1880.

Forms for parade and review of brigades, divisions and corps of infantry. By A. T. A. Torbert, captain U.S.A., brig. gen. vols., Army of the Potomac. Trenton, N.J.: Murphy & Bechtel, printers, 1864. 27p. NJHI 502

Torbert commanded the 1st New Jersey Brigade, 1862-1864.

UNITED STATES, DEFENDANT.

United States District Court, District of New Jersey. Before Field, j. [i.e., Richard S. Field, district judge] The United States vs. the schooner Etta, (formerly the Retribution.) Case. A. Q. Keasbey, U.S. district attorney, for U.S., Charles Edwards for claimants. Newark, N.J.: A. Stephen Holbrook, printer, 1865. 89p. NJHI

Copies of documents, interrogatories, arguments, and final decree (against the claimants). The case (1863-1864) resulted from seizure of the *Etta* at Jersey City, by U.S. authorities, under an "Act to confiscate property used for insurrectionary purposes," in the latter part of 1863. The ship, formerly a Confederate privateer, was ostensibly owned at this time by two British citizens, of Nassau, island of New Providence, carrying a cargo of fruit.

U.S. NAVY DEPT.

. . . Iron steam battery. Letter from the Secretary of the Navy, transmitting a report of the board of examiners on the iron steam battery constructing at Hoboken. January 6, 1862.—Referred to the Committee on Naval Affairs, and ordered to be printed. [Washington, D.C., 1862] 13p. (U.S. House of Representatives. 37th Congress, 2d session. Exec. doc. no. 23)

The report of the board (which is included) describes the vessel and analyzes its favorable and unfavorable features.

———————

. . . Letter of the Secretary of the Navy, in answer to a resolution of the Senate of the 18th instant, in relation to the contracts made with Robert L. Stevens for the construction of a steam floating battery. March 24, 1862.—Read, ordered to lie on the table, and be printed. [Washington, D.C., 1862] 11p. (U.S. Senate. 37th Congress, 2d session. Exec. doc. no. 34) PPLL 505

Caption title.

———————

. . . Stevens's Battery. Letter from the Secretary of the Navy, in relation to the expenditure of the appropriation for the completion of "Stevens's steam battery." May 28, 1862.—Laid on the table, and ordered to be printed. [Washington, D.C., 1862] 2p. (U.S. House of Representatives. 37th Congress, 2d session. Exec. doc. no. 121) 506

Following reports by a congressional committee and a board of experts, "I do not feel authorized to expend the money appropriated" for completion of the battery, "now partially constructed at Hoboken, New Jersey."

UNITED STATES SANITARY COMMISSION.

Narrative of privations and sufferings of United States officers & soldiers while prisoners of war in the hands of the Rebel authorities. Being the report of a commission of inquiry, appointed by the United States Sanitary Commission. With an appendix, containing the testimony . . . Boston: Published at the office of "Littell's living age" [1864] 87p. plates. [Loyal Publication Society. Publication no. 76] CSMH DLC NHI PP 507

"Testimony taken at Fort Delaware, June 21st, 1864": p.56-63.

An 86-page variant in NJN, NJR, and NHI has changes in letterpress on cover; also the four plates with preceding half-title (p.87) have been inserted between p.2 and p.3 with page number removed from half-title. None of these copies bears any reference to Loyal Publication Society.

———————

Narrative of privations and sufferings of United States officers and soldiers while prisoners of war in the hands of the Rebel authorities. Being the report of a commission of inquiry, appointed by the United States Sanitary Commission. With an appendix, containing the testimony. Philad'a: Printed for the U.S. Sanitary Commission, by King & Baird, prs., 1864. 283p. plates. CSMH NJHI NJP NJR NHI PHI PP PPLL 508

"Fort Delaware. Testimony taken at Fort Delaware, June 21st, 1864": p.199-219. Cf. also p.79-86.

"WARD" U.S. GENERAL HOSPITAL, NEWARK, N.J.

Special order. no. 15, Dec. 10, 1864. [Newark, N.J., 1864] Broadside. 8 x 5 in. NJR 509

Announces a program of weekly lectures, "to relieve the patients from the *ennui* incident to Hospital life."

WELLING, EDWARD LIVINGSTON, 1837-1897.

An address delivered before the Temperance Association of the Eleventh Regiment N.J. Vols. . . . April 25, 1864. By Dr. E. Livingston Welling, surgeon Eleventh Reg. N.J. volunteers. Published at the request of the society. Trenton, N.J.: Murphy & Bechtel, printers, 1864. 29p. NJR 510

"History of the Association" (p.[27]-29) signed: E. Clarke Cline, Chaplain 11th Regiment N.J. Vols., Secretary of the Society.

WIARD, NORMAN, 1825-1896.

. . . Communication of Norman Wiard, addressed to the Joint Committee on the Conduct of the War, upon the subject of great guns. February, 27, 1865.—Referred to the Committee on Naval Affairs and ordered to be printed. [Washington, D.C., 1865] 29p. illus., diagrs. (U.S. Senate. 38th Congress, 2d session. Miscel. doc. no. 47) NHI 511

Caption title.

Wiard, a munitions maker, lived in New York. His guns were fabricated in 1863 by the Trenton Locomotive Company. When the latter failed, he took over the establishment, renamed Trenton Wiard Ordnance Works. In 1865 it was seized for tax arrearages.

The author's year of birth is commonly given as 1826; but see G. K. Collins, *Wiard Family* (1912), p.33, 37-40.

———————

. . . Great guns. The cause of their failure, and the true method of constructing them. Addressed to the President, the members of his cabinet, the members of the Senate, the House of Representatives, and the officers of the Army and Navy of the United States. By Norman Wiard. New York: Holman, printer, 1863. 98p. illus. (incl. diagrs.) tables. DLC NJP NHI NN OCLWHI 512

———————

Inefficiency of heavy ordnance in this country and everywhere, and about Parrott and other hooped guns. Second edition—revised. By Norman Wiard. Washington: H. Polkinhorn & Son, printers, 1865. 32p. DLC NJP NHI NN OCLWHI 513

Introductory "notice" dated Washington, 10th Jan., 1865.

———————

[*Same: "third edition"*] Inefficiency of heavy ordnance in the United States service and in Europe. By Norman Wiard . . . Third edition revised. October, 1865. New-York: Sackett, Mackay & Lord, 1865. 44p. DLC 514

Not seen. Entry based on DLC catalog.

———————

The manufacture of small arms at home vs. their purchase abroad. By Norman Wiard . . . New York: Holman, printer, 1863. 29p. illus. DLC NHI NN 515

"Correspondence in relation to the manufacture of small arms": p.[15]-29.

———————

Marine artillery, as adapted for service on the coast, and on inland waters. The steamboats, the launches, the guns with sliding and field carriages, and implements described, as organized, invented, and adapted for service by Norman Wiard. New York: Holman, printer, 1863. 37p. illus. (incl. diagrs.) DLC NHI NN

———————

Memorial of Norman Wiard, addressed to the Joint Committee on the Conduct of the War, upon the subject of great guns. February 27, 1865.—Referred to the Committee on Naval Affairs and ordered to be printed. [Washington, D.C., 1865] 4p. NHI 517

———————

Memorial of Norman Wiard to the Senate and House of Representatives, in Congress assembled. To be accompanied by four pamphlets, entitled I.—Great guns, the cause of their failure, and the true method of constructing them. II.—Field artillery. III.—Marine artillery. IV.—Small arms. New York: Holman, printer, 1863. 12p. DLC DNW NHI 518

———————

[*Same: second edition*] Memorial of Norman Wiard, to the Senate and House of Representatives, in Congress assembled. To be accompanied by eight pamphlets, entitled I.—Great guns, the cause of their failure, and the true method of constructing them. II.—Field artillery. III.—Marine artillery. IV.—Small arms.

V.—Ships, rams, and forts. VI.—Proposals. VII.—Experiences of a contractor. VIII.—Review, in detail, of the annual report of the chief of the Navy Ordnance Bureau, 1862, with remarks on the present organization of the Washington Navy Yard, and its uses in connection with the said bureau. New York: Holman, printer, 1863. v, [7]-50p. DLC NHI NN 519

"Preface to second edition" (p.[iii]-v) dated New York, March 6, 1863.

———————

[*Same*] Memorial of Norman Wiard, to the Senate and House of Representatives, in Congress assembled. To be accompanied by eight pamphlets, entitled: I. Great guns . . . II. Field artillery. III. Marine artillery. IV. Small arms. V. Ships, rams, and forts. VI. Proposals. VII. Experiences of a contractor, with remarks on the management of the Army Ordnance Bureau, and its effect on the conduct of the war. VIII. Review, in detail, of the annual report of the chief of the Navy Ordnance Bureau, 1862, with remarks on the present organization of the Washington Navy Yard, and its uses in connection with the said bureau. New York: Holman, printer, 1863. v, [7]-60p. illus. DLC 520

———————

On a means of relieving the manufacturers of material of war, increasing the revenue, and reducing the expenses of the government. By Norman Wiard. Washington: H. Polkinhorn & Son, printers, 1865. 11p. DLC MB NHI NN 521

Dated (p.11): Washington, Jan. 1865.
Calls for development of arms export.

———————

Proposals for great guns. A letter to the Secretary of War. By Norman Wiard. New York: Holman, printer, 1863. 8p. illus. DLC NHI

———————

A system of marine artillery, as adapted for service on the coast, and on inland waters. The steamboats, the launches, the guns with sliding and field carriages, and implements described, and to form a part of the revenue service at all times, as organized, invented, and adapted for service by Norman Wiard. New York: Holman, printer, 1863. v, [3]-40p. illus. DLC NN 523

———————

Wiard's system of field artillery, as improved to meet the requirements of service. Commended by all the officers who have had it in their respective commands. [By] Norman Wiard. New York: Holman, printer, 1863. 38p. illus. (incl. diagrs.) NHI NN 524

———————

[*Same: second edition*] 46p. illus. (incl. diagrs.) DLC NHI NN OCLWHI 525

Text of title-page identical with that of 38-page edition except ". . . requirements of modern service . . ."

[WRIGLEY, HENRY E.]

Report on the defences of the Delaware River. 1863. [Philadelphia, 1863] 2p.l., [3]-16p. NJR (photo) 525a

Addressed to the governor of Pennsylvania: "By your kind permission I herewith present you a brief summary of an examination of suitable places and methods for the defence of the river approach to Philadelphia. The ideas it contains were matured while in the most active service, as an Engineer Officer in the Army . . . I would modestly present this report, simply with a desire to use the information possessed for the safety of our great city . . ."

Signed: Capt. Henry E. Wrigley, Engineer Office, Whipple's Division, Army of the Potomac. Philadelphia, Jan. 1, 1863.

CAMPAIGN LITERATURE, SPEECHES, DOCUMENTS, ETC.

General

NEW JERSEY. GOVERNOR.
. . . Annual message . . . 526

1862. Trenton, N.J.: Printed at the "True American" office, 1862. 16p. NJHI NJR
[n.p., 1862] cover-title (*Governor's message*), 8p. DLC
Copies without cover (caption title: Governor's message) seen, bound in *Legislative Documents*. NJJ NJN NJR

1863. Trenton, N.J.: Printed by David Naar, "True American" office, 1863. 9p. DLC NJ NJHI NJN NJP NJR

1864. Trenton, N.J.: Printed by David Naar, "True American" office, 1864. 31p. NJ NJHI NJJ NJN NJP NJR NN PHI
[*Same*] 37p. NN PHI. Title and text identical with those of the 31-page edition, but completely reset.

1865. Trenton: Printed at the "State Gazette" office, 1865. 24p. NJP NJR
Jersey City: Printed by John H. Lyon, 1865. 24p. NJ NJHI NJR NN
[*Same*] 28p. DLC NHI
["*. . . and accompanying documents*"] Jersey City: Printed by John H. Lyon and Jacob R. Freese, 1865. 154p. NJ NJJ NJN NJP NJR

Governors: 1860-1863, Charles S. Olden; 1863-1866, Joel Parker.

NEW JERSEY. STATE TREASURER'S OFFICE.
Annual report of . . . State Treasurer . . . for the year . . . 527

1861. Jersey City: Printed by John H. Lyon, 1862. 102, [1]p. DLC NJ NJJ NJN NJR
"Account current and balance sheet of the New Jersey war fund": p.[75]-102.

1862. Trenton, N.J.: Printed by David Naar, "True American" office, 1863. 125p., 1 leaf. DLC NJ NJN NJP NJR
"Account current and balance sheet of the New Jersey war fund": p.[83]-125.

1863. Trenton, N.J.: Printed by David Naar, "True American" office, 1864. 155p., 1 leaf. DLC NJJ NJN NJR
"Account current and balance sheet of the New Jersey war fund": p.[97]-155.

1864. Jersey City: Printed by John H. Lyon, 1865. 189p., 1 leaf. DLC NJ NJJ NJN NJR
"Account current and balance sheet of the New Jersey war fund": p.[103]-189.

1865. *Report of the Joint Committee on Treasurer's Accounts, to the Legislature, with the Treasurer's report to the governor, on the finances of the state.* Trenton, N.J.: Jacob R. Freese, printer, 1866. 216p. DLC
"War fund account": p.[83]-189.

State Treasurer, 1851-1865, was Rescarrick M. Smith.

THE OLD GUARD. June (and other issues?) 1862; v.1-8, Jan. 1863-Dec. 1870. Hackensack, N.J., 1862; New York, 1863-1870. 8 (9?) v. illus., plates (part col.) ports. NJJ (1866) NJP (1863-68) NJR (1864-67; incompl. 1863, 1868-70) NHI (1863-68, 1870) NN (1863-66; incompl. 1867-70) PHI (1863-65) 528

An important copperhead journal, published monthly except 1862, and Aug./Sept., Oct./Dec. 1863.

Publisher: 1862 (?) -1863, C. Chauncey Burr & Co.; 1864-1870, Van Evrie, Horton & Co. Title-page for v.8, 1870, bears imprint of English & Co., publisher.

Subtitle varies.

Issues for 1863 begin (Jan. and Feb.) as of v.2, changed (from March) to v.1.

No 1862 issues have been seen by the compiler. An editorial note (p.23) in January 1863 mentions publication of the first number in the preceding June, followed by suspension (due to mailing restrictions imposed by the "besotted tyrants at Washington"), and promises the "three numbers of the first half-yearly volume . . . due the subscribers who commenced with the beginning of the Work." "The office of publication has been removed from Hackensack to New York . . ." The editor offers a journal "of the pure Democracy that dates from other and better times," for states' rights and against "centralizing power," helping to free Democracy from the "half-companionship with revolutionary Black Republicanism, and even with bloody and inexorable Abolitionism. Hateful, disgraceful company! "

The editor, 1862-1869, was C. Chauncey Burr, formerly of the *Bergen County Democrat,* resident of Hackensack, contentious writer and speaker for the Democratic copperhead wing. In this period—except for a few signed pieces by others—all articles and departments (largely anonymous) were the work of Burr. Through 1864, the *Old Guard* dealt almost entirely with politics and war issues, incessantly attacking the federal administration, the Northern war effort generally, the War Democrats, etc., and variously endorsing the Southern cause. Although from 1865 also "devoted to literature, science and art" (including fiction and verse), the *Old Guard* retained much political content of the same tenor, extended into Reconstruction issues—e.g., numerous anti-Negro articles, some authored by racist Dr. John H. Van Evrie. Taking the editor's chair in January 1870, Thomas Dunn English (himself a wartime politician and copperhead) continued the *Old Guard* largely as a literary magazine, although with regular contributions by Burr.

Few of the *Old Guard* articles pertain directly to New Jersey. These, along with several other signed pieces by Burr and English, are recorded separately in this bibliography.

SCOVEL, JAMES MATLACK, 1833-1904.

Three speeches by Hon. Jas. M. Scovel, delivered in the Senate and House of Representatives of New Jersey, with an introduction. 1. New Jersey for the war. 2. New Jersey for the Union. 3. New Jersey for enfranchisement. Camden, N.J.: Published by Horace B. Dick, 1870. 64p. DLC NJP NHI PHI 529

The speeches were delivered, respectively, as follows: (1) Assembly, March 17, 1863, concerning the "peace resolutions"; (2) Senate, March 16, 1864, on the bill prohibiting enlistment of colored troops; (3) Senate, Feb. 27, 1866.

Biographical introduction by the publisher (Dick).

Ohio-born Scovel was a Camden attorney, a War Democrat, later Republican, member of the state Assembly, 1863, and Senate, 1864-1866.

1861

CROWELL, JOSEPH TUCKER, 1817-1891.

. . . Speech of Joseph T. Crowell, senator from Union County, at the Union convention, held at Scotch Plains, Tuesday, Oct. 29, 1861. [n.p., 1861] Broadside. 18¼ x 8 in. NJR 530

At head of title: Union County, (Second District,) people's candidate. For Assembly, John J. High, of Rahway, nominated by a convention composed of Republicans, Americans and Democrats who are opposed to the re-election of Israel O. Maxwell, in consequence of his disloyal votes in the last legislature.

Has little comment about High, but deals generally with the New Jersey political issues—interparty unity (i.e., Union Party), disloyalty of Democrats, particularly Maxwell.

Crowell was a Rahway printer, editor, and politician, a War Democrat and postwar Republican. During the 1840's he had lived in the South.

FIELD, RICHARD STOCKTON, 1803-1870.

The Constitution not a compact between sovereign states. An oration, delivered at Princeton, New Jersey, on the 4th of July, 1861, by Richard S. Field. Princeton, N.J.: J. T. Robinson, printer, 1861. 27p. DLC MH NJHI NN PPL 531

Princeton attorney, jurist, U.S. senator briefly (Dec. 1862-Jan. 1863), Republican.

"THE GREAT UNHUNG." INSCRIBED TO ALL whom it may concern. [n.p., 1861?] Broadside. 9¼ x 7½ in. NJR 532

A poetical assault on Col. James W. Wall ("confined of late within a fort"), one of New Jersey's copperheads, who had been arrested by federal authorities and imprisoned briefly in September 1861.

"HABEAS CORPUS." *Nassau literary magazine.* v.22, 1861/62. p.[97]-103 (Nov. 1861) 533

By a Princeton student.

"THE LIBERTY OF THE PRESS." *Ibid.*, p.32-40 (Sept. 1861) 534

Signed (p.40): Nassau.

Responding to the wartime controversy on this issue, a Princeton student argues for press freedom.

NEW JERSEY. GOVERNOR, 1860-1863 (OLDEN)

Message of his excellency Charles S. Olden, governor of New Jersey, delivered at the extra session of the Legislature, convened April 30, 1861. Trenton, N.J.: Printed at the "True American" office, 1861. 12p. DLC NJ NJHI NJR NN 535

Session convened to "meet the duty devolved on it by reason of the extended rebellion that exists against the Federal Government."

———————

Proclamation, by Charles S. Olden, governor of the state of New Jersey. [Trenton, N.J., 1861] Broadside. 10 x 7½ in. NJR 536

Thanksgiving proclamation, dated Nov. 1, 1861. Brief war allusions.

NEW JERSEY. LAWS, STATUTES, ETC.

An act authorizing a loan for the purposes of war, to repel invasion and suppress insurrection, and appropriating the same, and providing for the payment thereof. [Trenton, N.J., 1861] [2]p. 9¾ x 7¾ in. NJR 537

Caption title.

Included is a notice of the forthcoming sale of state bonds, dated May 28, 1861.

NEW JERSEY. LEGISLATURE.

. . . Resolutions of the Legislature of New Jersey, expressive of confidence in the government of that state in the present crisis in our national affairs; approving of the patriotic efforts of the President to maintain the Union, the Constitution, and the laws; and declaring their belief that the most speedy mode of restoring peace is by the vigorous prosecution of the war. August 2, 1861.—Ordered to lie on the table and be printed. [Washington, D.C., 1861] 2p. (U.S. Senate. 37th Congress, 1st session. Miscel. doc. no. 9) 538

"Concurrent resolutions adopted by the legislature at its extra session."

NEW JERSEY. LEGISLATURE. GENERAL ASSEMBLY. COMMITTEE ON JUDICIARY.

[Report of Committee on Judiciary on raising money for purposes of war, presented before the Assembly, May 1, 1861] 539

Not seen. Text of the report appears in *Minutes . . . of the Eighty-Fifth General Assembly of . . . New Jersey* (Jersey City, N.J., 1861), p.1124-1127. Double the usual number were ordered printed, which suggests that copies were issued in pamphlet form.

"Mr. [David] Mulford, Chairman of the Committee on Judiciary . . . to whom was referred that part of the Governor's message relating to the raising of money in this state . . . report . . . Assembly bill No. 5, entitled 'An act authorizing a loan for the purposes of war, to repel invasion and suppress insurrection, and appropriating the same and providing for the payment thereof.'"

PARKER, CORTLANDT, 1818-1907.

The present contest—our rightfulness in waging it—its necessity—our duty. An oration delivered at Newark, N.J., July 4, 1861, by Cortlandt Parker, Esq. . . . [Newark, N.J., 1861] 8p. NJR 540

Caption title.

The speaker was a Newark attorney and politician, a Republican, currently Essex County prosecutor.

PRINCETON, N.J. CITIZENS.

Celebration of the Fourth of July, 1861, in Princeton, N.J. Princeton, N.J.: J. T. Robinson, printer, 1861. 24p. NJP NJPT NJR NHI PPL 541

"The Constitution not a compact between sovereign states": p.[5]-24. Oration by Hon. Richard S. Field.

SCUDDER, ISAAC WILLIAMSON, 1816-1881.

Address delivered by Isaac W. Scudder, at Metropolitan Hall, Jersey City, July 4th, 1861. By request of the Common Council. New-York: C. F. Durant, book and job printer, 1861. 38p. NHI 542

Deals entirely with the war and its background. Scudder was a Jersey City attorney, associated with the New Jersey railroad monopoly; as a Republican, elected to Congress in the 1870's.

"SECESSION NEWSPAPERS." *Nassau literary magazine.* v.22, 1861/62 (Nov. 1861) p.117-121. 543

A Princeton student favors restrictive measures against the copperhead press.

TREASON! WHEREAS, CERTAIN ENEMIES OF the government have published a call for a meeting of the citizens of Monmouth County . . . at Middletown, on . . . the 29th inst. . . . Now, this is to give notice, that the above meeting is treasonable . . . being designed to give aid and comfort to the Southern conspirators . . . Citizens, arouse! . . . The Union! The whole Union, and nothing but the Union! . . . Keyport, N.J., 1861. Broadside. 9½ x 6 in. NJR 544

Dated: Keyport, Monmouth Co., N.J., August 27th, 1861.

UNION PARTY. NEW JERSEY. MIDDLESEX COUNTY.

To the people of Middlesex County. The Union convention, composed of Democrats and Union men of Middlesex County, met . . . the 15th of October . . . The convention made the following nominations: For senator, Amos Robins [i.e., Robbins], of Woodbridge [etc.] . . . New Brunswick: Printed at "the Times office" [1861] Broadside. 12 x 8½ in. NJR 545

Dated October 24th, 1861.

Includes text of the convention's resolutions supporting the war effort, gives names of the nominees, etc.

U.S. CONGRESS. SENATE.

. . . Mr. Ten Eyck [of New Jersey] submitted for consideration the following resolution. Resolved, That the present war is for the Union, according to the Constitution [etc.] . . . [Washington, D.C., 1861] [1]p. (U.S. Senate. 37th Congress, 2d session. Miscel. doc. no. 6) 546

At head of title: . . . In the Senate of the United States. December 16, 1861.—Ordered to be printed.

VANATTA, JACOB, 1824-1879.

Oration delivered by Hon. Jacob Vanatta, before the Society of the Sons of Liberty, of the city of Rahway, N.J., at the celebration of the anniversary of American independence, July 4, 1861. Published by the Society. Jersey City: John H. Lyon & Co., steam printers, 1861. 20p. NHI 547

Relates chiefly to the war.

The speaker was a Morristown attorney, Douglas Democrat, state assemblyman 1862-1863, etc.

———

Oration delivered by Jacob Vanatta, Esq., before the Society of the Sons of Liberty, of the city of Rahway, N.J., at the celebration of the anniversary of American independence, July 4, 1861. Published by the Society. Jersey City: John H. Lyon & Co., steam printers, 1861. 20p. NJP NJR 548

WALL, JAMES WALTER, 1820-1872.

Letter to Mr. Blair by James W. Wall, and his reception and speech, at Burlington, on Friday evening, Sept. 27th, 1861. [n.p., 1861] Broadside. 21½ x 13¾ in. NHI 549

Includes a copy of Wall's letter (Burlington, Aug. 26, 1861) to Postmaster General Blair, protesting the banning of certain newspapers from circulation by mail; Blair's response of Aug. 31; and an account of Wall's return to Burlington (following his release from Fort Lafayette after a short detention as a copperhead) and the text of his speech at the station platform before a welcoming crowd. The speech expresses gratitude for the reception, complains of his imprisonment, endorses the Constitution and Union, etc.

Wall was one of the most interesting figures in New Jersey's Civil War history. An attorney, Princeton graduate, son of Senator Garret D. Wall and brother-in-law of one-time governor Peter D. Vroom, he was a man of ability and considerable popularity. As a leader of the copperhead element of the Democracy, he freely expressed his views in speeches and writings, undeterred by his arrest in 1861, and was chosen in 1863 to fill a vacated U.S. Senate seat for about six weeks.

1862

BRADLEY, JOSEPH P., 1813-1892.

The political expressions of Joseph P. Bradley, compiled from speeches, and articles written by him, published in the Newark Daily Advertiser at different periods during the last two years. [Newark, N.J., 1862] 8p. NJR 550

Caption title.

Reprinted in J. P. Bradley, *Miscellaneous Writings* (Newark, 1902), p.[97]-123.

Bradley, a Newark attorney, was a candidate for Congress on the Union ticket at this time.

———

Speech of Joseph P. Bradley, Esq., at the Union administration meeting held in Newark, Oct. 22, 1862. [Newark, N.J., 1862] 4p. NJR

Caption title.

"From the Newark Daily Advertiser, Oct. 23, 1862."

Reprinted in J. P. Bradley, *Miscellaneous Writings* (Newark, 1902), p.[125]-137.

———

Speech of Joseph P. Bradley, Esq., the Union nominee for Congress, at Jersey City . . . Oct. 28, 1862. [n.p., 1862] 4p. NJR 552

Caption title.

Reprinted in J. P. Bradley, *Miscellaneous Writings* (Newark, 1902), p.[139]-149.

BROWNSON, ORESTES AUGUSTUS, 1803-1876.

The war for the Union. Speech by Dr. O. A. Brownson. How the war should be prosecuted. The duty of the government, and the duty of the citizen. New-York: George F. Nesbit & Co., printers and stationers, 1862. 16p. NHI NN OCLWHI 553

Address from the balcony of Willard's Hotel, Washington, on August 28, 1862, upholding abolitionist principles, colonization, prosecution of the war. Interspersed notations of audience reaction include a few heckling comments.

Brownson, a resident of Elizabeth, in 1862 ran unsuccessfully for Congress in the Third District of New Jersey as a Union candidate. He was a nationally-known writer, one-time Universalist clergyman, Catholic convert, and editor of *Brownson's Quarterly Review*.

CONGAR, HORACE NEWTON, 1817-1893.

"H. N. Congar's letters from Hong Kong. Edited by Maurice Tandler." *Proceedings of the New Jersey Historical Society*. v.84, 1966. p.[75]-88. 553a

Copies of four 1862 letters, Jan. 1 and 12, Aug. 16, and Dec. 31, the last two dealing considerably with current political and national issues in the United States, especially New Jersey. Congar, a Newark editor and politician, member of the 1860 Republican national convention, was appointed U.S. consul at Hong Kong in 1861.

DEMOCRATIC PARTY. NEW JERSEY.

Address of the New Jersey Democratic State Central Committee to the voters of the state. [Trenton, N.J., 1862] 16p. DLC NJ NJR 554

Caption title.
Signed at Trenton, Oct. 1862, by the Committee (p.16).
"Resolutions adopted at the Democratic State Convention, September 4, 1862": p.16.
Expresses "ardent devotion to the Union and the Constitution."

FINANCE. A LETTER ADDRESSED TO THE House Committee of Ways and Means, January 1, 1862, preliminary to the examination and discussion of "A bill to establish a national system of finance based on demand notes, currency bonds, and loan bonds." [Washington, D.C.: Scammell & Co., printers, 1862] 7p. MH NJR (photo) 555

Caption title.
Signed (p.7): New Jersey.
Sets forth a plan for a national paper currency. The pamphlet begins with (partial?) text of essentially the same proposal written during the panic of 1857, entitled "A National Exchequer," dated New Jersey, November 1, 1857, signed by (the same?) "New Jersey."

. . . FOURTH OF JULY IN SOMERVILLE, N.J. Order of exercises. [Somerville? 1862] Broadside. 6 x 6 in. NJR 556

Political satire aimed at alleged local "secesh" sympathizers (not identified by name).
"Printed at the Office of the 'Richmond Inquirer.'"

"NATIONAL DEBT." *Nassau literary magazine.* v.23, 1862/63. p.12-16 (Sept. 1862) 557

By a Princeton student.

NEW JERSEY. GOVERNOR, 1860-1863 (OLDEN)

Proclamation by Charles S. Olden, governor of the state of New Jersey. [Trenton, N.J., 1862] Broadside. 10 x 7½ in. NJR 558

Thanksgiving proclamation, dated Nov. 3, 1862. Reference to "troublous times," etc.

NIXON, JOHN THOMPSON, 1820-1889.

The rebellion: its origin, and the means of suppressing it. Speech . . . April 11, 1862. Washington, D.C., 1862. 14p. 559

Not seen (description from Sabin).

Nixon was a Bridgeton lawyer and politician, Republican, member of Congress 1859-1863, and from 1870 judge of the U.S. District Court.

———————

The rebellion: its origin, and the means of suppressing it. Speech of Hon. Jno. T. Nixon, of New Jersey, in the House of Representatives . . . April 11, 1862. Washington, D.C.: Scammell & Co., printers, 1862. 8p. DLC NJHI NJR NHI PHI PPL 560

Text in double columns.

PARKER, CORTLANDT, 1818-1907.

The moral guilt of the rebellion. An oration delivered at Newton, N.J., July 4, 1862, by Cortlandt Parker, Esq. [Newton, N.J.? 1862] 12p. NJHI NJR NHI 561

Caption title.
Text in double columns.

PERRY, NEHEMIAH, 1816-1881.

The Constitution and the Union, let them together be maintained. Speech of Hon. N. Perry, of New Jersey. Delivered in the House of Representatives, March 6, 1862. [Washington, D.C.: Printed by L. Towers & Co., 1862] 8p. DLC MB NJHI NJR NHI 562

Caption title.
Connecticut-born Perry was a prosperous Newark manufacturer, an officer of various corporations (including the New Jersey railroad monopoly). Originally a Whig, he became a Democrat; was a member of Congress 1861-1865, mayor of Newark after the war.

TEN EYCK, JOHN CONOVER, 1814-1879.

Remarks of Hon. J. C. Ten Eyck, of New Jersey, on the motion to postpone the confiscation bills, in order to take up the tax bill. Delivered in the Senate of the United States, May 21, 1862. [Washington, D.C.: L. Towers & Co., printers, 1862] 8p. DLC NJR NHI OCLWHI 563

Caption title.
Ten Eyck was a Burlington attorney, variously Whig and Republican. He served in the Senate 1859-1865.

TOWNSEND, SAMUEL P.

The great speech of the late political campaign. By Dr. S. P. Townsend. Delivered at Plainfield, New Jersey, on . . . October 30, 1862. On the subjects of conservatism, abolitionism, sham Democracy, paper money, the national finances, the war, our radical Congress and administration, etc., etc. . . . New York: Published by James Alexander Houston, November 25, 1862. [New York: Baker & Godwin, printers, 1862] 15, [1]p. DLC MH NJHI NJP NJR NHI OCLWHI 564

"This is a verbatim report of an extempore speech made by Dr. Townsend."

Text in double columns.

The speaker was of Quaker parents and a frequent visitor to the South, abolitionist, conservative, strongly pro-Union, etc.

[UNION PARTY. NEW JERSEY]

The war! Shall it be prosecuted? [n.p., 1862] 4p. NJR 565

Caption title.

Text in double columns.

A campaign tract favoring Marcus L. Ward for governor and attacking Democratic candidate Parker.

WALL, JAMES WALTER, 1820-1872.

Arbitrary arrests. Correspondence of James W. Wall with the New York World. [n.p., 1862] Broadside. About 19¼ x 12¾ in. NJR (photo) PPL 565a

Two letters, dated Burlington, Sept. 16 and 20, 1862, endorsing editorial protests against recent arrests by federal authorities and discussing additional cases of similar nature.

Text printed in four columns.

———————

The Constitution: originating in compromise, it can only be preserved by adhering to its spirit, and observing its every obligation. An address, delivered by James W. Wall, Esq., at the city hall, Burlington, February 20, 1862, by invitation of the Common Council of the city. Burlington: Printed at the office of the Dollar Newspaper, 1862. 22p. MB NJ NJR NHI 566

Text printed in two columns.

———————

The Constitution: originating in compromise, it can only be preserved by adhering to its spirit, and observing its every obligation. An address delivered by James W. Wall, Esq., at the city hall, Burlington, February 20, 1862, by invitation of the Common Council of the city. Philadelphia: King & Baird, printers, 1862. 60p. DLC MB NJ NJHI NJNBS NJP NJR NHI OCLWHI PHI PPL PU 567

1863

BURR, CHARLES CHAUNCEY, 1817-1883.

"The bowl of blood. By C. Chauncey Burr." *The Old guard.* v.1, 1863. p.124. 568

Four stanzas of verse. "Up, up, ye cowards! . . . Is this a time for rest? When 'loyal' treason madly rolls Its chains upon your breast! . . ."

Burr, Hackensack resident, editor of the *Old Guard*, was a noted copperhead spokesman.

———————

"Democratic policy." *Ibid.*, p.[258]-263. 569

Response to an article of the same title printed in "a paper professing to be democratic, published in New Jersey, which . . . more than intimates a policy which shakes hands with the black Republican party . . . It says that the party must 'emphatically discard and condemn the doctrine of secession or nullification,' and 'abjure all party affiliation and sympathy with the managers of the rebellion.' "

Anonymous but doubtless by editor Burr.

———————

"Drafting vs. enlisting." *Ibid.*, p.64-67. 570

In the form of a letter to "O. A. Brownson, LL.D.," signed (p.67): C. Chauncey Burr.

Copperhead editor of the *Old Guard* argues against the draft. Brownson, a resident of Elizabeth, N.J., in 1862 ran for Congress on the Union ticket.

———————

"Governor Parker's inaugural address." *Ibid.*, p.46. 571

Anonymous.

". . . We have seen no public document that goes more thoroughly to the root of the Executive usurpation and tyranny that have disgraced and justly alarmed the nation for the last two years . . ."

This issue of the *Old Guard* (February 1863), and that of January are identified as nos. 1 and 2 of vol. 2; succeeding issues of 1863 bear revised volume numbering (vol. 1).

———————

Speech of C. Chauncey Burr, delivered at the peace convention, New York, June 3d, 1863. [New York? 1863] 4p. NJR (photo) OCLWHI RP RPB 572

Caption title.

"Sir, I live in New Jersey—gallant, honest, glorious New Jersey—which was the only northern State that gave its electoral vote against Abraham Lincoln, and will be the last to submit to his intolerable despotism without a manly resistance." (Etc.)

BUTLER, BENJAMIN FRANKLIN, 1818-1893.

. . . Character and results of the war. A thrilling and eloquent speech, by Major-General B. F. Butler. New York, Sept., 1863. New York: Wm. C. Bryant & Co., printers, 1863. cover-title, 16p. NHI 573

Letterpress on covers.

At head of title: Printed for the Loyal National League of New Jersey, by the Loyal Publication Society, 863 Broadway. No. 7.

"THE CONSTITUTION—ITS SUSPENSION." *Nassau literary magazine.* v.24, 1863/64. p.17-22 (Sept. 1863) 574

Signed (p.22) : Id.

A Princeton student argues for restriction of individual liberty in the national interest.

CROWELL, JOSEPH TUCKER, 1817-1891.

Speech of Joseph T. Crowell, of Union County, in the Senate of New Jersey, January 22, 1863, on the motion to postpone indefinitely the anti-war resolutions offered by Hon. Daniel Holsman, of Bergen. [n.p., 1863] cover-title, 9p. DLC NJHI NJP NJR NHI NN 575

Caption title: The Democracy not submissionists. Speech of Jos. T. Crowell, against the anti-war resolutions, Trenton, January 22, 1863.

War Democrat versus copperhead.

DEMOCRATIC BATTLE SONG. Tune—Bruce's address. [n.p., 1863?] Broadside. 9½ x 3 in. NJR 576

Six stanzas of political verse urging Jerseymen to the defense of freedom, etc., in support of "Wright's rising star." Includes references to "a dark and dastard foe," who "With traitor hand and coward blow, Would lay the *Constitution* low," etc.

Apparently pertains either to William Wright, Democratic candidate for the U.S. Senate in 1863, or to Gen. E. R. V. Wright, Democratic candidate for governor in 1859, the "coward blow" in the latter case probably being John Brown's Harper's Ferry raid.

ENGLISH, THOMAS DUNN, 1819-1902.

Speech of Hon. Thomas Dunn English, of Bergen County, on the anti-abolition resolutions, in the House of Assembly of New Jersey, March 17th, 1863. Trenton: Printed at the True American office, 1863. 8p. DLC MH NJR NHI NN 577

The speaker was a physician, writer, poet, editor, politician, born in Philadelphia, lived in New York, Bergen County (from 1856), and Newark (from 1878). He was a Democrat, wartime copperhead, member of the state Assembly 1863-1864.

"THE FEDERAL CONSTITUTION." *Nassau literary magazine.* v.24, 1862/63. p.111-114 (Nov. 1863) 578

Signed (p.114) : "A . . ."

By a Princeton student.

FIELD, RICHARD STOCKTON, 1803-1870.

A charge to the grand jury in the District Court of the United States for the District of New Jersey, April 21, 1863. By R. S. Field, district judge . . . Trenton, N.J.: State Gazette and Republican print, 1863. 24p. DLC NJHI NJP NJR NHI 579

Chiefly deals with the nature of wartime crimes and offenses against the United States.

———————

Speech of Hon. R. S. Field, of New Jersey, on the discharge of state prisoners. Delivered in the Senate of the United States, January 7, 1863. Washington: Printed by L. Towers & Co., 1863. 16p. DLC NJP NJR NN OCLWHI PHI PPL 580

A statement made in connection with H.R. 362, a bill to provide for discharge of state prisoners and to authorize federal judges to take bail or recognizances for their trial. Senator Field, shortly afterward appointed U.S. district judge for New Jersey, deals here chiefly with suspension of the right of habeas corpus, which he believes to lie in the President's hands.

For a Democratic response, see no. 595.

FINANCE. NO. II. BILL — SYNOPSIS — AND explanatory remarks. [Washington, D.C.? 1863?] 6p. MH NJR (photo) 581

Caption title.

Signed (p.6) : New Jersey.

Contains the text of "A bill to establish a national system of finance, based on demand notes, currency bonds, and loan bonds" (p.[1]-3), followed (p.[4]-6) by "Synopsis and remarks exploratory" of the bill.

Copy in MH bears a longhand note above the title: "Finance / 1863," and is identified as a gift received Sept. 6, 1864.

"HABEAS CORPUS—ITS SUSPENSION." *Nassau literary magazine.* v.23, 1862/63. p.[193]-203 (Feb. 1863) 582

Signed (p.203) : Patriot.

A Princeton student essay justifying suspension.

LATHROP, CHARLES C. 1818-

Cause, course, effects, and ultimate results of the rebellion and the duties and rights of the federal government, consequent thereon. Address delivered by Hon. Charles C. Lathrop, before the Union League of Beverly, N.J., on . . . April 7, 1863. [n.p., 1863] 12p. DLC NHI

Reviews the issues of the war (slavery, etc.).

Lathrop (of Burlington County) was a Union candidate for the state Assembly, defeated 1863 in a contested election, elected 1864 and 1865. A native of Vermont, he had lived from about 1835 in Florida and Louisiana, removing to Philadelphia in 1856. Long active in politics (formerly a Whig and American Party man), he was appointed in 1862 collector of the port of New Orleans but resigned before occupying the office. For a defense against opponents of the appointment, see his pamphlet, *Biographical Sketch of Charles C. Lathrop, with Testimonials, Correspondence, &c., &c.* (Philadelphia, 1862). Copy in MB; photocopy in NJR.

LOYAL UNION LEAGUE OF NEWARK, N.J.

Constitution of the Loyal Union League of Newark, New Jersey. [Newark, N.J., 1863?] [4]p. 14 x 8½ in. NJHI 584

Caption title.

An organization devoted to support of the struggle against armed rebellion and copperhead elements, urging arrest and any other lawful measures against the latter.

McCLELLAN, GEORGE BRINTON, 1826-1885.

Soldiers read! Letter from Gen. McClellan. Orange, N.J., October 12th, 1863. [n.p., 1863] Broadside. 19 x 11¾ in. NJR 585

Addressed: Hon. Chas. J. Biddle.

Issued in support of Judge Woodward as candidate for governor of Pennsylvania, and denying reports that he had written to a Democratic meeting at Allentown (Pa.) favoring the candidacy of incumbent Governor Curtin. No New Jersey allusions.

NEW JERSEY. GOVERNOR, 1863-1866 (PARKER)

Annual thanksgiving. A proclamation by the governor of the state of New Jersey. [Trenton, N.J., 1863] Broadside. 10 x 8 in. NJR 586

Dated Nov. 7, 1863.

Contains war allusions.

———————

Inaugural address of Joel Parker, delivered at Trenton, upon taking the oath of office as governor of the state of New Jersey, January 20th, 1863. Trenton, N.J.: Printed by David Naar, "True American" office, 1863. 16p. DLC NJ NJHI NJN NJP NJR 587

Deals extensively with the war.

———————

[*Same*] 22p. DLC NHI NN 588

———————

[*Same: German edition*] Inaugural-Adresse von Joel Parker, gehalten zu Trenton bei Ablegung seines Amtseides als Gouverneur des Staates New Jersey, am 20. Januar 1863. Newark, N.J.: Druck von C. Hollinger („N.J. Volksmann" office) 1863. cover-title, 16p. DLC NHI

Caption title: Inaugural-Adresse des Gouverneurs Joel Parker.

Text in two columns.

———————

Proclamation by the governor of New Jersey. [Trenton, N.J., 1863] Broadside. 7¾ x 5 in. NJR 590

Designates April 30, 1863, as a day for "National Prayer, Fasting and Humiliation," to ask God "for the restoration of our now divided and suffering country . . ."

Dated April 14, 1863.

NEW JERSEY. LEGISLATURE.

List of officers and members of the eighty-seventh Legislature of New Jersey, with their residences in Trenton and post office address, and the joint and standing committees of both houses. Convened January 13th, 1863. Trenton, N.J.: Printed by David Naar, "True American" office [1863] Broadside. 21¾ x 15 in. NJR

NEW JERSEY. LEGISLATURE. GENERAL ASSEMBLY.

Diagram showing the location of the members composing the eighty-seventh Legislature of the state of New Jersey, and the counties which they represent. 1863. [Trenton, N.J.? 1863] Broadside. 14 x 17 in. NJR 592

Assembly only.

NIXON, JOHN THOMPSON, 1820-1889.

An address delivered before the Cliosophic and American Whig societies of the College of New Jersey, June 23, 1863, by the Hon. John T. Nixon, Bridgeton, N.J. . . . Philadelphia: Cax-

ton Press of C. Sherman, Son & Co., 1863. 36p.
DLC NJP NN PU 593

On the subject of patience and endurance, illustrated largely by examples from the distant past, with few references to the current war.

The speaker was a Princeton alumnus, lawyer and politician.

PERRY, NEHEMIAH, 1816-1881.

The omissions and commissions of the Administration. Speech of Hon. N. Perry, of New Jersey, delivered in the House of Representatives, February 2, 1863. Washington City: L. Towers & Co., printers [1863] cover-title, 8p.
NJR NHI 594

Caption title is similar, but with date: February 28 [*sic*], 1863.

Perry (Democrat) discusses executive usurpation of power, states' rights, confiscation, emancipation, the loyalty of New Jersey as a Democratic state (in reply to charges of Republican Senator R. S. Field).

[RANDOLPH, JOSEPH FITZ] 1803-1873.

Mr. Field and the habeas corpus. [n.p., 1863] 12p. NJR 595

Caption title.

A reply to Senator R. S. Field's *Speech . . . on the Discharge of State Prisoners* (no. 580). The author argues that "restraint on personal liberty which the emergency demands, may be obtained under the Constitution, through the Judiciary, in a much better and more satisfactory way than by . . . suspension of the habeas corpus by the Executive."

The copy in NJR bears a contemporary manuscript notation: "by Judge J. F. Randolph." Randolph was a Trenton lawyer, jurist, and member of the 1861 Peace Convention. He was a Democrat, formerly Whig, American, and Constitutional Union.

SCOVEL, JAMES MATLACK, 1833-1904.

New Jersey for the war. Speech of Hon. James M. Scovel, of Camden, New Jersey, on the peace resolutions, delivered in the New Jersey House of Assembly, March 17, 1863. Camden, N.J.: Printed at the "West Jersey Press" office, by S. Chew, 1863. 11p. CTY DLC MH NJJ NHI OCLWHI 596

Text in double columns.

TOWNSEND, SAMUEL P.

The speech of Dr. S. P. Townsend, delivered before the Union League, at New Providence, New Jersey . . . Nov. 9, 1863. On the subjects of the war a great national blessing—the barbarisms of the Southerners—a protective tariff—a national currency—the treasury notes—our national finances—the wealth of the nation—the slave oligarchs—the bullionists—capital and capitalists—the duty of farmers—New Jersey politics and politicians, etc., etc. New York: Published by the New Providence Union League, January 1st, 1864. 16p. MB NJR NHI

WALL, JAMES WALTER, 1820-1872.

Address delivered by Hon. James W. Wall, at Newark, N.J., July 4th, 1863. Newark, N.J.: Daily Journal print, 1863. 20p. NJHI NJP NHI OCLWHI PPL 598

Copperhead views of the war.

———

Speech of Hon. James W. Wall, of New Jersey, on the indemnification bill; delivered in the Senate of the United States, March 2, 1863. Washington, 1863. 13p. DLC NJP NJR OCLWHI PHI PPL 599

Printed in double columns.

———

Speech of Hon. James W. Wall, of N.J., on the Missouri emancipation bill, delivered in the United States Senate, February 7th, 1863. Washington: M'Gill & Witherow, printers, 1863. 16p. DLC NJ NJP NJR PHI 600

At least one of the copies located (in NJ) has a misprint on the title-page—"Mislouri."

———

Speeches for the times. By Hon. James W. Wall, of New Jersey. With a sketch of his personal and political history . . . New York: Published by J. Walter & Co., 1864. 63p. CTY DLC DNW MB NJ NJJ NJP NJR NHI NN NNC OCLWHI PHI PPL 601

Includes texts of three speeches: p.11-32, "The Indemnification bill" (U.S. Senate, March 2, 1863); p.32-53, "Peace or separation" (Democratic Club, Philadelphia, May 9, 1863); p.53-63, "Civil liberty overthrown" (mass meeting, Mount Holly, N.J., Sept. 28, 1863).

Publisher's advertisement on outside of back cover.

[WRIGHT, WILLIAM]

A word of warning to Democrats, from a life-long voter with the party. Philadelphia: U.S.

Steam-Power Book and Job Printing Office, 1863. 16p. DLC OCLWHI 602

Signed: W.

Supports the government's war effort and warns against political action which could weaken the national cause.

"This pamphlet is intended for gratuitous distribution, and to be read around the camp-fires . . ."—p.16.

The author, William Wright (cf. no. 603, following), was probably the Philadelphia physician of that name who was party to a number of Burlington deeds in the late 1840's and early 1850's. In a few deeds of 1864 he is described as a resident of Burlington.

———————

[*Same: variant*] A word of warning to Democrats, from a life-long voter with the party. For gratuitous distribution. Philadelphia: U.S. Steam-Power Book and Job Printing Office, 1863. 16p. DLC MB NJR (photo) NHI 603

Signed: Wm. Wright, Meadow Lawn, Burlington, N.J., January, 1863.

1864

BURR, CHARLES CHAUNCEY, 1817-1883.

"The doom, and the regeneration of Democracy. The speech in full of C. Chauncey Burr, delivered in Bergen County, N.J., the afternoon before the late election." *The Old guard.* v.2, 1864. p.274-280. 604

Copperhead views, and a criticism of the Democratic party organization for its more moderate stand.

[BURR, CHARLES CHAUNCEY?] 1817-1883.

"The first gun of state sovereignty fired in New Jersey." *Ibid.*, p.110-113. 605

A response to Governor Parker's message [March 23, 1864] opposing, as an infringement of state sovereignty, proposed federal legislation injurious to the existing New Jersey railroad monopoly. The writer calls for a consistent state-sovereignty stand against the federal conscription act.

———————

"The messages of Governors Seymour and Parker." *Ibid.*, p.37-39. 606

Reviewing the recent governors' messages of New York and New Jersey, the writer attacks both War Democrats and the Lincoln administration as disunionist in their prosecution of an unconstitutional war.

CONGAR, HORACE NEWTON, 1817-1893.

Circular from H. N. Congar. [Newark, N.J.? 1864] Broadside. 16¾ x 10 in. NJHI NJR

Text in two columns.

"To the Union Citizens of Newark, New Jersey: From my transient home in the far East, I send Greeting to the Union men of my native City. In the midst of a struggle for the preservation of the Nation, and on the eve of a political contest in which are involved its highest interests, I feel that duty calls me to labor in your ranks . . ."

Signed: H. N. Congar. Hong Kong, June 7th, 1864.

A rhetorical summary of the war issues and Union heroics, and a call for support of Lincoln in the presidential campaign.

Congar was a Newark attorney and Republican leader, one-time owner of the anti-slavery Newark *Mercury.* Lincoln in 1861 appointed him consul at Hong Kong, and he later held other state and national offices.

THE DAILY TIMES, JERSEY CITY, N.J.

. . . Great railroad disaster . . . Jersey City, N.J., 1864. Broadside. 14 x 8 in. NJR NHI

Text in two columns.

A satiric picture of McClellan's defeat for the presidency, set in terms of a train trip from Orange, N.J., to Washington, with McClellan as engineer. The train, loaded with New Jersey (and other) politicians, is halted by a wreck.

At head of title: The Daily Times. Jersey City, N.J., Friday, November 11, 1864. <The following editorial from Wednesday's Times is republished at the request of numbers of subscribers.>

DEMOCRATIC PARTY. NEW JERSEY. BERGEN COUNTY. SECOND ASSEMBLY DISTRICT.

McClellan men, attention! There will be a meeting of the Democracy, of the 2d Assembly District, of Bergen County, on Tuesday ev'g, Sept. 20th . . . at the drill-room of the National Guard, for the purpose of organizing a Democratic campaign McClellan club! for the 2d Assembly District, of Bergen County. The following speakers will address the meeting, Hon. A. J. Rogers, Hon. Rodman M. Price, Hon. Dan. Holsman. All conservative, constitutional men are invited to attend. By order of committee. [Paterson, N.J.] Paterson Guardian print [1864] Broadside. 18¾ x 12 in. NJR 609

DEMOCRATIC PARTY. NEW JERSEY. BRIDGEWATER TOWNSHIP.

Liberty and Union! Ex-Chancellor Benj. Williamson, will positively address the Bridgewater Club at Doughty's Hall, on . . . Nov. 2d. Somerville, Oct. 31, 1864. Somerville, N.J.: Somerset Messenger print [1864] Broadside. 17¼ x 12 in. NJR 610

Bears a cut of an eagle with names, "McClellan & Pendleton."

DEMOCRATIC PARTY. NEW JERSEY. GREENVILLE TOWNSHIP.

Patriotism and love of country under the Constitution and laws, as opposed to loyalty, either to kings, princes, or presidents. The Democrats of the township of Greenville, are invited to attend a meeting of the Democratic McClellan Club, at the hall of Frederick Thau, on Saturday [*changed by hand to* "Monday"] evening, ["Sep. 12." *entered by hand*] 1864, at eight o'clock. Good speaking and singing. Ye Democrats, who love your country, come. By order, Stephen Terhune, pres't. Thomas Carey, sec'y. [n.p., 1864] Broadside. 17 x 14 in. NJR 611

DEMOCRATIC PARTY. NEW JERSEY. HILLSBOROUGH TOWNSHIP.

Old Hillsborough arouse! All persons in favor of constitutional law, good government, civil and religious liberty, and opposed to all unwarranted usurpation of arbitrary power, are cordially invited to attend a grand mass meeting at Neshanic, on . . . November 2nd, 1864 . . . Gen. Theodore Runyon, Hon. R. J. Ludlow, of Phila., and others, will address the meeting. The McClellan clubs of the surrounding country are invited to be present. Neshanic, Oct. 25, 1864. By order of committee. Somerville, N.J.: Somerset Messenger print [1864] Broadside. 26 x 19 in. NJR 612

THE DRAFT! THE LIBERTY OF THE PRESS! Account of the presentation of a sword-cane to Edward N. Fuller, Esq., editor of the "Daily Journal," Newark, N.J., by a delegation of New York Democrats, July 30th, 1864. [n.p., 1864] 8p. NHI OCLWHI 613

Caption title.
Fuller, a vociferous copperhead, had published on July 19, 1864, an article hostile to the draft, for which he was arrested by U.S. authorities. The sword-cane (inscribed "'Resistance to tyrants is obedience to God.' . . .") was presented by "admirers of his patriotic and fearless course in opposition to the unjust war of the Lincoln Administration upon the Southern States."

Contains texts of the address by C. Chauncey Burr, chairman (p.2-4), and the response by Fuller (p.4-8), both following the copperhead line.

[LATHROP, CHARLES C.] 1818-

Reports and depositions in the contested election of the Second Assembly District of Burlington County. Printed by order of the Legislature. Camden, N.J.: Morris R. Hamilton, printer, 1864. 248p. NJR 614

Concerns the protest of Charles C. Lathrop (Union or Republican Assembly candidate) against Jarrett Stokes (Democrat) ; relating only in a limited way to wartime conditions, but does present a picture of contemporary political practices.

McCLELLAN, GEORGE BRINTON, 1826-1885.

General McClellan's letter of acceptance, together with his West-Point oration. New-York City: Published by E. P. Patten [1864] 8p. CSMH DLC NJR OCLWHI 615

Caption title.
Text in two columns.
Letter of acceptance (p.[1]-2) headed Orange, N.J., Sept. 8, 1864, but has no New Jersey allusions.

———

Letter of Geo. B. McClellan, in acceptance of the nomination of the Chicago convention. Orange, N.J., Sept. 8, 1864. [New York, 1864] Broadside. 24 x 19 in. NJR 616

Text in two columns.

McCLELLAN. THE PRIDE OF "JERSEY BLUE." Phila:. Mason & Co. [1864] Broadside. 9¼ x 6 in. NJR (photo) PPL 616a

Song sheet (words only). "Tune:—'Hoist up the Flag.'"
Although this Democratic campaign broadside is not primarily a New Jersey item, it is included because of the allusion to "Jersey Blue." The term "Jersey Blues" long had been applied, rather loosely, to New Jersey militia units, both individually and collectively.

NEW JERSEY. COMMITTEE ON BEHALF OF THE NEW JERSEY STATE BANKS.

An appeal to the Congress of the United States on the subject of bank tax and bank currency, by a committee of New Jersey state bank officers. Trenton, N.J.: Printed at the "True American" office, 1864. 18p. NJR NHI

Signed (p.18): S. Broadwell, B. M. Price, Thos. D. Armstrong, committee.

The "Committe [*sic*] on behalf of the New Jersey state banks" was appointed by a convention of said banks held at Trenton, Jan. 14, 1864. (Cf. p.[3].)

NEW JERSEY. GOVERNOR, 1863-1866 (PARKER)

A proclamation. [Trenton, N.J., 1864] Broadside. 10 x 8 in. NJR 618

Thanksgiving proclamation. War allusions.

Dated Nov. 12, 1864, and signed in holograph by the governor and his secretary.

———————

A proclamation by the governor. [Trenton, N.J., 1864] Broadside. 9¾ x 7¾ in. NJR 619

Appointing a day of humiliation and prayer, "that He [the Lord] will not destroy this Nation; that the effusion of blood may be stayed, unity be restored and peace established . . ."

Dated July 30, 1864, and signed in holograph by Governor Joel Parker and his secretary.

NEW JERSEY. LEGISLATURE.

List of officers and members of the eighty-eighth Legislature of New Jersey, with their residences in Trenton and post office address, and the joint and standing committees of both houses. Convened January 12th, 1864. [Trenton, N.J.? 1864] Broadside. 21¾ x 15 in. NJR

NEW JERSEY. LEGISLATURE. GENERAL ASSEMBLY.

. . . An act to prevent the admixture of races in the state of New Jersey. [Trenton, N.J., 1864] Broadside. 13¼ x 8 in. NJR 621

At head of title: Assembly—no. 267. State of New Jersey.

Prohibits marriages between whites and Negroes.

NEW JERSEY. LEGISLATURE. GENERAL ASSEMBLY. COMMITTEE ON ELECTIONS.

Reports of the majority and minority of the Committee on Elections, to whom was referred Assembly bill no. 190, entitled "An act to enable qualified voters of this state in the military service of this state, or of the United States, to exercise the right of suffrage," and concurrent resolutions on the same subject. Trenton, N.J.: Printed by David Naar, "True American" office, 1864. 19p., 1 leaf. NJ NJJ NJP NJR NHI 622

With text of the bill.

———————

Reports of the majority and minority of the Committee on Elections, to whom was referred the petition of Charles C. Lathrop, claiming the seat of Jarrett Stokes. Trenton, N.J.: Printed by David Naar, "True American" office, 1864. 35p. NJ NJJ NJP NJR 623

NEW JERSEY. LEGISLATURE. SENATE.

Diagram showing the location of the members composing the twentieth Senate of the state of New Jersey, and the counties which they represent. 1864. [Trenton, N.J., 1864] Broadside. 17 x 14 in. NJR 623a

PARKER, JOEL, 1816-1887.

Speech of Governor Parker, at Freehold, N.J., Aug. 20, 1864. Subject: our national troubles—their causes and the remedy. [New York, 1864] 8p. NHI 624

Caption title.

Text in double columns.

The three variants (nos. 624a, 625-626), except for minor title changes in one case and insertions preceding the title in the other two cases, are identical with the present publication.

———————

Speech of Governor Parker, at Freehold, N.J., August 20, 1864. Subject—our national troubles—their causes and the remedy. [New York, 1864] 8p. NJJ 624a

Caption title.

Text in double columns.

———————

. . . Speech of Governor Parker, at Freehold, N.J., Aug. 20, 1864. Subject: our national troubles—their causes and the remedy. [New York, 1864] 8p. NHI 625

Caption title.

Text in double columns.

At head of title: Campaign document, no. 4.

———————

[*Same*] 8p. DLC MB NJP NJR NHI PHI 626

Caption title.

Text in double columns.

At head of title: . . . Campaign document, no. 6.

"Sold at 13 Park Row, New York, and at all Democratic Newspaper Offices, at $1 per 1,000 pages."

PENNSYLVANIA. GENERAL ASSEMBLY.

Ceremonies of the second inauguration of Andrew G. Curtin, governor of Pennsylvania, with the proceedings of the presentation of Audubon's works by the loyal citizens of New Jersey. Harrisburg: Singerly & Myers, state printers, 1864. 22p. NN 627

Pages 14-22 devoted to the ceremony, addresses, and description of the volumes presented (Audubon's "Birds" and "Quadrupeds") by a group of South Jersey "loyal citizens" as a testimonial "of his patriotism and energy, in the cause of our common country" (at the recent election and in the war effort). Largely relates to the war.

PERRY, NEHEMIAH, 1816-1881.

Rebellious states. Speech of Hon. Nehemiah Perry, of New Jersey, delivered in the House of Representatives . . . May 3, 1864. [Washington: Gibson Brothers, printers, 1864] 8p. DLC MB NHI OCLWHI 628

Caption title.

POTTS, WILLIAM D.

Campaign songs for Christian patriots and true Democrats, accompanied with notes. By Rev. William D. Potts, M.D., Newark, N.J. New York: Published by the author, 1864. 24p. illus. (music) DLC NJP NHI OCLWHI 629

Lyrics by Potts attacking the Republican administration for causing the war, calling for immediate peace, ranting against abolitionism, etc.

Letterpress on covers.

———————

Freemen's guide to the polls. And a solemn appeal to American patriots. By Rev. Wm. D. Potts, M.D., author of "Lectures on the true development of man," "Honorable courtship and true marriage," "Our country vindicated." Newark, N.J. New York: Published by the author, 1864. 125 (i.e., 120) p. DLC NJP NHI RPB

A rather wild attack on the Lincoln administration and an appeal for McClellan's election.

Letterpress on covers.

ROGERS, ANDREW JACKSON, 1828-1900.

Confiscation of rebel property. Speech of Hon. Andrew J. Rogers, of New Jersey, delivered in the House of Representatives, January 21, 1864. [Washington, D.C.: McGill & Witherow, printers and stereotypers, 1864] 8p. DLC NHI 631

Caption title.

Text in double columns.

———————

Speech of Hon. Andrew J. Rogers, of N.J., delivered in the House of Representatives, April 12, 1864, on the resolution to expel Hon. Alexander Long, of Ohio, for words spoken in debate. [Washington, D.C., 1864] 15p. CTY DLC NHI 632

Caption title.

Text in double columns.

The words spoken by Long expressed opposition to the war's further prosecution, etc. Rogers, a Democrat, supports Long's right of free speech, attacks abolitionism, endorses the principle of an honorable compromise, etc.

———————

Speech of Hon. Andrew J. Rogers, of New Jersey, on the confiscation of rebel property. Delivered in the House of Representatives, January 21, 1864. Washington, D.C.: Printed at the "Constitutional Union" office, 1864. 16p. NJR NHI 633

SCOVEL, JAMES MATLACK, 1833-1904.

New Jersey for the Union. Speech of Hon. James M. Scovel, senator from Camden, upon the bill prohibiting the enlistment of Negro troops in New Jersey, under a penalty of $500, or imprisonment for five years, delivered March 16, 1864. Trenton: Murphy & Bechtel, printers, 1864. 16p. DLC NJJ NJP NHI 634

———————

[*Same: variant*] Trenton, N.J.: Murphy & Bechtel, printers, 1864. 16p. NJR 635

SHALL THE SOLDIERS VOTE? [n.p., 1864] 4p. NJR 636

Caption title.

A Union Party tract, reviewing the party's efforts, public petitions, etc., supporting the bill to permit absentee voting by New Jersey soldiers, defeated April 6, 1864, by majority Democratic members of the House. Included is the text of the minority (Union) report of the Committee on Elections.

Signed: Mercer.

TEN EYCK, JOHN CONOVER, 1814-1879.

Reconstruction in the states. Speech of Hon. John C. Ten Eyck, of New Jersey. Delivered in the Senate of the United States, May 6, 1864. [Washington: Printed by L. Towers for the

Union Congressional Committee, 1864] 7, [1]p. DLC NJHI NJR NHI OCLWHI PHI 637

Caption title.

———————

Reconstruction in the states. Speech of Hon. John C. Ten Eyck, of New Jersey. Delivered in the Senate of the United States on . . . Jan. 5, 1864. [Washington, D.C.: L. Towers & Co., printers, 1864] 8p. NJR NN 638

Caption title.

TO THE DELEGATES TO THE DEMOCRATIC convention of the Fourth Congressional District of New Jersey. [n.p., 1864] [2]p. 10 x 8 in. NJR 639

Caption title.

Signed: "Peace," and dated Essex County, August 15th, 1864.

An attack against A. J. Rogers, a contender for the Democratic congressional nomination, presenting his recent service in Congress as inconsistent, etc., especially in his position on conduct of the war.

The 4th District included the counties of Sussex, Morris, Passaic, Bergen, and all Essex except Newark.

TO THE PUBLIC. [Mount Holly, N.J.? 1864] Broadside. 12½ x 9 in. NJR 640

Signed: An Inquirer.

An attack on Charles C. Lathrop (of Delanco, N.J.), Union-Republican candidate for state Assembly from Burlington County against Jarrett Stokes, Democrat. Deals considerably with the contested election of 1863 involving the same candidates.

Text in three columns.

TOWNSEND, SAMUEL P.

A speech by Dr. S. P. Townsend. The nation saved by interposition of providence—the abolitionists—Wm. Lloyd Garrison—Abraham Lincoln—the financial question, etc., etc. Delivered November 3d, 1864, at Elizabeth City, New Jersey . . . [n.p., 1864] 16p. CSMH DLC MB NHI NN 641

At bottom of title-page is the admonition: "Organize leagues. Postscript.—It is an important duty that our merchants, manufacturers, farmers, &c., owe to their pecuniary interests, to at once organize leagues . . ."

WALL, JAMES WALTER, 1820-1872.

Oration of Hon. James W. Wall, at Keyport, New Jersey, on the 22d of February, 1864, by invitation of the Democratic Central Committee of the Third Assembly District of Monmouth County . . . Middletown Point, N.J.: J. F. Warner & Son, book and job printers, 1864. 8p. NJR NHI NN 642

Text in two columns.

"For Sale at the Drug and Stationery Store of Geo. W. Bell, Middletown Point, N.J."

WINFIELD, CHARLES HARDENBURG, 1829-1898.

Oration delivered by C. H. Winfield, of Jersey City, at Hackensack, N.J., July 4th, 1864. Jersey City: Printed by John H. Lyon, 1864. 21p. NJJ 643

Deals entirely with issues of the war, chiefly the nature of the Union and the question of secession. Winfield was a Jersey City lawyer, elected the following year as a Democrat to the state Senate.

WRIGHT, WILLIAM, 1824-1866.

To the Metropolitan Sanitary Fair. A simple remedy for a sore evil, or The necessity of making early nominations to secure competent public officers. By William Wright. Paterson, N.J.: Printed and presented by Wright & Chiswell, office of the daily and weekly "Press," 1864. cover-title, 14p. DLC NJR (photo) 644

Caption title: A simple remedy, &c.

Presenting a detailed non-partisan picture of corrupt political practice, the author (Paterson writer, editor, and Republican) proposes as a remedy the requirement that candidates be selected from three to twelve months before the election date, so as to permit full public exposure.

1865

BRADLEY, JOSEPH P., 1813-1892.

The constitutional amendment. Letter from Joseph P. Bradley, Esq., of New Jersey, to Mr. Charles Knap, on the question of the number of states requisite to ratify an amendment to the Constitution. Washington: Gideon & Pearson, printers, 1865. cover-title, 11p. MB MH NJP NJR NHI 645

Dated: Washington, February 18, 1865.

Relates to the 13th Amendment.

Reprinted in Bradley's *Miscellaneous Writings* (Newark, 1902), p.[151]-163.

The writer was a prominent Newark attorney, jurist, and public figure.

———————

The constitutional amendment. Letter from Hon. Joseph P. Bradley, of New Jersey, to Mr.

Charles Knap, on the question of the number of states requisite to ratify an amendment to the Constitution. [Washington, D.C., 1865] 4p. DLC 645a

Caption title.
Not seen. Entry based on DLC catalog.

NEW JERSEY. LEGISLATURE. GENERAL ASSEMBLY.

Debates in the eighty-ninth General Assembly of the state of New Jersey, on the bill to ratify an amendment to the Constitution of the United States . . . Trenton, N.J.: Printed by J. R. Freese, "State Gazette" office, 1865. 107p. DLC NJ NJP NJR NN 646

Largely texts of speeches concerned with the 13th Amendment, introduced for ratification on Feb. 9, 1865.

———————

[*Same: German edition*] Debatten in der neunundachtzigsten Generalversammlung des Staates New Jersey, über den Gesetzentwurf für Ratifizirung eines Amendements zur Constitution der Vereinigten Staaten . . . Newark, N.J.: Gedruckt bei B. Prieth, New Jersey freie Zeitung office, 1865. 124p. NHI 647

Largely (p.6-122) texts of addresses by numerous members of the Assembly.

———————

Extracts from Debates in the eighty-ninth General Assembly of the state of New Jersey, on the bill to ratify an amendment to the Constitution of the United States. Speech of Hon. P. C. Brinck, of Camden . . . Trenton, N.J.: Printed by J. R. Freese, "State Gazette" office, 1865. 23p. NJR 648

Text of Brinck's speech and some legislative proceedings.
Same as the initial pages (through top of p. 23) of *Debates . . . on the Bill to Ratify an Amendment to the Constitution* (no. 646).

———————

Washington's birthday. Celebration of the birthday of Washington, and of the victories of the Union arms: by the House of Assembly of the lxxxixth Legislature of New Jersey, February 22d, 1865 . . . Trenton, N.J.: Printed by J. R. Freese, "State Gazette" office, 1865. 22p. DLC NJ NJHI NJJ NJP NJR NHI NN 649

Included are addresses by Charles C. Lathrop, assemblyman from Burlington County, and Leon Abbett, from Hudson County. Both deal more with Washington than the Civil War.

NEW JERSEY. LEGISLATURE. GENERAL ASSEMBLY. COMMITTEE OF THE JUDICIARY.

Reports of the majority and minority of the Committee of the Judiciary, on the bill to ratify an amendment to the Constitution of the United States. Presented to the House of Assembly Feb. 23d, and ordered to be printed. Trenton, N.J.: Printed by J. R. Freese, "State Gazette" office, 1865. 5, [1]p. NJHI 650

The majority report offers amendments to the bill, providing for submission of the 13th Amendment to a referendum. The minority report proposes passage of the bill without change.

ROGERS, ANDREW JACKSON, 1828-1900.

The power of amending the Constitution. Speech of Hon. Andrew J. Rogers, of New Jersey, delivered in the House of Representatives of the United States, January 9, 1865. [Washington, D.C., 1865] 8p. DLC NJR NHI

Caption title.
Delivered in connection with a joint resolution, under consideration, proposing an amendment to the Constitution (the 13th Amendment).
Text printed in double columns.

"WARD" U.S. GENERAL HOSPITAL, NEWARK, N.J. INMATES.

. . . To the Honorable Senate and General Assembly of the state of New Jersey. [Newark, N.J., 1865] Broadside. 12½ x 7¾ in. NJR

Headed: "Ward" U.S. General Hospital, Newark, N.J., February 15, 1865.
A petition from inmates of the hospital, "citizens of New Jersey . . . and representing every Regiment which this State has sent to the field," urging ratification of the 13th Amendment, abolishing slavery.

THE RAILROAD CONTROVERSY

A significant factor in New Jersey history for many years was "the Monopoly," so-called—a transportation combine controlling the important route between New York and Philadelphia. The monopoly franchise was granted in the 1830's to what became known informally as the Joint Companies (dominated by the Camden and Amboy Railroad), which grew prosperous, arrogant, and decisively active in New Jersey politics, despite irregular opposition within the state and perennial attacks from without.

The Civil War armed a new assault upon the monopoly, a struggle centered in the halls of Congress. It began with various representations deploring the quality of military rail service between New York and Philadelphia (or Washington). Subsequently legislation was introduced which would have weakened the monopoly group, one bill providing federal support for a competing line (headed by the Raritan and Delaware Bay Railroad) which indirectly covered the same route as the Joint Companies. The latter defended themselves vigorously, with the help of New Jersey's governor, legislature, and congressional delegation; nevertheless, their day was nearing its end. After the war, they reorganized (soon renamed the United New Jersey Railroad and Canal Company) and in 1871 "the Monopoly" disappeared into the Pennsylvania Railroad system by way of a 999-year lease.

BUTLER, WILLIAM ALLEN, 1825-1902.

Railway communication between New York and Washington. Remarks and opinion of counsel in reference to the bill pending before Congress to legalize the Raritan & Delaware Bay Railroad, and the Camden & Atlantic Railroad and their branches as a postal and military route. Wm. Allen Butler, Edwards Pierrepont, counsel. [New York? 1864] cover-title, 11p. DBRE DLC NJR (photo) 653

Dated New York, January 27th, 1864.

"THE CAMDEN AND AMBOY NUISANCE." *Harper's weekly*. v.8, 1864. p.787 (Dec. 10, 1864) 653a

Short editorial.

CAMDEN AND AMBOY RAILROAD AND TRANSPORTATION COMPANY.

[Affidavits of Edwin A. Stevens and others in regard to transportation of troops by the Company. n.p., 1864] 8p. DBRE NJR (photo) 654

Statements of Feb. 1 and 2, 1864, by Stevens (president) and employees, etc., describing the Company's exertions in the shipping of troops, its readiness and ample facilities for the purpose, particularly in comparison with its rival, the Raritan & Delaware Bay Railroad.

[CAMDEN AND AMBOY RAILROAD AND TRANSPORTATION COMPANY]

Considerations upon the question whether Congress should authorize a new railroad between Washington and New York. [Washington, D.C.] G. S. Gideon & Co., printers [1863] cover-title, 15p. NJHI NJR 655

Caption title: Should Congress authorize a new railroad line from Washington to New York?

Dated (p.15) "Washington, January 29th, 1863"; signed: Jos. P. Bradley, Wm. Wheeler Hubbell, Geo. Ashmun, Attorneys for the R.R. Companies.

———

Points against the Raritan and Delaware Bay and Camden and Atlantic Railroad application: <House bill, no. 307.> Washington: Gideon & Pearson, printers [1864] cover-title, 6p. CSMH DLC MB NJR (photo) 656

Signed (p.6): J. P. Bradley, W. W. Hubbell, Geo. Ashmun, On Behalf of the Camden and Amboy R.R. Co.

"DEATH ON THE RAIL." *Harper's weekly*. v.9, 1865. p.178 (March 25, 1865) 656a

Editorializing account of a recent accident on the Camden and Amboy Railroad.

A DEFENCE OF NEW JERSEY IN RELATION to the Camden and Amboy Railroad and its privileges. Washington: Gideon & Pearson, printers, 1864. cover-title, 13p. DBRE DLC MH NJR NHI NN 657

Two letters, addressed to the editors of the New York *Evening Post*, by "A Citizen of New Jersey," relating to the transit duties (attacked by out-of-state interests) and the monopoly. The author is described as a "prominent supporter of the present National administration, in New Jersey." Followed by "Railroad Facilities of New Jersey," extract from a speech of Hon. L. D. M. Sweat.

JOHNSON, REVERDY, 1796-1876.

Railroads in New Jersey. Power of the United States over state charters. Speech of the Hon. Reverdy Johnson, of Maryland, in the United States Senate, January 19, 1865; on House bill, no. 307, to regulate commerce among the states. [Washington, D.C.: Gibson Brothers, printers, 1865] 16p. DLC NJHI NHI OCLWHI 658

Caption title.

JOINT SENATE AND ASSEMBLY.–NO. 10,780. State of New Jersey. An act to incorporate the nation's main trunk triple track agricultural railroad company. [n.p., 186–] Broadside. 12 x 6¼ in. NJR 659

A satiric piece in the form of a bill in the New Jersey legislature. Incorporators of the mythical railroad include both state and national figures (e.g., Lincoln). The railroad is to run from a "convenient" point in New Jersey to a convenient point anywhere in the United States, providing it is not used to compete with the New Jersey Railroad, etc.

MAINE. LEGISLATURE.

. . . Transportation of troops between New York and Washington. Resolutions of the Legislature of Maine, in relation to a new railroad route between New York and Washington. January 27, 1864.–Referred to the Select Committee on New Railroad Route. [Washington, D.C., 1864] [1]p. (U.S. House of Representatives. 38th Congress, 1st session. Miscel. doc. no. 23) 660

"Resolves relating to the inadequate facilities for travel and transportation of troops . . ."

METROPOLITAN RAILROAD COMPANY.

. . . Railroad communication between New York and Washington city. <To accompany bill H.R. no. 396.> Proposition of the Metropolitan Railroad Company to build the Metropolitan Railroad, making direct communication between Washington city and New York. April 10, 1862.–Ordered to be printed. [Washington, D.C., 1862] 6p. (U.S. House of Representatives. 37th Congress, 2d session. Miscel. doc. no. 65) 661

Dated: Metropolitan Railroad Company Office, Washington, November 13, 1861.

NEW JERSEY. COURT OF CHANCERY.

. . . Opinion of Chancellor Green, on final hearing in the case of the Delaware and Raritan Canal and Camden and Amboy Railroad and Transportation companies v. the Camden and Atlantic Railroad Company, the Raritan and Delaware Bay Railroad Company, and others. Delivered February 3d, 1864. Trenton, N.J.: "True American" print [1864?] 31p. DBRE DLC NJP 662

Caption title.

NEW JERSEY. GOVERNOR, 1863-1866 (PARKER)

Message of Joel Parker, governor of New Jersey, to the Legislature, in relation to the bill pending before the U.S. House of Representatives concerning the Camden and Atlantic Railroad Company and the Raritan and Delaware Bay Railroad Co. With the concurrent resolutions adopted by the New Jersey Legislature. Trenton, N.J.: Printed at the "True American" office, 1864. 8p. DLC NJ NJJ NJN NJP NJR NN 663

The bill, declaring the companies "to be lawful structures and public highways of the United States," is opposed as conflicting with New Jersey's monopoly agreement with "certain companies" (i.e., the Camden & Amboy and the New Jersey Railroad companies) and as an encroachment on states' rights.

Essentially the same as no. 665.

———————

[*Same: another edition?*] cover-title, 8p. DBRE 664

Not seen. The DLC catalog card (from Bureau of Railway Economics) indicates identical title, with two exceptions: ". . . Delaware Bay Railroad Company, with . . ." and ". . . Legislature. Ordered to be printed."

———————

Proclamation of the governor and joint resolution of the Senate and House of Assembly of the state of New Jersey, in relation to the Raritan & Delaware Bay and Camden & Amboy railroad companies. Washington: Gideon & Pearson, printers [1864] cover-title, 7p. DBRE DLC NJR (photo) NHI 665

Dated March 23, 1864.

Opposes the bill pending in the House of Representatives to provide federal sanction and privileges to the Camden & Atlantic and Raritan & Delaware Bay railroads.

Essentially the same text as in nos. 663 and 664.

NEW YORK (STATE) LEGISLATURE.

. . . Resolutions of the Assembly of New York, in favor of an increase of the facilities for convenient and expeditious travel and transportation of troops between the cities of New York and Washington. February 8, 1864.—Referred to the Committee on Military Affairs and the Militia and ordered to be printed. [Washington, D.C., 1864] [1]p. (U.S. Senate 38th Congress, 1st session. Miscel. doc. no. 24) 666

"Whereas the facilities for convenient and expeditious travel and transportation of troops . . . especially between New York and Philadelphia, are at present notoriously inconvenient and inadequate . . ."

[RARITAN AND DELAWARE BAY RAILROAD COMPANY]

Additional reasons why the bill introduced in Congress to authorize a new line of railway communication between New York and Philadelphia should be sustained. Washington, D.C.: Gibson Brothers, printers, 1864. 8p. CST NHI

Signed (p.8): B. Williamson, C. A. Seward, Ashbel Green, of counsel for the Raritan and Delaware Bay railroad company.

Printed also as part of no. 671.

RARITAN AND DELAWARE BAY RAILROAD COMPANY.

In the Court of Errors and Appeals of the state of New Jersey. Between the Raritan and Delaware Bay Rail Road Company, and the Camden and Atlantic Rail Road Company, appellants, and the Delaware and Raritan Canal, and the Camden and Amboy Rail Road and Transportation companies, respondents. On appeal . . . Jersey City: Printed by John H. Lyon, 1865. 404p. fold. tables. DBRE NJ 668

———————

. . . In the Court of Errors and Appeals in the last resort in all causes. Between the Raritan & Delaware Bay Railroad Company and the Camden & Atlantic Railroad Company, appellants, and the Delaware & Raritan Canal and Camden & Amboy Railroad and Transportation companies, respondents. Appeal from decree in Chancery. New York: Wm. C. Bryant & Co., printers, 1866. viii, 390p. NJ 669

At head of title: State of New Jersey.

[RARITAN AND DELAWARE BAY RAILROAD COMPANY]

Reasons why the Raritan & Delaware Bay Railroad Company should not be destroyed by the Camden & Amboy monopoly. Washington, D.C.: Gibson Brothers, printers, 1864. cover-title, 15p. fold. map. DLC MB NH NJP NJR (photo) 670

Signed by C. A. Seward, Jonathan Edwards, and Ashbel Green.

Dated: Washington City, February 1, 1864.

———————

Reasons why the Raritan and Delaware Bay R.R. Co. should not be destroyed by the Camden and Amboy monopoly. [Washington? 1864] 23p. DLC NJR (photo) 671

Caption title.

Signed (p.10) by C. A. Seward, Jonathan Edwards, Ashbel Green.

First part (p.1-14) contains virtually the same text as the Company's 15-page pamphlet of the same title (see no. 670, preceding). Added material (p.14-20) consists of extracts from an 1841 John R. Thomson letter and from 1864 speeches in Congress by Representatives Schenck and Garfield; also (p.20-23) "Additional reasons why the bill introduced in Congress to authorize a new line of railway communication between New York and Philadelphia should be sustained" (note pamphlet of this same title, no. 667 above).

ROGERS, ANDREW JACKSON, 1828-1900.

Speech of Hon. Andrew J. Rogers, of New Jersey, on a bill to authorize the Camden and Atlantic and the Raritan and Delaware Bay Railroad companies, of the state of New Jersey, to transport passengers and merchandise across the state from New York to Philadelphia, in violation of the laws of the state and the decision of her courts. Delivered in the House of Representatives, March 22, 1864. Washington, D.C.: Printed at the Constitutional Union office, 1864. 16p. NHI 672

In reference to the bill to declare certain railroads military and post roads, and to regulate commerce.

SCOVEL, JAMES MATLACK, 1833-1904.

Speech of the Hon. James M. Scovel, before the anti-monopoly convention, at Trenton, N.J., Feb. 1, 1865. Trenton: Murphy & Bechtel, printers, 1865. 12p. DLC NJHI 673

———————

Speech of Hon. James M. Scovel, in the New Jersey Senate, on the resolutions in response to the "Governor's message on the proposed action of Congress on the air-line railroad bill." [n.p., 1864] 8p. DLC MH NJHI NJR NHI OCLWHI 674

The "Republican party has no vitality in New Jersey, (else New Jersey would not be the only disloyal Northern State) and it never will have till it ceases to be a parasite of the Camden and Amboy Railroad Company."

SHALL THE EXTENSION OR RECREATING of the Camden & Amboy Railroad monopoly be permitted by the people of New Jersey, and made perpetual? . . . [n.p.] 1864. cover-title, 15p. DBRE DLC MH NH NJHI NJR NHI NN 675

Caption title: The steady progress of the Camden and Amboy Railroad Company and the Delaware and Raritan Canal Company, toward the complete control of the whole Government of . . . New Jersey considered, and commended to the consideration of the people.

STATEMENT MADE BY THE RAILROAD companies owning the lines between Washington and New York to the Postmaster General. Washington: Gideon & Pearson, printers, 1864. 12p. DBRE NJR (photo) 676

Caption title: Improvements in progress in the railroad lines between Washington and New York.

Dated Jan. 14, 1864, and signed by F. Wolcott Jackson, E. A. Stevens, and three others, representing, in part, the New Jersey railroad monopoly interests. Written in response to complaints of delay and irregularity in the delivery of mail, with explanations and promises of improvement.

A variant in NN has imprint date 1863 (presumably an error) but appears identical otherwise.

STOCKTON, ROBERT FIELD, 1795-1866.

Defence of the system of internal improvements, of the state of New Jersey. By R. F. Stockton. Philadelphia: King & Baird, printers, 1864. 48p. DBRE DLC NH NJN NJP NJR NJT NHI NN PHI PPL PU 677

Cover-title: Letters of Commodore Stockton to the New York Evening Post.

Consists of two letters, May 25 and April 5, 1864, defending the Joint Companies. Stockton was president of the canal company, chief strategist and strong man of the monopoly.

———————

Letter to the editors of the N.Y. Evening Post, in reply to a citizen of New Jersey. By R. F. Stockton. Philadelphia: King & Baird, printers, 1864. cover-title, [3]-26p. DBRE DLC MH NJ NJHI NJP NJR NHI NN PHI 678

Caption title: To the editors of the New York Evening Post: Princeton, May 25, 1864.

Text is identical with that of p.[3]-26 in Stockton's *Defence of the System of Internal Improvements* (no. 677, preceding).

———————

Letter to William C. Bryant, Esq., from R. F. Stockton. [Philadelphia: Duross Brothers, printers, 1864] 16p. CT DBRE DLC MB NJR PHI

Cover-title: Defence of the system of internal improvements, of the state of New Jersey. By the president of the Delaware and Raritan Canal Company . . .

Letter "to William C. Bryant, Esq., Publisher of the New York Evening Post," headed Princeton, April 5th, 1864.

STORY, JOSEPH, 1779-1845.

State monopolies and restrictions upon commerce, unconstitutional. Opinion of Mr. Justice Story . . . New York: G. A. Whitehorne, printer, 1864. cover-title, 16p. DLC NHI 680

Caption title: The power of Congress to establish post offices and post roads. By Joseph Story, LL.D.

A reprint of sections 1125 to 1145 of the 18th chapter of Story's *Commentaries on the Constitution of the United States.*

"Action of state legislatures [on the Camden & Amboy monopoly]": p.15-16.

Although not written to deal with the Camden and Amboy, it obviously was published to serve in opposition to the railroad.

SUMNER, CHARLES, 1811-1874.

Rail-road usurpation of New Jersey. Speech of Hon. Charles Sumner, of Massachusetts, on the Act to regulate commerce among the several states, in the Senate of the United States, February 14th, 1865. [New York] New York Young Men's Republican Union, 1865. 12p. DBRE DLC MB NJP NJR NN 681

An attack on New Jersey's railroad monopoly—particularly the transit duty imposed on through passengers.

Published also in Charles Sumner, *Works* (Boston, 1870-1883), v.9, p.[237]-265.

———————

[*Same: "second edition"*] . . . Unconstitutionality of the Camden & Amboy monopoly. Speech of Hon. Charles Sumner, of Massachusetts. On the Act to regulate commerce among the several states, in the Senate of the United States, February 14, 1865. [Trenton, N.J.: Trenton Weekly Monitor, 1865] 12p. NJR

Caption title.

At head of title: Supplement to the Monitor. Second edition . . .

———————

[*Same: "third edition"*] NJR 683

At head of title: Supplement to the Monitor. Third edition . . .

TEN EYCK, JOHN CONOVER, 1814-1879.

Railroads in New Jersey. Power of the United States over state charters. Speech of the Hon. John C. Ten Eyck, of New Jersey, in the United States Senate, February 16, 1865; on House bill, no. 307, to regulate commerce among the states. [Washington, D.C.: Gibson Brothers, printers, 1865] 16p. PHI 684

Caption title.

Defense of the monopoly interests.

U.S. CONGRESS. HOUSE. COMMITTEE ON MILITARY AFFAIRS.

. . . Delaware and Raritan Bay Railroad Company. <To accompany bill H.R. no. 307.> March 9, 1864.—Ordered to be printed. Mr. Deming, from the Committee on Military Affairs, made the following report. The Committee on Military Affairs, to whom was referred the petition of the Raritan and Delaware Bay Railroad Company, respectfully report . . . [Washington, D.C., 1864] 5p. (U.S. House of Representatives. 38th Congress, 1st session. Rept. no. 31) 685

"The Committee . . . unanimously recommend the passage of the accompanying bill."

U.S. CONGRESS. HOUSE. COMMITTEE ON ROADS AND CANALS.

. . . Railroad facilities between New York and Washington. <To accompany bill H.R. no. 361.> March 13, 1862.—Ordered to be printed. Mr. Johnson, from the Committee on Roads and Canals, made the following report. The Committee on Roads and Canals, to whom was referred a bill entitled "An act to secure increased railroad facilities between the cities of New York and Washington," . . . report . . . [Washington, D.C., 1862] 7p. (U.S. House of Representatives. 37th Congress, 2d session. Rept. no. 61) 686

U.S. CONGRESS. HOUSE. SELECT COMMITTEE TO INQUIRE INTO THE EXPEDIENCY AND NECESSITY OF ESTABLISHING A MILITARY AND POST ROAD FROM NEW YORK TO WASHINGTON.

. . . Railroad from Washington city to New York. <To accompany bill H.R. no. 793.> March 3, 1863.—Laid on the table, and ordered to be printed. Mr. Fenton, from the select committee appointed by resolution, made the following report. The select committee, appointed in pursuance of the resolution of the House, passed January 12, 1863, to inquire into the expediency and necessity of establishing a military and post road from the city of New York to the city of Washington, in order to facilitate the transportation of the mails and arms, troops and munitions of war . . . submit the following report . . . [Washington, D.C., 1863] 5p. (U.S. House of Representatives. 37th Congress, 3d session. Rept. no. 63) 687

The Committee "unanimously recommend its passage."

THE CHURCHES: SERMONS, ESSAYS, ETC.

Baptist

APPLETON, JAMES H.

Piety and patriotism, the demand of the times, sanctioned and enjoined by Christ: a discourse delivered before the Union Baptist Church, Jersey City, N.J., on . . . August 24th, 1862. By J. H. Appleton. New-York: C. S. Westcott & Co., printers, 1862. 28p. NRAB 688

FISH, HENRY CLAY, 1820-1877.

The duty of the hour: or, Lessons from our reverses. A discourse, by Henry C. Fish, D.D., pastor of the First Baptist Church, Newark, N.J. New York: Sheldon & Company, 1862. 23p. NJHI NJR NHI NRAB 689

The address was delivered July 20 and repeated July 27.

On verso of title-page: John F. Trow, printer and electrotyper . . .

——————

The valley of Achor a door of hope; or, The grand issues of the war. A discourse, delivered on Thanksgiving Day, Nov. 26, 1863. By Henry Clay Fish, D.D., pastor of First Baptist Church, Newark, N.J. New-York: Sheldon & Co., 1863. 24p. DLC MB NJHI NJJ NJP NJR NHI NRAB OCLWHI PHI 690

Evidently the address was not given before his own congregation.

For a hostile response, see no. 321.

[FISHER, ROBERT] 1817?-

A greater rebellion. [New York: American Tract Society, 186–] 12p. NJP 690a

Caption title.

Included as no. 3 in *Sixteen Envelope Tracts for Soldiers. Selected from Tracts Offered for the Thompson Premium* (New York: Published by the American Tract Society [186–]), whose contents-list identifies the author as Rev. R. Fisher, Mount Salem, N.J.

Also included, anonymously, in the American Tract Society's *Twenty-Four Pocket Tracts for Soldiers. Short, Pithy, and Attractive* (n.d.). Copy in NJP.

The New Jersey Baptist State Convention minutes for 1857-1861 list Robert Fisher as pastor of the Baptist Church at Mount Salem (in Sussex County). He is recorded in the 1860 census schedule for Wantage Township as a native of "Brittan."

LEVY, EDGAR MORTIMER, 1822-1906.

God's proclamation of freedom. A discourse, preached in the Baptist Church, Flemington, N.J., at the twenty-fifth anniversary of the New Jersey Baptist State Convention, November 15th, 1864. By Rev. Edgar M. Levy, pastor of the South Baptist Church, Newark, N.J. Newark, N.J.: Printed for the Convention, by Francis Starbuck, 1864. 16p. NRAB 691

Deals with slavery and the Civil War.

Not seen (description from NRAB).

——————

National thanksgiving. A sermon, preached in the North Baptist Church, Newark, N.J., before the united Baptist congregations of the city . . . Nov. 24, 1864. By Edgar M. Levy, pastor of the South Baptist Church. New York: Holman, book and job printer, 1864. 18p. DLC NJHI NHI NRAB 692

——————

"Sermon." New Jersey Baptist State Convention. *Minutes of the thirty-fifth anniversary.* Newark, 1865. p.[27]-38. NJR 693

Annual sermon preached Nov. 15, 1864, before the Convention.

Printed separately under the title, *God's Proclamation of Freedom* (no. 691, above).

RIDDELL, MORTIMER SHELDON, 1827-1870.

The law of sacrifice: a sermon, by Rev. M. S. Riddell, pastor of the Baptist Church, New Brunswick, N.J. Newark, N.J.: Francis Starbuck, book and job printer, 1864. 16p. 694

In memory of four members of the congregation who died in military service, "martyrs of the Republic": George C. Boice, William Hendricks, Woodbury H. Staley, and Peter Hoagland.

Copy owned by Baptist Church of New Brunswick.

——————

Principle and passion in conflict. A thanksgiving sermon. Preached Nov. 28, 1861, in the First Baptist Church, New-Brunswick, N.J., by the pastor, Rev. M. S. Riddell. New-Brunswick, N.J.: Printed at the Fredonian office, 1861. 24p. CSMH NJR NHI NN 695

SMITH, HENRY FERDINAND, 1828-1887.

Hindrances to the efficiency of the ministry: a sermon preached before the East New Jersey Pastoral Conference, at the annual meeting in Newark, Sept. 15, 1863, by H. F. Smith, pastor of the First Baptist Church, Bloomfield, N.J. Newark, N.J.: Printed for the Conference by F. Starbuck, 1863. 28p. NJP NJR NRAB 696

Uses the battle of Gettysburg as a point of departure, but the text is almost entirely theological.

Methodist

DOBBINS, JOSEPH B.

The Bible against slavery; a vindication of the sacred Scriptures against the charge of authorizing slavery. A reply to Bishop Hopkins. By Rev. J. B. Dobbins, pastor of the Third Street Methodist Episcopal Church, Camden, N.J. Philadelphia: King & Baird, printers, 1864. 24p. DLC NJR NHI 697

The contents, appearing originally in a series of (newspaper?) articles, were published in the present form at the request of Council no. 3 (Camden), Union League of America.

The copy in DLC has a prefixed letter of presentation from P. C. Brinck to Abraham Lincoln.

The Third Street church is the present First Methodist Church.

DUNN, LEWIS ROMAINE, 1822-1898.

An oration delivered at Morristown, N.J., July 4th, 1863, by Rev. L. R. Dunn, pastor of the M.E. Church . . . Morristown, N.J.: A. A. Vance, printer, 1863. 23p. NJHI NJP NJR NHI

Relates somewhat to the war.

HAVEN, GILBERT, 1821-1880.

"The day dawns." Haven, Gilbert. *National sermons*. Boston, 1869. p.269-290. DLC MB NJP NJR NN OCLWHI 699

Preached March 9, 1862, in the Clinton Street Methodist Episcopal Church, Newark, "on the occasion of the first Abolition Proclamation."

WILEY, ISAAC WILLIAM, 1825-1884.

How we got in. How to get out. Two lectures, delivered at Temperance Hall, Trenton, N.J., on . . . Feb. 16 & 23, 1864. By Rev. I. W. Wiley, A.M., M.D. Reported by James Ristine, A.M. Trenton, N.J.: Thomas U. Baker, printer, 1864. 53p. DLC MB NJJ NJP NJR NJT NHI OCLWHI PHI

Addresses delivered in behalf of the Sanitary Commission (although the contents do not relate to the Commission).

Wiley, for several years principal of Pennington School (then Pennington Seminary and Female Institute), was a Methodist clergyman.

———————

Two lectures on the rebellion. Subjects: How we got in. How to get out. Delivered at Temperance Hall, Trenton, N.J., by Rev. I. W. Wiley, A.M., M.D. Reported by James Ristine, A.M., for the benefit of the Sanitary Commission. Second edition. Trenton, N.J.: Thomas U. Baker, printer, 1864. 53p. NJP NHI RPB

Differs from first edition by slight textual changes.

Presbyterian

[ANONYMOUS]

"Religious instruction in the Army." 702

See entry no. 734a.

[ATWATER, LYMAN HOTCHKISS] 1813-1883.

"The war and national wealth." *Biblical repertory and Princeton review*. v.36, 1864. p.449-483. 703

The author was a Presbyterian and Congregational clergyman, on the faculty of Princeton College since 1854, lecturing also at Princeton Theological Seminary.

[BAIRD, SAMUEL JOHN] 1817-1893.

"African colonization." *Biblical repertory and Princeton review*. v.34, 1862. p.686-711. 704

Historical review and Christian argument for colonization.

Author identified in Poole, *Index to Periodical Literature* (1882), p.278.

Baird was pastor of the Woodbury, N.J., Presbyterian Church, born in Ohio, had lived and married in the South.

———————

"Slavery and the slave trade." *Ibid.*, p.524-548.

Historical account, ending in condemnation.

For authorship see *The Biblical Repertory and Princeton Review. Index Volume from 1825 to 1868*, p.101.

————————

". . . The Union and the Constitution." *The Danville quarterly review.* v.3, 1863. p.345-370, 539-568. 706

The author is identified in Bartlett, *Literature of the Rebellion,* no. 247.

BROWN, WILLIAM YOUNG, 1827-1914.

The Christian hero: his conflicts, victories and crown. A sermon, preached in the chapel of the Douglas Hospital, Washington, D.C. . . . August 3d, 1862, by Rev. W. Y. Brown, A.M., hospital chaplain, U.S.A. Salem, New Jersey: Printed at the Standard office, 1862. 16p. NJP

The author studied at Princeton Theological Seminary 1852-1853, served various Presbyterian congregations (none in New Jersey); was principal, Shippenburg, Pa., Academy, 1860-1861; U.S. Army chaplain, 1861-1865.

BUSH, GEORGE CLINTON, 1815-1890.

Sermon delivered by the Rev. George C. Bush, at Stewartsville, N.J., May 19, 1861, on "The state of the Union." [n.p., 1861] 11p. NJHI NJP 708

Caption title.

Bush was pastor of the Stewartsville Presbyterian Church.

BUTLER, FRANCIS EUGENE, 1825-1863.

Our prospects and duties. A sermon on the war, preached at Paterson, N.J., on . . . April 28th, 1861, by F. E. Butler. Paterson: Printed by Van Derhoven & Irish, Guardian office, 1861. 12p. DLC NJJ NJPT OCLWHI 709

Graduate of Yale (1857) and Princeton Theological Seminary (1860), ordained by the Presbytery of Passaic, Butler supplied several churches, including the Congregational Church of Paterson. As chaplain of the 25th N.J. Vols., he died in May 1863 of wounds received at Suffolk, Va. The NJR manuscript collection includes a series of Butler's war letters, 1862-1863, and his prewar diaries, 1846-1862.

CATTELL, WILLIAM CASSADAY, 1827-1898.

Quit you like men: Be strong. Address delivered before the American Whig and Cliosophic societies of the College of New Jersey, June 25th, 1861. By William C. Cattell . . . Newark, N.J.: Printed at the Daily Advertiser office, 1861. 29p. DLC MH NJP NJPT NJR NN PHI PU 710

Instructive in a negative way. Despite the audience of young men facing the military obligations of a war just begun, Cattell deals almost entirely with religious and moral points, giving virtually no attention to the national conflict.

The author, a Presbyterian clergyman, graduate of Princeton University and the Princeton Theological Seminary, was professor of Latin (from 1863, president) at Lafayette College.

CLARK, JOSEPH, 1825-1865.

"The history and theory of revolutions, as applied to the present Southern rebellion." *Biblical repertory and Princeton review.* v.34, 1862. p.244-276. 711

Clark was a Presbyterian clergyman, for a few years pastor at Chambersburg, Pa., but 1859-1865 engaged in business, occasionally supplying vacant pulpits.

————————

The history and theory of revolutions. From the Princeton review for April 1862. By Rev. Joseph Clark, A.M., Chambersburg, Pa. Philadelphia: William S. & Alfred Martien, 1862. 35p. DLC MB NJHI OCLWHI PHI PU 712

CUYLER, THEODORE LEDYARD, 1822-1909.

Intellect; and how to use it. An address delivered before the Cliosophic and American Whig societies of the College of New Jersey, June 24th, 1862. By Rev. Theodore L. Cuyler, Brooklyn, N.Y. Newark, N.J.: Printed at the Daily Advertiser office, 1863. 26p. DLC NJHI NJP NJPT NJR PU 713

Various allusions to the war and its background.

Cuyler was a Princeton alumnus and Presbyterian clergyman.

FEW SMITH, JOSEPH, 1816-1888.

". . . The glorious liberty of the children of God." *The national preacher.* 3rd series. v.1, 1862. p.276-286. 714

At head of title: Sermon XIX. By Rev. J. Few Smith, D.D., pastor of the Second Presbyterian Church, Newark, N.J.

"Preached on the Sabbath following the fourth of July 1862."

Various war allusions.

FRENCH, EDWARD WARNER, 1829-1885.

Our present duty: a sermon, preached in the First Presbyterian Church, South Bergen, N.J., by Edward W. French, pastor. July 20th, 1862.

New York: Wm. C. Bryant & Co., printers, 1862. 16p. DLC NJHI NJP NHI NN OCLWHI 715

[HODGE, CHARLES] 1797-1878.

"England and America." *Biblical repertory and Princeton review.* v.34, 1862. p.147-177.

An effort "to convince the few readers we have in Great Britain" that their sympathy and support for the rebellion were "inconsistent with all their avowed principles and a grievous wrong to this country."—[Charles Hodge] *The Princeton Review on the State of the Country and of the Church* (1865), p.632.

Hodge was a noted theologian, Princeton Theological Seminary professor, and editor of the *Review.* The original of the present essay is in the NJR manuscript collection.

———————

England and America. From the Princeton review. [n.p., 1862] 1 p.l., p.147-177. NN 717

———————

England and America. From the Princeton review for January 1862. Second edition. Philadelphia: William S. & Alfred Martien, 1862. cover-title, 31p. DLC NJHI NJPT NJR NHI OCLWHI PP PU 718

———————

"The Princeton review on the state of the country and of the church." *Biblical repertory and Princeton review.* v.37, 1865. p.627-657.

An editorial survey and restatement of the *Review's* strong Union stand during the war years, with comments on the pertinent wartime articles, contemporary reactions to them, etc.

———————

The Princeton review on the state of the country and of the church. October 1865. [Philadelphia: Peter Walker, 1865] 1p.l., p.[627]-657, [1] NJPT NJR NN 720

———————

"The war." *Biblical repertory and Princeton review.* v.35, 1863. p.140-169. 721

HORNBLOWER, WILLIAM HENRY, 1820-1883.

The duty of the General Assembly to all the churches under its care. A vindication of the minority in opposition to the resolutions on the state of the country, by W. H. Hornblower. Paterson: A. Mead, printer, Register office, 1861. cover-title, 10p. DLC NJHI NJP NJPT NHI OCLWHI

Text in two columns.

A sermon before the author's congregation in Paterson, supporting a minority view that the recent Presbyterian General Assembly resolutions endorsing the Union cause were improper, injurious and disruptive to the Presbyterian Church in America.

Letter of transmittal (p.[1]) dated June 10, 1861.

———————

Sermon on the war, by W. H. Hornblower, delivered in the First Presbyterian Church of Paterson, N.J., April 21, 1861. Paterson: A. Mead, printer, Register office, 1861. cover-title, 7p. DLC NJHI NJPT NJR NHI OCLWHI 723

Text in two columns.

HOYT, JAMES, 1817-1866.

God with the nation: a thanksgiving sermon; delivered Nov. 27, 1862, in the First Presbyterian Church, Orange, N.J., by James Hoyt, pastor of the church. Orange, N.J.: Edward Gardner, printer, "Journal" office, 1862. 26p. NJHI NHI 724

KEMPSHALL, EVERARD, 1830-1904.

A thanksgiving sermon, delivered by Rev. Everard Kempshall, pastor of the First Presbyterian Church, Elizabeth, N.J., November 26th, 1863 . . . New-York: Wm. C. Martien, printer, 1863. 20p. NJHI NJPT NHI 725

Relates largely to the war.

MACDONALD, JAMES MADISON, 1812-1876.

On praying and giving thanks for victories; a correspondence between Rev. J. M. Macdonald, and the Rev. Dr. [Charles] Hodge. [Princeton, N.J.? 1864] 6p. NJPT 726

Caption title.

Concerns Macdonald's thanksgiving sermon delivered August 6, 1863, at Princeton.

McGILL, ALEXANDER TAGGART, 1807-1889.

American slavery, as viewed and acted on by the Presbyterian Church in the United States of America. Compiled . . . by the Rev. A. T. McGill, D.D., stated clerk of the General Assembly. Philadelphia: Presbyterian Board of Publication [c1865] 72p. DLC NJPT NHI NN 727

Historical survey.

———————

The hand of God with the black race. A discourse delivered before the Pennsylvania Colonization Society, by Rev. Alexander T. McGill, D.D., professor in the Theological Seminary, at Princeton, N.J. . . . Philadelphia: William F. Geddes, printer, 1862. 19p. CTY DLC MB NJP NJPT NJR NHI NN OCLWHI PHI 728

A plea for colonization.

Reviewed in *Biblical Repertory and Princeton Review,* v.34, 1862, p.557.

———————

". . . Life by faith." *The national preacher.* 3rd series. v.1, 1862. p.[353]-363. 729

At head of title: Sermon XXIII. By Alexander T. M'Gill, D.D., Princeton, New-Jersey.

"A sermon preached before the Synod of New-Jersey, at the opening of the sessions at Rahway, on . . . Oct. 21st, 1862. Published by request of Synod."

Various war allusions.

———————

Life by faith. A sermon preached before the Synod of New-Jersey, at the opening of its sessions, at Rahway, New-Jersey . . . October 21st, 1862. By Alexander T. M'Gill, D.D., of Princeton, New-Jersey. Published by request of the Synod. New-York: Published in the National preacher for December, by W. H. Bidwell, 1862. 15p. CSMH DLC NJP NJR 730

[McILVAINE, JOSHUA HALL] 1815-1897.

"American nationality." *Biblical repertory and Princeton review.* v.33, 1861. p.611-645 (Oct. 1861) 731

Deals extensively with the nature of the Constitution, causes of secession, and the need for vigorous prosecution of the war.

The author was a Presbyterian clergyman, graduate of Princeton College and Princeton Theological Seminary, and held the chair of belles lettres at the College 1860-1870, preaching also in neighboring cities.

———————

American nationality. From the Biblical repertory and Princeton review for October 1861. Philadelphia: Published by Peter Walker [1861?] 37p. NJR NHI 732

MAGIE, DAVID, 1795-1865.

A discourse delivered in the Second Presbyterian Church, Elizabeth, N.J., August 6th, 1863, on occasion of the public thanksgiving appointed by Abraham Lincoln, President of the United States, to commemorate the signal victories vouchsafed to the federal arms. By Rev. David Magie, D.D. New-York: Printed by Francis Hart & Co., 1863. 28p. DLC IHI NJHI NJJ NJP NJPT NJR NHI OCLWHI PHI 733

———————

Public thanksgiving. A sermon, preached in the Second Presbyterian Church, Elizabeth, N.J., November 28th, 1861, by David Magie, D.D. . . . New-York: Printed by Francis Hart & Co., 1861. 23p. DLC NJHI NJP NJPT NJR NHI

[MATTHEWS, JAMES] 1820-

"Religious instruction in the Army." *Biblical repertory and Princeton review.* v.35, 1863. p.383-403. 734a

Role of the chaplain, etc.

MILLARD, NELSON, 1834-1910.

A discourse preached Thanksgiving Day, Nov. 26, 1863, by Rev. Nelson Millard, at the Presbyterian Church, Montclair, N.J. . . . New-York: D. D. Nicholson, book & job printer, 1863. cover-title, 24p. NJR 735

Largely concerned with the war.

MILLER, SAMUEL, 1816-1883.

Prayer for our country. Three sermons. By Samuel Miller. Philadelphia: Henry B. Ashmead, book and job printer, 1862. 46p. DLC NJP NJPT OCLWHI 736

The sermons: The righteous war of a Christian people; National prayer; The union prayer meeting.

The author, a Presbyterian clergyman, was a supply pastor at Columbus, Tuckerton, and Bass River during this period.

MOTT, GEORGE SCUDDER, 1829-1901.

Seven weeks of prayer, held in Newton, N.J., from February 22 to April 8, 1865. Prepared by Rev. George S. Mott. [n.p., 1865] 1p.l., 34p. NJPT NJR NHI 737

Chronological account of a religious revival conducted by local Presbyterian, Methodist, and Baptist churches. Only very slight allusions to the war.

PLITT, JOHN KELLER, 1828-1898.

God's doings for the nation. A sermon preached in the First Presbyterian Church,

Greenwich, New Jersey, on the day of national thanksgiving, November 24th, 1864, by Rev. J. K. Plitt, A.M., pastor of St. James' Evangelical Lutheran Church, Greenwich, N.J. Easton, Pa.: Printed by L. Gordon, 1864. 21p. DLC NJR (photo) 738

REED, VILLEROY DIBBLE, 1815-1901.

The morning cometh. A sermon preached in the First Presbyterian Church, Camden, N.J., on the day of national thanksgiving. November 24, 1864. By Villeroy D. Reed, pastor of the church. Philadelphia: Collins, printer, 1864. 18p. PHI PPL 739

Many allusions to the war and its issues.

RODGERS, RAVAUD KEARNEY, 1796-1879.

Thanksgiving. A sermon preached in the Presbyterian Church, Bound Brook, N.J., November 28th, 1861, the day of thanksgiving appointed by the governor of the state, by Ravaud K. Rodgers, D.D., pastor of the church of Bound Brook, N.J. . . . New-Brunswick, N.J.: Terhune & Van Anglen's press, 1861. 18p. DLC NJHI NJJ NJP NJR 740

Allusions to the war.

SPRAGUE, ISAAC NEWTON, 1801-1890.

The duty of sustaining the government. A sermon preached in the Presbyterian Church at Caldwell, N.J., on . . . May 19, 1861, by Rev. I. N. Sprague, pastor of the church. Newark, N.J.: Printed at the Daily Advertiser office, 1861. 20p. DLC NJHI NJJ NJNBS NHI 741

———————

God's purposes in the war. A sermon delivered in the Presbyterian Church at Caldwell, N.J., on the day of national thanksgiving, August 6, 1863. By Rev. I. N. Sprague, (pastor.) Newark, N.J.: Printed at the Daily Advertiser office, 1863. 29p. DLC NJHI NJR NHI 742

STEARNS, JONATHAN FRENCH, 1808-1889.

". . . The powers of darkness have their hour." *The national preacher.* 3rd series. v.1, 1862. p.[65]-76. 743

At head of title: Sermon V. By Rev. Jonathan F. Stearns, D.D., pastor of the First Presbyterian church, Newark, New-Jersey.

SYMMES, JOSEPH GASTON, 1826-1894.

National thanksgiving: a sermon, preached in the First Presbyterian Church of Cranbury, New Jersey, on November 26, 1863. By Joseph G. Symmes, pastor of the church. Philadelphia: William S. & Alfred Martien, 1864. 40p. DLC NJP NJPT NHI PHI 744

VAN DYKE, JOSEPH SMITH, 1832-1915.

Elements and evidences of national decay. A lecture delivered in the Presbyterian Church, Bloomsbury, N.J., Aug. 7, 1862, by the pastor, Rev. Joseph S. Van Dyke. Philadelphia: McLaughlin Brothers' book & job printing establishment, 1862. 16p. DLC MB NJ NJHI NJPT NJR NHI OCLWHI PHI PPL 745

WALLACE, CHARLES CLARK, 1832-1889.

The situation, and duty of the hour. A discourse delivered on the national thanksgiving day, August 6, 1863. By Rev. Charles C. Wallace, pastor of First Presbyterian Church, Perth Amboy, N.J. New-York: John A. Gray & Green, printers, stereotypers, and binders, 1863. 24p. NJR (photo) PCC PPPRHI 746

WORRELL, CHARLES FLAVEL, 1805-1881.

A thanksgiving sermon, preached in the First Presbyterian Church of Millstone, Monmouth County, N.J., by the pastor, Rev. C. F. Worrell, D.D., on . . . November 26, 1863, the day appointed by the President of these United States and the governor of New Jersey as a day of thanksgiving for mercies received. Hightstown, N.J.: Jacob Stults, printer, 1864. 31p. MH NJP NJPT NJR 747

Cover-title: God in our country's calamities.

The congregation's request for publication is headed Perrineville, Nov. 27, 1863.

Protestant Episcopal

BRUCE VANDERVOORT, -1893.

The cloud of human experience. A token of God's protection. A sermon delivered in St. Paul's Church, Hoboken, November 2, 1862. By Rev. V. Bruce. Hoboken: A. O. Evans, 1863. 10p. 748

Not seen. Description taken from Sabin (8729), Bartlett (708); also James Kelly, *American Catalogue,* 1861-1866, p.245.

DOANE, WILLIAM CROSWELL, 1832-1913.

The sorrow of Lent for sin, and not for suffering; the morning sermon in St. Mary's Church, Burlington, on the first Sunday in Lent, February 22d, A.D., 1863. By the rector, the Rev. Wm. Croswell Doane, B.D. . . . Philadelphia: J. B. Chandler, printer, 1863. 14p. NJ OCLWHI

———

The statesman and the state: in uno, plura; e pluribus unum: The oration before the citizens of Burlington . . . at their public celebration of the birthday of Washington, February 22d, A.D. 1862, by the Rev. Wm. Croswell Doane, rector of St. Mary's parish. Philadelphia: James B. Chandler, printer, 1862. 21p. CSMH NJR PHI 750

Reflections of the war, although few direct allusions.

NEVILLE, EDMUND.

Rebellion and witchcraft. A thanksgiving sermon, preached [Nov. 28, 1861] in Trinity Church, Newark, N.J., by the Rev. Edmund Neville, D.D., rector. Newark, N.J.: Printed at the office of the Daily Advertiser, 1861. 16p. MB NJHI NJP NJR NHI NN PHI PPPRHI PU 751

SMITH, MARSHALL B. 1832-1882.

God's mighty doings for the nation. A sermon preached on the day of national thanksgiving . . . November 24, 1864, in St. John's Church, Passaic, N.J., by the Rev. M. B. Smith, A.M., rector . . . New-York: John A. Gray & Green, printers, stereotypers, and binders, 1864. 19p. CTY MWA NJNBS NHI NN 752

———

The nation's danger and the nation's duty. A sermon, preached in St. John's parish, Passaic, New-Jersey . . . April 21st, 1861. By the Rev. M. B. Smith, A.M., rector elect . . . New-York: John A. Gray, printer, stereotyper, and binder, 1861. 14p. DLC MWA NJR (photo) NHI PPL 753

———

Thanksgiving for victory. A sermon preached at a union service in the Reformed Protestant Dutch Church, Passaic, N.J., on the day of national thanksgiving for victory . . . August 6th, 1863. By M. B. Smith, rector of St. John's Church, Passaic . . . New-York: John A. Gray & Green, printers, stereotypers, and binders, 1863. 15p. NJNBS NHI OCLWHI 754

STEARNS, EDWARD JOSIAH, 1810-1890.

The sword of the Lord: a sermon, preached in the House of Prayer, Newark, New Jersey, on . . . September 26, 1861, being the national fast day. By Edward J. Stearns, A.M., of the Diocese of Maryland,—minister in charge . . . Baltimore: James S. Waters, 1861. iv, [5]-15p. DLC MB NJHI NJP NJR NHI PHI 755

The author, who had been supplying the Newark pulpit, here presents the Southern viewpoint.

Reformed

BERRY, JAMES ROMEYN, 1827-1891.

God's voice of encouragement to the nation. A sermon, delivered in the Third Reformed Dutch Church, Jersey City, N.J., on the . . . day of national humiliation and prayer, August 4th, 1864. And repeated . . . August, 7th, by Rev. J. Romeyn Berry. Jersey City: Printed at the Daily Times office, 1864. 24p. NJNBS NJP NJPT NJR 756

CORNELL, WILLIAM, 1834-1876.

"Our thanksgivings." A sermon preached at Freehold, N.J., August 6, 1863. By Rev. William Cornell, instructor in Latin and chemistry in the Freehold Institute. Freehold: James S. Yard, printer, 1863. 15p. NJNBS NHI 757

DEMAREST, JAMES, 1832-1913.

The present duty of American Christians. A sermon preached in the Second Reformed Dutch Church, Hackensack, N.J., on . . . July 7th, 1861. By Rev. James Demarest, Jr., pastor . . . New-York: John A. Gray, printer, stereotyper, and binder, 1861. 15p. NJHI NJJ NJNBS NJP NJR NHI PPPRHI RP RPB 758

Largely concerned with the war.

———

Thanksgiving sermon. A sermon preached in the Second Reformed Dutch Church, Hackensack, N.J., on Thanksgiving morning, Nov. 28, 1861. By Rev. James Demarest, Jr., pastor . . . Hackensack: Printed at the office of the Bergen

County Patriot, 1861. 16p. DLC NJJ NJNBS NJR NHI PPPRHI 759

Concerned with the war.

[DURYEE, WILLIAM RANKIN] 1838-1897.

Sentinels for the soul. [New York: American Tract Society, 186–] 16p. NJP 760

Caption title.

Included as no. 3 in *Ten Premium Tracts for Soldiers. Written for Premiums Offered by the Widow of Col. Alexander R. Thompson, U.S.A., Who Fell in the Florida War* (New York: Published by the American Tract Society [186–]), whose contents-list identifies the author as William R. Duryee, Newark, N.J.

Duryee, a Reformed clergyman from Newark, served 1862-1863 as chaplain of a Kentucky regiment.

GORDON, WILLIAM ROBERT, 1811-1897.

Reliance on God, our hope of victory. A sermon preached on the day of fasting and prayer, September 26th, 1861. By Rev. W. R. Gordon, D.D., pastor of the Reformed Dutch Church, Schraalenburgh, N.J. . . . New-York: John A. Gray, printer, stereotyper, and binder, 1861. 30p. DLC NJNBS NJR NHI 761

McKELVEY, ALEXANDER, 1827-1908.

A thanks-giving sermon, by Rev. Alex'r McKelvey, pastor of First Reformed Dutch Church, Paterson, N.J. . . . Paterson: A. Mead, printer, Register office, 1861. 18p. DLC NJR 762

PROUDFIT, JOHN WILLIAMS, 1803-1870.

The sanctuary of God, consulted in the present crisis. A sermon preached in the First Reformed Dutch Church, New-Brunswick, N.J. . . . April 21st, 1861. By John Proudfit, D.D. . . . New-Brunswick, N.J.: Terhune & Van Anglen, printers, 1861. 22p. NJNBS NJPT NJR NN 763

———————

[*Same: "second edition"*] CSMH DLC NJHI NJNBS NJP NJR NHI OCLWHI PHI PPPRHI 764

ROMEYN, THEODORE BAYARD, 1827-1885.

Continual praise. A thanksgiving sermon, preached in the Reformed Dutch Church of Blawenburgh, N.J., on . . . November 28th, 1861, by Rev. Theodore B. Romeyn. New-Brunswick, N.J.: Terhune & Van Anglen's press, 1861. 21p. NJR NN 765

Various allusions to the war.

STUDDIFORD, PETER AUGUSTUS, 1828-1886.

A nation's responsibility to God. A thanksgiving sermon, preached in the Reformed Dutch Church at Belleville, N.J., November 27th, 1862, by Rev. P. A. Studdiford, pastor of the church. Newark, N.J.: Printed at the Daily Advertiser office, 1862. 23p. NJJ NHI PPPRHI 766

THOMPSON, JOHN BODINE, 1830-1907.

"Our country.—Signs of danger and promise." *The evangelical quarterly.* v.2, 1861. p.[529]-581 (Oct. 1861) 767

Anonymous, but author's own copy is in NJR.

Thompson was pastor of the Metuchen, N.J., Reformed Church, 1859-1866.

———————

. . . Signs of promise: a thanksgiving discourse. By the Reverend John Bodine Thompson. New York: Schermerhorn, Bancroft & Co., 1864. cover-title, 24p. (The pulpit and rostrum. no. 32. Dec. 1864) DLC NJ NJNBS NJR NHI

Various reflections of the war.

Delivered in the Metuchen Reformed Church, Nov. 24, 1864.

WELLS, CORNELIUS LOW, 1833-1904.

The present condition of our national affairs a theme for thankfulness, and not for lamentation. A sermon, preached in the Third Reformed Dutch Church, Jersey City, N.J., on . . . December 1st, 1861, by Rev. C. L. Wells, pastor . . . New-York: George Russell, printer, 1861. 24p. NJJ NJNBS NHI 769

WORTMAN, DENIS, 1835-1922.

Living for principles; or, The right against the expedient. An address before the Anti-Secret Association of Rutgers College, New Brunswick, N.J., at its anniversary, May 7th, 1862. By Rev. Denis Wortman, Jr., Bushwick Avenue Reformed Dutch Church, Brooklyn, E.D. New York: Hosford & Ketcham, stationers and printers, 1862. 16p. DLC NJR NHI NN 770

Various allusions to the war.

Society of Friends

ALLINSON, WILLIAM JAMES, 1810-1874.

"Right in the abstract. A lecture prepared for the New York 'Friends' Lyceum' course, by Wm. J. Allinson; and delivered 1st mo. 2d, 1862." *Friends' review.* v.16, 1862/63. p.3-6, 27-30, 42-44, 58-60, 76-78. 771

Condemnation of slavery and a review of the controversy, deploring past equivocation by the federal government. Allinson (a Burlington Quaker), while gratified that abolition will result from the war, endorses Friends' adherence to their pacifist beliefs.

———————

Right in the abstract: one of the course of Friends' Lyceum lectures. Delivered in the lecture room of Friends' meeting house on 20th Street, New York, First Month 20th, 1862. By William J. Allinson. Philadelphia: Henry Longstreth, 1862. 68p. MH NJR (photo) PHC

"The following Lecture is copied from the columns of Friends' Review . . ."—p.[3].

———————

[*Same: "third edition"*] Right in the abstract: one of the course of Friends' Lyceum lectures delivered in the lecture room of Friends' meeting house, on 20th St., New York, First Month 20th, 1862. By William J. Allinson. Third edition. Philadelphia: Henry Longstreth, 1863. 72p. PHC 771b

FRIENDS, SOCIETY OF. PHILADELPHIA YEARLY MEETING.

"Address to the members of Philadelphia Yearly Meeting, from the Meeting for Sufferings." *Friends' review.* v.15, 1861/62. p.387-389.

Dated Jan. 17, 1862.

A reaffirmation of Quaker opposition to war, urging members of the Society to abstain from support of the present conflict, either by service or contribution.

Editorial comment: *ibid.*, p.392-393.

———————

[*Same*] To the members of Philadelphia Yearly Meeting. [Philadelphia, 1862] [4]p. NJR PHC 771d

Caption title.

"Signed on behalf and by direction of a Meeting for Sufferings, held in Philadelphia, the 17th of First month, 1862. Joseph Snowden, Clerk."

Printed docketing (p.[4]): Address to the members of Philadelphia Yearly Meeting. 1862.

———————

Epistle to the members of the Yearly Meeting of Friends held in Philadelphia. Philadelphia: Printed by William K. Bellows, (successor to Joseph Rakestraw,) 1863. 12p. DLC 772

Expresses loyalty to the government, opposition to war, and urges Friends not to support the military effort.

"From a Meeting . . . held in Philadelphia the 18th day of the 12th month, 1863."

Signed (p.12): Joseph Snowden, Clerk.

Miscellany

BACON, GEORGE BLAGDEN, 1836-1876.

A plea for the sacredness of human life. A sermon preached at Orange, New Jersey, January 8th, 1865. By George B. Bacon, pastor of the Orange Valley Church. Published by request of the congregation. New York: John F. Trow, printer, 1865. 16p. CTY NJP NJPT 772a

Bacon, pastor of the Orange Valley Congregational Church, is moved by a local (railroad?) disaster of the past week. This and other current evidences of callousness about human life and safety he attributes to the present war.

APPENDIX I

The Prewar Period

The Prewar Period

HISTORY

DUDLEY, THOMAS HAINES, 1819-1893.

"The inside facts of Lincoln's nomination." *Century illustrated monthly magazine.* v.40, 1890. p.477-479. 773

The role of New Jersey's delegation (including the author) at the 1860 Chicago Republican convention.

Signed (p.479) : Camden, N.J. Thomas H. Dudley.

Reprinted in the American Iron and Steel Association *Bulletin,* no. 26, July 14, 1890.

FURMAN, DAVID DICKSON, 1917-

"New Jersey in 1861." An address by David D. Furman, attorney general, state of New Jersey, at the convocation arranged for Fairleigh-Dickinson University by the New Jersey Civil War Centennial Commission, February 7, 1961, Madison, New Jersey. [Trenton, N.J.: Civil War Centennial Commission, 1961] [1], 6 leaves. NJ NJR 774

Mimeographed.

Historical setting for New Jersey on the eve of war.

GOLDSMITH, BERTHOLD HENRY, 1882-

"Ante-bellum politics [in New Jersey]. By B. H. Goldsmith, historian and author." Kull, I. S., *New Jersey, a history.* New York, 1930. v.3, p.[745]-753. plates. 775

KNAPP, CHARLES MERRIAM, 1892-

"From peace to war." *Ibid.,* p.[757]-769. 776

———————

"The presidential campaign of 1860 in New Jersey." *Ibid.,* p.[787]-800. 777

LAWSON, EVALD BENJAMIN, 1904-1965.

When Lincoln visited New Jersey [1861] he won the public heart by the manly simplicity of his character. By Evald Benjamin Lawson, president of Upsala College. [n.p., 1943] [4]p. illus. (incl. port.) NJN NJR 777a

Caption title.

"Reprinted from *Contemporary Life,* February-March, 1943."

MAYNARD, DOUGLAS H.

"Dudley of New Jersey and the nomination of Lincoln." *Pennsylvania magazine of history and biography.* v.82, 1958. p.100-108. 778

An account of the significant part played by Thomas H. Dudley and his fellow delegates from New Jersey at the 1860 Republican national convention, based in some degree on the Dudley papers in the Henry E. Huntington Library.

MEARNS, DAVID CHAMBERS, 1899-

"Who in triumph advances. [By] David C. Mearns." *Proceedings of the New Jersey Historical Society.* v.77, 1959. p.[111]-127. 779

Address delivered Feb. 20, 1959, before the New Brunswick Historical Club.

An account of Lincoln's visit to New Jersey on Feb. 21, 1861—his triumphal passage through the towns along his route, Jersey City to Trenton, and his reception in the chambers of the state legislature.

Reprinted in no. 21; also in David C. Mearns, *Largely Lincoln* (New York, 1961), p.[61]-84.

NIXON, JOHN THOMPSON, 1820-1889.

"The circumstances attending the election [February 1860] of William Pennington, of New Jersey, as speaker of the thirty-sixth Congress. Read before the New Jersey Historical Society, January 18th, 1872. By Hon. John T. Nixon, judge of the United States District Court." *Ibid.* 2nd series. v.2, 1870/72. p.[205]-220. 780

Both Pennington and Nixon were newly-elected congressmen, then representing the "Opposition" party.

———————

The circumstances attending the election of William Pennington, of New Jersey, as speaker of the thirty-sixth Congress. Read before the New Jersey Historical Society, January 18th, 1872. By Hon. John T. Nixon, judge of the

United States District Court. Newark: Printed at the Daily Advertiser office, 1872. 16p. NJ NJP 780a

REILLY, GEORGE LOVE ANTHONY.

"'Old Abe' passes through New Jersey [February 1861]. By George L. A. Reilly." *Journal of the Rutgers University Library.* v.13, 1949/50. p.[51]-54. 781

SMITH, CHARLES PERRIN, 1819-1883.

"The nomination of Lincoln. By Charles P. Smith." *Beecher's magazine.* v.5, 1872. p.332-335. 781a

Shows the part played by New Jersey's delegation to the 1860 Republican national convention. Smith, a member of the delegation, lived for many years in Trenton, a man of influence in New Jersey Republican politics. His reminiscences (see no. 282) are an invaluable tool for historians of the period.

WEART, JACOB, 1829-1905.

". . . Speaker William Pennington." *New Jersey law journal.* v.20, 1897. p.196-204, 230-239. 782

Deals particularly with his political history: nomination and campaign for Congress in 1858; election to the speakership, and service in Congress until his death in 1862. Pennington was a Newark attorney and jurist, governor 1837-1843, Whig, "Opposition" party, and Republican adherent.

Part of a series, "Reminiscences of Some Former Noted Members of the New Jersey Bar."

POLITICS

Campaign Literature, Speeches, Documents, Etc.

ADRAIN, GARNETT BOWDITCH, 1815-1878.

Great right of self-government—and the Union. Speech of Hon. G. B. Adrain, of New Jersey, on the election of speaker. Delivered in the House of Representatives, December 14, 1859. [Washington, D.C.] Printed by Lemuel Towers [1859] 16p. DLC NJR OCLWHI 783

Caption title.

Adrain was a New Brunswick attorney who served in Congress 1857-1861. Here, opposing the Administration candidate for speaker (T. S. Bocock of Virginia), he defends himself as an anti-Lecompton Democrat against charges of party disloyalty, reviewing the pertinent national issues (Kansas-Nebraska act, slavery, union, etc.), and urging Douglas as a presidential candidate.

———

State of the Union. Speech of Hon. Garnett B. Adrain, of New Jersey, in the House of Representatives, January 15, 1861. [Washington, D.C.: Printed at the office of the Congressional Globe, 1861] 8p. DLC NJR OCLWHI 784

Caption title.

Text in two columns.

ALEXANDER, WILLIAM COWPER, 1806-1874.

Letter from Col. Alexander. [n.p., 1859] Broadside. 12 x 6¼ in. NJR 784a

Two letters to an unnamed Democrat, the first by William C. Alexander (New York, Oct. 26, 1859). The second, headed "Letter from Gov. Vroom" (Trenton, Sept. 24, 1859), bears the misprint signature of "Peter V. Vroom," i.e., Peter D. Vroom. The writers, declining invitations to attend political rallies at (respectively) Newark and Jersey City, duly record their support of the party and its current gubernatorial candidate, Gen. Edwin R. V. Wright, Hudson County attorney and politician, later member of Congress.

Former-governor Vroom also had been considered for the 1859 nomination. Alexander, a Princeton lawyer, had run unsuccessfully for the governorship in 1856. Both men were delegates to the 1861 Washington Peace Convention.

DEMOCRATIC PARTY. NEW JERSEY.

Douglas & Johnson! Regular Democratic nominees. Address to the Democratic electors of the state of New-Jersey, by the State Central Committee, as directed to be issued by the Democratic state convention, held at Trenton, July 25, 1860 . . . Trenton: Published by the Committee, 1860. cover-title, 23p. NJHI NJR

Caption title: To the Democratic electors of the state of New Jersey . . .

Sub-title (p.[1]): Popular sovereignty and non-intervention in New Jersey.

Signed (p.19) at Trenton, Aug. 10, 1860, by the State Central Committee, Rodman M. Price chairman.

Proceedings of the Democratic state convention, July 25, 1860: p.20-23.

DEMOCRATIC PARTY. NEW JERSEY. CRANBURY.

Grand union rally. Breckinridge, Douglas & Bell. The friends of the union electoral ticket who are willing to unite as one man in support of the same, and all others opposed to the election of Lincoln and Hamlin, the Republican-abolition candidates, and to preserve our Union from the dangers with which it is threatened by the ascendancy of that party, are requested to meet in mass meeting, at Vanderveer's Hotel, village of Cranbury, on Friday evening, Nov. 2, at 7 1-2 o'clock. The meeting will be addressed by Hon. Jas. W. Wall, of Burlington, A. M. Johnson, Esq., of Trenton, A. R. Speer, Esq., of New Brunswick, J. Elmer Stout, Esq., of New Brunswick, Robert Green, Esq., of Elizabeth, and others. Gen. Leslie Combs, of Kentucky, and J. Randolph Appleby, of Old Bridge, have been invited and are expected to attend. The Minute Men of New Brunswick, Hightstown Zouaves, Union Club, of Spottswood, and the Union Club of Princeton, will positively be in attendance to enliven the occasion by a grand torchlight procession. By order of the Committee. Trenton, N.J.: "True American" print [1860] Broadside. 38 x 24 in. NJP 786

This item reflects the union or fusion movement involving three New Jersey parties hostile to Lincoln —the Breckinridge and Douglas Democrats, and the Constitutional Union Party (supporting Bell).

DEMOCRATIC PARTY. NEW JERSEY. EAST WINDSOR TOWNSHIP.

The abolition boat "Nigger Worshipper." Will leave the only state that is true to the Union for the fertile shores of Big Salt River during the following week. The splendid craft "Nigger Worshipper" will positively start at 6 A.M. from Smock's dock. The Pioneer Battalion of the East Windsor Lincoln and Hamlin Club, with the enormous cart wheel will take passage in the first trip . . . [n.p., 1860] Broadside. 9 x 3 in. NJR 787

Campaign satire.

———————

Turn out Democrats!! Come to Windsor this evening, (Tuesday,) October the 30th, at 7 o'clock, and see the Hightstown Zouaves parade, and hear some good Democratic talk. All come! By order of many Democrats. Windsor, Oct'r 30, 1860. Hightstown, N.J.: Printed at the "Excelsior" office [1860] Broadside. 19 x 12¼ in. NJR 787a

Bears an 11-inch cut of an eagle and scroll with the words "Green & Early!"

[DEMOCRATIC PARTY. NEW JERSEY. HUNTERDON COUNTY]

To the people of the county of Hunterdon. The lovers of the Union and the Constitution, and of the rights of the states and of the people under this hallowed charter, all who entertain feelings of fraternal regard to our brethren of Virginia, in this, their day of darkness and peril, and to all our brethren of the South, all who are opposed to the ceaseless agitation of slavery and sectionalism, the fruits of which have been only evil, and that continually, 'till the dissolution of the ties that unite and bind us together as one people in these United States, is seriously threatened, all who are willing to leave the rights and duties of the master and the slave where our forefathers left them under the guarantees of the Constitution, and all who love the peace, union, and harmony of the great American family, are hereby respectfully and earnestly requested to meet in the court house, in Flemington, on Wednesday, the 14th inst., and at seven o'clock, P.M., then and there to take such course as duty and patriotism may demand of us in this emergency of our history. Peter I Clark, A. Wurts, Adam Bellis [and 133 other names, arranged in seven columns] . . . Dated Flemington, N.J., December 9th, 1859. Flemington, New Jersey: Adam Bellis, printer, "Democrat office" [1859] Broadside. 24 x 20 in. NJFLHI 788

Apparently a meeting of Democrats and other anti-Republican elements.

DEMOCRATIC PARTY. NEW JERSEY. TRENTON.

Grand union demonstration! In the city of Trenton, on Friday ev'g, Nov. 2, at Kay's United States Hotel. All citizens of Trenton and vicinity opposed to the election of Lincoln and Hamlin, Stratton and Boswell, are invited to assemble in front of Kay's hotel, on Friday ev'g, Nov. 2, at 7 o'clock, to express a determined and energetic effort to save our gallant little state from the disgrace of casting her electoral vote for the abolition Republican party, and of being misrepresented in our national and state legislatures. Come, all true sons of New Jersey who love their state and our glorious Union, one grand rally for the union electoral ticket, farmer Green, and the Trenton blacksmith. The following gentlemen have been invited, and are expected to be present and address the meeting. Hon. Robert J. Walker, Hon. Jonathan Pickel, Thos. Dunn English, Hon. Daniel Holsman, Hon. James W. Wall, Charles W. Jay, Robert S. Green, and others. The Bordentown Union Zouave Club, and the Union Zouave Club of Burlington, have accepted an invitation and will be present. Trenton, N.J.: "True American" print [1860] Broadside. 38 x 24 in. NJP 789

Three New Jersey anti-Lincoln parties (Breckinridge and Douglas Democrats, and the Constitutional Union Party) were concerned in the union movement.

INGLIS, CHARLES.

To the electors of Passaic County! In yielding to the wishes of my friends of the Union Party, and permitting the use of my name as candidate for the office of surrogate [etc.] . . . [Paterson, N.J., 1860] Broadside. 8 x 5½ in. NJR 790

Signed: Charles Inglis. Paterson, November 2nd., 1860.

MECHANICS AND WORKING-MEN OF NEWARK! [Newark, N.J., 1860] Broadside. 9½ x 6 in. NJHI 791

A Democratic appeal for defeat of Lincoln, arguing that Republican victory will bring war and damaging effects to Newark industry.

Signed: Truth.

Illustrated in John T. Cunningham, *Newark* (1966), p.151.

NEW JERSEY. COMMISSIONERS TO THE PEACE CONVENTION, 1861.

Report of the commissioners appointed by the Legislature of New Jersey to meet commissioners of Virginia and other states, at Washington, February 4, 1861 . . . Trenton: Printed at the "True American" office, 1861. 7p. NJ NJR NN 792

Dated Trenton, March 2, 1861.

The commissioners: Charles S. Olden, P. D. Vroom, R. F. Stockton, B. Williamson, Jos. F. Randolph, F. T. Frelinghuysen, R. M. Price, Wm. C. Alexander, T. J. Stryker.

"Proposed amendments to the Constitution, adopted by the Peace Conference": p.[5]-7.

NEW JERSEY. GOVERNOR, 1860-1863 (OLDEN)

Message of Charles S. Olden, governor of New Jersey, to the Senate and House of Assembly. Read January 12th [*sic*], 1861, and ordered to be printed. Trenton: Printed at the "True Democrat" office, 1861. 14p. DLC NJR 793

About a quarter of the text concerns the North-South conflict.

———————

Message of Hon. Charles S. Olden, governor of New Jersey, to the Senate and House of Assembly. Read January 10, 1861 . . . Trenton, N.J.: Printed at the "True American" office, 1861. 17p. NJR NN 794

———————

Message of Hon. Charles S. Olden, governor of New Jersey, with accompanying documents. Read January 10, 1861 . . . Trenton, N.J.: Printed at the "True American" office, 1861. 46p. fold. table. NJR 795

The accompanying documents (p.[19]-46) are reports of the adjutant-general and quartermaster-general.

NEW JERSEY. LEGISLATURE.

. . . National disturbances. Resolutions of the Legislature of the state of New Jersey, in regard to the pending troubles between the North and the South. January 28, 1861.—Ordered to be printed. Joint resolutions on the state of the Union passed by the Legislature of New Jersey. [Washington, D.C., 1861] 2p. (U.S. House of Representatives. 36th Congress, 2d session. Miscel. doc. no. 28) 796

The resolution [approved Jan. 29] endorsed the Crittenden Compromise and appointed nine commissioners to represent New Jersey at the Washington Peace Convention of February 1861.

———————

Resolutions of the Republican members of the New Jersey Legislature, on the present state of the Union. [n.p., 1861] 4p. NJR 797

Caption title.

Dissent against resolutions passed by the Democratic-controlled legislature endorsing the Crittenden Compromise.

Signed by Jonathan Cook, William F. Brown, and other Republican members.

Undated but of late January or early February 1861. Cf. C. M. Knapp, *New Jersey Politics During the . . . Civil War and Reconstruction* (1924), p.50.

———————

. . . The union of the states. Preamble and joint resolutions of the Legislature of the state of New Jersey, in in [*sic*] relation to the union of the states. January 31, 1861.—Ordered to be printed . . . [Washington, D.C., 1861] 3p. (U.S. House of Representatives. 36th Congress, 2d session. Miscel. doc. no. 31) 797a

Same text as no. 796, with added notations of passage and governor's approval, etc.

NEW JERSEY. LEGISLATURE. SENATE.

Diagram showing the location of the members composing the fifteenth Senate of the state of New Jersey, and the counties which they represent. 1859. [Trenton, N.J., 1859] Broadside. 14½ x 11 in. NJR 798

PEDDIE & MORRISON, NEWARK, N.J.

The following letter was written to one of our Southern friends in answer to one received with reference to the state of things now existing, and the probable election of Lincoln, which we thought would not be out of place in other sections of the South. [Newark, N.J., 1860] 4p. NJR 798a

Caption title.

The text of the letter follows, headed "Newark, N.J. Oct. 31, 1860," and addressed to "Messrs. ——— ——— Richmond, Va." In a detailed analysis, intended to quiet Southern fears, it states that the dominant Republican view is not radically anti-slavery, although Lincoln might possibly oppose the admission of further slave states. It is increasingly realized that the Negro is "only prosperous and happy under subjection," and means should be undertaken to disseminate in the North "more just and equitable views" of Southern slavery and its benefits to the Negro and mankind in general. "A Paper that will present these considerations, we intend to get up in Newark as soon as possible." Although partisans of Bell and Everett, the writers consider their election dubious; hence, reluctantly, they intend to support Douglas, "of whose morality we have not the highest opinion."

Signed (p.4): Peddie & Morrison. This was a trunk-manufacturing concern. Of the two partners, Thomas B. Peddie (a native of Scotland) served 1864-1865 in the state Assembly, actively supporting the Union cause, and was elected to Congress in 1876 as a Republican. John Morrison, born in England, died eight months after the above letter was written.

POTTS, JOSEPH COLLINS, 1808-1880.

Letter from Joseph C. Potts, Esq., to Hon. Caleb H. Valentine, setting forth the basis upon which to establish the union, harmony and success of the Democratic Party. Trenton, N.J.: Printed at the "True American" office, 1859. 12p. NJ NJR (photo) 798b

An extended letter (Trenton, May 10, 1859) preceded by a short letter from Valentine to Potts (Hackettstown, April 26, 1859); both originally appeared in the *True American* of May 24, 1859.

Published by the Democratic Central Committee of Mercer County. Cf. p.[3].

RICHARDSON, WILLIAM ALEXANDER, 1811-1875.

Speech of Hon. W. A. Richardson of Illinois, delivered in Burlington, New Jersey . . . July 17, 1860. [Phila.: Ringwalt & Brown, printers, 1860] 8p. DLC IHI NJR (photo) 799

Caption title.

"Ridicule of Lincoln, based upon six years' association with him in the Illinois legislature and in the 30th Congress."—Monaghan, *Lincoln Bibliography,* no. 78.

STOCKTON, ROBERT FIELD, 1795-1866.

Speech of Commodore Robert F. Stockton, on the past, present and future of the American Party. Delivered in the city of Camden, N.J., August 4th, 1859. Published by order of the State Executive Committee. Camden, N.J.: J. H. Jones & Co., printers, 1859. 24p. DLC NJ NJP NJR OCLWHI 800

In the face of Democratic and Republican confusion on sectional issues, Stockton calls for reorganization of the American Party as a force for conservatism, preservation of the Union, etc.

"Resolutions": p.[21]-24.

TEN EYCK, JOHN CONOVER, 1814-1879.

Speech of Hon. John C. Ten Eyck, of New Jersey. Delivered in the United States Senate, April 2, 1860. [n.p.: Republican Executive Congressional Committee, 1860] 7, [1]p. DLC NJR OCLWHI RP RPB 801

Caption title.

Deals with states' rights, slavery, fugitive slave laws, etc.

Printed in double columns.

———————

Speech of Hon. John C. Ten Eyck, of N.J., on the presentation of the resolutions of that state on "The state of the Union." Delivered in the United States Senate February 1, 1861. [Washington: H. Polkinhorn, printer, 1861] 8p. DLC MH NJHI NHI OCLWHI 802

Caption title.

THOMSON, JOHN RENSHAW, 1800-1862.

Speech of Senator Thomson, of New Jersey, on presenting the resolutions of that state on "The state of the Union." Delivered in the Senate of the United States, February 7, 1861. Washington: Henry Polkinhorn, printer, 1861. 14p. NJJ NJP NJR OCLWHI 803

TO THE REPUBLICAN WIDE AWAKE LADIES of Hartford: The Wide Awakes of Newark, N.J., numbering about two hundred, will arrive in this city Thursday evening, July 26th, on their visit to the Wide Awakes of Hartford . . . Per order Committee of Arrangements, E. N. Kellogg, chairman. H. T. Sperry, sec'y. . . . [Hartford, Conn., 1860] Broadside. 4½ x 7¼ in. NHI 804

A call for assistance of "the Republican Ladies of Hartford."

. . . TO THE REPUBLICAN WIDE-AWAKE ladies, of Hartford: Your generous response to the call of the Committee at the Newark reception last spring, gladdened all our hearts and rendered our city distinguished among strangers, for its noble hospitalities . . . Per order Committee of Arrangements, H. T. Sperry, chairman. C. A. Stillman, sec'y. . . . [Hartford, Conn., 1860] Broadside. 9¾ x 7½ in. NHI 805

At head of title: Wide-Awake head-quarters, 311 Main street. Hartford, Nov. 12, 1860.

Calls for further assistance by the ladies at a victory celebration on November 14.

ULLMANN, DANIEL, 1810-1892.

Speech of Hon. Daniel Ullmann, of New York, at the Lincoln and Hamlin ratification meeting in Newark, N.J., June 12, 1860. [n.p., 1860] 4p. NJR RPB 806

Caption title.

WALL, JAMES WALTER, 1820-1872.

Speech of James W. Wall, Esq., delivered at the great union meeting, held at Concert Hall, Newark, December 23d, 1859. [Newark, N.J.? 1860?] 15p. NJR PHI 806a

"We have come up here, if I understand the full purport of your call, to give assurance to those of our brethren at the South, now excited by apprehensions of our loyalty, that the Northern heart still pulsates in unison with theirs . . ."—p.[3].

Responding, apparently, to the recent raid on Harper's Ferry, Wall deplores conditions which threaten the national union—chiefly abolitionist fanaticism and other unreasonable pressures from the North which he sees driving the South to a dangerous point.

WOODRUFF, ABSALOM B. 1819-1886.

Speech of Absalom B. Woodruff, Esq., before the Olden Club, at Paterson, Oct. 12, 1859. [Paterson, N.J.? 1859] 6p. NJR 807

Caption title.

Text printed in double columns.

The speaker (Paterson attorney, editor, and politician) compares the past records of gubernatorial candidate Olden and his Democratic opponent, Gen. E. R. V. Wright, to the disadvantage of the latter.

THE CHURCHES: SERMONS, ESSAYS, ETC.

BAIRD, SAMUEL JOHN, 1817-1893.

Southern rights and Northern duties in the present crisis. A letter to Hon. William Pennington. By Rev. Samuel J. Baird, D.D. Philadelphia: For sale by Lindsay & Blakiston; Smith, English & Co. and other booksellers, 1861. 32p. CTY MB MH NJHI NJNBS NJR NHI NN OCLWHI PHI PP PPL PU RPB 808

Signed (p.32): Samuel J. Baird. Woodbury, N.J., February 6, 1861.

Addressed (p.[3]) "To the Hon. William Pennington, of New Jersey, Speaker of the House of Representatives of the United States."

A review of slavery, abolitionism, states' rights, etc., expressed in sympathy for the South.

Baird, a native of Ohio, taught schools and held Presbyterian charges in the South, and married a South Carolina woman. After several years as pastor of the Woodbury Presbyterian Church, he resigned in 1865.—*Biblical Repertory . . . Index Volume . . . 1825 to 1868* (Phila., 1871), p.99-101.

BROWN, ISAAC VAN ARSDALE, 1784-1861.

White diamonds better than "black diamonds;" slave states impoverished by slave labor. Read the appendix, and decide from fact. By Isaac V. Brown, D.D. Trenton, N.J.: Printed for the proprietor, by Murphy & Bechtel, 1860. 144p. DLC NJR NHI 809

"As the subject of Slavery is unavoidably a principle *Issue* in the contested election for President and Vice President of these United States, now presented to the people, this Essay is intended to prove, I. That Slavery is irreconcilable with Christianity. II. By extracts from the Census of the United States, in an appendix, to show that Slavery has always impoverished the States within which it has existed. This is a question of fact between *Free* and *Slave* labor . . ."—Preface (Trenton, July, 1860).

Originally published (1858) under the title: Slavery irreconcilable with Christianity and sound reason.

The author, a Presbyterian clergyman and founder of the Lawrenceville School, lived in Trenton during his last years.

CRANE, JONATHAN TOWNLEY, 1819-1880.

Christian duty in regard to American slavery. A sermon preached in the Trinity Methodist Episcopal Church, Jersey City, on . . . December 11, 1859, by Rev. J. T. Crane, D.D., pastor . . . Jersey City: R. B. Kashow, 1860. 22p. NJP NHI NN-SC 810

"When the popular excitement over the affair at Harper's Ferry was at its height, the following Sermon was prepared . . ."—Author's preface, dated Jersey City, Jan. 24, 1860.

A call for moderation, for freeing of the slaves by non-violent measures.

J. T. Crane's son Stephen (1871-1900) was the noted American writer, author of *The Red Badge of Courage.*

FEW SMITH, JOSEPH, 1816-1888.

Prayer for rulers: hope for our country. A sermon preached in the Second Presbyterian Church, Newark, N.J., Thanksgiving Day, November 29, 1860, by the pastor, J. Few Smith . . . Newark, N.J.: A. Stephen Holbrook, printer, 1860. 32p. NJHI NJR NN 811

GORDON, WILLIAM ROBERT, 1811-1897.

The peril of our ship of state: a sermon on the day of fasting and prayer, January 4th, 1861 . . . [and] The folly of our speculations: a New-Year's sermon, January 6, 1861 . . . [and] Strictures on a recent sermon of Rev. H. J. Van Dyke. By Rev. W. R. Gordon, D.D., pastor of the Reformed Dutch Church of Schraalenbergh, N.J. . . . New-York: John A. Gray, printer, stereotyper, and binder, 1861. 38p. DLC NJNBS NJP NJR NHI OCLWHI PPPRHI 812

The "strictures" are in rebuttal of Rev. Henry J. Van Dyke's sermon, *The Character and Influence of Abolitionism,* Dec. 9, 1860, of which several editions were published in 1860 and 1861 (e.g., nos. 825, 825a).

[GRAYSON, WILLIAM JOHN] 1788-1863.

Reply to Professor Hodge, on the "State of the country." Charleston: Steam-power presses of Evans & Cogswell, 1861. 32p. DLC NJP NJPT NHI NN OCLWHI PHI 813

Answering, from the Southern viewpoint, Hodge's article (see no. 815) in the January 1861 *Biblical Repertory and Princeton Review.*

Signed (p.32): Friends in Council.

[HODGE, CHARLES] 1797-1878.

"The church and the country." *Biblical repertory and Princeton review.* v.33, 1861. p.322-376 (April 1861) 814

Written just before the outbreak of war, the article sets forth the pertinent issues (chiefly slavery) and considers the possible effect of the conflict upon Presbyterian unity. Hodge, editor of the *Review* for many years, was influential in Presbyterian affairs; graduate of Princeton and of the Princeton Theological Seminary, long a professor in the latter.

———————

"The state of the country." *Ibid.,* p.1-36 (Jan. 1861) 815

Written by the editor of the *Review* in the shadow of imminent secession, the article takes a firm Union stand. It was circulated widely in pamphlet form and attracted considerable response, both northern and southern (e.g., no. 813).

———————

The state of the country . . . [Philadelphia? 1861?] cover-title, 36p. DLC NJP NN 816

"Advance sheets of the Princeton Review [January 1861]."

———————

. . . The state of the country. From the Princeton review, January, 1861. [New York? Sold at the New-York office of the Princeton review,

1861?] 32p. DLC MB NJHI NJNBS NJP NJPT NHI OCLWHI PPL PU 817

Caption title.

IRVING, DAVID, 1821-1885.

Former times contrasted with the present. A sermon preached by Rev. David Irving, on Thanksgiving Day, November 29, 1860, in the First Presbyterian Church, Morristown, N.J. New York: Printed by Edward O. Jenkins, 1860. 19p. NJHI 818

Discusses issues of the times, threat of secession, etc.

MACDONALD, JAMES MADISON, 1812-1876.

Prayer for the country. A discourse preached on Thanksgiving Day, November 29, 1860, in the First Presbyterian Church, Princeton, N.J. By James M. Macdonald, D.D. . . . New York: John F. Trow, printer, 1860. 16p. DLC NJ NJP NJPT

McGILL, ALEXANDER TAGGART, 1807-1889.

Sinful but not forsaken. A sermon, preached in the Presbyterian Church, Fifth Avenue and Nineteenth Street, New York, on the day of national fasting, January 4, 1861. By Alexander T. McGill, of Princeton, New Jersey . . . New York: John F. Trow, printer, 1861. 22p. NJPT NHI NN PHI 820

Allusions to current politics and threatened disunion.
The author, a Presbyterian clergyman, was a member of the Princeton Theological Seminary faculty, also clerk of the Presbyterian General Assembly.

———————

[*Same*] New York: Anson D. F. Randolph, 1861. 22p. DLC NJP NN 821

PUTNAM, FERNANDO C. 1812?-1886.

The true safety of the nation. A sermon preached in Bergen, N.J., January 4, 1861, the day recommended by the President to be observed as a day of fasting, humiliation and prayer; by the Rev. F. C. Putnam, rector (elect) of St. Paul's Church. Jersey City: John H. Lyon & Co., steam book printers, 1861. 15p. CSMH NJPT NJR 822

Minor reflections of current national problems.

RANKIN, JOHN CHAMBERS, 1816-1900.

Our danger and duty. A sermon preached by Rev. John C. Rankin, pastor of the Presbyterian Church at Basking Ridge, N.J., on the national fast day, January 4, 1861 . . . Jersey City: John H. Lyon & Co., printers, 1861. 7p. MH NJR 823

Text printed in double columns.

———————

Our danger and duty, a sermon preached by Rev. John C. Rankin, pastor of the Presbyterian Church, at Basking Ridge, N.J., on the national fast day, January 4, 1861 . . . Jersey City: John H. Lyon & Co., steam book printers, 1861. 14p. NJPT NJR 824

VAN DYKE, HENRY JACKSON, 1822-1891.

The character and influence of abolitionism. A sermon preached in the First Presbyterian Church, Brooklyn, on Sabbath evening, December 9th, 1860, by Rev. Henry J. Van Dyke, pastor . . . Trenton, N.J.: Printed at the "True American" office, 1861. 23p. NJR 825

An attack on abolitionism, of which several other editions were published outside New Jersey. For "strictures" on this sermon, see no. 812.

———————

The character and influence of abolitionism. Sermon preached in the First Presbyterian Church, Brooklyn, Sunday evening, Dec. 9th, 1860. By Rev. Henry J. Van Dyke. [Jersey City: John H. Lyon & Co., steam printers, 1860?] 8p. NN 825a

Caption title.
Printed in two columns.

WILSON, JAMES PATRIOT, 1808-1889.

Our national fast. A sermon preached in the South Park Presbyterian Church, January 4th, 1861, by Rev. James P. Wilson, D.D., pastor . . . Newark, N.J.: A. Stephen Holbrook, printer, 1861. 22p. DLC NJHI NJN 826

PREWAR MISCELLANY

[ANONYMOUS]

"The Crittenden amendment." *Youth's gazette* (Moorestown, N.J.) v.2, 1860/61. p.43-47 (Jan. 19, 1861) 827

The writer (who identifies himself only as "Othello") strongly criticizes the proposed amendment.

"For the Youth's Gazette." The *Gazette* was a semi-monthly publication (1859-1861) of the Moorestown Reading Circle, made up largely of essays and poems contributed anonymously by the members, many or perhaps all of them Quakers. The only file of this periodical known to the compiler is in NJR

For a response and Othello's subsequent rejoinder to the latter, see nos. 827e and 827a, respectively.

———————

"The Crittenden compromise.—No. 2." *Ibid.*, p.72-82 (Feb. 16, 1861) 827a

Signed (p.82) : Othello.

"For the Youth's Gazette."

An answer to no. 827e. See preceding entry (827) for the original article by Othello.

———————

"Disunion is the cry." *Ibid.*, p.84-85 (March 9, 1861) 827b

Poetry. Signed: I.

"For the Youth's Gazette."

———————

"John Brown." *Ibid.* v.1, 1859/60. p.6-8 (Dec. 10, 1859) 827c

An essay (dated "Nov. 24th") expressing disapproval of Brown and his illegal acts and urging persuasion as a better means to free the slaves.

———————

"Lines suggested by the execution of John Brown. 12th Month, 2d, 1859." *Ibid.*, p.5-6 (Dec. 10, 1859) 827d

Poetry. Disapproval and pity for Brown.

———————

"Reply to The Crittenden amendment." *Ibid.* v.2, 1860/61. p.53-58 (Feb. 2, "1860," i.e., 1861) 827e

"For the Youth's Gazette."

In response to an earlier article (see no. 827), the writer, while not condoning slavery, defends the compromise as a measure necessary for the support of constitutional rights (those of slaveholders) and the reduction of hostilities which threaten revolution, resulting from abolitionist pressures.

For a rejoinder, see no. 827a.

———————

"Sentiments of a member [of the Moorestown Reading Circle]." *Ibid.*, p.83-84 (March 9, 1861) 827f

"For the Youth's Gazette."

The writer condemns secession, calling for a strong Union stand and support of the Lincoln administration.

[LIPPINCOTT, W. R.]

"On the dissolution of the Union." *Ibid.*, p.67-68 (Feb. 2, "1860," i.e., 1861) 827g

Poetry.

"For the Youth's Gazette."

Manuscript note identifies the author: "W. R. Lippincott."

NEW JERSEY MILITARY ASSOCIATION.

Organization and proceedings of the New Jersey Military Association at the meetings held in . . . Trenton, February, 1860. Trenton, N.J.: State Gazette & Republican steam power press print, 1860. 64p. NJ NJP NJR 827h

Includes list of members, list of military (i.e., militia) companies in New Jersey, text and analysis of militia laws.

For proceedings of the 3rd-5th meetings, Jan. 22, Feb. 5, and March 5, 1861, with president's address of the last date, see no. 829; for later meetings see nos. 486-488.

RUNYON, THEODORE, 1822-1896.

The militia: its place in our governmental system. An address delivered before the New Jersey Military Association, March 5, 1861, by the president, Gen. Theodore Runyon . . . Newark, N.J.: A. Stephen Holbrook, printer, 1861. 18p. NJHI NJJ NJR 828

Runyon was a Newark attorney, jurist, Douglas Democrat, politician (gubernatorial candidate, 1865), militia officer, and commander of the three-month New Jersey Brigade sent to Washington at the outbreak of war in 1861.

———————

The militia system. Address by Gen. Theodore Runyon, president of the N.J. Military Association. Delivered before the Association at a meeting held at Jersey City . . . March 5, 1861. Trenton: Printed at the State Gazette and Republican office, 1861. 25p. NJ NJP NJR 829

Cover-title: New Jersey Military Association. The president's address, minutes of meetings, and a revised list of members. 1861.

"Officers. 1861": p.[18].

"Additional meetings of the Association" (Jan. 22, Feb. 5, and March 5, 1861): p.[19]-23. Minutes of the earlier two meetings were published in no. 827h.

"List of members" (with rank, name of militia unit, and address): p.24-25.

U.S. CENSUS OFFICE. 8TH CENSUS, 1860.

Abstract of the population and statistics of the state of New Jersey, according to the census of 1860. Prepared under the direction of the superintendent of the Census Department, at Washington. Ordered to be printed under the supervision of the secretary of state, by a resolution of the last Legislature. Trenton: Phillips and Boswell, printers, 1862. 100p. tables. DLC NJN NJR 830

Population, real estate, paupers and defectives, education, industry, etc.

WEBSTER, WILLIAM STEWART CROSS, 1844-1922.

"How two Princeton students saw Lincoln in 1861. [Edited by Lilliam M. Blease.]" *Princeton University Library chronicle.* v.5, 1943/44. p.154-157. 831

Letter written Feb. 23, 1861. Webster (a Princeton freshman) describes the events of Lincoln's passage through Princeton and his own experiences, following Lincoln to Trenton, in company with an older brother, also a student of the College.

WETMORE, WILLIAM JARVIS, 1809-

. . . "Anthem of the free." [Trenton, N.J.] State Gazette & Republican print [1860] Broadside. 8¼ x 5½ in. NJR 832

"Written and Composed by Wm. J. Wetmore, M.D., for the Fourth of July, 1860. To be sung by the Trenton Glee Club."

Words only.

APPENDIX II

The Postwar Period

The Postwar Period

HISTORY

CUMMINGS, WARREN D.

"Sussex County campaigners in 1865. [By] Warren D. Cummings." *Proceedings of the New Jersey Historical Society.* v.78, 1960. p.[22]-32.

Concerns the gubernatorial contest, in which Ward (Union Party) defeated Runyon (Democrat) —especially the debates and other campaign machinations of their chief Sussex County supporters, respectively General Kilpatrick and Congressman A. J. Rogers.

GAINES, ABNER J. 1923-

"New Jersey and the Fourteenth Amendment. [By] Abner J. Gaines." *Ibid.* v.70, 1952. p.[37]-55. 834

An account (based chiefly on contemporary newspapers) of New Jersey's ratification of the amendment (1866), its subsequent effort to rescind the ratification (1868), and the 1866 conflict over election of a U.S. senator from New Jersey.

In NJ is a 76-page typescript of the same author and title (1949). This is probably the original, and more extended, version of the present article. "Bibliographical Note" and "Citations": leaves [67-76].

GOLDSMITH, BERTHOLD HENRY, 1882-

"Post bellum politics and conditions. By B. H. Goldsmith, historian and author." Kull, I. S., *New Jersey, a history.* New York, 1930. v.3, p.[883]-891. 835

POLITICS

Campaign Literature, Speeches, Documents, Etc.

1865

DEMOCRATIC PARTY. NEW JERSEY.

List of delegates to the Democratic state convention, August 30, 1865. Compiled from the official returns in the secretary of state's office, by order of Hon. P. D. Vroom, chairman of Democratic State Central Committee. [n.p., 1865] Broadside. 11 x 10½ in. NJFLHI 836

Main text in four columns: lists of communities (grouped by county) with respective numbers of voters and delegates.

[DEMOCRATIC PARTY. NEW JERSEY]

Negro suffrage. The new Republican plank. [n.p., 1865] 7p. NJR 837

Caption title.

[DEMOCRATIC PARTY. NEW JERSEY. BERGEN COUNTY]

Bergen County tracts. No. 1. Our national dangers. [n.p., 1865] 4p. NJR 838

Caption title.

Campaign literature. The national dangers are "Radicalism in Politics, and Infidelity in Religion."

"Democrats of Bergen County, prepare for duty." —p.4. No other reflection of local politics.

———————

Bergen County tracts. No. 2. To the farmers and mechanics of Bergen County. [n.p., 1865] 4p. NJR 839

Caption title.

Campaign literature, chiefly attacking the iniquities of the radical Republicans in Washington.

EQUAL RIGHTS LEAGUE OF THE STATE OF NEW JERSEY.

Proceedings of the State Convention of Colored Men of the State of New Jersey, held in the city of Trenton, N.J., July 13th and 14th, 1865. With a short address to the loyal people of New Jersey, together with the constitution of the Equal Rights League of the State of New Jersey. Published for the Executive Committee of the Equal Rights League of the State of New Jersey, by order of the Convention, by William Steward, recording secretary of the E.R.L. of N.J. Bridgeton, New Jersey: J. B. Ferguson, printer, 1865. 15p. NJR (photo) NN-SC 840

The League, formed by the convention, had as its object "to secure to ALL men *all* equal political rights and immunities."

FIGHTING WITH THE BALLOT! AS SUNG BY G. C. B. Holloway . . . Jersey City: From the "Times" publishing house [1865] Broadside. 9 x 5¾ in. NJHI 841

"Air: 'Tramp, Tramp,' &c."

Political verse supporting Marcus L. Ward against the copperheads in the forthcoming gubernatorial election.

"Entered according to Act of Congress, in the year 1865, by T. F. Holloway . . ."

HOLLOWAY, G. C. B.

The squirming copperhead. Written and sung by Master G. C. B. Holloway. Jersey City: From the "Times" publishing house [1865] Broadside. 9½ x 5¾ in. NJHI 842

"Air: 'Dixey's Land.' "

Verse supporting Marcus L. Ward, Union candidate for governor.

"NEW JERSEY." *Harper's weekly.* v.9, 1865. p.483 (Aug. 5, 1865) 842a

Editorial endorsement of Marcus L. Ward, for the governorship.

NICOL, R. B.

The battle-cry, in New Jersey, Forward! for Ward. (A parody, on "The battle-cry of freedom.") . . . Washington, D.C.: R. B. Nicol, care of Gibson Brothers, printers [1865] Broadside. 8 x 5¾ in. NJHI NJP NJR 843

Song sheet (verse only).

Supporting the Union candidate for governor, Marcus L. Ward.

———————

Campaign song for the great question, Who will be governor of New Jersey. (Air—The elfin waltz.) . . . Washington, D.C.: R. B. Nicol, care of Gibson Brothers, printers [1865] Broadside. 7⅞ x 5½ in. NJHI NJP NJR 844

Song sheet (verse only).

For Marcus L. Ward, Union gubernatorial candidate. "The Copperhead Candidate, / Runyon, we know / Was noted for running, / Some four years ago. / Since then he has run / In this traitorous train, / . . ."

———————

Gen. Runyon, the copperhead candidate, running for governor of New Jersey. (Air—King of the cannibal islands.) . . . Washington, D.C.: R. B. Nicol, care of Gibson Brothers, printers [1865] Broadside. 7¾ x 5⅜ in. NJP NJR

Song sheet (verse only).

"The Author of this Song, (a discharged, crippled Soldier) . . ."

———————

. . . Kilpatrick's march through New Jersey . . . Washington, D.C.: R. B. Nicol, in care of Gibson Brothers, printers [1865] Broadside. 8 x 5¼ in. NJHI NJP 846

Song sheet (verse only).

"The Author of this, and a variety of other Patriotic Songs, is a discharged trooper, crippled in the bridle arm, but finds employment for the sword arm by wielding the pen in defence of The Union."

In support of the Union campaign (M. L. Ward for governor), backed by speeches and other activities in New Jersey by Gen. Judson Kilpatrick.

———————

Marcus L. Ward, the soldier's friend, for governor of New Jersey. (Air—Tramp, tramp, tramp.) . . . Washington, D.C.: R. B. Nicol, care of Gibson Brothers, printers [1865] Broadside. 8 x 5½ in. NJHI NJP NJR 847

Song sheet (verse only).

NJHI has a second copy, printed in silver on black calendered paper.

Illustrated in John T. Cunningham, *Newark* (1966), p.163.

PYATT, ASA, 1800?-

A song of victory. By Asa Pyatt, Esq. [New Brunswick, N.J., 1865?] Broadside. 7½ x 6 in. NJR 848

Seven stanzas of verse, apparently celebrating the Democratic defeat in 1865. "The Copperheads they rule no more / In our beloved State, / Which makes them moan, and sigh, and groan— / The Union men berate."

The poet was a New Brunswick school teacher.

RALLY, BOYS! FOR MARCUS WARD. New York: Baker & Godwin [1865] Broadside. 9½ x 6 in. NJR 849

Campaign verse.

SICKLES, DANIEL EDGAR, 1825-1914.

Democrats, will you read this? General Sickles on the New Jersey Democrats. [n.p., 1865] Broadside. 11½ x 8 in. NJR 850

A letter, dated Boston, September 25, 1865, addressed to Major General Kilpatrick, answering his invitation to visit the Sussex County (N.J.) fair. He attacks the current treasonable position of the Democratic organization in New Jersey—particularly their platform of Aug. 30, 1865.

Signed: D. E. Sickles.

———————

Gen. Sickles's letter. [n.p., 1865] 2p. NJR

Caption title.

Both pages printed on one side of a sheet measuring 9 x 12 in.

Dated Boston, Sept. 25, 1865. (See preceding entry.)

Signed: D. Sickles.

A SOLDIER'S ANSWER TO A REPUBLICAN tract. [n.p., 1865] 7p. NJR NHI 852

Caption title.

Signed (p.7): Veteran.

The author, a four-year army veteran (apparently of Trenton), attacks the Republican record as regards treatment of New Jersey soldiers—inadequate pay and provisions, lack of absentee voting rights, etc.

SONG OF THE LOYAL BAND. TUNE—TRAMP, tramp, tramp, the boys are marching. [Newark, N.J., 1865] Broadside. 9¼ x 5¾ in. NJR

Campaign song (words only), supporting Marcus L. Ward for governor.

Two lines at bottom: Old North Ward, Newark, N.J. / **33**.

"THANK THEM AGAIN! THE VOICE OF loyal New Jersey after the election Nov. 7, 1865." *Harper's weekly*. v.9, 1865. p.742 (Nov. 25, 1865) 853a

Verse.

UNION LEAGUE OF NEW JERSEY.

. . . Brothers: The time is at hand for us to commence a thorough canvass. We must not lose a day . . . Newark, N.J., 1865. Broadside. 10 x 7¾ in. NJR 854

At head of title: <Circular no. 7.> Union League of New Jersey, State Council, Newark, August, 1865.

A call to the local councils for intensified political activity and development of League membership, etc.

Signed by A. D. Hope, president; John F. Starr and Chas. P. Smith, vice presidents; Benj. S. Morehouse, secretary.

[UNION PARTY. NEW JERSEY]

Copperhead love for the soldier. [n.p., 1865] 12p. NJHI NJR 855

Caption title.

"The right of soldiers to vote": p.3-10.

———————

Duties of American citizens. New York: Edward O. Jenkins, printer [1865] 16p. NJHI

Caption title.

A Union Party tract charging the Democrats with disloyalty, etc.

Signed (p.16): "By order of the Committee, B. Aycrigg, Chairman. Passaic, N.J., May 3, 1865."

———————

Facts for voters. New Jersey during the war. Democratic treatment of the soldiers! Jersey City: From the "Times" publishing house [1865] 8p. NJR 857

Caption title.

"The right of soldiers to vote denied by New Jersey copperheads": p.[6]-8.

UNION PARTY. NEW JERSEY.

. . . Marcus L. Ward, "the soldiers' friend." Let all who love truth, honor & goodness, please read carefully. Paterson, N.J.: Printed by Chiswell & Wurts, "Press" office, 1865. 12p. DLC NJHI NJN NJR NHI 858

At head of title: Issued by the New Jersey Union Executive Committee.

Supports Ward as Union candidate for governor, with a detailed account of his wartime activities, particularly in aiding New Jersey soldiers and their families.

———————

The two platforms . . . Jersey City: From the "Times" printing house [1865] Broadside. 16 x 11¼ in. NJR 859

Printed in two columns, the first headed: "Look on this picture, / Union platform, / adopted at Trenton, July 20, 1865." The second is headed: "And then on this! / Copperhead platform, / adopted at Trenton, August 30, 1865."

———————

The Union platform, adopted by the Union state convention at Trenton, July twentieth, eighteen hundred and sixty-five. Jersey City: From the "Times" printing house [1865] Broadside. 15¾ x 11½ in. NJHI NJP NJR 860

Text in two columns.

———————

. . . The war debt. The two parties in New Jersey in relation to it. Jersey City: From the "Times" publishing house [1865] 8p. NJP 861

Caption title.

A campaign tract, published not long before the fall election of 1865, urging that the national war debt be honored, and attacking the Democratic stand on this and other war matters.

[UNION PARTY. NEW JERSEY. ELIZABETH]

Attention, battalion! All returned soldiers and sailors of Elizabeth and vicinity, who favor the election of Marcus L. Ward, the Union candidate for governor, are requested to meet . . . in Library Hall, Friday evening next, Sept. 15 . . . for the purpose of organizing a campaign club . . . Elizabeth: New Jersey Journal print [1865] Broadside. 23½ x 18 in. NJHI 862

[UNION PARTY. NEW JERSEY. NEW BRUNSWICK]

Change of programme. In consequence of the storm, the Union meeting will take place at Greer's Hall, instead of court house square, this afternoon and evening . . . Ex-Gov. Curtin, of Pennsylvania, will be present . . . [New Brunswick, N.J.] Fredonian steam power press print [1865?] Broadside. 8 x 5½ in. NJR 863

1865/66

The Senatorial Election

[ANONYMOUS]

An examination into the validity of the New Jersey senatorial election of March 15, 1865. [n.p., 1865 or 1866] 52p. DLC NJP NJR 864

Caption title.

An account of the election, and arguments favoring its validity.

The legislature in joint session had elected to the U.S. Senate—by plurality rather than majority vote—John P. Stockton (1826-1900), chairman of the state delegation to the 1864 Democratic national convention, a Princeton lawyer of influence (son of Robert F. Stockton, strong man of the New Jersey railroad monopoly; brother of Attorney-General R. F. Stockton, Jr.; cousin of U.S. district judge R. S. Field; etc.). Although admitted to the Senate, he was unseated in March 1866 after a controversy as to the legality of his election—and, incidentally, his own right to vote on the issue when a tie developed.

Several of the pamphlets involved in the argument are without date, but probably appeared between December 1865 and March 1866.

———————

New Jersey senatorial election. A reply to the arguments submitted to the Judiciary Committee in favor of the protest. [n.p., 1866] 20p. DLC MH NJR 865

Caption title.

Supports the legality of Stockton's election, particularly refuting arguments in two pamphlets (nos. 872 and 868, respectively), one by A. O. Zabriskie, the other [Cortlandt Parker's] *Was the Hon. John P. Stockton Duly Elected Senator from New Jersey?*

———————

The New Jersey senatorial question. [n.p., 1865 or 1866] 4, 4p. MH NJR 866

Caption title.

The first four pages present an argument against the legality of Stockton's election by a plurality vote (rather than majority).

The second four-page section (for which the preceding section was intended as a preliminary statement) contains a protest [of March 20, 1865] by thirty-eight dissenting members of the legislature, opposing Stockton's admission to the Senate. The text of this protest is published also in U.S. Senate, Committee on the Judiciary, *Report*, Jan. 30, 1866 (39th Congress, 1st session, Rep. com. no. 4), p.5-7.

Sabin gives date 1866.

———————

Statement. [n.p., 1866?] 21p. NJR 867

Caption title.

A professional-sounding legal argument against the validity of Stockton's election of March 15, 1865.

The copy in NJR, evidently distributed by mail, bears a postmark of Burlington, N.J., Jan. 10 (doubtless 1866).

NEW JERSEY. LEGISLATURE.

Protest of the Democratic members of the New Jersey Legislature against the attempt to elect a United States senator. Read in the Senate and General Assembly. September 18, 1866. Trenton, N.J.: Printed at the "True American" office, 1866. 8p. NJP 867a

[PARKER, CORTLANDT] 1818-1907.

Was the Hon. John P. Stockton duly elected senator from New Jersey? [n.p., 1865 or 1866] cover-title, 24p. DLC NJHI 868

Copy in NJHI has a manuscript note on the cover: "by Cortlandt Parker."

An argument against the validity of the election. For a rebuttal, see no. 865.

SUMNER, CHARLES, 1811-1874.

"Majority or plurality in the election of senators. Speech in the Senate, on the contested election of Hon. John P. Stockton, of New Jersey, March 23, 1866." Sumner, Charles. *Works.* Boston, 1870-1883. v.10, p.[377]-390.

———————

"A senator cannot vote for himself. Speech in the Senate, on the vote of Hon. John P. Stockton affirming his seat in the Senate, March 26, 1866." *Ibid.*, p.[391]-405. 870

U.S. CONGRESS. SENATE. COMMITTEE ON THE JUDICIARY.

. . . Report. The Committee on the Judiciary, to whom were referred the credentials of John P. Stockton, claiming to have been elected a senator from the state of New Jersey, for six years, from the fourth day of March, eighteen hundred and sixty-five, together with the protest of certain members of the Legislature of said state against the validity of his election, submit the following report . . . [Washington, D.C., 1866] 20p. (U.S. Senate. 39th Congress, 1st session. Rept. no. 4) NJR 871

Caption title.
Submitted by Mr. Trumbull. Ordered printed Jan. 30, 1866.
"Minutes of the proceedings of the several joint meetings [Feb. 15, March 1, and March 15] of the senate and general assembly of the State of New Jersey, for the session of 1865": p.7-20.
Includes a copy of the memorial by certain New Jersey legislators, March 20, 1865, protesting against Stockton's admission to the Senate seat.
The Committee recommended seating of Stockton.

ZABRISKIE, ABRAHAM OOTHOUT, 1807-1873.

The New Jersey senatorial question. Opinion of A. O. Zabriskie. [n.p., 1866] 1p.l., 10p. NJR (photo) PPL 872

Signed (p.10): A. O. Zabriskie. January 2d, 1866.
A legal argument against the validity of Stockton's election. Zabriskie was a respected Jersey City attorney and jurist.
This is one of two pamphlets, sent to the Senate Judiciary Committee early in 1866, rebutted anonymously in another pamphlet (no. 865): *New Jersey Senatorial Election. A Reply.*

1866

COOPER, PETER, 1791-1883.

Reconstruction. Letter from Peter Cooper to President Johnson. [New York, 1866] 4p. MH NJR 872a

Caption title.
Cooper deplores the President's conflict with Congress over reconstruction issues, and in particular his opposition to the recently-passed Fourteenth Amendment.

DAVIDSON, JOHN, 1837-1911.

Letter of Hon. John Davidson, Union candidate for Congress in the Third Congressional District of New Jersey, in reply to the letter of Hon. Charles Sitgreaves. [Elizabeth, N.J.? 1866] 4p. NJR 873

Caption title.
Text in two columns.
Davidson, a native of Scotland, lived in the United States from the age of ten, and in Elizabeth, N.J., from about 1864, practicing law in New York City. For some years he was active in Republican affairs, as a delegate to state conventions, congressional aspirant, etc. He is said to have been offered several public appointments, including the governorship of Wyoming Territory.

[DEMOCRATIC PARTY. NEW JERSEY. SECOND CONGRESSIONAL DISTRICT]

Newell's record! Let the intelligent voters of the Second District read! [n.p., 1866] 4p. NJR

Caption title.
Opposes former-governor William A. Newell, of Allentown, N.J., Union Republican candidate for Congress (to which he had been elected previously in 1864). An attack particularly on his do-nothing record in the 1866 session, his alleged prejudice against persons of foreign birth, and support of Negro suffrage.

FRELINGHUYSEN, FREDERICK THEODORE, 1817-1885.

Remarks of Hon. F. T. Frelinghuysen, of New Jersey, on the bill extending the elective franchise in the District of Columbia, and on the death of Hon. William Wright, of New Jersey; delivered in the Senate of the United States, December 11, 13, and 17, 1866. Washington: Printed at the Congressional Globe office, 1867. 7p. DLC 873b

"Death of Senator Wright": p.[6]-7.
Text in two columns.

NEW JERSEY. GOVERNOR, 1863-1866 (PARKER)

Correspondence referred to in the governor's message. [n.p., 1866] 26, [3]p. NJR 874

Caption title.
Signatures: [1]-4. Seems to be an independent publication of documents accompanying the governor's annual message of January 1866.

Contents include: "War claims" (p.[11]-12); "Bounties" (p.[13]-14); "Children's Home" (p.[15]-16).

Text corresponds to that in no. 875, p.[27]-35 and [109]-114, but is a different printing.

———————

Documents accompanying Governor Parker's message . . . for the year 1865. Trenton, N.J.: Printed at the "State Gazette" office, 1866. 114p. DLC NJR NN 875

"Antietam National Cemetery" (reports, estimates of expenses, lists of the dead from various states, etc.): p.[63]-88.

"Correspondence with the President and the heads of the various departments in relation to military matters, etc.": p.[89]-108.

"War claims": p.[109]-110.

"Bounties": p.[111]-112.

"Soldiers' Children's Home": p.[113]-114.

NEW JERSEY. GOVERNOR, 1866-1869 (WARD)

. . . Governor Ward's message . . . [Newark, N.J.] Newark Daily Advertiser [1866] Broadside. 10¾ x 7¾ in. NJHI 876

Addressed to the New Jersey legislature convened in special session to consider ratification of the proposed 14th Amendment and also to fill a New Jersey vacancy in the U.S. Senate.

Signed: Marcus L. Ward. Trenton, N.J., September 10, 1866.

In two columns. Evidently reprinted from the *Daily Advertiser*.

———————

Inaugural address of Marcus L. Ward, governor of New Jersey, to the Senate and General Assembly. Delivered January 16th, 1866, and ordered to be printed. Trenton, N.J.: Printed at the "State Gazette" office, 1866. 9p. DLC NJR 876a

———————

Inauguration of his excellency Marcus L. Ward, governor of New Jersey, January 16, 1866. Trenton, N.J.: Printed at the "State Gazette" office, 1866. 18p. NJN NJR 876b

"Inaugural address": p.[11]-18.

———————

Message of Governor Marcus L. Ward, with accompanying documents, to the Legislature of the state of New Jersey, September 10, 1866. Trenton, N.J.: Printed at the "State Gazette" office, 1866. 8p. NJR 877

NEW JERSEY. LEGISLATURE.

. . . Increase of pay to officers of the Navy. Resolutions of the Legislature of New Jersey, asking for increase of pay to officers of the Navy. April 16, 1866.—Referred to the Committee on Naval Affairs and ordered to be printed. [Washington, D.C., 1866] [1]p. (U.S. House of Representatives. 39th Congress, 1st session. Miscel. doc. no. 86) 878

———————

. . . Resolution of the Legislature of New Jersey, in favor of retaining the Veteran Reserve Corps in the military service of the United States.—March 1, 1866.—Referred to the Committee on Military Affairs and the Militia and ordered to be printed. [Washington, D.C., 1866] [1]p. (U.S. Senate. 39th Congress, 1st session. Miscel. doc. no. 70) 879

———————

. . . Resolution of the Legislature of New Jersey, in favor of the passage of a law for the equalization of bounties to volunteers. March 1, 1866.—Referred to the Committee on Military Affairs and the Militia and ordered to be printed. [Washington, D.C., 1866] [1]p. (U.S. Senate. 39th Congress, 1st session. Miscel. doc. no. 71) 880

"Joint resolution relative to bounty to New Jersey soldiers mustered into the service of the United States . . ."

———————

. . . Veteran Reserve Corps. Resolution of the Legislature of New Jersey, in regard to the Veteran Reserve Corps. February 27, 1866.—Referred to the Committee on Military Affairs and ordered to be printed. [Washington, D.C., 1866] [1]p. (U.S. House of Representatives. 39th Congress, 1st session. Miscel. doc. no. 51)

NEW JERSEY REVIEW. v.1, nos. 1-12. Jan.-Dec. 1866. Newark, N.J., 1866. 1v. 13 x 9½ in. NJR 881a

No more published.

A monthly periodical edited and published by Edward N. Fuller, previously editor of the copperhead *Newark Daily Journal*, "which for various reasons of political and personal consistency, we deemed it wise to relinquish in the month of April last." Conducted, with comparative moderation, as a Democratic organ "devoted to the independent discussion of topics of general interest, including Politics, State and National, the necessity of a radical and comprehensive reform in our system of government . . . excluding the trading politicians of all parties, and replacing them by men of worth and character. Some attention will be paid to . . . matters outside the range of politics . . ."

Opposes radical Republicanism, Negro suffrage, Loyal Leagues, etc., expressing sympathy for the defeated South, qualified support for President Johnson, and adherence to states'-rights principles.

NEWELL, WILLIAM AUGUSTUS, 1819-1901.

Reconstruction. Speech of Hon. William A. Newell, of New Jersey, in the House of Representatives, February 15, 1866. [Washington, D.C.: Printed at the Congressional Globe office, 1866] 8p. DLC NJR 882

Caption title.
Text in two columns.

READ, THOMAS BUCHANAN, 1822-1872.

. . . The soldier's friend. Inscribed to Marcus L. Ward, governor of New Jersey. [n.p., 1866?] Broadside. 12 x 6 in. NJR 883

At head of title: From the New York Tribune.

Verse extolling Ward's assistance to the soldiers and their families (many being of Newark) during the war.

" 'Tis fitting, then, the grand old State . . . Should seat thee in the Ruler's chair And blessed the hour that placed thee there. I need not bid thee, still be true . . ." Apparently written following Ward's inauguration (or possibly just after the November 1865 election preceding).

Signed at end: Thomas Buchanan Read.

ROGERS, ANDREW JACKSON, 1828-1900.

Assumption of rebel debt, etc. Speech of Hon. A. J. Rogers, of New Jersey, in the House of Representatives, March 26, 1866. [Washington: Printed at the Congressional Globe office, 1866] 8p. DLC NJP NHI 884

Caption title.
Text in two columns.
Proceedings during the consideration of resolutions submitted by Rogers.

———————

. . . The Constitution is the Union. Old issues in regard to slavery are dead, and new issues are upon us. Speech of Hon. A. J. Rogers, of New Jersey, on amending the Constitution and reconstructing the Union. Delivered in the House of Representatives, February 26, 1866 . . . Washington, D.C.: Printed at the "Constitutional Union" office, 1866. 16p. DLC NJP NJR 885

Text in two columns.

———————

Speech of Hon. Andrew J. Rogers, of New Jersey, on reconstruction; delivered in the House of Representatives, June 13, 1866. Washington: Printed at the Congressional Globe office, 1866. 8p. CSMH NJR (photo) 885a

Text printed in two columns.

———————

A white man's government. Speech of Hon. Andrew J. Rogers, of New Jersey, delivered in the House of Representatives, January 11, 1866. The only hope of liberty and union, is in the white men of this country. Washington, D.C.: Printed at "the Constitutional Union" office, 1866. 19, [1]p. CTY DLC NJP NHI PHI 886

Text in two columns.
Proceedings in connection with a bill (H.R. no. 1) extending suffrage rights in the District of Columbia.

SCOVEL, JAMES MATLACK, 1833-1904.

Our relations with the rebellious states. Speech of Hon. James M. Scovel, delivered in the New Jersey Senate, February 27th, 1866. [Trenton, N.J.: Murphy & Bechtel, printers, 1866] 16p. DLC NJ NJP PHI PPL 887

Caption title.

SITGREAVES, CHARLES, 1803-1878.

Defense of the New Jersey Democracy. Remarks of Hon. Charles Sitgreaves, of New Jersey, delivered in the House of Representatives, January 16, 1866. [Washington, D.C.: Printed at the Congressional Globe office, 1866] 3p. DLC 887a

Caption title.
Text in two columns.
Answer to criticism of the Democratic Party's wartime record in New Jersey, especially its part in withholding from soldiers the right to vote.

———————

Speech of Hon. Charles Sitgreaves, of New Jersey, on radicalism and reconstruction; Saturday, June 16, 1866. Washington: Printed at the Congressional Globe office, 1866. 14p. DLC NJJ NJP 888

Delivered in the House of Representatives. Sitgreaves was a Warren County Democrat.

Text in two columns.

WILLIAMS, STEPHEN K.

Speech of Hon. S. K. Williams, on the political issues of the day, delivered in Newark, Oct. 22, 1866. [Newark, N.J.: Newark Courier power print, 1866] 12p. NJR 889

Caption title.

A radical Republican attack on the moderation of President Johnson. Williams was a member of the New York Senate, from Wayne County, N.Y.

WRIGHT, EDWIN RUTHVEN VINCENT, 1812-1876.

Speech of Hon. E. R. V. Wright, of New Jersey, on reconstruction—justice to all men; delivered in the House of Representatives, January 26, 1866. Washington: Printed at the Congressional Globe office, 1866. 8p. CSMH DLC NJR 890

"The House having under consideration the proposition to amend the Constitution apportioning representation and taxation . . ."

1867

CATTELL, ALEXANDER GILMORE, 1816-1894.

Speech of Hon. Alexander G. Cattell, of New Jersey, on the bill to authorize the Secretary of the Navy to accept League Island for naval purposes; delivered in the Senate of the United States, February 13, 1867. Washington: Printed at the Congressional Globe office, 1867. 15p. DLC OCLWHI PHI 891

Text in two columns.

Argument for removal of the navy yard from Philadelphia to League Island, in the Delaware River.

[DEMOCRATIC PARTY. NEW JERSEY]

Negro suffrage! Is it not the only question in the pending election? [n.p., 1867] 14p. NN-SC

Caption title.

FRELINGHUYSEN, FREDERICK THEODORE, 1817-1885.

Speech of Hon. F. T. Frelinghuysen, of New Jersey, on the constitutionality of the reconstruction act of March 2, 1867, being an amplification of remarks made in the Senate, delivered and published at the request of the Republican Association of Washington, D.C., and a speech in review of the opinion of the Attorney General on the reconstruction measures of Congress, in the Senate, July 9, 1867. Washington: Printed at the Congressional Globe office, 1867. 13, [1]p. DLC 891aa

Text in two columns.

JONES, ALFRED W. 1834?-

Depositions in the contested election between Jones vs. Tyrrell, in the Second Assembly District of Middlesex County. Trenton, N.J.: Printed at the office of the State Gazette, 1867. 147p. NJR 891b

Deals with charges of irregularity at the polls in 1866, and with the respective allegations that (1) the New Jersey Railroad had connived in Tyrrell's election, and (2) Jones had been a Confederate. Nathaniel H. Tyrrell was a Perth Amboy Republican. Jones, born in Virginia, had lived in Kansas and Missouri before removing to Woodbridge in the fall of 1864. He was a lawyer (practicing recently in New York City with a former Confederate), later editor of Perth Amboy and Woodbridge newspapers, and a successful Assembly candidate in 1867 and 1868.

NEW JERSEY. LEGISLATURE. GENERAL ASSEMBLY.

Diagram showing the location of the members composing the ninety-first General Assembly of the state of New Jersey, and the counties which they represent. 1867. [Trenton, N.J., 1867] Broadside. 13 x 16 in. NJR 891c

NEW JERSEY. LEGISLATURE. GENERAL ASSEMBLY. COMMITTEE ON ELECTIONS.

Report of Committee in the contested election between Jones vs. Tyrrell, in the Second Assembly District of Middlesex County. [n.p., 1867] 11p. NJR 892

Dated (p.11): April 10th, 1867.

NEWELL, WILLIAM AUGUSTUS, 1819-1901.

Restoration of the rebellious states. Speech of Hon. William A. Newell, of New Jersey, in the House of Representatives, January 4, 1867. [Washington, D.C.: Printed at the Congressional Globe office, 1867] 8p. DLC NJR NN PHI 893

Caption title.

"The House . . . having under consideration the President's annual message . . ."

Printed in double columns.

REPUBLICAN PARTY. NATIONAL UNION COMMITTEE.

Newark, N.J., May 30, 1867. Dear sir: We take the liberty of sending you the appeal of the National Union Committee for funds to aid the re-organization of the Southern states on the basis of our principles . . . Please send any contribution . . . to my order as treasurer. Respectfully yours, Marcus L. Ward. [Newark, N.J., 1867] Broadside. 7¾ x 5 in. NJHI 894

To the Republicans of the Union. [New York, 1867] Broadside. 9¾ x 7¾ in. NJR 895

A call for action and financial contributions to develop Republican strength in the Southern states.

Signed: Marcus L. Ward, N.J. [and others] . . . Executive Committee of the National Union Committee. New York, May 16, 1867.

"Address letters and contributions to Gov. Marcus L. Ward, Chairman and Treasurer, Newark, N.J."

ROGERS, ANDREW JACKSON, 1828-1900.

Reconstruction. Speech of Hon. A. J. Rogers, of New Jersey, delivered in the House of Representatives, February 7, 1867. [Washington, D.C., 1867] 8p. NJR 896

Caption title.

Text in two columns.

"The House having under consideration the bill (H.R. no. 1143) to provide for the more effectual government of the insurrectionary States."

1868

BRADLEY, JOSEPH P., 1813-1892.

Opinion relative to the rights of deserters & rebels to vote. [Newark, N.J., 1868] Broadside. 10 x 8 in. NJHI 897

A legal opinion, signed: Joseph P. Bradley. Newark, N.J., November 2, 1868.

CATTELL, ALEXANDER GILMORE, 1816-1894.

Opinion of Mr. Cattell, of New Jersey, on the impeachment of the President. [n.p., 1868] 13p. MH NJR 898

A legalistic argument for the impeachment.

[DEMOCRATIC PARTY. NEW JERSEY]

A few facts for thoughtful men. [n.p., 1868] 16p. NJR 899

Caption title.

Addressed "To the People of New Jersey." Chiefly an attack on the Radical administration and policies —Reconstruction issues, Negro suffrage, the national debt, etc.

"Platform of the Democratic Party, adopted in New York, July 7, 1868": p.[12]-16.

"Resolutions of the New Jersey Democratic State Convention, adopted July 22, 1868": p.16.

Political record of Ex. Gov. Joel Parker, of New Jersey. [New York? 1868] 8p. NN 900

Caption title.

Presented to the National Democratic Convention by the New Jersey delegates, to urge Parker as the presidential candidate. A review of his career, etc.

Signed (p.8): "St. James Hotel, N.Y., July 4, 1868."

FIRST WARD GRANT AND COLFAX CLUB, NEWARK, N.J.

. . . Dear sir: Permit us to call your attention to the necessity of getting out every Republican vote at the election . . . on . . . November 3rd. . . . [Newark, N.J., 1868] Broadside. 8 x 5 in. NJHI 901

Dated: Newark, N.J., October 30th, 1868.

Signed: By order of Committee, C. G. Crane, president. Charles B. Smith, secretary.

FRELINGHUYSEN, FREDERICK THEODORE, 1817-1885.

Opinion of Mr. Frelinghuysen, of New Jersey, on the impeachment of the President. [n.p., 1868] 9p. NHI 902

An analysis of the legal aspects of Johnson's impeachment (". . . and I shall vote for conviction").

Frelinghuysen was a Newark lawyer, member of the 1861 Peace Convention, wartime attorney-general of New Jersey, U.S. senator at this time, and a Republican.

Reconstruction. Speech of Hon. F. T. Frelinghuysen, of New Jersey, delivered in the Senate of the United States, January 28, 1868. Washington: F. & J. Rives & Geo. A. Bailey, printers and reporters of the debates of Congress, 1868. 14p. CSMH DLC MH NJ NJP NJR OCLWHI 903

Text printed in two columns.

HAIGHT, CHARLES, 1838-1891.

Impeachment of the President. Speeches of Hon. Charles Haight, and Hon. Charles Sitgreaves, of New Jersey, delivered in the House of Representatives, February 24, 1868. Washington: F. & J. Rives & Geo. A. Bailey, reporters and printers of the debates of Congress, 1868. 8p. NJR 904

Both speakers were attorneys and Democrats, Haight (of Freehold) and Sitgreaves (of Phillipsburg) representing the Second and Third congressional districts, respectively.

KILPATRICK, HUGH JUDSON, 1836-1881.

Great speech of Maj.-Gen. Kilpatrick, at Salem [Mass.], on Tuesday evening, Oct. 27, 1868, in opposition to the re-election of Gen. Butler to Congress. [n.p., 1868] 24p. DLC MB OCLWHI 904a

Caption title.
Numerous reflections of the war.

NEW JERSEY. GOVERNOR, 1866-1869 (WARD)

The constitutional amendment. Message of his excellency, Marcus L. Ward, (governor of New Jersey,) vetoing Senate joint resolution no. 1. [n.p., 1868] 4p. NJR 905

Caption title.
Dated Trenton, Feb. 25, 1868.
The resolution was an attempt to rescind New Jersey's ratification of the Fourteenth Amendment.

———————

. . . To the honourable the Senate of the state of New Jersey. [n.p., 1868] Broadside. 19 (?) x 6¾ in. NJR 906

At head of title: State of New Jersey, Executive Department, Trenton, February 25, 1868.
Message vetoing Senate joint resolution no. 1, "withdrawing the consent of this State to the proposed amendment of the Constitution of the United States, entitled 'Article fourteen,' . . ."
Text in two columns (probably a newspaper reprint).
Only copy seen is in fragmentary condition, all but the top one-third missing.

NEW JERSEY. LEGISLATURE.

Joint resolution withdrawing the consent of the state of New Jersey to the proposed amendment to the Constitution of the U.S., and the message of Marcus L. Ward, governor, vetoing the same. Ordered to be printed by the General Assembly, March 17, 1868. Trenton, N.J.: Printed at the True American office, 1868. 13p. NJ 906a

Fourteenth Amendment.

———————

List of officers and members of the ninety-second Legislature of New Jersey, with their residences in Trenton, and post office address, and the joint and standing committees of both houses. Convened January 14, 1868. [Trenton, N.J., 1868] Broadside. 21 x 15¼ in. NJFLHI

NEW JERSEY. LEGISLATURE. GENERAL ASSEMBLY.

Diagram showing the location of the members composing the ninety-second General Assembly of the state of New Jersey, and the counties which they represent. 1868. [Trenton, N.J., 1868] Broadside. 14 x 17 in. NJFLHI 908

"POLITICAL RELIGION." *The Old guard.* v.6, 1868. p.855. 909

Four stanzas of poetry in Negro dialect, introduced by the editor (C. Chauncey Burr): "A Methodist clergyman . . . sends us the following verses, which he says a brother clergyman [ostensibly Negro] in New Jersey not long since sung in a religious meeting, to the great edification of the white brothers and sisters . . ."
Unflattering image of the Negro character, fitted to Burr's stand against Reconstruction.

RUSLING, JAMES FOWLER, 1834-1918.

Address of General James F. Rusling, before the district convention at Toms River, August 27, 1868. [n.p., 1868] 7p. NJR 910

Caption title.
Rusling, a Trenton lawyer and wartime officer, here accepts the Second District Union Republican nomination for Congress.
Included also are addresses by William A. Newell (late unsuccessful congressional candidate) and Mahlon Hutchinson.

SITGREAVES, CHARLES, 1803-1878.

The state of the Union viewed from a Christian stand-point. Speech of Hon. Charles Sitgreaves, of New Jersey, in the House of Representatives, January 25, 1868. [Washington, D.C.: Printed at the Congressional Globe office, 1868] 8p. DLC NJR 911

Caption title.
Text in two columns.

UNION REPUBLICAN PARTY. NEW JERSEY.

Address of the Union Republican State Executive Committee of New Jersey. [Trenton, N.J.? 1868] 8p. NJR 912

Signed (p.8): "Charles P. Smith [and eleven others] . . . Union Republican State Ex. Com. Trenton, Aug. 10, 1868."

WHITE SOLDIERS' AND SAILORS' UNION.

White boys in blue! Attention! Phillipsburg, New Jersey: Sigman & Werkheiser, printers, "Democrat" office [1868] Broadside. 20¾ x 13 in. NJR 913

A bloody-shirt appeal for Seymour and Blair.

Signed: By Order of the White Soldiers' and Sailors' Union. Gen. C. A. Heckman, Chairman. Capt. Chas. Sitgreaves, Secretary. Capt. Samuel Mutchler, Serg't. William Hoff, Ass't Secretaries.

WINFIELD, CHARLES HARDENBURG, 1829-1898.

Constitutional amendment. Speech of Hon. C. H. Winfield, in the New Jersey Senate, delivered February 19, 1868, on the resolution to withdraw the assent of New Jersey to the proposed Fourteenth Amendment to the Constitution of the United States. Jersey City: Printed by John H. Lyon, 1868. 31p. NJR 914

Winfield, a Democrat from Hudson County, argues for rescinding the 1866 ratification and offers supporting expressions of opinion by Reverdy Johnson, George T. Tichenor, etc. Winfield served one term in the state Senate, 1866-1868.

UNIT VETERANS' ASSOCIATIONS

1ST N.J. BRIGADE

BALDWIN, SAMUEL H. 1839?-1893.

The Society of Kearny's First New Jersey Brigade. Fifth annual reunion held at Kearny's homestead Sept. 14, 1886. Oration, The First New Jersey Brigade, by Samuel H. Baldwin, private, Co. K, 2d Regt. Newark: The Holbrook Printing Co., 1887. 19p. NJ NJHI NJN 915

Same text (except for added introductory paragraph) published previously in the Society's 5th *Report of Proceedings* (see no. 917).

[MCALLISTER, ROBERT] 1813-1891.

[Address prepared for delivery at the second annual reunion of the Society of Kearny's First New Jersey Brigade. n.p., 1883?] 5p. NJR 916

Untitled. Text begins: "Mr. President and Comrades."

Includes reminiscences of the Brigade's wartime experiences.

Copy in NJR (from Robert McAllister papers) has manuscript note in McAllister's hand at top of p.[1]: "Was not delivered. But may at some meeting of the next reunion of the old 1st New Jersey Brigade. Our meeting on the 9th was the 2d."

SOCIETY OF KEARNY'S FIRST NEW JERSEY BRIGADE.

Minutes of the . . . annual reunion . . . DLC (5th, 1886) DNW (5th-6th, 11th-14th, 16th; 1886-87, 1892-94, 1896-97) NJ (5th-6th, 1886-87) NJHI (5th, 1886) NJN (22nd, 28th; 1903, 1909) NJR (12th, 1893) NHI (5th, 17th; 1886, 1898) 917

A metal box in the base of the Kearny monument, Military Park, Newark, contains the best (and totally inaccessible) run: 11th-14th, 16th-32nd; 1892-1894, 1896-1913).

Title varies: 5th, *Report of proceedings;* 6th, 11th not known; 12th-14th, *Proceedings of the . . . annual meeting;* 16th-32nd, *Minutes . . .*

5th (1886) includes brief accounts of 1st-4th meetings, 1882-1885; also (p.12-24) "Oration. By Samuel H. Baldwin. Co. K, 2d Reg't."

11th (1892) covers also 8th-10th meetings, 1889-1891.

List of members since 1885 included in 12th report (and others?).

30th and 31st (1911/12) combined in one publication.

No meeting held in 1895.

War Dept. bibliography lists also 15th (1897). Cf. 10th, same year.

2ND N.J. BRIGADE

KING, HORATIO COLLINS, 1837-1918.

. . . The phantom column. Poem by Horatio C. King, brevet col. U.S. vols. Read at the reunion of the Second New Jersey Brigade at Elizabeth, N.J., Sept. 26, 1889. [New York? 1889] cover-title, 7p. DLC NHI OCLWHI 918

At head of title: Compliments of Horatio C. King, no. 38 Park row, N.Y.

No specific allusions to the 2nd Brigade.

Printed also (p.[19]-26) in his *The Army of the Potomac: Sketch. The Phantom Column: Poem* [n.p., 1898?]; 26p., ports. Copies in DLC, NJN, NHI.

SECOND NEW JERSEY BRIGADE SOCIETY.

Program and menu. [n.p., 1911?] cover-title, [4]p. 919

Twenty-fourth reunion, 1911, at Trenton.

Not seen. Description from U.S. War Dept. *Bibliography of State Participation in the Civil War* (3d ed., 1913), p.458.

———————

. . . Report of the . . . annual reunion . . . CSMH (1st-3rd, 1888-90) DLC (2nd, 9th; 1889, 1896) DNW (1st-11th, 13th, 16th-17th; 1888-98, 1900, 1903-04) NJ (1st-8th, 1888-95) NJR (4th, 1891; also incompl. copies: 1st, 3rd-6th, 8th) NHI (1st-3rd, 1888-90) 920

Contents of 4th report (and others?) include addresses with war reminiscences.

13th (1900) includes 12th meeting, 1899.

16th (1903) includes 14th-15th meetings, 1901-1902.

———————

. . . The third annual reunion of the Second New Jersey Brigade Society (5th, 6th, 7th, 8th and 11th N.J., 2d and 120th N.Y., and other regiments serving with that brigade) will be held at Newark, N.J., Wednesday, June 18th, 1890 . . . Trenton, N.J., 1890. Broadside. 10 x 8 in. NJR 920a

At head of title: Second New Jersey Brigade Society. Trenton, N.J., May 24th, 1890.

Signed: Gen. Robt. McAllister, President. U. B. Titus, Secretary.

1ST N.J. CAVALRY. COMPANY A

RE-UNION OF COMPANY A, First New Jersey Cavalry. [Doylestown: Press of Doylestown Democrat, 1886] Broadside. 15½ x 11¼ in. CSMH 921

Imprint details taken from J. P. Nicholson *Catalogue*, p.221.

Includes "Address of General [William Watts Hart] Davis."

7TH N.J. INFANTRY

SEVENTH REGIMENT VETERAN ASSOCIATION OF NEW JERSEY.

By-laws of the Seventh Regiment Veteran Asso'n, of New Jersey. Newark, N.J.: Wm. H. Holloway, printer, 1896. 16p. NHI 922

"Roster": p.10-16.

8TH N.J. INFANTRY

VETERAN ASSOCIATION, 8TH REGIMENT NEW JERSEY VOLUNTEERS.

14th annual reunion and banquet, Veteran Association, 8th Regiment N.J. Volunteers, "Hooker's Old Guard," Tuesday evening, Nov. 18, '90, at L. Achtel Stetter's, 842 Broad Street, Newark, N.J. [Newark, N.J.: W. H. Shurts, printer, 1890] 4p. 4¼ x 3¼ in. NJR 923

Menu and program.

9TH N.J. INFANTRY

HIGHTSTOWN GAZETTE, *Hightstown, N.J.*

The Gazette souvenir, fifth reunion of the Ninth Regt. New Jersey Veteran Vols., held at Hightstown, N.J., September 16th, 1890 . . . [Hightstown, N.J.] The Hightstown Gazette [1890] cover-title, 2p.l., 3-14p. incl. port. NJR

Proceedings of the reunion events and texts of addresses by local persons and by Surgeon F[idelio] B. Gillette (with some wartime reminiscences).

"This Souvenir is composed of reprints from the report of the exercises in the Hightstown Gazette."

NINTH NEW JERSEY VETERAN VOLUNTEERS' ASSOCIATION.

. . . Reunion . . . 925

1st, 1887. *Twenty-fifth anniversary of the battle of Roanoke Island. First annual reunion of the 9th New Jersey Veteran Volunteers at the Veteran Zouaves' armory, Elizabeth, N.J. . . . Feb. 8, 1887.* Elizabeth, N.J.: Cook & Hall, book and job printers, 1887. 27p. illus. (ports.) Cover-title: "First annual reunion . . ." Contains minutes, constitution, and by-laws of the Association; proceedings of reunion events; addresses of Gen. Heckman, Charles Scranton, James Stewart, Jr., and J. Madison Drake; biographical sketches, with portraits, of Heckman, Stewart, Abram Zabriskie, and Benjamin W. Hopper; list of members. CSMH DLC NJ NJJ NJP NJR NHI PPL

2nd, 1887. *Twenty-sixth anniversary of the muster-in of the regiment. Second reunion of the Ninth N.J. Veteran Volunteers at the rooms of Aaron Wilkes Post, no. 23, G.A.R., Trenton, N.J. . . . September 13, 1887.* Elizabeth, N.J.: Cook & Hall, book and job printers, 1887. 20p. illus. (ports.) Includes biographies and portraits of Lt. Col. William B. Curlis and Capt. Morris C. Runyon (i.e., Runyan). DLC NJ NJHI NJP NHI

8th, 1893. Camden, 1893. 9, [2]p. Not seen by the compiler. DNW

12TH N.J. INFANTRY

REUNION SOCIETY OF THE TWELFTH REGIMENT NEW JERSEY VOLUNTEERS.

Proceedings of the first[-sixth] annual reunion of the Society of the Twelfth Regiment New Jersey Volunteers, held at Woodbury, February 22, 1875[-February 23, 1880] [Woodbury, N.J.? 1880?] 56p. CSMH NJ NHI 926

Caption title.

Possibly published in two or more sections—e.g., 4th-6th reunions (1878-1880), p.43-56. Cf. p.55.

13TH N.J. INFANTRY

VETERAN ASSOCIATION OF THE THIRTEENTH REGIMENT, NEW JERSEY VOLUNTEERS.

Report of the monument committee of the Veteran Association of the 13th Regiment, New Jersey Volunteers, 1862-1865, and dedicatory exercises at Gettysburg . . . July 1st, 1887. And the camp-fire on . . . June 30th, with a list of the contributors to the monument fund. New Brunswick, N.J.: Fredonian Publishing Co.'s print, 1887. 63p. CSMH DLC NJ NJHI NJN NJP NJR PPL 927

———————

. . . Reunion . . . 1st-29th, 1886-1914. CSMH (1st-9th) DLC (1st 7th, 13th) DNW (6th, 8th-12th, 14th-20th) NJ (1st-18th) NJHI (1st-16th, 18th, 21st-24th, 26th-27th) NJJ (1st-5th) NJN (1st-12th) NJP (1st, 6th-7th) NJR (1st-19th, 28th-29th) NHI (1st-20th) PPL (1st) 928

Proceedings, including addresses, etc.
Title varies.

13TH N.J. INFANTRY. COMPANY D

"D" SOCIETY.

Some rhymes read at the annual re-union of "D" Society, held at the Continental Hotel, Newark, N.J. . . . January 15, 1907. [n.p., 1907] [4]p. NJR 929

Caption title.
Society organized by veterans of Co. D, 13th N.J. Vols.

14TH N.J. INFANTRY

[REUNION ASSOCIATION OF THE SURVIVORS OF THE FOURTEENTH REGIMENT NEW JERSEY VOLUNTEERS]

. . . Report of the fiftieth anniversary of the muster in of the Fourteenth Regiment N.J. volunteers and the thirty-fourth annual reunion at the home of James B. Vredenburgh, Esq., Freehold, N.J., August 26, 1912. [n.p., 1912] 40p. incl. front. (ports.) illus. (incl. ports.) NJ

At head of title: 1862 1912.

15TH N.J. INFANTRY

FIFTEENTH REGIMENT NEW JERSEY VOLUNTEERS' VETERAN ASSOCIATION.

Fourth annual pilgrimage of the Fifteenth Regiment New Jersey Volunteers' Veteran Association, May 11th to 15th, 1909, Fredericksburg, Washington and Gettysburg. Washington, N.J.: The Washington Star printery [1909] 2p.l., 7-81p. illus., ports. NJ NJHI 931

Cover-title: Back to the old battlefields.
Frank G. Andrews, pilgrimage historian.

———————

15th New Jersey Regiment Volunteer Veteran's Association. Second annual personally conducted pilgrimage to Gettysburg and the Shenandoah Valley, Penna., returning via Washington. Five days, May 21st to 25th, inclusive, 1907. [n.p., 1907?] 12p. fold. map. CSMH NJR (photo) 932

Contents include "Movements of the Fifteenth New Jersey Volunteer Regiment in the Shenandoah Valley campaign" (1864), p.[2]-[3]; itinerary of the 1907 pilgrimage, p.[4]-[8].

———————

Pilgrimage of the Fifteenth Regiment New Jersey Volunteers' Veteran Association to Gettysburg and the Shenandoah Valley, May 21st to 25th, 1907. Elizabeth, N.J.: The Henry Cook Printshop [1907] 61, [1]p. illus. (incl. map, ports.) NJN NJR 932a

———————

Pilgrimage of the Fifteenth Regiment New Jersey Volunteers' Veteran Association to White Oak Church camp ground and battlefields of Fredericksburg, Va., and vicinity, May 22 to 26, 1906. Newark, N.J.: Madison & Co., stationers and printers [1906] 2p.l., 7-62, [1]p. illus. (incl. map, ports.) NJR NHI 933

"J. Frank Lindsley, Historian."

———————

Re-union . . . 934

[1st] Hackettstown, 1880. Dover: "Iron Era" print, 1880. 24p. CSMH NJ NJHI NJP NJR NHI PPL
2nd, Flemington, 1881. Trenton: Wm. S. Sharp, printer, 1881. 20p. CSMH NJ NJHI NJP NHI PPL
3rd, Morristown, 1882. Morristown: "Chronicle" book and job print, 1883. 8p. CSMH NJ NJP NHI

———————

Roster of the officers and men of the 15th Regiment Association, New Jersey Volunteers. Somerville, N.J.: The Somerville Publishing Company steam print, 1896. 37p. DLC NHI

23RD N.J. INFANTRY

RE-UNION SOCIETY OF THE TWENTY-THIRD REGIMENT NEW JERSEY VOLUNTEERS.

History of the Re-union Society of the 23d Regiment N.J. Volunteers, organized December 13, 1888. Philadelphia: Keystone Printing Co., 1890. 111p. front. (port.) plates. DLC NJ NJHI NJR NHI 936

Minutes of meetings, historical addresses and reminiscences by E. Burd Grubb (p.7-23) and Edward K. Donaldson (p.35-46), regimental rolls, constitution and membership list of the Society, etc.

27TH N.J. INFANTRY

RICHMOND, JOHN BROWN, 1829-1911.

Our deceased comrades. Read at the reunion of the Twenty-Seventh Regiment, New Jersey volunteers, at Morristown N.J., October 7, 1896. By John B. Richmond major and surgeon. [n.p., 1896] 8p. CSMH NJJ NJR (photo) NHI 937

"It has been thoughtlessly made by some a subject of reproach that the dead of the 27th were not slain by bullets, and that it was not a 'fighting regiment.' Its history, course, and line of service *were* in some respects peculiar." Some details are given concerning loss of 33 men in a Cumberland River crossing (1863); also biographical sketch of Major Auguste Durest Blanchet (1816-1896) of Madison and Morristown (p.7-8).

29TH N.J. INFANTRY

TWENTY-NINTH REGIMENTAL ASSOCIATION.

Souvenir program, unveiling of the monument in commemoration of the services of the Twenty-Ninth Regiment New Jersey volunteer infantry in the war between the states: 1861-1865. Fairview Cemetery [near Red Bank], Monmouth County, New Jersey, Memorial Day . . . May 30th, 1925 . . . [n.p., 1925] [8]p. NHI 938

Mounted colored illus. on cover; port. inserted.
"The survivors of the 29th Regiment . . . and their addresses . . .": p.[2] of front cover.
Verses on back cover.
The regiment was recruited in Monmouth County and part of Ocean County.

33RD N.J. INFANTRY

THIRTY-THIRD NEW JERSEY VOLUNTEERS ASSOCIATION.

Roster, surviving members, Thirty-Third New Jersey Volunteers. [Morristown, N.J.? 1893] 7p. NJR (photo) 939

Caption title.
Arranged by company, with ranks and addresses.
Dated Morristown, N.J., Sept. 4, 1893. Evidently prepared by the Association's secretary, John C. Smith.

37TH N.J. INFANTRY

[37TH REGIMENT N.J. VOLUNTEERS ASSOCIATION]

. . . Souvenir of the first annual reunion, 37th Regiment New Jersey volunteers, at the home of Gen. E. Burd Grubb. Edgewater Park [near Burlington], New Jersey, September 12th. 1889. [New York: J. Henry Probst, printer, 1889] 26p., 1 leaf. DLC NJR (photo) NHI 940

At head of title: 1864 1889.
Contains list of Association officers, historical details about the regiment, and a verse, "Colonel Grubb's—1864—chickens" (signed: "37th Reg't'l 'Poet'"), eulogizing Grubb's war services.

MISCELLANEOUS VETERANS' ORGANIZATIONS (SELECTED MATERIAL)

AVERELL, WILLIAM WOODS, 1832-1900.

1883. Memorial Day at Hackensack, N.J. Address of Major-General W. W. Averell, delivered in "the Church on the Green," before James B. McPherson Post 52, G.A.R. New York: Hotel Mail Publishing Company [1883] 16p. NN 941

List of officers on back cover.

BENSON, CORNELIUS HENRY.

"Yank" and "Reb," a history of a fraternal visit paid by Lincoln Post, no. 11, G.A.R., of Newark, N.J., to Robt. E. Lee Camp, no. 1, Confederate Veterans, and Phil. Kearney [i.e., Kearny?] Post, no. 10, G.A.R., of Richmond, Va., October 15th, to October 18th, inclusive. By Comrade C. H. Benson . . . Newark, N.J.: M. H. Neuhut, printer, 1884. 124p. DLC NJHI NJJ NJN NIC NN 942

"Comrade C. H. Benson, historian of the expedition."

BRUCE, WILLIAM J. -1894.

Address delivered before the Society of the Officers of the New Jersey Battalion at Yorktown. Upon its second anniversary at Edgewater [near Burlington], on . . . October 20, 1884, by William J. Bruce, historian. [Camden, N.J.: C. S. Magrath, Democrat printing house, 1884] 44p. incl. col. plates. NJ PP 943

"One hundred copies printed."

Contains numerous reminiscent details.

———————

Historical sketch: read before the Society of the Officers of the New Jersey Battalion at Yorktown, upon the occasion of its second annual meeting at Edgewater, on . . . October 20, 1883, by William J. Bruce, historian. [Philadelphia: Times printing house, 1883] 39p. incl. col. plate. NJP PP 943a

"One hundred copies printed."

The New Jersey Battalion of 1881 was a military-type delegation which represented the state, with some distinction, at the Battle of Yorktown (Va.) centennial celebration. A year later, the Battalion's officers formed the present organization, modeled after the hereditary Society of the Cincinnati. Although rooted in a Revolutionary War anniversary, the Society (its members being also Civil War and National Guard officers) in its publications gave some attention to the war of 1861-1865. The four yearly meetings held 1882-1885 (cf. also nos. 146 and 943) were at Edgewater, the home of its president, Col. E. Burd Grubb, near Burlington.

FROM THE ATLANTIC TO THE PACIFIC, by the Veteran Zouaves, of Elizabeth, New Jersey. Bt. Brig. General J. Madison Drake, commanding. July-August, 1886. Elizabeth, N.J.: Cook & Hall, printers, 1886. 66p. illus. (incl. port.) DNW NJ NJJ NJN 944

Account of a trip from Elizabeth to California and return; descriptions (including newspaper excerpts) of the ceremonies and receptions at various points, etc.

"Rebellion record of the Veteran Zouaves": p.55-56. Roster of members, with names of their respective wartime units.

GILE, AUGUSTINE CHARLES, 1845-1939.

An outline of the history of the New Jersey departments, Grand Army of the Republic, Sons of the Union Veterans of the Civil War, Daughters of Union Veterans, National Women's Relief Corps, Ladies of the Grand Army of the Republic, Sons of Veterans Auxiliary. Written by comrade Gile, of Cape May, and published by the city of Cape May . . . in connection with the fifty-eighth state encampment, Department of New Jersey, G.A.R., Cape May, June 24, 25, 26, 1925. [Wildwood, N.J.: Leader Publishing Co., 1925] cover-title, 16p. NJR 945

GOSSON, LOUIS C.

Post-bellum campaigns of the blue and gray. 1881-1882 . . . By Louis C. Gosson, aide-de-camp to the commander-in-chief of the Grand Army of the Republic, past commander of Aaron Wilkes Post, no. 23, Department of New Jersey, G.A.R. Trenton, N.J.: Naar, Day & Naar, printers, 1882. 192p. front. CSMH DLC NJ NJHI NJP NJR NJT PHI PPL 946

Describes a visit to Richmond in 1881 by members of Aaron Wilkes Post, No. 23, G.A.R., a second visit in 1882 to present punch bowls to their hosts of 1881, and a return visit to Trenton later in 1882 by veterans of three Confederate units. Followed by press reports and comments.

See also no. 950.

GRAND ARMY OF THE REPUBLIC. DEPARTMENT OF NEW JERSEY. AARON WILKES POST, NO. 23, TRENTON.

On to Richmond! Post no. 23, G.A.R., Department of New Jersey, and its friends, October 16th, 1881. Bishop W. Mains, publisher. Illustrated by Joseph W. Phillips. Trenton, N.J.: John L. Murphy, book and job printer, 1881. 81p. plates. NJ NJHI NJR NJT 947

Narrative of a visit to Richmond.

GRAND ARMY OF THE REPUBLIC. DEPARTMENT OF NEW JERSEY. PHIL KEARNY POST, NO. 1, NEWARK.

The Kearney statue. [Newark, N.J., 1867] Broadside. 9¾ x 7¾ in. NJHI 948

"At a meeting of Newark Post, G.A.R., held in this city on . . . April 25, 1867, a committee, appointed at a previous meeting, reported the following Address and Resolutions on the subject of erecting a statue of General Phllip [*sic*] Kearney [i.e., Kearny] in the Hall of Statuary in the Capitol at Washington."

Text printed in three columns.

GRAND ARMY OF THE REPUBLIC. DEPARTMENT OF NEW JERSEY. LYON POST, NO. 10, VINELAND.

"Members of Lyon Post, G.A.R., Vineland, N.J." *Vineland historical magazine.* v.10/12,

1925/27, p.78-80, continued serially through v.13/15, 1928/30, p.143-144. 949

Alphabetical roster, with brief service records, some biographical details.

[McCARTHY, CARLTON]

"Ex-Confederates in New Jersey." *Southern Historical Society papers*. v.10, 1882. p.233-235.

Signed (p.235): C. McC.

An account of a visit to Trenton by more than seventy-five Confederate veterans (chiefly from Richmond) in April 1882, as guests of Aaron Wilkes Post, No. 23, G.A.R.

Reprinted in no. 946.

NEW JERSEY UNION OFFICERS' ASSOCIATION.

Constitution and by-laws of the New Jersey Union Officers' Association . . . Trenton, N.J.: Murphy & Bechtel, book and job printers, 1875. 16p. CSMH MB NJR PPLL 951

"Roll of members": p.[9]-16. With name of unit and place of residence.

PARKER, CORTLANDT, 1818-1907.

Address before the Society of the Army of the Potomac, delivered at their re-union in Orange, N.J., June 12th, 1889. By Cortlandt Parker. [n.p., 1889] 31p. CSMH NJR 952

WORLOCK, WILBUR WILLISTON.

Poetic war record of Drake's Veteran Zouaves, of Elizabeth, New Jersey. By Wilbur Williston Worlock. Elizabeth, N.J.: Journal steam printing house, 1885. 17, [1]p. NN 953

Individual war records of the members in verse, varying from a single line each to the more-than-two-pages devoted to J. Madison Drake; also some details concerning the Zouaves, which he organized Jan. 19, 1878, "as an independent military command."

"The within Poem was recited by the Author at a reception tendered him by Drake's Veteran Zouaves at their Armory in Elizabeth, N.J., on . . . April 28, 1885, on which occasion the command appeared in their new and gorgeous uniforms for the first time."

Dated Brooklyn, N.Y., April, 1885.

VETERANS' WELFARE (SELECTED MATERIAL)

BARBER, JAMES.

The nation's defenders. The Dayton National Soldiers' Home. How the disabled are cared for. By James Barber. Eighth New Jersey Regiment. Dayton, Ohio: United Brethren Publishing House, 1872. 42p. DLC 954

———————

The nation's defenders. The New Jersey and the national homes for disabled volunteer soldiers. How they are cared for. (Second edition, enlarged.) By James Barber, Eighth New Jersey Regiment. Newark, N.J.: Published by Martin R. Dennis, 1874. 82p. CSMH NJ NJHI NJN NJR NHI 954a

"The New Jersey Home for Disabled Soldiers" (Newark): p.6-23. History and description.

NEW JERSEY. AGENCY FOR THE COLLECTION OF MILITARY CLAIMS.

Annual report of the agent [E. L. Campbell] for collection of military claims of the state of New Jersey, for the year 1868. Trenton, N.J.: Printed at the True American office, 1869. 5p. NJ NJHI NJR 955

The office was established chiefly for the "collection of additional bounty granted by act of Congress, approved July 28, 1866," and for settlement of other similar claims on the national government by New Jersey soldiers and their families.

No more published.

NEW JERSEY. COMMISSIONERS OF THE NEW JERSEY HOME FOR DISABLED SOLDIERS.

Report of the Commissioners of the New Jersey Home for Disabled Soldiers, to his excellency Joel Parker. Trenton, N.J.: Printed at the "State Gazette" office, 1866. 4p. DLC NHI

Signed (p.4): Marcus L. Ward, Daniel Haines, William A. Newell, Charles S. Olden, Edwin A. Stevens, Rynear H. Veghte, commissioners. December 30, 1865.

The commissioners, appointed under an act of March 23, 1865, "to authorize the establishment of the New Jersey Home for Disabled Soldiers," recommend a site, and urge passage of a law to implement the project.

The Home, located at Newark, was removed to Kearny in the late 1880's. Its history can be traced in the annual reports published 1866-1931.

NEW JERSEY. COMMITTEE APPOINTED TO INQUIRE INTO THE CONDITION AND MANAGEMENT OF THE SOLDIERS' CHILDREN'S HOME.

Report of the Committee appointed by his excellency Gov. Parker, to inquire into the condition and management of the Soldiers' Childrens' Home of New Jersey. Freehold, N.J.: Printed at the "Monmouth Democrat" office, 1872. 26p. NJR NJT 957

The committee, appointed Aug. 30, 1872, in response to charges of abuse, neglect, and general mismanagement, was composed of Charles E. Elmer, Gen. Gershom Mott, and Charles D. Deshler.

The Home, originally planned for Jersey City, was removed to Trenton in the year of its establishment, 1865. It closed March 7, 1876. For details, see annual reports, published regularly, 1865-1876; also in volumes of the *Legislative Documents*.

NEW JERSEY. HOME FOR DISABLED SOLDIERS, SAILORS OR MARINES AND THEIR WIVES, VINELAND.

"Graveyard inscriptions from the old soldier's home, Vineland, N.J. Taken September 10, 1928." *Vineland historical magazine.* v.13/15, 1928/30. p.166-168, 187-190. 958

The home was established by an act of 1898.

NEW JERSEY. LEGISLATURE. JOINT COMMITTEE ON SOLDIERS' CHILDREN'S HOME.

Report of the Joint Committee on Soldiers' Children's Home. March 20, 1876. Trenton, N.J.: John L. Murphy, State Gazette printing house, 1876. 7p. NJ 959

NEW JERSEY. SOLDIERS' CHILDREN'S HOME.

Charter, constitution and by-laws of the Soldiers Children's Home, of New Jersey. Jersey City: Printed by John H. Lyon, 1865. 12p. NJR 960

First expected to be at Jersey City, the home was very soon located at Trenton.

————————

Constitution and by-laws of the Soldiers' Children's Home of New Jersey . . . Trenton, N.J.: Murphy and Bechtel, printers, 1866. 14, [1]p. NJ NJHI NJT 961

MONUMENTS (BATTLEFIELD AND LOCAL)

ANDERSONVILLE

NEW JERSEY. ANDERSONVILLE MONUMENT COMMISSION.

Report of the New Jersey Andersonville Monument Commissioners . . . 1899. Somerville, N.J.: The Unionist-Gazette Association, state printers, 1899. 18p. front., plates. CSMH DNW NJ NJR (photo) 962

"List of New Jersey troops buried in Andersonville, Ga., National Cemetery, so far reported to the Quartermaster General's office, U.S.A.": p.13-18. With rank, unit, death date, and grave number.

Signed (p.12): C. F. Hopkins, R. A. Clark, Commissioners.

ANTIETAM

NEW JERSEY. ANTIETAM BATTLEFIELD MONUMENT COMMISSION.

Addresses delivered on the occasion of the dedication of the New Jersey monument on the battlefield of Antietam, September 17th, 1903, by James O. Smith, chairman of the Commission, Governor Franklin Murphy, President Theodore Roosevelt. [Newark, N.J.: M. Plum, 1903] 31p. NJ NJHI NJR 963

————————

. . . Report of the New Jersey Battle Monument Commissioners. 1903. [Trenton, N.J., 1904] 14p. NJ 964

At head of title: Document no. 54.

Signed (p.14): James O. Smith, Joseph E. Crowell, John J. Toffey, Commissioners.

Dated Jan. 9, 1904.

The commission was authorized, under legislation of 1902-1903, to provide for erection of a monument commemorating the participation of New Jersey units in the battle of Antietam.

Includes copies of the inscriptions for various New Jersey units, an account of the dedication ceremony on Sept. 17, 1903, etc.

BEVERLY, N.J.

BEVERLY WEEKLY VISITOR, *Beverly, N.J.*

Unveiling of the soldiers' monument, Beverly, N.J. [Beverly, N.J.: Beverly Weekly Visitor, 1875] Broadside. 15 x 10½ in. illus. 965

"From the Beverly Weekly Visitor." Evidently reprint of a newspaper article.

No copy seen. Description based on 1894 reprint.

———————

[*Same: reprint*] [Beverly, N.J.? 1894] NJR

At head of title: Fac-simile of the original sheet, issued at the unveiling of the Monument, June 28, 1875.

Copy in NJR has pencil notation at end: "Republished by Mrs. Scattergood May 23, 1894."

[NEW JERSEY. COMMITTEE FOR THE ERECTION OF A SOLDIERS' MONUMENT IN THE BEVERLY NATIONAL CEMETERY]

An appeal in behalf of the soldiers' state monument, at Beverly, N.J. [n.p., 1873] 3p. NJR (photo) PHI 966a

Caption title.

Signed (p.3): John Jameson, Chairman. E. P. Townsend, M.D., Secretary. Beverly, N.J., May 1, 1873.

The Committee solicits private contributions to supplement the state appropriation of $10,000.

CHICKAMAUGA

NEW JERSEY. CHICKAMAUGA AND CHATTANOOGA PARK COMMISSION.

Report of the New Jersey Chickamauga and Chattanooga Park Commissioners, to his excellency, Hon. John W. Griggs, governor . . . Somerville, N.J.: The Unionist Gazette print, 1897. 32p. DNW NJ PP 967

Includes texts of dedication addresses.

The commissioners were John J. Toffey and Francis Child.

ELIZABETH, N.J.

FOWLER, CHARLES NEWELL, 1852-1932.

Memorial address by Hon. Charles N. Fowler at the laying of the corner stone of the soldiers' and sailors' monument, Elizabeth, New Jersey . . . May thirtieth, 1906. [Elizabeth, N.J.? 1906] 15p. DLC NJR (photo) 968

FLEMINGTON, N.J.

SUNDERLIN, J. C.

"The soldier's monument at Flemington, New Jersey." *The Jerseyman.* v.2, 1893. p.[17]-19. plate. 969

GETTYSBURG

NEW JERSEY. COMMISSIONERS TO CARE FOR GETTYSBURG BATTLE MONUMENTS.

. . . Report of Commissioners to Care for Gettysburg Battle Monuments. 1892. Trenton, N.J.: Naar, Day & Naar, printers, 1893. 19p. front., plates. CSMH DNW NJ NJHI NJN NJP NJR NN 970

Commissioners appointed under an act of 1889.

Appears also with half-title only: Document no. 22. Report of the Gettysburg Battle-field Commission of New Jersey. 1892. (Copy in NJ.)

[NEW JERSEY. GETTYSBURG BATTLEFIELD COMMISSION]

Programme. Dedication of the New Jersey monuments on the battlefield of Gettysburg . . . June 30, 1888 . . . [Jersey City, N.J.: The Jersey City Printing Company, 1888] [8]p. NJHI

"Inscription on the monuments": p.[3]-[7].

NEW JERSEY. GETTYSBURG BATTLEFIELD COMMISSION.

Report of the Gettysburg Battle-field Commission of New Jersey . . . December 7th, 1886. Trenton, N.J.: The John L. Murphy Publishing Co., printers, 1887. 18p. CSMH DLC DNW NJ NJHI NJN NJP NJR 972

Also found with half-title only, headed "Document no. 35." (Copy in NJ.)

The commission was appointed May 27, 1886, under an act "to provide for the erection of suitable monuments to mark the position of New Jersey regiments upon the battlefield of Gettysburg."

———————

[*Same:* 1887] Report of the Gettysburg Battle-field Commission of New Jersey . . . December 15th, 1887. Trenton, N.J.: The John L. Murphy Co., printers, 1887. 20p. front. DNW NJ NJHI NJP NJR 973

"Dedication of the monument to the Thirteenth New Jersey Volunteers": p.[11]-20. Proceedings and addresses.

Also found with half-title only, headed "Document no. 32." (Copy in NJ.)

———————

[*Same:* 1891] Final report of the Gettysburg Battle-field Commission of New Jersey . . . Trenton, N.J.: Printed by the John L. Murphy Publishing Company, 1891. 165p. front., plates. CSMH DLC DNW NJ NJHI NJR NN 974

"Dedication of the New Jersey monuments . . . June 30th, 1888": p.[45]-94. Report of proceedings and texts of addresses in behalf of the various regiments and batteries, by former members of each.

"Extracts from letters and memoranda of interest from officers and men engaged in battle of Gettysburg": p.[103]-124.

"Table of losses in New Jersey commands . . .": p.[131].

"Official reports of New Jersey commanders, of the battle of Gettysburg": p.[133]-157.

Also found with half-title only, headed "Document no. 21." (Copy in NJ.)

NEW JERSEY. LAWS, STATUTES, ETC.

. . . An act to authorize the governor to detail a suitable portion of the National Guard of this state to act as an escort to the state officers, veteran soldiers and guests, on the occasion of the dedication of the state monuments at Gettysburg . . . Trenton, N.J., 1888. Broadside. 8 x 5 in. NJR 974a

At head of title: State of New Jersey. Office of Adjutant General. Trenton, March 8, 1888. <Circular.>

Signed: William S. Stryker, Adjutant General.

HIGHTSTOWN, N.J.

GREEN, EDWARD T.

Oration delivered before the East Windsor Soldiers' Monument Association, at Hightstown, N.J., July 5th, 1875, by Edward T. Green . . . Trenton, N.J.: Murphy & Bechtel, steam power book and job printers, 1875. 14p. NJR 975

HOBOKEN, N.J.

HOBOKEN, N.J.

Headquarters grand marshal of the soldiers' monument celebration . . . General orders, no. 2. Hoboken, N.J., May 26, 1888. [Hoboken, N.J.? 1888] [5]p. DLC NJR (photo) 976

Caption title.

Gives order of march and other parade directions.

JERSEY CITY, N.J.

JERSEY CITY, N.J. COMMITTEE ON SOLDIERS' AND SAILORS' MONUMENT.

Souvenir programme, issued in connection with the unveiling of the soldiers' and sailors' monument, Memorial Day, May 30, 1899. Containing a brief history of the movement towards the erection of the monument, together with the names and portraits of those who conceived the patriotic idea, and to whom is owing the successful accomplishment of the project. [n.p., 1899] [46]p. illus. (incl. ports.) ports. NJJ

Includes advertising matter.

MONOCACY

NESS, GEORGE T.

"Forgotten New Jersey monument. By George T. Ness, Jr. . . ." *Proceedings of the New Jersey Historical Society*. v.59, 1941. p.257-261. 978

Erected 1907 on the Monocacy battlefield, in memory of the 14th N.J. Vols.

NEW JERSEY. COMMISSIONERS ON FOURTEENTH REGIMENT MONUMENT AT MONOCACY, MD.

Report of the commissioners appointed by Edward C. Stokes, governor of New Jersey, to erect a monument to commemorate the services of the 14th Reg't N.J. volunteers in the Civil War of 1861 to 1865. Services of dedication at Monocacy, Frederick County, Maryland, July 9, 1907. [Asbury Park, N.J.: Pennypacker Press, 1907] 34p. front. (ports.) plates, ports. DLC NHI 979

"History of the regiment": p.13-19. By Maj. John C. Patterson, president of the commission.

Roll of comrades present: p.31-33.

NEW BERNE

NEW JERSEY. COMMISSION FOR ERECTION OF MONUMENT TO NINTH NEW JERSEY VOLUNTEERS AT NEW BERNE, N.C.

. . . Report of State Commission for Erection of Monument to Ninth New Jersey Volunteers at New Berne, North Carolina. Dedication, National Cemetery, New Berne, N.C., May 18, 1905. Published by authority of the Commission. [Philadelphia: International Press, the John C. Winston Co.] 1905. 112p. incl. front., ports. CSMH DLC NJ NJHI NJJ NJN NJP NJR NJT NHI NN PP 980

"General Stewart's address": p.65-74. Historical. James Stewart was president of the Commission, former regimental commander.

"Survivors of the Ninth Regiment": p.108-110. Name, company, place of residence for each.

"List of New Jersey soldiers [i.e., 9th Regt. soldiers] buried in the National Cemetery at New Berne, N.C.": p.110-112. Name, company, and death date of each.

NEW BRUNSWICK, N.J.

MacMahon, Alexander.

Souvenir program. Dedication of the soldiers and sailors monument. New Brunswick, N.J., November 15, 1893. Compiled by Alexander MacMahon. New Brunswick, N.J.: Press of Times Publishing Company [1893] 42, [2]p. illus. NJR 981

Contains an account of the "Soldiers' and Sailors' Monument Association of the County of Middlesex" (p.9-13).
Text interspersed with local advertisements.

[Soldiers' and Sailors' Monument Association of the County of Middlesex, N.J.]

Opera House, New Brunswick, N.J. Production of the beautiful fairy operetta, "Titania;" or, The butterflies' carnival, by two hundred children under the personal direction of Mr. Edwin Osmond, for the benefit of the soldiers' and sailors' monument fund. Wednesday eve'g, May 30, 1888 . . . [New Brunswick, N.J.: Fredonian job print, 1888] 32p. NJR 981a

Includes advertising matter; letterpress on covers.
"The Monument Association": p.25-31. History, etc.; list of officers and trustees.

SALEM CHURCH

New Jersey. Commission to Erect a Monument on Battlefield of Salem Church and to Place Tablet on Battlefield of Spottsylvania, Va.

Report of monument commissioners appointed to erect a monument on battlefield of Salem Church, and to place a tablet on the battlefield of Spottsylvania, Va. Transmitted by the governor to the Legislature, session of 1910. Trenton, N.J.: MacCrellish & Quigley, state printers, 1910. 7p. DLC DNW NN 982

To "commemorate the services of the Fifteenth Regiment, New Jersey Volunteer Infantry, in the battles of Salem Church and Spottsylvania, and other engagements of the Civil War . . ."
The commissioners: John F. Dryden, chairman; J. W. Plume, and others.
Dated Newark, N.J., January 6th, 1910.

———————

[*Same: another edition*] 4p. NN 983

Only copy seen, bound in a pamphlet volume, is without title. Otherwise the text is the same as in the 7-page edition, described immediately preceding, except for transfer of two lines from top of p.6 to bottom of p.5 (i.e., p. 3 and p. 2, respectively, of renumbered 4-page edition).

TRENTON, N.J.

Rusling, James Fowler, 1834-1918.

Mercer County soldiers' and sailors' monument. History, laying of corner stone, dedication, roll of honor, officers and members, etc. By James F. Rusling. Trenton, N.J., 1910. 46p. front. (port.) plates (incl. ports.) CSMH NJP NJR PHI 983a

The monument, dedicated June 19, 1909, was erected at Trenton through public subscription, by the Mercer County Soldiers' and Sailors' Monument Association.

WOODBURY, N.J.

Gloucester County, N.J.

Addresses, delivered at the dedication of the soldiers' monument, erected by the county of Gloucester, to the soldiers who fell in the late rebellion, by Rev. Mr. J. F. Garrison, James Wilson, Esq., Senator F. T. Frelinghuysen, at Woodbury, N.J., May 30th, 1867. Woodbury, N.J.: Printed at the Constitution office, 1867. 16p. DLC 984

Text printed in two columns.

LINCOLN MEMORIAL ADDRESSES

BLACKBURN, WILLIAM MAXWELL, 1828-1898.

The crime against the Presidency. A sermon, delivered . . . April 16, 1865, in the Fourth Presbyterian Church, Trenton, N.J., by the pastor, Rev. William M. Blackburn. Trenton, N.J.: Murphy & Bechtel, printers, 1865. 24p. CSMH DLC IHI MB NJHI NJNBS NJPT NJR NJT OCLWHI PHI PPPRHI 985

BUSH, JAMES SMITH, 1825-1889.

Death of President Lincoln. A sermon, preached in Grace Church, Orange, N.J., Easter, April 16, 1865, by the rector, James S. Bush, M.A. Orange, N.J.: E. Gardner, power-press printer, 1865. 8p. CSMH DLC NN RPB 986

DAVIDSON, JOHN, 1837-1911.

Address on the death of Abraham Lincoln, President of the United States. Delivered before the Lexington Literary Association, New York, April 19, 1865. By John Davidson. New York: John J. Reed, book and job printer, 1865. 16p. CSMH DLC IHI MB NJP NN OCLWHI 987

DEMUND, ISAAC S. 1803-1888.

Lamentation on the death of Abraham Lincoln, President of the United States. By Isaac S. Demund, pastor of the Reformed Dutch Church, Paramus, New-Jersey, May, 1865. New-York: John A. Gray & Green, printers, 1865. 15p. CSMH DLC IHI NJNBS OCLWHI 988

DISCOURSES MEMORIAL OF ABRAHAM Lincoln, sixteenth President of the United States, delivered in Flemington, N.J., by the pastors of the different churches, on . . . April 19th, 1865. Published by the citizens. Lambertville, N.J.: Clark Pierson, printer, "Beacon" office, 1865. 2p.l., [3]-22, 16, 13p. DLC IHI NJNBS NJR OCLWHI 989

The speakers: Thomas Swaim (Baptist), J. L. Janeway (Presbyterian), and J. P. Dailey (Methodist Episcopal). Of these, John Livingston Janeway (1815-1906) had been chaplain of the 30th N.J. Vols., 1862-1863.

GARRISON, JOSEPH FITHIAN, 1823-1892.

The teachings of the crisis. Address delivered in St. Paul's Church, Camden, N.J., on the occasion of the funeral of Abraham Lincoln, April 19, 1865, by Rev. J. F. Garrison, M.D. . . . Camden, N.J.: Printed by S. Chew, at the office of the "West Jersey Press," 1865. 20p. DLC IHI NJHI NJNBS PHI 990

———————

[*Same: "second edition"*] The teachings of the crisis. Address delivered in St. Paul's Church, Camden, N.J., on the occasion of the funeral of Abraham Lincoln, April 19, 1865. By Rev. J. F. Garrison, M.D. Second edition. Camden, N.J.: Printed by S. Chew, at the office of the "West Jersey Press," 1865. 20p. DLC IHI NJR (photo) OCLWHI PHI 991

GORDON, WILLIAM ROBERT, 1811-1897.

The sin of reviling, and its work. A funeral sermon, occasioned by the assassination of President Lincoln, April 14th, 1865. By W. R. Gordon, D.D., pastor of the Ref. Prot. Dutch Church of Schraalenberg, N.J. Preached on May 7, 1865 . . . New-York: John A. Gray & Green, printers, 1865. 24p. DLC IHI MB NJHI NJNBS NJN NJP OCLWHI PHI PPL PPPRHI 992

GRAY, GEORGE ZABRISKIE, 1838-1889.

The proper use of the memory of a good man's life. A sermon preached June 1st., 1865, being the day of national humiliation in commemoration of the death of President Lincoln, in Trinity Church, Bergen Point, N.J., by Rev. George Zabriskie Gray, rector . . . New York: Martin & Fulkerson, stationers and printers [1865] 17p. CSMH NJHI 993

HAMILL, SAMUEL McCLINTOCK, 1812-1889.

President Lincoln, a faithful son. An address delivered before the High School at Lawrenceville, N.J., by Samuel M. Hamill, D.D., June 1st, 1865. Trenton: Murphy & Bechtel, printers, 1865. 11p. CSMH DLC IHI MB NJHI OCLWHI PHI PPL PPPRHI 994

[HODGE, CHARLES] 1797-1878.

"President Lincoln." *Biblical repertory and Princeton review.* v.37, 1865. p.435-458 (July 1865) 995

———————

President Lincoln. From the Princeton review, July 1865. [Philadelphia: P. Walker, 1865] 1p.l., p.435-458. CTY DLC NJHI NJP NJR OCLWHI

HORNBLOWER, WILLIAM HENRY, 1820-1883.

Sermon occasioned by the assassination of President Lincoln. Delivered April 16, 1865. In First Presbyterian Church, of Paterson, N.J. By W. H. Hornblower, pastor. Paterson, N.J.: Printed by Chiswell & Wurts, "Press" office, 1865. 15p. CSMH DLC IHI MB NJHI NJJ NJP NJPT NJR OCLWHI 997

MACDONALD, JAMES MADISON, 1812-1876.

President Lincoln; his figure in history: a discourse delivered in the First Presbyterian Church, Princeton, New Jersey, June 1st, 1865. By James M. Macdonald, D.D. New York: Charles Scribner & Co., 1865. 23p. CSMH DLC IHI MB NJP NJPT NN OCLWHI 998

MESSLER, ABRAHAM, 1800-1882.

Dr. Messler's sermon. In commemoration of the death of President Lincoln. [Somerville, N.J.? 1865] Broadside. 21 x $10\frac{1}{2}$ in. NJHI NJR 999

In three columns.

The sermon, "The Importance of Being Prepared to Die," was delivered April 19, 1865, in the Reformed Church of Raritan, N.J., of which Messler was pastor.

MOORE, WILLIAM LEWIS, 1833-1905.

A discourse on the assassination of Abraham Lincoln, sixteenth President of the United States, April 14th, 1865. Delivered in the Presbyterian Church of New Providence, New Jersey, by Rev. William Lewis Moore, pastor, on . . . April 16th, 1865 . . . New York: French and Wheat, book and job printers [1865] 12p. NJHI 1000

MORRIS, SAMUEL JAMES, 1829-1906.

A sermon on the assassination of Abraham Lincoln, preached in the M. E. Church, Pine Brook, N.J., April 23d, 1865, by Rev. S. J. Morris . . . Newark, N.J.: A. Stephen Holbrook, printer, 1865. 12p. NJR 1001

NEWARK, N.J. CITIZENS.

Obsequies of Abraham Lincoln, in Newark, N.J., April 19, 1865. Oration by Frederick T. Frelinghuysen, Esq. Newark, N.J.: Printed at the Daily Advertiser office, 1865. 23p. CTY DLC IHI MB NJHI NJP NJR NN PHI PPL PPPRHI RPB

"Oration": p.[9]-21.

———————

[*Same: reprint*] [Newark, N.J.: Reprinted by Baker Printing Co., 1910] 23p. NJJ NJN NJR

SPRAGUE, ISAAC NEWTON, 1801-1896.

President Lincoln's death. A discourse delivered in the Presbyterian Church in Caldwell, N.J., on the day of national mourning, June 1st, 1865, by Rev. I. N. Sprague, pastor . . . Newark, N.J.: Printed at the Daily Advertiser office, 1865. 20p. DLC IHI MB NJPT NJR 1004

STEARNS, JONATHAN FRENCH, 1808-1889.

Death of President Lincoln; a sermon delivered in the First Presbyterian Church, Newark, N.J., Sunday morning, April 16, 1865, by the pastor, Jonathan F. Stearns, D.D. Champlain [N.Y.] Privately printed, 1919. 19, [1]p. CSMH CTY DLC NJR OCLWHI 1004a

"This Sermon has been composed from the Original Manuscript in the Collection of the late Charles Woodberry McLellan, and printed in the Month of July, 1919 at the Moorsfield Press in an edition of Fifty Copies . . ."—p.[2].

———————

Rejoice with trembling, fast after the assassination of President Lincoln; a sermon delivered in the First Church of Newark, N.J., Sunday morning June 1st, 1865, by the pastor, Jonathan French Stearns . . . Champlain [N.Y.] Privately printed at the Moorsfield Press, 1933. iv, [1], 7-25p., 1 leaf. CSMH 1004b

"This sermon has been composed from the original manuscript presented by Hon. Seargent Prentiss Stearns to the late Charles Woodberry McLellan, and now deposited in the McLellan Lincoln collection at Brown university."

"Fifty-two copies were printed in the month of May, 1933 . . ."

Preface signed: Hugh McLellan.

Not seen. Entry based on CSMH catalog card.

STEELE, RICHARD HOLLOWAY, 1824-1900.

Victory and mourning. A sermon occasioned by the death of Abraham Lincoln . . . Preached in the First Reformed Dutch Church, New-Brunswick, N.J., June 1st, 1865, by Rev. Richard H. Steele, pastor of the church. New-Brunswick, N.J.: Terhune & Van Anglen's press, 1865. 27p. DLC IHI MB NJHI NJNBS NJP NJR OCLWHI 1005

SYMMES, JOSEPH GASTON, 1826-1894.

"To what purpose is this waste?" Address delivered before the Loyal Leagues of South-Brunswick and Monroe, June 1, 1865, by Rev. Joseph G. Symmes, pastor First Presbyterian Church, Cranbury, N.J. Published by request of the Leagues. New-Brunswick, N.J.: Printed at the Fredonian book and job office, August 1865. 29p. DLC IHI NJHI OCLWHI 1006

THOMPSON, HENRY POST, 1831-1891.

In memoriam. A sermon delivered on . . . April 16, 1865, in the Reformed Prot. Dutch Church of Peapack, N.J. By Rev. Henry P. Thompson. New York: John F. Trow, printer, 1865. 16p. (The pulpit and rostrum. no. 36. June 1865) DLC MB NJ NJHI NJNBS NJR NHI PHI PPPRHI RPB 1007

———————

"In memoriam; a sermon delivered on . . . April 16, 1865, in the Reformed Protestant Dutch Church of Peapack, N.J. By Rev. Henry P. Thompson." *Magazine of history. Extra number* 32, 1914. p.[5]-16. DLC NJN NJP NHI NN

Reprint of no. 1007.

WELLES, THEODORE WYCKOFF, 1839-1923.

Victory turned to mourning. A memorial sermon on the occasion of the assassination of Abraham Lincoln . . . Preached in the Reformed Dutch Church, Bayonne, N.J. . . . April 23, 1865, by Theodore W. Wells [*sic*]. Jersey City: Printed at the Daily Times office, 1865. 23p. DLC IHI NJR (photo) 1009

YARD, ROBERT BOYD, 1828-1875.

The providential significance of the death of Abraham Lincoln: a discourse delivered in the Central M. E. Church, Newark, N.J., on the day of national humiliation, June 1st, 1865. By Rev. Robert B. Yard, pastor of Clinton St. M. E. Church: late chaplain of 1st Regiment N.J. volunteers, 6th Corps . . . Newark, N.J.: H. Harris, publisher and stationer [1865] 23p. CSMH DLC IHI MB NJHI NJN NJP OCLWHI 1010

———————

"The providential significance of the death of Abraham Lincoln: a discourse delivered in the Central M. E. Church, Newark, N.J., on the day of national humiliation, June 1st, 1865. By Rev. Robert B. Yard, pastor of Clinton Street M. E. Church: late chaplain of 1st Regiment N.J. volunteers, 6th Corps . . . Newark, N.J., H. Harris, publisher and stationer . . ." *Magazine of history. Extra number* 73, 1921. p.[7]-30. DLC IHI NJN NJP 1011

Reprint of no. 1010.

POSTWAR MISCELLANY

ADAMS, HENRY WRIGHT, 1818-1881.

The past, present, and future of America. An oration delivered in the First Presbyterian Church, Orange, New Jersey, July 4th, 1865. By Prof. Henry W. Adams, M.A., M.D., of Irvington, N.J. New York: Printed by John F. Trow & Co., 1865. 52p. DLC MB NJHI NHI OCLWHI PHI 1012

Concerned largely with the war and its issues.

AERIAL NAVIGATION COMPANY.

The aereon, or flying-ship, invented by Solomon Andrews . . . New York: John F. Trow & Co., publishers, for the Aerial Navigation Company, 1866. cover-title, 15, [1]p. DLC NJP NJR (photo) 1013

Contains a description of Andrews' invention, a review of his wartime efforts to interest the federal government in its military development. The Company was formed in November 1865 to exploit the commercial possibilities of the invention.

Woodcut on outside of back cover: "The first aereon, 1863."

ALEXANDER, STEPHEN, 1806-1883.

Address delivered on the eighty-ninth anniversary of our national independence, at Princeton, N.J. By Prof. Stephen Alexander, LL.D. Princeton: Printed at the Standard book and job office, 1865. 25, [1]p. NJP NJPT NJR NHI NN

The speaker, member of the College of New Jersey (Princeton) faculty, deals considerably with the war and related matters.

ANDREWS, SOLOMON, 1806-1872.

Aerial navigation and a proposal to form an Aerial Navigation Company. By Solomon Andrews, M.D., the inventor. [New York: John F. Trow, printer] 1865. 32p. CSMH DNW NJR (photo) NN PHI 1015

Cover-title: The art of flying. By Solomon Andrews, the inventor . . .

Dated (p.30): Perth Amboy, N.J., May 10th, 1865.

"The object of the following publication is twofold, viz.: to inaugurate a new mode of transportation by air lines, and to preserve the true history of its origin and development."—p.[3].

"Brief history of the origin of, and experiments which have resulted in aerial navigation": p.[5]-30. Chiefly an account (including copies of correspondence, documents, newspaper articles, etc.) of Andrews' futile efforts, 1862-1865, to interest the federal government in the use of his dirigible ("aerostat") for reconnaisance and other military purposes. After building and testing the ship at his own expense without securing any official acceptance, he turned to the possibility of commercial development. Andrews, a Perth Amboy physician and inventor of some reputation, served for a time during 1862 in the Sanitary Commission.

"Proposal for the formation of an Aerial Navigation Company for commercial purposes": p.[31]-32.

The "brief history" includes (p.17-23) the text of a pamphlet published early in 1864, *The Aereon*, addressed to the members of Congress. (See no. 463a.)

BRIDGETON, N.J.

Proclamation! Mayor's office, city of Bridgeton, April 18, 1865. Whereas, the fearful tragedy enacted at Washington has converted an occasion of rejoicing over the national victories into one of national mourning . . . I, James Hood, mayor of . . . Bridgeton, do hereby request the various religious denominations throughout the city to meet in their respective places of worship on . . . the 19th inst., at 12 o'clock (noon), for humiliation and prayer . . . and I also request that all places of business be closed during the day . . . Bridgeton, N.J.: G. F. Nixon, printer, "Chronicle" office [1865] Broadside. 9 x 12 in. NJR 1016

Lincoln's assassination.

DAVIDSON, JOHN, 1837-1911.

Oration delivered before the Legislature of New Jersey, upon "Our sleeping heroes," February 22d, 1866, by John Davidson, Esq., of Elizabeth, N.J. Trenton, N.J.: Printed at the "State Gazette" office, 1866. 27p. CSMH DLC NJ NJHI NJJ NJP NJR NHI NN PPL PU 1017

———————

Our sleeping heroes, an address by John Davidson, delivered in Elizabeth city, N.J., February 12, 1866. Published by request. Elizabeth, N.J.: Printed at the New Jersey Journal office [1866] 15p. CSMH NHI OCLWHI 1018

Cover-title: Our sleeping heroes, an address by John Davidson, Esq., of Elizabeth. Delivered at Elizabeth, February 12, 1866. Repeated before the Legislature of New Jersey, in the Assembly chamber, Trenton, February 22, 1866 . . .

DOOLITTLE, THEODORE SANDFORD, 1836-1893.

A sermon delivered in the First Reformed Dutch Church, of Schenectady, N.Y., before the congregations of the Presbyterian & First R. D. churches, on the national thanksgiving day . . . December 7, 1865, by Rev. T. Sandford Doolittle, A.M., professor of logic, rhetoric, and mental philosophy, in Rutgers College, New Brunswick, N.J. Schenectady: Young & Graham, printers, 1866. 22p. CSMH DLC MH NJNBS NJR NHI OCLWHI 1019

Many war allusions.

FIELD, RICHARD STOCKTON, 1803-1870.

Address on the life and character of Abraham Lincoln, by the Hon. Richard S. Field. Delivered before the Legislature of New Jersey, February 12, 1866. Trenton, N.J.: Printed at the "State Gazette" office, 1866. 40p. CSMH DLC IHI MB NJ NJHI NJJ NJP NJT NN OCLWHI PHI PPL 1020

FISH, HENRY CLAY, 1820-1877.

God's hand in the rebellion; or, Special providences of the late war. A discourse preached . . . July 2, 1865. By Henry Clay Fish, D.D., pastor of the First Baptist Church, Newark, N.J. New York: Sheldon & Co., 1865. 32p. 1021

Evidently issued separately; however, the only copies seen form part of no. 1043, *War Record of the First Baptist Church, Newark, N.J.* (New York, 1865). Copies in CSMH, MB, NJHI, NJR (photo), NHI, NRAB.

FOSTER, JOHN YOUNG, 1831-1896.

Report of John Y. Foster, Esq., on the war history of New Jersey, for the year 1866. Trenton, N.J.: Printed at the office of the State Gazette, 1867. cover-title, 3p. NJP NJR NHI NN OCLWHI PP 1022

Progress report on the proposed Civil War history of New Jersey which the governor, in April 1866, had commissioned Foster to prepare.

Dated Trenton, December 24, 1866; addressed to Marcus L. Ward, Governor.

Foster's *New Jersey and the Rebellion* was published in 1868 (see no. 2).

JERSEY CITY, N.J.

Proclamation! Glorious news! Lee and his whole army captured! The question of "self government" settled forever. The glorious old Union already restored and peace and prosperity within our grasp. God be praised! Our citizens are requested to illuminate private and public buildings to-night, in honor of the glorious news received this morning. [*Signed*] Orestes Cleveland, mayor. Monday, April 10, '56 [i.e., '65] [Jersey City, N.J., 1865] Broadside. NJJ 1022a

Facsimile reproduction in William H. Richardson, *The "Mahings" of the Lincoln Association of Jersey City* (1919), p.28.

JERSEY CITY, N.J. COMMON COUNCIL. COMMITTEE ON ENLISTMENTS.

Report of the Committee on Enlistments, made February 3, 1866. Printed by order of Common Council. Jersey City: Printed by John H. Lyon, 1866. 24p. NJJ NJP NHI 1023

A "full and complete exhibit of all the transactions of the Committee, and of the Mayor [Orestes Cleveland]" in response to "statements industriously circulated during the past ten months, of great frauds in the operations of the Committee."

The Committee had been appointed "to procure a sufficient number of recruits, volunteers and substitutes to fill the quota assigned to Jersey City under the call of . . . December 19th, 1864."

[KILPATRICK, HUGH JUDSON] 1836-1881.

The Irish soldier in the War of the Rebellion. [Deckertown, N.J.: Independent steam print, 1880?] 1p.l., 11p. CSMH NJR (photo) NN 1024

Engraving of the author on cover.

"Gen. Kilpatrick's Great Lecture as delivered six years ago [1874] in Boston Theatre, Boston, Mass., for the benefit of the Catholic Orphan Children of that city, and repeated in New York City for the benefit of the Sisters of Mercy, at Cooper Institute, and repeated hundreds of times in all the large cities. Reported by the *Boston Pilot* and New York *Irish World*."

Includes personal reminiscences.

KIRKLAND, CHARLES PINCKNEY, 1830-1904.

A letter to Peter Cooper, on "The treatment to be extended to the rebels individually," and "The mode of restoring the rebel states to the Union." With an appendix containing a reprint of a review of Judge Curtis' paper on the Emancipation Proclamation, with a letter from President Lincoln. By Charles P. Kirkland. New York: Anson D. F. Randolph, 1865. 46, [3], [3]-20p. CSMH DLC IHI NJP NJR NN PP

Dated New York, June 14, 1865.

Jay Monaghan, *Lincoln Bibliography* (1943), notes other editions.

LAWSON, ALBERT GALLATIN, 1842-1929.

An address to the pupils of the Eagleswood Military Academy, during their encampment in Eagleswood Park, June, 1865, by Rev. A. G. Lawson. Eagleswood, Perth Amboy, New Jersey, June, 1865. New York: Baptist & Taylor, book and job printers, 1865. 16p. NJR NN NRAB

"The encampment at Eagleswood": p.[15]-16. Signed: H. J. C. (Probably Horace J. Canfield, academic superintendent and teacher at Eagleswood.)

Various reflections on the war and victory. The address deals with "lessons of the hour" (i.e., at war's end), its purpose to strengthen patriotism and increase respect for education.

LECTURE IN AID OF THE DESTITUTE OF the South. Hon. James W. Wall, will deliver a lecture at the court house, Hudson City, on . . . May 7, 1867 . . . Subject: "Woman's true mission," . . . [n.p., 1867] Broadside. 9¼ x 6 in. NJR 1027

Signed: Committee, G. D. Van Reipen, Wm. E. Benjamin [and others].

MATLOCK, ROBERT KENNEDY, 1804-1877.

The address of welcome from Gloucester County, to her veteran soldiers, at Mullica Hill, New Jersey, September 14th, 1865, by R. K. Matlock, appointee . . . Printed for the soldiers.

Woodbury, N.J.: Constitution office, 1865. 15p. NJHI NHI 1028

NEW JERSEY. ADJUTANT-GENERAL'S OFFICE.

. . . Circular. [Trenton, N.J., 1882] 8p. MB NJR (photo) 1028a

Caption title.

At head of title: State of New Jersey, Office of Adjutant General. Trenton, May 1st, 1882.

"The honorable discharges of the following named soldiers and sailors of the late war are filed in this office, and will be returned to their owners on application." The several hundred names are listed alphabetically, each with identification of former rank and unit, in some cases regiments of other states than New Jersey.

———

[Communication to the New Jersey Senate, Feb. 28, 1888 (in response to its resolution of Feb. 22), providing information and statistics on the number of New Jersey service men and dependents entitled to state pay under the act of May 11, 1861, and supplement of March 31, 1865, as provided by Senate bill 156, pending] [Trenton? 1888] 1029

No copy seen. Text appears in Senate *Journal,* 1888, p.401-404. "On motion of Mr. Pfeiffer, two hundred copies of the same were ordered to be printed."

———

Report of Adjutant General in reference to the number of citizens of New Jersey serving in regiments of other states during the Civil War of 1861-65. To the Senate of New Jersey. Trenton, N.J.: John L. Murphy, book and job printer, 1880. [3]p. DLC MB NJ NJHI 1030

A brief listing of Pennsylvania and New York units recruited in New Jersey.

NEW JERSEY. BAR.

Proceedings at the dinner given by the bar of New Jersey, to Thomas H. Dudley, Esq., Nov. 25, 1868. Newark: Printed at the Daily Advertiser office, 1868. 18p. NJ 1031

Includes an extended address by Dudley.

———

Trenton, N.J., November 11th, 1868. Dear sir: Thomas H. Dudley, Esq., our consul at Liverpool, England, has recently returned to his home in this state, on temporary leave of absence. During the late Civil War . . . Mr. Dudley rendered us the most signal service by the extraordinary efforts which he made in England and in Europe to prevent the violation of our blockade, and the fitting out of piratical cruisers designed to prey upon American commerce [etc.] . . . It is proposed to invite him to a public dinner to be given at the Trenton House, Trenton, on . . . Nov. 25th inst. . . . [Trenton, N.J., 1868] Broadside. 9¾ x 8¾ in. NJHI 1032

A solicitation of subscriptions ($10), signed by A. O. Zabriskie and nine others. "Committee of Arrangements" listed.

NEW JERSEY. COMMISSIONERS ON THE PLAN OF THE STEVENS BATTERY.

Report of the Commissioners on the Plan of the Stevens Battery, to the Legislature of New Jersey, with a report of the engineer in charge. Trenton, N.J.: Printed at the True American office, 1870. 6p. NN 1033

NEW JERSEY. COMMISSIONERS ON THE SOLDIERS' NATIONAL CEMETERY AT GETTYSBURG.

Report of the commissioners for New Jersey on the soldiers' national cemetery at Gettysburg, Pennsylvania. Trenton, N.J.: Printed at the True American office, 1869. 4p. NJHI 1034

NEW JERSEY. GOVERNOR, 1863-1866 (PARKER)

A proclamation by the governor of New Jersey. [Trenton, 1865] Broadside. 9¾ x 7¾ in. NJR NHI 1035

Appointing a day of thanksgiving and prayer (Dec. 7). Primarily relates to the war.

Dated Nov. 13, 1865.

NEW JERSEY. GOVERNOR, 1866-1869 (WARD)

. . . Proclamation by the governor. For a day of public thanksgiving and praise. [Trenton, 1866] Broadside. 10 x 8 in. NJP 1036

At head of title: State of New Jersey.

Comments deal in part with peace and reconstruction.

Dated Nov. 5, 1866; signed in holograph by Gov. Marcus L. Ward and his secretary.

NEW JERSEY. GOVERNOR, 1872-1875 (PARKER)

Message of the governor relative to the Stockton and Kearney [i.e., Kearny] statues, to the

Legislature, session of 1872. [n.p., 1872] 5p. DLC NJP NN 1037

Dated Trenton, February 21, 1872.
Proposed statues of Richard Stockton (signer of the Declaration of Independence) and General Philip Kearny for a National Statuary Hall in Washington, D.C.

NEW JERSEY. LAWS, STATUTES, ETC.

Militia law of the state of New Jersey. Trenton, N.J., 1866. 42p. DLC NJHI NJR NHI NN 1038

With statement of promulgation from the Adjutant-General's office (General Orders no. 3, Trenton, December 31, 1865): p.[3]. Compiled under an act of April 6, 1865.

NEW JERSEY. LEGISLATURE. GENERAL ASSEMBLY.

. . . An act to equalize the payment of bounties in the township of Alexandria, in the county of Hunterdon. [Trenton, N.J., 1870] 2p. 14 x 7¾ in. NJR 1039

Caption title.
At head of title: Assembly—no. 281. State of New Jersey.

NEW JERSEY. LEGISLATURE. GENERAL ASSEMBLY. COMMITTEE TO PROCURE A PORTRAIT OF ABRAHAM LINCOLN.

Addresses delivered at the presentation of the portrait of Abraham Lincoln, by the Committee of the House of Assembly, February 12, 1867. Trenton, N.J.: Printed at the office of the State Gazette, 1867. 33, [1]p. DLC IHI NJ NJR NN

Various reflections on the war.

———————

[*Same: variant*] 36p. IHI NJJ NJP 1041

Identical with no. 1040 except p.[35]-36: Second inaugural address of President Lincoln.

NEW JERSEY RAILROAD AND TRANSPORTATION COMPANY.

New Jersey Railroad & Transportation Co. Special arrangement for the transportation of the remains of the late President Abraham Lincoln, over the New Jersey Railroad, on Monday, April 24, 1865, under instructions from the War Department . . . [n.p., 1865] Broadside. 1041a

Timetable and special instructions, covering the route between New Brunswick and New York.

Signed: F. Wolcott Jackson, Gen'l Sup't. J. W. Woodruff, Ass't Sup't.
Illustrated in John T. Cunningham, *Newark* (1966), p.[164].

NEWARK, N.J. CITIZENS.

Programme of the celebration of the ninety-second anniversary of American independence, at Newark, N.J., July 4th, 1868, together with the address of Hon. Lyman Tremain, of New York. Newark, N.J.: Evening Courier print, 1868. 18p. NJP NJR 1042

The address (p.[6]-18) deals considerably with the Civil War and slavery.

[NEWARK, N.J. FIRST BAPTIST PEDDIE MEMORIAL CHURCH]

War record of the First Baptist Church, Newark, N.J., during the four year's [*sic*] national struggle, from 1861 to 1865. Containing its official declarations, roll of honor, etc. With a discourse by the pastor, Henry Clay Fish, D.D. . . . New York: Sheldon and Company, 1865. 26p., 1 leaf, [31]-38p., 2 leaves, 32p. CSMH MB NJHI NJR (photo) NHI NRAB 1043

Composed partly of official declarations (chiefly in letters to the Baptist association), excerpts from sermons, both strongly supporting the war and the federal administration. A section, "The Pastor Drafted," is made up of newspaper items (some sarcastic) and correspondence relating to the drafting in 1864 of the Rev. Mr. Fish, a vociferous Unionist, for whom the congregation thereupon arranged to procure a substitute. Other sections contain notes and newspaper excerpts concerning further wartime activities of the church.

"The roll of honor of First Baptist Church and congregation . . . containing the names of the gallant one hundred and seventy, who served in the Union Army or Navy in the war of 1861-1865": p.[31]-38.

"A tribute to our gallant one hundred and seventy. By L[ewis] V. F. Randolph": first unnumbered leaf following p.38. Poetry.

Incorporated as the final section is Henry Clay Fish, *God's Hand in the Rebellion*, with its own complete title-page, separate pagination and running head, and composed of two full signatures ([1]-2[8]). Apparently intended to serve also as a separate pamphlet (see entry no. 1021).

The collation given above is from the CSMH copy. Contents of the NRAB copy (per letter of Dr. E. C. Starr, curator, June 3, 1964) are differently arranged: 26p., 1 leaf, 32p., 1 leaf, [31]-38p., 1 leaf (i.e., with *God's Hand in the Rebellion*, preceded by unnumbered half-title ["Discourse"], placed before the "Roll of Honor" with its own unnumbered half-title; the "Tribute" by L.V.F.R. is on the unnumbered final leaf).

The First Baptist Church took its present name in the 1880's.

PARKER, CORTLANDT, 1818-1907.

Our triumph and our new duties. Oration delivered by Cortlandt Parker, Esq., at Bloomfield, N.J., July 4, 1865. Newark, N.J.: A. Stephen Holbrook, printer, 1865. 38p. DLC NJHI NJJ NJP NJR NHI OCLWHI PPL 1044

PLUMLEY, GARDINER SPRING, 1827-1894.

Piety secures the nation's prosperity. A thanksgiving discourse, by Rev. G. S. Plumley. Preached in the First Presbyterian Church, Metuchen, New Jersey, on . . . December 7, 1865 . . . New York: F. Somers, printer, 1866. 24p. DLC NJHI NJP NJR NN PPL PPPRHI 1045

PRINCETON TOWNSHIP, N.J., COMPLAINANT.

. . . William V. Scudder, collector of the township of Princeton, &c. vs. the state—Elias C. Baker, and others, relators. Error to the Supreme Court. Writ ret'ble 2d Tues. Mar. 1867, and duly returned. [n.p., 1867?] 8p. NJ 1046

Caption title.

At head of title: New Jersey Court of Errors and Appeals.

Concerns non-payment of taxes under an assessment authorized for the raising of funds to fill draft quotas.

PUGH, JOHN HOWARD, 1827-1905.

The success and promise of the American union, an oration, delivered before the citizens of Burlington, N.J., on . . . July 4th, 1865. By J. Howard Pugh, M.D. Philadelphia: King & Baird, printers, 1865. 24p. DLC NJP NJR NHI PHI 1047

"The jubilee of freedom. By John Collins": p.23-24. Verse.

REED, VILLEROY DIBBLE, 1815-1901.

The conflict of truth. A sermon preached in the First Presbyterian Church, Camden, N.J., April 30, 1865, by Rev. V. D. Reed, D.D. Camden, N.J.: Printed by S. Chew, at the office of the "West Jersey Press," 1865. 29p. DLC IHI NJHI NJPT NJR OCLWHI PHI 1048

Deals considerably with the war; to a lesser degree with Lincoln's assassination.

RHODES, JACOB.

The nation's loss: a poem on the life and death of the Hon. Abraham Lincoln, late President of the United States, who departed this life, in Washington, D.C., April 15, 1865. By Jacob Rhodes . . . Newark: F. Starbuck, printer, 1866. 18p. CSMH DLC NJR (photo) 1049

"The alleged author was a colored man, a gardener, residing in Newark, and the same poem has been published in broadside with the name of 'Rev. Peter W. Brister' as the author, but without any printer's name, place or date.—Boyd's *Lincoln Bibliography*" (quoted in Frank P. Hill, *Books, Pamphlets and Newspapers Printed at Newark,* 1902, no. 473).

RUCKMAN, ELISHA, 1812- PLAINTIFF.

. . . New Jersey Court of Errors and Appeals. The state—Elisha Ruckman, plaintiff in error, vs. Peter A. Demarest, collector, &c., defendant in error. In error to Supreme Court. Returnable November term, 1865. A. S. Jackson, attorney, &c. Trenton: Hough & Yard, printers [1865?] 69p. tables. NJ 1050

Caption title.

Case involves non-payment of taxes (Harrington Township, Bergen County, N.J.) by Ruckman as a protest against the raising of troops by means of bounty payments. The various depositions and exhibits contain much detail on draft procedures and bounties.

[RUSLING, JAMES FOWLER] 1834-1918.

"National cemeteries." *Harper's new monthly magazine.* v.33, 1866. p.310-322. illus. 1051

No personal allusions.

STEVENS, C. A.

Memorial, testimony, and letters of federal prisoners, on the claim of P. F. Frazee, a loyal citizen of New Jersey, for property destroyed at Columbia, S.C., February 17, 1865, by the forces of Maj. Gen. Sherman. C. A. Stevens, solicitor . . . Washington: McGill & Witherow, printers and stereotypers, 1866. cover-title, 39p. NJP NHI 1052

In 1850, Phineas F. Frazee (of Rahway, N.J.) had set up a carriage factory at Columbia, developing this and other property there to a value of $200,000. Although he remained in Columbia throughout the war, the present depositions, etc., are intended to demonstrate his pro-Union sympathies (also describing the pertinent events and the extent of his loss).

THE STEVENS IRON CLAD BATTERY. New York: D. Van Nostrand, publisher, 1874. 2p.l., 46p. illus., plates (part fold.) diagram. DLC NJHI NJR NHI NN PPLL 1053

Engraved portrait of Edwin A. Stevens on title-page.

"For transmission abroad."

Prospectus for sale of the unfinished vessel lying in dry dock at Hoboken. The will of Edwin A. Stevens, who began the construction, had directed his executors to complete the ship (if the cost not exceed one million dollars) and present it to the state of New Jersey. The legislature passed an act in 1869 accepting the vessel, but the funds proved insufficient, and a subsequent act (March 27, 1874) provided for the battery's sale.

The pamphlet contains a description of the ship, numerous pertinent engineering details, copies of documents, etc.

The "commission to effect sale" consisted of Gov. Joel Parker and Vice-Chancellor Amzi Dodd representing the state, and W. W. Shippen and Rev. Samuel B. Dod, executors.

STRYKER, WILLIAM SCUDDER, 1838-1900.

. . . Dear sir: At the solicitation of a number of officers of New Jersey regiments during the late war, I propose compiling a volume of memoirs of their deceased comrades . . . Trenton, 1869. [4]p. NJR 1054

Dated Trenton, April 22, 1869, and signed: William S. Stryker, Adjutant General of N.J.

A form letter containing a list of New Jersey officers who died in service and requesting data concerning them.

TO RETURNED OFFICERS, SOLDIERS AND sailors in the city of Elizabeth and vicinity. Gentlemen: You are cordially invited to participate in the public celebration on the fourth day of July next in this city, in honor of the Declaration of American Independence, the success of our arms, and the return of peace . . . [Elizabeth, N.J.] New Jersey Journal print [1865] Broadside. 23 x 13½ in. NJHI 1055

Signed by Chauncey Harris and ten other officers.

WARD, MARCUS LAWRENCE, 1812-1884.

Bounties. Speech of Hon. Marcus L. Ward, of New Jersey, in the House of Representatives, June 19, 1874. Washington: Government Printing Office, 1874. 10p. NJR 1056

Concerns a bill, previously introduced by Ward, which provided bounty payments to the families of soldiers who (1) had enlisted for less than a year, and (2) had died in service or from service-connected causes. Particular note is made of the short-term militia organizations that served in the first months of the war.

WIARD, NORMAN, 1825-1896.

About great guns. The pressure of powder and the unequal heating of metals, by Norman Wiard. Washington: Printed by Lemuel Towers, 1867. 12p. illus. DLC 1056a

———————

Facts about ordnance and the frauds and mismanagement of the Ordnance Department. By Norman Wiard. [Washington, D.C.? 1866?] 16p. DLC NN 1057

Caption title.

———————

Memorial of Norman Wiard, asking compensation for alterations in certain iron-clad steam transports. [Washington, D.C.? 1866?] cover-title, 27p. DLC 1057a

———————

Memorial of Norman Wiard, asking reimbursement of expenses incurred [Jan.-Feb. 1865] in delivery of the steamers Augusta and Savannah, at Hilton Head. [n.p., 1866?] cover-title, 21p. DLC MH 1057b

———————

Memorial of Norman Wiard, relating to the arbitrary annulment of a contract with the Secretary of the Navy, for xv-inch guns. [n.p., 1866] cover-title, 52p. illus., plates. DLC NHI

———————

More exposures of the jobbery of the Ordnance Department. Dyer & Rodman . . . [By] Norman Wiard. Washington, D.C.: Powell, O'Brien & Co., printers, 1869. 72p. illus. DLC NHI 1059

Index

Index

BY I. KAY LIONIKIS AND ANTHONY S. NICOLOSI

ALL REFERENCES ARE TO ENTRY NUMBERS

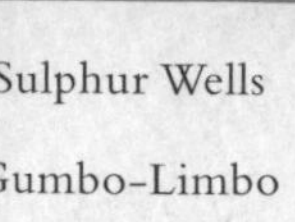

Doc Ford Country

Sulphur Wells
Gumbo-Limbo
Matlacha
Sandy Hook
CAPE CORAL
PINE ISLAND
Bull Sharks
St. James City
Sound
Causeway Blvd.
Woodring's Point
Sanibel Flats
Tarpon Bay
No Más
Doc Ford's Lab
Dinkin's Bay Marina
Sanibel Marina
Periwinkle Way
Bait Box
Sanibel Lighthouse
Sanibel – Captiva Rd.
Nave's
Timbers
Tarpon Bay Rd.
Casa Ybel Rd.
Bailey's General
W. Gulf Dr.
Gray Gables
FLORIDA

FORT MYERS RSW INTERNATIONAL AIRPORT (25 miles) →

Rendering by Meighan Cavanaugh

CHASING MIDNIGHT

ALSO BY RANDY WAYNE WHITE

Sanibel Flats
The Heat Islands
The Man Who Invented Florida
Captiva
North of Havana
The Mangrove Coast
Ten Thousand Islands
Shark River
Twelve Mile Limit
Everglades
Tampa Burn
Dead of Night
Dark Light
Hunter's Moon
Black Widow
Dead Silence
Deep Shadow
Night Vision

NONFICTION

Randy Wayne White's Ultimate Tarpon Book
Batfishing in the Rainforest
The Sharks of Lake Nicaragua
Last Flight Out
An American Traveler
Randy Wayne White's Gulf Coast Cookbook
(with Carlene Fredericka Brennen)
Tarpon Fishing in Mexico and Florida (An Introduction)

FICTION AS RANDY STRIKER

Key West Connection
The Deep Six
Cuban Death-Lift
The Deadlier Sex
Assassin's Shadow
Grand Cayman Slam
Everglades Assault

CHASING MIDNIGHT

Randy Wayne White

G. P. PUTNAM'S SONS NEW YORK

PUTNAM

G. P. PUTNAM'S SONS
Publishers Since 1838
Published by the Penguin Group
Penguin Group (USA) Inc., 375 Hudson Street, New York, New York 10014, USA • Penguin Group (Canada), 90 Eglinton Avenue East, Suite 700, Toronto, Ontario M4P 2Y3, Canada (a division of Pearson Penguin Canada Inc.) • Penguin Books Ltd, 80 Strand, London WC2R 0RL, England • Penguin Ireland, 25 St Stephen's Green, Dublin 2, Ireland (a division of Penguin Books Ltd) • Penguin Group (Australia), 250 Camberwell Road, Camberwell, Victoria 3124, Australia (a division of Pearson Australia Group Pty Ltd) • Penguin Books India Pvt Ltd, 11 Community Centre, Panchsheel Park, New Delhi–110 017, India • Penguin Group (NZ), 67 Apollo Drive, Rosedale, North Shore 0632, New Zealand (a division of Pearson New Zealand Ltd) • Penguin Books (South Africa) (Pty) Ltd, 24 Sturdee Avenue, Rosebank, Johannesburg 2196, South Africa

Penguin Books Ltd, Registered Offices: 80 Strand, London WC2R 0RL, England

Published simultaneously in Canada

Library of Congress Cataloging-in-Publication Data

White, Randy Wayne.
Chasing midnight / Randy Wayne White.
p. cm.
ISBN 978-0-399-15831-5
1. Ford, Doc (Fictitious character)—Fiction. 2. Marine biologists—Fiction. 3. Florida—Fiction. I. Title.
PS3573.H47473C47 2012 2011047133
813'.54—dc23

Printed in the United States of America
1 3 5 7 9 10 8 6 4 2

BOOK DESIGN BY AMANDA DEWEY

This is a work of fiction. Names, characters, places, and incidents either are the product of the author's imagination or are used fictitiously, and any resemblance to actual persons, living or dead, businesses, companies, events, or locales is entirely coincidental.

While the author has made every effort to provide accurate telephone numbers and Internet addresses at the time of publication, neither the publisher nor the author assumes any responsibility for errors, or for changes that occur after publication. Further, the publisher does not have any control over and does not assume any responsibility for author or third-party websites or their content.

There is no room for moral baggage on a small island. Anything bigger than a bikini is better left at home.

—S. M. Tomlinson,
One Fathom Above Sea Level

If religion is opium to the masses, the Internet is a crack, crank, pixel-huffing orgy that deafens the brain, numbs the senses, and scrambles our peer list to include every anonymous loser, twisted deviant and freak, as well as people we normally wouldn't give the time of day.

—S. M. Tomlinson,
Sudden Internet Isolation Response
In an Unprepared Society
(Excerpted from *Zen Me the Pillow You Dream On*)

This book is for two respected travel companions, on the road and off:
Allan W. Eckert and Peter Matthiessen

Sanibel and Captiva Islands are real places, faithfully described, but used fictitiously in this novel. The same is true of certain businesses, marinas, bars and other places frequented by Doc Ford, Tomlinson and pals.

In all other respects, however, this novel is a work of fiction. Names (unless used by permission), characters, places and incidents are either the product of the author's imagination or are used fictitiously. Any resemblance to actual persons, living or dead, or to actual events or locales is unintentional and coincidental.

Contact Mr. White at WWW.DOCFORD.COM

AUTHOR'S NOTE

I learned long ago, whether writing fiction or nonfiction, an author loses credibility if he's caught in a factual error. Because of this, I do extensive research before starting a new Doc Ford novel, and *Chasing Midnight* required more research than most. Before recognizing those who provided assistance, I would first like to remind the reader that all errors, exaggerations and/or misinterpretations of fact, if any, are entirely the fault of the author.

Much thanks goes to the dedicated professionals of Mote Marine Laboratories, most particularly Jim Michaels, for his patient advice and attention regarding sturgeon and caviar. A visit to Mote's Sarasota, Florida, facility is highly recommended, as is the superb Siberian caviar produced and processed there in the most well-thought-out Earth-friendly facility the author has visited.

Without the extensive use and testing of an extraordinary piece of tactical equipment, the TAM-14, a thermal acquisition monocular, this would have been a very different book, indeed. The author owes much thanks to Bob Alexander and Nivisys Industries of Tempe, Arizona. Nivisys is a low-profile company that, consistently, takes an innovative lead in engineering and producing some of the world's finest tactical optics systems, and the author would like to thank all involved for allowing him to use the TAM-14 in a very public way.

Others providing expert advice on equipage were Kevin Parsons, founder of Armament Systems and Procedures (ASP, Inc.), Chuck Bunstock of Golight, Inc., Nebraska, and Dr. John Patterson of Bathys Hawaii Watches.

Sports psychologist Don Carman, once again, contributed unerring insights into human behavior, aberrant and otherwise, and his advice regarding Marion Ford's fitness routine is much appreciated. Dr. Brian Hummel, Dr. Denis Kuehner, of Sanibel Island, and Dr. Timothy S. Sigman provided expert medical advice.

Bill Lee, and his orbiting star, Diana, as always, have guided the author, safely—for the most part—into the strange but fun and enlightened world of our mutual friend, the Rev. Sighurdhr M. Tomlinson. Equal thanks go to Gary and Donna Terwilliger for helping the author to escape, undamaged. Steven Dougherty of New York and California has also provided useful insights into the mind-set of hipsterdom and various modes of übercoolness.

The author's black ops advisers, Hon. Cdr. Tony Johnson, Capt. Galen Hanselman and Capt. Dan O'Shea, were of especial help, as were international intelligence correspondents T. B. Thomas Pattison, Capt. Bobby Dollar, Capt. James Hull of Costa Rica, Jay Blues Sielman and Harlow Montague—wherever they may be.

Others who provided help or insights, information or advice include: Dr. Pearl D. Miller of Tampa, Dr. Dave Melzer, Darryl Pottorf, Mark Pace, Kirsten Martin of VersaClimber, and friend and attorney Steve Carta.

Special thanks goes to Wendy Webb, my life companion, adviser and trusted friend, as well as Stephen Grendon, the author's devoted SOB, Mrs. Iris Tanner, guardian angel, and my partners and pals Mark Marinello, Marty and Brenda Harrity and my surfing buddy, Gus Landl.

Much of this novel was written at corner tables before and after hours at Doc Ford's Rum Bar and Grille on Sanibel Island and San Carlos Island, where staff were tolerant beyond the call of duty. Thanks go to Raynauld Bentley, Dan Howes, Brian Cunningham, Mojito Greg Barker, Liz Harris, Capt. Bryce Randall Harris, Milita Kennedy, Sam Khussan Ismatullaev, Olga Jearrard, Rachel Songalewski of Michigan, Jean Crenshaw, Amanda Gardana Rodriguez, Bette Roberts, Brian Cunningham, Amazing Cindy Porter, Ethan Salley, Fernando Garrido, Greg Barker, Jessica Shell, Jim Rainville, Kevin Filowich, Kimberly McGonnell, Laurie Yakubov, Lisa Reynolds, Michelle Boninsegna, Sarah DeGeorge, Shawn Scott and Dale Hempseed and master chef Chris Zook.

At the Rum Bar on San Carlos Island, Fort Myers Beach, thanks go to Wade Craft, Kandice Salvador, Herberto Ramos, Brian Obrien, lovelies Latoya Trotta, Magen Wooley, Meghan Miller, Meredith Mullins, Nicole Hinchcliffe, Nora Billheimer, Ali Pereira, Andrea Aguayo, Brian Sarfati, Catherine Mawyer, Corey Allen, Crissy McCain, Deon Schoeman, Dusty Rickards, Erin Montgomery, Jacqi Schultz, Justin Dorfman, Keil Fuller, Kerra Pike, Kevin Boyce, Kevin Tully, Kim Aylesworth, Kylie Pryll, Patrick John, Robert Deiss, Sally Couillard, Steve Johnson, Sue Mora and Tiffany Forehand.

At Timber's Sanibel Grille, my pals Matt Asen, Mary Jo, Audrey, Becky, Bart and Bobby were, once again, stalwarts.

Finally, I would like to thank my two sons, Rogan and Lee White, for helping me finish, yet again, another book.

— Randy Wayne White, Casa de Chico's
Sanibel Island, Florida

1

I was beneath fifteen feet of water, at night, observing a dinosaurian fish, when something exploded and knocked out the island's underwater lights.

The fish, a Gulf sturgeon, was armor plated, three feet long, hunkered close to the bottom as it fed. Its close relative, the beluga sturgeon, is the gold standard of caviar lovers, and a sacred cow to the global, billion-dollar caviar trade.

My interest in sturgeon, and the often corrupt caviar industry, was a secondary reason for spending this new moon evening, in June, on one of Florida's exclusive private islands—Vanderbilt Island on the Gulf of Mexico. The retreat is forty acres of palms, sand and Old Florida architecture, north of Vanderbilt Beach, east of Lovers Key and south of Sanibel Island, a small enclave concealed by swamp and shallow water in a remote corner of Estero Bay.

A handful of the caviar trade's elite was on the island for a weekend get-together, hosted by a Russian black market millionaire. Officially, he was rallying interest in a new U.S. import company.

Privately, he claimed to have found a legal way around the international ban on beluga products. It had something to do with altering the Gulf sturgeon's DNA to produce larger eggs like its Caspian Sea cousin.

"Eggs firm and finely skinned so they burst between the teeth with hints of butter, almonds and fresh ocean air—each pearl black as a Caspian midnight," according to literature in my gift bag when I checked in.

Gulf sturgeon were common in Florida until the 1930s, when they were netted almost into nonexistence between Tampa Bay and the Florida Keys. The idea of a genetically altered hybrid was fanciful, considering the legalities involved, but it had merit—on paper, anyway.

But I was dubious. Sufficiently so to make some unofficial inquiries, and then try to finagle invitations for myself and my pal Tomlinson. As I soon discovered, though, the Russian wasn't handing out invitations to just anyone.

"Impossible," a woman with a Russian accent had told me, "unless you are wholesaler. Restaurateur, maybe, but *established* restaurants. And willing to pay fee—in advance—to reserve spot."

The price was so steep it had strengthened my impression that the black marketeer didn't want outsiders at his caviar party. After a bit more research, and after discovering a couple of impressive names on the guest list, I had become doubly determined to go. There had to be a way.

There was. Tomlinson is founder of two thriving gourmet rum bars, and I was an investor. That made us both "established restaurateurs." Sort of. The woman then told me I had to send documentation before she would accept my credit card.

"It worth the money," the woman had added. "First night, guests treated to night of gambling and caviar at famous resort across bay. They have dolphin show and Jet Skis."

Flipper and Jet Skis—I could hardly wait.

She was referring to the Bare Key Regency Resort and Offshore Casino Boat, a particularly noxious tourist trap, four miles by water from Vanderbilt Island. But I had sent the papers, anyway, and finally closed the deal.

I wanted Tomlinson along for more than just his restaurant connections. The man may look like the Scarecrow in a New Age *Wizard of Oz*, but he has rock star qualities that make him a favorite of poor boat bums and yachtsmen alike. To almost everyone, Tomlinson is Everyman, his aggressive edges worn smooth by demons, hallucinogenics and his daily use of cannabis. As an author, he is revered by spiritualist types. As an ordained Zen Buddhist monk, he has a devoted cult following—even though the man is anything but monklike in his appetites and behaviors.

My pal is, frankly, a pain in the ass more than occasionally. But he is also one of the smartest people I know. It was one of the reasons I wanted Tomlinson along. But not the main reason. The Russian host would check my background and be understandably suspicious. The same with three other men I'd found on the guest list. They were the Russian's caviar competitors from Iran and Turkmenia, and also a Chinese mega-millionaire by the name of Lien Hai Bohai.

Their suspicions about me would be well founded. I'm a marine biologist who is sometimes contracted by the same governmental agencies, state and federal, that are mandated to protect endangered species such as the beluga sturgeon. I hoped my association with Tomlinson—an unrepentant hipster who reeked of patchouli oil and enlightenment—would veil my true intentions.

Fact is, after my unofficial inquiries, a government agency had instructed me to attend the party. Which is why I had paid the heavy fee. The agency's interest in the Russian—Viktor Kazlov—and his guests, was classified for reasons that had less to do with caviar than with their business dealings in the Middle East.

Kazlov and his Eastern European associates were my primary reasons for being on the island. Because China is now the world's leading producer of aquaculture products—and the most expert at stealing aquaculture technology—Lien Bohai was of interest, too.

I had grown tired of the formal reception, though, that was still going strong in the island's main lodge. The bar and dining room were tiny, and I'm uncomfortable in crowded spaces. Then Tomlinson had introduced me to one of the most abrasive women I'd ever met, an environmentalist named Winifred Densler. "Eco-elitist" would be a more accurate way to describe her, because it includes iconoclasts from both political wings, right and left.

Densler, it turned out, had crashed the party, along with four male associates. Worse, as I discovered later, Tomlinson had "possibly but unknowingly" helped the trespassers by posting key information about the caviar meeting on their web page after donating money to the group six months earlier.

Something else I noticed while at the reception: Kazlov's bodyguard was watching me a little too closely.

I wanted out. I had things to do. I was particularly curious about what the Russian's luxury yacht looked like from beneath the surface. It was a twenty-some-meter Dragos Voyager, black hull, white upper deck, built in Turkey. One glance at its bright red waterline told me it was a false line, and the craft was carrying something heavy.

So I had given Kazlov's security guy the slip, and left Tomlinson to deal with the poisonous Ms. Densler and her techy-looking associates, all members of a controversial organization, Third Planet Peace Force—3P2, as it was commonly abbreviated.

Alone at last, beneath a starry June sky, I had donned scuba gear and slipped into the water. I wanted to spend some time observing the Gulf sturgeon penned there as an exhibit, and enjoy the solitude of depth and darkness, before getting serious about inspecting Kazlov's yacht.

Not total darkness, of course. The docks were illuminated by rows of underwater lights, which provided both visibility and entertainment. Underwater lights attract baitfish. Baitfish attract bigger fish. Big fish attract the true oceangoing predators. There was no telling what was swimming around out there in the gloom.

The night sea is relentless theater, one small drama after another, alive with sounds. With my scuba exhaust bubbles as a metronome, catfish bawled, distant dolphins pinged, pistol shrimp crackled among pilings where spadefish and sheepshead grazed.

Mostly, though, my attention was fixed on the Gulf sturgeon. At a yard long, and fifty pounds, the animal was probably around ten years old—less than a third of its probable life span. As it moved along the bottom, suction-feeding sandworms and isopods, it reacted to my presence with the guarded indifference of a species that has survived for two hundred million years.

If Batman had a boat, it might resemble the Gothic symmetry that defines the twenty-some species in the family *Acipenseridae*. The Gulf sturgeon I was watching was a tri-edged submarine, shaped like a spear from the Bronze Age. Its armored scutes were suggestive of helmets worn by jousting knights, its lateral lines were effective, timeless shields. Had the Civil War ironclads enjoyed the same protection, their battles might have survived the harbor.

The sturgeon is among the few bony fishes to have flourished through ice ages, meteorite assaults and volcanic upheavals that dinosaurs and a million other long-gone species could not endure. Only in the last hundred years has the animal's genetic virtuosity been tested. Loss of habitat and pollution play roles. But it is the global love of caviar that has put the fish on the endangered species list.

Female sturgeon, of all species, are slow to mature—ten to twenty-five years before they can produce the eggs for which they are caught and killed by poachers and black marketeers. Even then, the timing must be exactly right. The eggs must be harvested *before* the fish ovulates. After ovulation, the shell of the egg—the chorion—is riddled with tiny holes to accept sperm. Salt, and sometimes borax, which are added as preservatives to caviar, convert ovulated eggs into mush. They are uneatable, not marketable. Which is why even farm-raised female sturgeon must be sacrificed, and why there are ever-fewer mature sturgeon swimming wild in our global waters.

This fish, only yards away, was a prime example of a healthy Gulf sturgeon—and why I didn't want to miss this rare opportunity to observe it feeding at night.

So I was enjoying myself.

Until the explosion.

I had been underwater for about twenty minutes when it happened. I heard a percussive thud that jarred the soft tissue of my inner ears, and left me blinking in the sudden darkness. Then I felt a delayed, radiating pressure that caused me to grab for a dock piling as a mild shock wave rolled past, my swim fins fluttering, but not much.

I didn't know, of course, but the explosion also took out every light on the island, along with the island's emergency redundancy systems—backup lighting, generators, computers and the land-based communication systems.

Also unknown to me, a military-grade GSM mobile blocking

device had been simultaneously activated to jam cell phones, wireless Internet and VHF radios.

Suddenly, for the first time since a telephone had been installed, Vanderbilt Island was actually an island.

Instead of suspecting that a hostile group was taking the island hostage—something I should have given serious consideration—my first thought was lightning strike.

It made sense. Only a few minutes before, a rain squall, ion-charged, had strafed the coast, moving westward in darkness toward the Yucatán. I had waited until I thought the danger was past, but summer storms are tricky to predict. The night clouds had still been incandescent, rumbling spires when I had entered the water.

Lightning hit a transformer and the transformer exploded.

That's the way my mind accounted for what had happened. It explained the power outage that, just as abruptly, changed the underwater world I now inhabited.

In the space of those few seconds, the sturgeon I was observing ascended several million years in the hierarchy of fish and primates.

I was demoted proportionally.

On the Darwinian ladder, the fish was now far more advanced than some dumbass, bat-blind marine biologist who happened to be underwater and alone, breathing air from an aluminum tank.

Me, the dumbass biologist.

A moment later, it got worse. My sense of direction was skewed, and I somehow ended up under the docks. How far, I wasn't sure, but I banged into enough pilings to know it had happened.

Calmly, very calmly, I attempted to surface. Fifteen feet is a short distance, unless you are underwater—and unless the valve of your scuba tank snags a cable tethered to the bottom.

It happened.

For a spooky moment, I strained against the cable. It stretched but wouldn't break. Then, instead of dumping my gear and swimming to the surface, I made the stupid decision to try to free myself rather than leave so much expensive equipment behind.

More than one diver has killed himself for the sake of a few hundred dollars.

Steadying myself against a piling, I used my right hand to search for whatever it was I had snagged. Finally, I found it: a jumble of nylon rope. Even through my leather gloves, I could tell. Maybe it was the line from a crab trap that had been blown in by the squall.

Strapped to my belt was a perfectly good dive knife. A superb knife, in fact. One of the last stainless steel survival knives made personally by the late Bo Randall of Orlando.

But, once again, I put the value of my equipment ahead of my own safety. If I pulled the knife from its scabbard, I risked dropping it—probably never to be found in the silt below.

Instead, I traced the nylon line until it became taut. I got a couple of wraps around my hand, used the piling as my anchor and gave a violent yank.

Suddenly, instead of just being snagged, I was tangled in what felt like an ascending web of rope.

Another very poor decision. Me, the dumbass, indeed. So my reality was now this: I was underwater, alone, in total darkness, tangled and tethered to the bottom.

Yet . . . I still wasn't worried. Not really. I had plenty of options, plenty of air, and I have lived an unusual life. I had been in tougher spots than this and survived. Marion D. Ford, world traveler, expert waterman, drown in a marina basin in four meters of water? Not likely.

Ego, again.

Diving alone at night isn't for amateurs, nor the poorly equipped. In that way, at least, I was prepared. I had a good knife. And looped to my dive vest, a brilliant little ASP LED flashlight.

I decided to have a look at what I was dealing with before going to work with my knife. Methodical action, taking small, careful steps, is my way of neutralizing panic. When I freed the flashlight, though, my hand banged what might have been a piling crosstie, which caused me to fumble and drop the thing.

Uckkin Id-ot!

Even though I spoke through my regulator, a dive buddy—had I been wise enough to have recruited one—would have understood that I was getting frustrated.

Fortunately, I'd hit the flashlight's pressure switch before it tumbled to the bottom. It landed on its side.

Visibility was better than usual after a storm—which meant the viz was poor, only a few yards at most. Even so, the little LED speared a dazzling column of light toward a buoyed ring of netting where the sturgeon I had been watching was penned.

A second sturgeon had joined the animal, I noted through the murk. Both appeared unfazed as they hugged the bottom, silt blooming from their gills, as they suctioned crustaceans and worms from unseen holes. I was amused by the notion the fish were now observing me, but I knew better. Even in temporary captivity, wild Florida sturgeon had better things to do than watch a primate drown.

The flashlight provided enough ancillary light for me to take stock of the situation. Yes, I was tangled in a dozen yards of crab line, a weighted trap somewhere off in the darkness.

For the next ten minutes, I stayed very busy trying to recover from my error, and the snowballing series of small mistakes that no diver with my experience should have made. Underwater, the only expert divers worthy of the term have scales, or fluked tails. No matter how shallow, or close to shore, that reality doesn't change. Primates are rank tourists whenever depth exceeds the distance between our feet and our nose.

For me, the "expert diver," it was a much deserved kick in the butt. And a reminder that "the unexpected" only surprises amateurs, drunks and children.

It was not, however, the most compelling reminder of the night.

A stranger, pointing a semiautomatic pistol at my head, would provide that.

2

I was a little shaky when I finally surfaced. And mad enough to have exhausted the profanities that accurately described my incompetence—and there were many.

A dazzling tube of light still marked my flashlight's location. It was beneath a dock in the deepest part of the basin. Seeing it was frustrating enough to cause me to swear at myself again. My damn tank and regulator were down there, too. Plus a weight belt!

I had gotten so badly tangled that I had jettisoned everything but my buoyancy compensator vest. Worse, I hadn't managed to get a look at the underside of the Russian's yacht, which was moored in deep water along the outside T-dock. The vessel sat alone, tethered to shore power by an electrical umbilical cable, which explained why its cabin had gone black, and why its pumps were no longer bilging water that is omnipresent in a craft her size.

Thinking, *Her emergency generator will kick on soon,* I treaded water above the flashlight, vaguely aware the generator did *not* start automatically—a fact that would prove of grave importance by early the next morning.

I was more concerned with what had just happened. Finally, I decided, screw it. Enough for one night. I could always buy more scuba equipment. More likely, though, I'd recover my gear in the morning.

To regroup, I rolled onto my back, inflated my vest and took a look around. The power was still out; no backup generators running on shore, either, which I found odd. The marina was a gray scaffolding of docks; the island, a density of shadows pocked by rooflines, coconut palms, the opaque glint of windows. Miles to the northwest, though, a pearlescent glow told me that Bare Key Regency Resort, and its floating casino, hadn't lost power. Farther north, Sanibel was an inverted island of luminous ivory, moored beneath the stars.

Seeing the lights of Sanibel reminded me that Vanderbilt Island is only a thirty-minute boat ride from my fish house and laboratory on Dinkin's Bay. Fast, unless you come by sailboat, which I had (against my better judgment), arriving earlier that day aboard Tomlinson's old live-aboard Morgan, *No Más*.

The decision seemed harmless at the time because Vanderbilt ranks as one of the most insulated and safest retreats in the world. The acreage is a tropical garden of blooming flowers and coconut palms, with a historic fishing lodge built atop the remnants of a pre-Columbian pyramid. That's right, a shell pyramid in Florida. Vanderbilt is one of several ancient places on the Gulf Coast once inhabited by contemporaries of the Maya.

Now, though, as I floated in darkness, I began to regret coming by sailboat. There was no telling how long the island's power would be out. More than a few hours, and I'd be forced to bunk aboard *No Más* instead of the air-conditioned suite in the main lodge, where I had already stowed my overnight bag.

Tomlinson snores. He barks and chortles as he dreams. If I'd arrived in my overpowered fishing skiff, I could sleep in my own bed and be back on Vanderbilt Island before breakfast.

Then the prospect became even more unsavory. What if Tomlinson had lured his eco-elitist friend, Winifred Densler, aboard *No Más* while I was underwater? By God, I'd sleep on the dock before enduring close quarters with someone like her. It wouldn't be the first time I'd slept outside to escape Tomlinson's craziness.

I flutter-kicked into deeper water for a better view of the very few boats among the network of dockage. My friend's old Morgan was moored thirty yards from where I'd surfaced, so it wasn't hard to spot. No oil lamp showing through the porthole, though . . . no sounds that I could hear.

Reassuring, but it wasn't proof.

I checked my Chronofighter dive watch: 9:45 p.m. Early, by island standards, where days are shortened in favor of long nights spent partying.

Tomlinson probably was still at the main lodge, getting determinedly drunk by candlelight. Or entertaining his eco-elitist lady friend, or some equally determined female—or females. The man is open-minded when it comes to excess. And he's a resourceful opportunist when it comes to power failures.

No one else was around, either. The caviar reception again. The island's summer population, which was zero, had been displaced by a dozen weekend caviar-minded dignitaries, which was why the marina was now a ghost village of a few empty boats and silence.

That was okay.

It was nice to be in the water, alone at night—particularly after coming so close to being killed by my own ineptitude. I decided it was the perfect time to drift for a while and look at stars. After being reminded of my personal deficiencies, it might be comforting to reaffirm that, above me, were a trillion indifferent solar systems that simply didn't give a damn what happened to me, and never would.

That's exactly what I was doing—floating on my back, looking at the sky—when I noticed a lone figure coming down the dock toward me.

It was a man, walking fast, hands in his pockets. Was he wearing a crewneck? It crossed my mind because Tomlinson's environmentalist friends had all worn black crewnecks, the organization's yellow logo on the breast pocket. Maybe the visitor had come searching for Tomlinson and the outspoken Ms. Densler.

My glasses were around my neck on fishing line, but I also use a prescription dive mask. I seated the mask on my face, but there wasn't enough light to see. So I tilted the mask to my forehead and waited.

There was something so determined—no, aggressive—about the man's body language, it stopped me from calling out a greeting. Or asking, *What knocked out the power?* which I would probably have done under different circumstances. Small islands are throwbacks to small towns of the previous century—even a retreat for the ultra-wealthy. Strangers interact. People smile. They wave. They make inane remarks about the weather, totally out of character with the aloof and guarded lives they've probably left behind.

Not with this guy, though. He wasn't out for a stroll. He was on a mission.

I used my fins to rudder me safely into the shadows, closer to shore, where, if need be, I could be out of the water quickly.

The man continued along the main dock, still walking fast. That's when I realized he had spotted my flashlight. The one I had dropped and left on the bottom. Its beam created a murky corona beneath the dock, noticeable from a long distance because it was the only light for miles.

Yeah . . . the guy's attention was focused on the light, because he didn't stop until he was standing directly above it. I watched the man squat to get a closer look. Then he was talking into what must have been a cuff link–sized transmitter, because he touched a finger to an earbud as spoke into his wrist.

"I think find him at marina. You hear? I see underwater light, I see bubbles." Then, to himself, he muttered, "Damn radio amateurs!"

I wasn't sure what that meant, other than my regulator was leaking residual air (I had closed the valve after jettisoning my tank.) And the man had some professional training of some sort or his tone wouldn't have been so contemptuous.

He was having radio problems, obviously. I watched him slap at the transceiver before he asked again, "You goddamn hear me or not?"

The accent was Russian. For a moment, I assumed the accent confirmed it was Kazlov's bodyguard, or an employee of one of his competitors. He definitely wasn't with the Chinese mega-millionaire. But then I remembered that Densler and her party crashers were part of an international organization. I'd been told there were five Third Planet members on the island, but only three were at the reception. I'd gotten a quick look at the other two, though, before I'd fled the fishing lodge, a pair of chubby blond-haired twins who, Densler had said, drove their van from California. Were the twins originally from the Caspian Sea region, the epicenter of the organization's work?

Possibly. If so, I guessed they would soon be enjoying a night in an American jail, compliments of one pissed-off Viktor Kazlov.

The prospect buoyed my spirits as I watched the man bang the transceiver with his fist, then curse it with a string of Russian profanities. Finally, he said, "Transmission jammed! Bastards have jamming device, you hear?"

A jamming device? On Vanderbilt Island? Hilarious. I actually smiled. I didn't believe it, of course, but at least the guy was entertaining.

That's when I heard him say, "What is happening now? Answer me! Who is shooting?"

Shooting?

Suddenly, I wasn't smiling. Yes, shooting. Not firecrackers. Gunshots. I heard them, too. Three shots, rapid-fire, followed by two shots, a gun of heavier caliber. Then another burst of rapid fire from the opposite end of the island. It was like a small war was erupting around us.

For a moment, I felt detached from reality. People on Vanderbilt Island didn't carry weapons. The explosion I had heard was just that—an explosion. Lightning, a faulty wire—it could be explained. In a peaceful place like this, though, gunshots were an aberration. What the hell was happening?

Now the man had the transceiver out of his pocket and was tapping it on a piling. Frustrated, he held his wrist to his mouth and said, very loud, "If you hear me, I find Ford. Take no more chances. Understand? He is here . . . at marina. Out!"

It was startling to hear my name, but I was shocked at what happened next.

As I floated motionless, only fifteen yards away, the man drew a semiautomatic pistol and took his time mounting an oversized sound suppressor on the barrel. Then he chose a section of water above my sunken flashlight, pointed the weapon toward the bottom and fired four muffled shots in rapid succession.

After waiting a few seconds, he went to the other side of the dock and fired four more rounds. The bullets pocked the water with miniature geysers of light, each report no louder than an air rifle.

I wasn't dreaming—it was *happening.*

Slowly, then faster, I began kicking quietly toward the dock because I realized what was happening. Not why, but what, and I didn't like it. The sound suppressor implied the shooter was a pro, and he intended to kill me. But to do it, he either had to make a lucky shot or scare me to the surface.

The odds favored me surfacing, and the shooter knew it. That's why he took his eyes off the water long enough to check his watch. It was also why I was swimming toward the man instead of panicking and racing for shore.

I had to get under the dock before he spotted me. It was the only available cover, and the shooter's next move was obvious: he would produce a flashlight and search the area before firing randomly again.

A flashlight . . . it scared me more than the gun. But that's what the shooter was doing now, taking a cop-sized Maglite from a pack strapped around his waist.

As I swam, I watched him check his watch again, then use the flashlight, shining the beam down into the water, then panning it in my direction.

I didn't see what the man did next. I was busy slipping free of my inflatable vest, submerging silently, then kicking hard in darkness, in the direction of the dock.

3

Underwater, from old habit, I counted each kick-stroke with my left fin. It's an effective navigational tool. And the only aid available, under the circumstances, except for the faint glow of my lost flashlight, off to my left, which helped me maintain a straight course.

Or so I hoped.

I guessed the dock was twenty yards away. I knew that, for me, twenty-five yards requires at total of eighteen to twenty fin strokes. Nine to ten, if counting only my left leg.

It varies, of course, depending on tidal current. Or whether I'm in a pool or open water. So, the seventh time I kicked with my left fin, I thrust my hands ahead of me, anticipating a collision with a piling.

Something else I anticipated was the shooter spotting me, and that bullets would soon pierce the surface. I've heard bullets from underwater before. They make a keening sound. Their punch creates an uncomfortable shock wave as they arc past.

There were no shots fired, though. Nor did my hands make contact with a piling as expected.

Because adrenaline was firing my muscles, I was burning air fast. But holding my breath was the least of my problems, I decided, when I still hadn't found the dock after a total of twenty-four fin strokes. Twelve with my left leg.

Could I have possibly swam beyond the dock? That was unlikely. It would have required navigating a perfect line between rows of pilings, a feat similar to threading a needle in darkness. If I'd wanted to do it, I couldn't have done it.

Apparently, though, I had swum too far. So I jettisoned air to reduce buoyancy, balled my legs beneath me and spun around, pulling hard with my arms, attempting to retrace my course.

Yes, it turned out, I had threaded the needle. I knew almost immediately because, mid-glide, before I could get my hands in front of me, my head collided with a piling.

Thunk.

It was the sound of an ax rebounding off green wood. I hit so hard, I was disoriented by the impact and the acid sting of barnacles that lacerated my forehead.

I surfaced without deciding to surface, still woozy and unsure what had happened. Then it took me a moment to realize that the light suddenly blinding me was unrelated to the starbursts firing inside my head.

From above, I heard a voice say, "Hah! Blood on your face! Is dangerous, you know, to produce blood when swimming. Sharks everywhere in water—Dr. Ford."

A joke, I realized. Someone was making a joke before shooting me—something only a cold-blooded killer would do.

The man also had a head full of rage. It was in his tone.

I blinked my eyes, the taste of salt water and blood warm on my lips, as I looked up. The shooter was a vague silhouette behind the flashlight's glare. He was on the dock above me, only a few feet away. Too close to miss with the pistol he was pointing at my face . . . now getting ready to squeeze the trigger—I could tell by the way he leaned to reduce the distance that separated us.

Why? That's the question I wanted answered.

Instead, I haggled for a few extra seconds of life, sputtering, "If you shoot me, I won't be able to tell you what I know. It's worth a lot of money."

The lie was as desperate as it was baseless, but it caused the man to stop what he was about to do.

The shooter lowered the gun slightly. "You have secrets to sell? In our work line, who does not?"

In our line of work, he meant. Not good news for me. It suggested that I'd been right from the start. He was Viktor Kazlov's bodyguard, whom I'd seen earlier in the bar. Big slope-shouldered man, hairy as a bear, and former KGB, my guess. A professional who was also furious about something, so he didn't mind waiting while I humiliated myself by trying to negotiate.

I took a chance and said, "Government secrets—who cares anymore? Beluga caviar, though, that's valuable."

Yes, the guy was taking his time, enjoying himself, because he replied, "Beluga, of course. Better exchange rate than gold. Diamonds are shit to beluga. This is information you selling? Maybe you working for competitors and make me better offer."

Another joke.

My head was clearing, I was putting elements together: an explosion, several gunshots, then a man aiming a pistol at me. It meshed with the gangster tactics common in the black market caviar industry.

I was also assembling a vague plan. My right hand confirmed that my dive knife was still secure in its scabbard as I replied. "I'm not going to risk lying. You'd just shoot me later. Let's talk. How about you start by telling me your name."

I wasn't being polite, I was employing the hostage's first rule of survival: use first names, make it personal.

In reply, I heard laughter with a derisive edge. "Putin—Vladimir Putin. What you think of that?"

Yep, a funny guy. I used the name, anyway, saying, "You can drop the doctor stuff . . . *Vladimir*. Give me time to get out of the water and I'll tell you why I'm worth more alive than dead."

Suddenly, the shooter was tired of the game. "Enough talk. I see you and long-haired friend at bar tonight—he like to talk too much, I think. I know you steal from Mr. Kazlov's yacht today. That stupid. Then, tonight, you shoot Mr. Kazlov. That very stupid."

Kazlov, shot?

No wonder the guy was furious. I hadn't been aboard the yacht, but, otherwise, the shooter, Vladimir, was uncomfortably accurate in suspecting I had targeted his boss. Not to kill him—not yet, anyway. Even so, what the hell had Tomlinson said to make me a suspect?

The conversation had taken a dangerous turn, but going for my dive knife was the wrong move now. Instead, I said, "How badly was Kazlov hurt?"

Vladimir was staring at me, letting his anger build. "There is only one secret you have I want. Where is explosives? You and hippie friend put bomb somewhere, kill everything on island? Or poison gas, maybe, huh? Where is?"

Bomb? What in the hell had Tomlinson told the man?

I exhaled, and sank imperceptibly as I said, "If there's an explosive somewhere, I didn't set it—but I'll help you find it. And I didn't shoot your boss. In fact, we had a friendly talk today. Kazlov will confirm that, if he still can."

"One more chance, I give you. Where is explosives? No more time for lies."

I started calm and tried to reason with the man. "Vladimir, listen to me. What you're saying makes no sense. I live in this area. I'm known in Florida. Why would I risk all of that? Put the pistol away and let's talk, okay?" As I said it, I allowed my body to sink another few inches. Now only my face was visible above the water. Beneath me, through contact with the fins, my toes sensed the bottom only a few inches below.

The timing was right because Vladimir was shaking his head, done talking. I waited as he extended the pistol toward me again. Four feet separated us . . . then three feet. It was impossible for him to miss, yet I fought the urge to throw my hands up as a shield. My hands had to remain where they were, in the water, to provide thrust when I needed it. Another reason I couldn't use my knife.

I heard the first syllable of something the man was going to say, some parting word, before he pulled the trigger. As he began to speak, I sank deeper. Then, when my fins touched bottom, I used that tiny momentum to vault upward, kicking furiously, as I butterfly-stroked once with both arms.

The combined thrust dolphined me out of the water, my hands soaring above dock level, high enough to grab for the pistol. As I did, Vladimir made a grunting sound of surprise and fired two, maybe three, wild rounds. Impossible to be sure because it all happened so fast.

Instead of finding the weapon, though, my hands made contact with the man's right wrist. It was all I had and I wasn't letting go.

My fingers buried themselves tendon-deep in the guy's forearm.

He fought back, but my descending weight was too much. Vladimir made a bellowing sound as I pulled him into the water on top of me.

We went straight to the bottom, the bodyguard kicking and clawing, as I wrestled for hand control. By the time we'd surfaced, I had confirmed that the semiauto pistol and the flashlight were both gone, lost during the fall.

I was relieved, at first. Then vaguely disappointed. I spent years as an amateur wrestler learning hard lessons from tough technicians. Then more years learning lethal, unconventional techniques from military studs, usually at the Jungle Operations Training Center, Fort Sherman, Panama. I knew within seconds that Vladimir had the grappling abilities of an average adult male—few skills at all, in other words. Unless he'd gotten very, very lucky, I could have stripped the weapon from him, no problem.

Or maybe I'd badly misjudged the man.

When we surfaced, I was facing the shooter. I tried to slip behind him, but he pivoted with me, which was impressive, considering the man wasn't wearing fins. When I grabbed for his elbow, he used the palm of his free hand to try to knock my jaw crooked, then swung a wild right fist that numbed my ear, then deadened my shoulder. Vladimir, I realized, was a boxer with some martial arts skills. Worse, he possessed what's called "heavy hands." If he landed a punch, it might be the end of the fight, and the end of Marion D. Ford. The possibility scared the hell out of me, so I retreated by exhaling and diving for the bottom.

When I reappeared, I was kicking so hard that I launched my body over the man, smothered him with my arms, and took him under for several seconds. This time, when we surfaced, I was behind him. I had an ankle grapevined around his right leg to ensure body control, leaving one fin free to keep us afloat. My right forearm was across the man's throat, my left hand was behind his head. The configuration resembled a figure four: my right hand locked over my left arm to create a fulcrum. I had sufficient leverage to snap the man's neck, if I chose to do it. Deadly—as I knew better than most.

Or, with the sharp edge of my wrist, I could slow the flow of blood through the man's carotid artery until he chose to surrender rather than black out. The finesse provided me options—persuasive, debilitating or deadly—depending on how much pressure was applied.

I was glad I hadn't risked using my dive knife now.

Vladimir was a fighter, though, and wouldn't quit. He bucked and thrashed; rested for a few seconds, then bucked and thrashed some more. His efforts reminded me of a grazing animal that had been surprised by one of the big constrictor snakes. A python or anaconda. His was a gradual surrender interrupted by frenzied bursts of desperation.

Finally, when I felt the man's body go limp, I pushed his head under long enough to confirm he wasn't faking. It was a judgment call—I didn't want to drown him. I wanted the guy alive so I could find out what the hell was going on. Afterward, I'd call the cops—if they weren't already on their way to arrest the trespassing environmentalists. Or I would use the sailboat's VHF to raise the Coast Guard—depending on the man's answers.

There was a reason why his answers were important to me.

Inside the boundaries of the United States, I'm just another face in the crowd, a low-profile citizen. And that's the way I want to keep it because I live a very different life when I'm in other countries. Which made it risky for me to get law enforcement involved—especially the feds—so I had to be very, very careful.

What worried me was the possibility that Vladimir, and Kazlov, knew about my other life—my "shadow life," as an NSA associate once described it. I'm a biologist by profession, true. But I also use my research as plausible cover to travel the world, gathering intelligence for an agency that remains classified, as well as to carry out less traditional assignments.

The euphemisms vary throughout the intelligence community, although few agencies have cause to use them—only one deep cover team, as far as I know. Special duties. Executive reassignment. Kinetic military action—just a few of the code phrases used in my shadow life and my work overseas.

On those rare occasions when I'm assigned a specific target, a human objective. "Eternalize" is a better word choice. Spoken or written, it might be "internalize," which could be explained away as a typo. Or a word that was misheard.

Always give yourself an out.

Early in my secret career, I sometimes struggled with the moral ambiguities. No longer. For better or worse, I've come to terms with who I am, what I am. Darwinism explains the human condition as accurately as it describes the competitive process that is natural selection. It was possible that the bodyguard had been assigned to eliminate me for reasons just as cold, just as impersonal. Reasons that had nothing to with a supposed theft, or the shooting of Viktor Kazlov—if the man had, indeed, been shot.

From the instant I saw Vladimir mounting a sound arrester on his weapon, that possibility had been in my mind. There are at least three foreign governments, and two foreign black ops organizations, that would me shoot on sight, given the opportunity. It was not improbable that one of those groups had been tracking me for a while and had chosen Vanderbilt Island because the caviar gathering provided plausible cover. After all, that's what had brought *me* here.

How much did the bodyguard know? That's what I had to find out. And I would—as soon as the man regained consciousness.

How I handled the situation depended on how he answered my questions. I didn't want to go to extremes—in fact, dreaded the tight-sphincter complexities of disposing of a body or staging an accident.

If the man posed a threat to my career, my group or my freedom, however, I wouldn't hesitate.

4

As I swam Vladimir into the shallows, I heard more gunshots in the distance. Someone was burning a lot of ammunition. Because the reports lacked the distinctive give-and-take rhythm of enemies trading fire, the random bursts suggested chaos . . . or panic. It was as puzzling as it was surreal.

Nor did my interrogation of Vladimir go as smoothly as expected. I discovered that I hadn't kept the man underwater long enough to confirm he was unconscious. The instant our feet touched bottom, he surprised me by hammering me in the ribs with his elbow, then caught me with a right fist to the forehead as he turned.

It was a glancing blow. I was wearing fins, though, which put me at a disadvantage. As if wearing clown shoes, I went stumbling and splashing sideways, struggling to keep my balance. When I finally went down, Vladimir was charging me through knee-deep water to continue the fight—a mistake on his part.

The man should have run for shore and escaped into the shadows. It might have saved him from what happened minutes later.

I was wearing old-style Rocket fins. They're heavy, but I like them because they don't float, and because they're big enough to allow me to wear jungle boots rather than booties, if the situation requires.

Tonight I was wearing worn-out Nikes, not boots, but that didn't make it any easier to pry the fin straps over the heels of my shoes. That's what I was trying to do when the man threw himself on me, yelling something in Russian.

As he clubbed at me with his fists, I managed to get one fin off and toss it toward the dock before deciding I'd better fight back. If he connected solidly, knocked me out, he might be able accomplish with his hands what he'd failed to do with the pistol.

I became an armadillo—pulled my knees to my chest and wrapped my arms over my head for protection. It gave the bodyguard enough confidence to do what I anticipated. I waited until I felt the man's body weight move to my shoulders as he tried to get a clean shot at my face. He was riding too high, in wrestling jargon, something he wouldn't have understood. That subtle change in balance allowed me to crab-crawl backward from beneath his legs and escape behind him. Out the back door—more wrestling jargon.

That quick, our positions were reversed—me on top, him on his belly in the water. Twice, he tried to slam the back of his head into my face, but I was pressed too close for him to connect. The positioning allowed me enough control to free one hand, pry off my second fin and lob it close to where the other fin had landed.

When I did, he attempted to elbow me. I caught his left wrist and levered it up between his shoulder blades. At the same time, I grabbed his throat with my right hand, lifted his face out of the water and leaned close enough to his ear to whisper, "Why are you doing this? I didn't shoot Kazlov, damn it!"

Struggling to breathe, Vladimir made a guttural sound of pain but didn't answer.

I jammed the man's face into the water, pushed it to the bottom and held him there while I refueled with ten deep breaths. As I did, my eyes scanned the docks, then moved to the island. The bodyguard had been in contact with someone before he'd had radio problems. Soon, they would come looking for him.

I leaned and squinted, trying to discern details. Was there someone in the shadows, moving toward us? My glasses were still on the fishing line around my neck, so I couldn't be sure.

I watched for a couple of more seconds, then returned my attention to Vladimir. After levering the man's head up, I waited until he was done coughing water before I tried again.

"Tell me what the hell's going on and I'll let you go."

When he refused, I pushed his face to the bottom for another ten count, as my head swiveled toward the island. Yes, there had been someone standing near a tree—possibly the shooter's ally. I knew for certain only because the blurry shape I'd seen was now gone.

Where?

I couldn't risk remaining in the open, an easy target. Not with so many trigger-happy people around. So I grabbed the bodyguard's belt and dragged him closer to the dock in case I needed cover . . . or a safe exit.

Then I waited as Vladimir tried to stand. He was so winded and disoriented that he staggered and fell before finally making it to his feet. For several seconds, he stood at leaning rest, hands on his knees, fighting to get his breath.

There didn't appear to be much fight left in the guy, but he had fooled me before. By the time he'd recovered enough to stand erect, and look at me, I was holding my dive knife, palm up, because I wanted him to see it.

"You didn't try to kill me because of explosives," I said in a low voice, straightening my glasses. "Or because Kazlov was shot. This has something to do with his boat being robbed, doesn't it? *Doesn't it?*"

The man snorted as if I was too stupid to understand, his eyes moving from me to the Russian's yacht moored at the T-dock, seventy-some yards in the distance. His contempt caused me to think of another explanation for why the night had suddenly turned violent.

No . . . there were several possibilities, in fact—explanations that were as varied as the three powerful men who had come to Vanderbilt Island as Viktor Kazlov's guests.

Earlier in the day, Kazlov had told me he was disappointed in the turnout for his caviar party. I doubted that, considering the difficult time I'd had finessing invitations, but hadn't challenged the point. The Russian claimed he had invited experts from around the world, but the only notables who'd showed were his three most powerful rivals, an Iranian, a Turkmenian and the millionaire from China.

Later, I had made it my business to meet them all—introductions filled with meaningless niceties to deflect conversation. It is a device that powerful people use to keep their inferiors at a respectable distance.

Lien Hai Bohai was Chinese, but he had been educated in Hong Kong, so his English was as polished as his manners. He owned a fleet of fishing boats that were actually floating fish factories. Bohai also owned three aquaculture facilities and was among the primary reasons that China is now the world's leading exporter of farm-raised caviar. Since China began encouraging private enterprise and entrepreneurialism more than a decade ago, men like Bohai had turned the behemoth's economy around.

The surname of Kazlov's Iranian competitor was Armanie. Because I'd done research, I knew Armanie's given name was Abdul, but the man rarely used it.

The third man, from Turkmenia, was Darius Talas—a massively fat man whose first name stuck with me because I associated his silver hair and mustache with the fictional Dorian Gray.

Like Kazlov, his guests had spent the previous two days gambling, partying and watching dolphins humiliate themselves at the resort across the bay—a spectacle Tomlinson and I had intentionally missed.

"Bonding," the Russian called it.

Like Kazlov, both Caspian neighbors had brought a security "assistant" to the island—high-stakes businessmen hire bodyguards for a reason. Unlike Kazlov, his competitors had business interests that included more than caviar and black marketeering. Talas and Armanie were also making a fortune drilling for oil in the Caspian Sea, so caviar wasn't their primary source of income.

Lien Hai Bohai was different from his rivals in several ways (although he, too, had enjoyed the casino, I'd been told). Kazlov and Armanie were seldom separated from their bodyguards while Bohai, a frail man, in his seventies, seemed unconcerned with security. He was traveling with two women, no security guys. And, unlike the others, he had made his fortune stripping the sea bottom of life rather than probing it for fossil fuels.

All three of Kazlov's rivals were rich—an important similarity, if one of them had something to do with breaking into the Russian's yacht. If they'd done it, they weren't looking for money.

"Someone stole information," I said to the bodyguard, as we stood facing each other in thigh-deep water. "That's what this is all about. You didn't ask me anything about what was stolen, so it has to be data of some type. The thieves were after something that had no value once it was compromised. That's why you don't care about recovering it."

I made sure he saw my knife before I said, "That's why you didn't ask me about the robbery before you tried to shoot me. Nothing else explains it. What did they take, a computer? A hard drive?"

Photographs were another possibility, but I was thinking about Kazlov's claim that he had discovered a way to create a hybrid caviar using DNA from beluga and Gulf sturgeon. The Russian had explained the process to me, but in vague terms, when I'd met him earlier.

Vague or not, I understood more than Kazlov realized, because sturgeon aquaculture was another subject I had researched. In fact, I had spent a couple of days in nearby Sarasota, at Mote Marine Laboratory's seventeen-acre research facility, talking to experts. There, Jim Michaels, one of the world's leading authorities on sturgeon farming, had provided me with the latest data.

Thanks to Michaels, I had learned more from what Kazlov *didn't* say, during our half-hour conversation, than from the few details he provided. I had come away from the talk convinced that Kazlov, and his aquaculture specialists, were working on something unusual. A unique protocol, possibly, that had more to do with manipulating chromosomal sets in sturgeon than disguising beluga DNA. Research on transgenic fish has been around just long enough to earn the process an acronym: GMOs. Genetically modified organisms. And also long enough to prove its profitability.

The fact that I knew this in advance caused me to suspect that Kazlov was lying about developing a sturgeon hybrid. Why would he bother? More important, why would Kazlov's three powerful competitors pretend to be interested? They were knowledgeable men.

They had to know already what I myself had only recently learned. According to the experts at Mote Marine Lab, there are only two true holy grails in the world of producing beluga-grade caviar.

1. Develop a female sturgeon that will produce preovulated eggs, on a regular basis, that can be removed without killing the female. As an analogy, Michaels had used dairy farms and milk cows.
2. Develop a female beluga that will mature in five to ten years instead of twenty years and thus take the deadly pressure off the world's wild brood stock population.

If Kazlov had discovered either of these holy grails, his research was well worth stealing. It would be worth *billions*, not millions of dollars. And it *could* be stolen—if the Russian's research was incomplete and not yet patentable as an exclusive intellectual property.

I didn't consciously think about all this as I stood, holding the knife, questioning Kazlov's bodyguard. I had been going over it in my mind all afternoon. Genetic engineering, in all fields, requires exacting protocols if the results are to be duplicated. If Kazlov had made an unprecedented breakthrough, his beluga protocols and research records had to exist. Which is why I immediately suspected that a computer hard drive had been stolen

Kazlov's research data would have been backed up in many places, of course, so it was pointless to recover a missing hard drive or to question the thief who'd stolen it. But killing the thief before he shared data worth billions of dollars made good business sense—to a black marketeer like Kazlov, anyway.

Once again, I said to Vladimir, "Someone stole a hard drive. Or a computer. Nothing else adds up. But why suspect me?"

I got an uneasy feeling in my stomach when the bodyguard

shrugged and said, "I once work for Russian State Security Committee. For man who does not exist, you are very famous, Dr. Ford. Of course you are first person I suspect."

Russian State Security Committee and the KGB—the same organization.

I replied, "That doesn't mean I shot your boss or rigged an explosive device—or broke into his damn boat."

Probably fearing I now had reason to kill him, Vladimir offered me an alternative, saying, "You come to fishing lodge and help me find Mr. Kazlov, if you don't believe. We in same work line, you and me. Tonight"—the man took a look over his shoulder before continuing—"tonight, everyone go crazy. Never seen such craziness. Maybe you need our help. Maybe we need yours."

The man couldn't be serious. It was a ploy to lure me back to the enemy's camp. Even so, I was willing. Judging from all the gunfire, the enemy's camp was a hell of a lot safer than standing in the water out in the open.

I used the knife to point toward shore, telling Vladimir, "You lead the way. I'll buy you a vodka or two—we've both earned it."

I would have preferred to watch cops handcuff the big hairy bastard. But first I wanted to humor the guy because there was a lot I wanted to know—including what Tomlinson had said to convince the bodyguard or Kazlov that I'd broken into his yacht. First, my old pal somehow helps a group of eco-extremist trespassers, then he implicates me in a crime? I wanted some answers.

Instead of moving, though, Vladimir stood motionless, his attention fixed on something ashore. Because it was so dark, and because my glasses were hazed with salt, I was slower to figure out what he was looking at.

Someone was standing beneath trees near the reception office. That's what had caught his attention. No . . . not standing. It was the vague shape of a man dressed in dark clothing, his face covered with maybe a scarf, walking toward us. He was carrying what looked like a professor's laser pointer. The pointer slashed a red streak on the ground with every swing of his arm.

Instantly, I stepped behind Vladimir, using him as a shield because I knew it wasn't a laser pointer. Too many shots had been fired tonight. It had to be a laser gun sight, probably mounted on a semiautomatic pistol. But maybe the situation wasn't as threatening as it seemed.

The man coming toward us was inexperienced, that was obvious. No pro would give away his position before he was ready to fire. The guy was probably nervous, unknowingly activating the laser's pressure switch, his fingers too tight around the pistol grip.

Vladimir realized what we were seeing, too, because he said something in Russian that sounded like "Piz-do-BOL!" and crouched low. I did the same because the laser was suddenly a smoky red cable that panned across the water, then painted a shaky Z stripe on my chest.

I was diving toward the dock when the first round was fired.

5

Three pistol shots later, I was hiding under the dock, near where I had tossed my Rocket fins. As I used feet and hands to search for the fins, my attention shifted from the dark shoreline, to Vladimir, who had been hit at least once.

He lay thrashing on his back, then managed to get to his knees. His face was featureless in the darkness, blank from shock. His left arm dangled in the water, a useless deadweight.

I wondered if he'd been hit anywhere else.

The man's head turned toward the gunman, then to the dock, where I was crouching. Vladimir's brain was still working, at least, because he began to crawl toward me. Not crawl, actually. Because of his dead arm, he had to lunge forward, find his balance, then worm his knees beneath him before lunging again—pathetic to witness.

I should have kept moving—especially after I found one fin, then the second, lying on the bottom nearby. With fins, the dock became an effective exit tunnel into deeper water. From there, I could transit beneath a couple of nearby boats to the freedom of open water. Or

I could hide until the gunman tired of searching and then maybe use a VHF radio on one of the boats to call for help.

I couldn't bring myself to leave, though. It wasn't because I felt any allegiance to the wounded man—why would I? But I was adrenaline drained and suddenly indecisive—a by-product of fear. Until I understood what was happening, it was impossible to know what to do next or who to trust.

It had been a confusing night, but now I was completely baffled. Had Vladimir just been shot by one of his own people? Or were Kazlov, his two Caspian competitors, or possibly even Lien Bohai, engaged in a private war?

Bohai could be eliminated, I'd decided—the man was in his seventies and he'd arrived without a bodyguard. It was plausible, though, that the men from the Caspian Sea—Talas, Armanie and Kazlov—had squabbled and were now shooting it out.

Black marketeers of Eastern Europe don't get as much publicity as Mexican narco gangs, but they are as murderous, and markedly more dangerous, because they operated on a more sophisticated level. Circumventing international laws requires political connections, money and brains.

Caviar traffickers commonly recruit key people from special ops teams around the Caspian Sea. It explains the trade's reputation for precise and ruthless action against anyone who crosses them.

As Vladimir dragged himself toward me, I got an answer to one of my questions—maybe two answers—when the gunman opened fire again.

The pistol didn't have a silencer, and I ducked instinctively as bullets slapped the water nearby, *WHAP-WHAP-WHAP-WHAP.*

Four quick rounds . . . then two more, all hitting close enough to Vladimir to confirm that he wasn't the victim of friendly fire.

Yes . . . Kazlov's people were being targeted. It suggested that his Iranian or Turkmenian competitor—maybe both—had decided to stop the Russian's work on beluga sturgeon or to steal his methodology . . . or they wanted to settle some old debt.

When the gunman fired twice more, however—and missed both times—I began to doubt my own theory. How could a trained professional score only one hit out of twelve or thirteen rounds? True, it was dark. Yes, the gunman was twenty-some yards away—a very long shot for a pistol—and he was moving. But thirteen rounds?

It caused me to reconsider another possibility—an explanation I had already contemplated but didn't like because it implicated old enemies . . . or maybe even an old friend.

Tomlinson.

Exhausted, Vladimir dropped to his belly in water too shallow for him to submerge. When a bullet plowed a furrow near his head, though, he got to his knees and lunged again, landing only two body lengths from where I was hiding.

The gunman was closer, too, but I didn't know exactly where. Soon, he would be on the dock, probably with a flashlight. I'd been through that once tonight, and once was more than enough. I couldn't delay my escape much longer.

Intellectually, I knew I should put on my fins and head for deeper water. I hadn't learned all I wanted to know from the wounded man, but I had seen enough to be convinced there was no safe place on the island. Risky or not, I had to contact law enforcement. Then I had to find Tomlinson and try to help him and anyone else who had been caught in the middle of this lunacy.

Yet, instead of escaping, I remained hidden as Vladimir collapsed on his belly again only yards away. In the sudden silence of wind and lapping waves, I realized the gunman had stopped firing.

There had to be a reason. Had his weapon misfired? Or was he reloading?

Reloading, probably. There are semiautomatic pistols with extended magazines that hold thirty rounds or more. Most, though, have half that capacity. If the gunman was changing magazines, it would take only a few seconds.

I decided to risk a quick look.

Hooking an arm around a piling, I poked my head above the dock for a couple of seconds, then ducked back into the shadows.

The gunman was at the water's edge, fifteen yards away, his back to me. The way he was hunched over, concentrating, gave the impression that his gun had jammed. Or maybe he didn't have a second magazine so was now reloading one cartridge at a time.

If I'd been sure that's what he was doing, I would have charged the guy. It was tempting. The only way to find out, though, was to actually try it. I decided to take another look to confirm.

That's what I was getting ready to do when I realized that Vladimir was floating facedown, head bobbing in a freshening breeze, his body very still.

Without thinking, I took a long, silent step and grabbed the back of the man's shirt. As I dragged him under the dock, supporting his head, he inhaled several deep breaths, still alive and possibly conscious.

If the gunman heard us, there was no telltale yelp of protest.

When Vladimir coughed, then opened his eyes, I touched a finger to my lips—a waste of time because it was so dark. Even so, the man seemed to understand, because he turned his head to listen as I whispered, "I need a weapon. Is there anything on Kazlov's boat?"

The man blinked at me and said, "I bleed to death. Yes?"

Yes . . . probably. I didn't want that to happen, though. Not yet, anyway.

Hurrying, I drew my knife and slit his shirtsleeve to the shoulder. The arm was black with shadows and blood, so I felt around until I discovered a chunk of his deltoid missing, meat and muscle, but no bone fragments that I could feel.

I told him, "It's not too bad. But, yeah, you're losing blood."

The man winced when I applied pressure, but he was alert enough to understand when I asked again if there were weapons aboard Kazlov's yacht.

"Up there," he said. "Everything left up there."

My interpretation: the bodyguard's extra weapons were housed at the fishing lodge.

With a swipe, I cut the man's shirtsleeve free and made two fast wraps around his arm. When I clove-hitched the material tight over the wound, he grunted, but that's all. A tough guy.

I waited for him to take a couple of breaths before motioning toward shore to indicate the gunman. "How many shooters, you think?"

Vladimir's reaction was unexpected. He grabbed my shirt and yanked me close to his face. "Damn liar! You and him"—the man was talking about the gunman—"him and your longhair friend, they plan this, I think! And you are lying about goddamn bomb!"

He gave me a shove as he released me. "Chemical weapons. Kill people with bombs—something only cowards do. Pretend you do not know."

I snapped, "Are you talking about those idiot activists? I don't think they have the brains. You should have called the cops the moment they walked into the fishing lodge."

Vladimir hissed, "I *tried*. You know reason cannot call!"

We were running out of time. It had been only a minute since I'd seen the gunman working on his pistol. If the weapon was jammed, we might have another minute. If he was only reloading, though, our time was up.

Holding the knife as a reminder, I whispered, "I didn't save your ass because I'm a nice person. There's something you're not telling me."

Vladimir looked at me for a second—a look of reappraisal, perhaps. Before he could reply, though, he turned an ear to listen.

I heard it, too. The gunman had entered the shallows, water splashing with each careful step. Seconds later, the beam of a flashlight found the dock, panning back and forth.

Not only was the guy a bad marksman, he had chosen the worst possible approach. The dock was high ground. It provided a better vantage point. It would allow him a faster egress if he had to move. In knee-deep water, there's no such thing as a sprinter.

It was yet more evidence the gunman was not a special ops pro working for caviar traffickers. Worse, it added some validity to Vladimir's claim that my long-haired pal was involved.

Tomlinson and his fellow members of the eco-elitist group Third Planet Peace Force. If true, they hadn't come just to crash a party. Tomlinson's new friends had come to declare war on Kazlov and his fellow "environmental gangsters."

I motioned for Vladimir to follow me before moving to a piling on the opposite side of the dock. The water was shallow enough, so I kept my fins over my shoulder as I floated myself into the open, hands pulling me along the bottom.

A hedge of mangrove trees, twenty-five yards away, wasn't the closest cover, but that's the direction I headed. It was the safest line of escape because the gunman was stupid. As his flashlight probed among the pilings, the dock shielded us from his view instead of providing the guy an elevated killing platform.

After a minute or so, a glance over my shoulder confirmed that

Vladimir was still with me. He was on his belly, using his feet and one good arm to propel him along the bottom. Impressive, but he was going too slow. Sooner or later, the gunman would figure out that he'd made a strategic error. He would use the dock.

Turned out, it was later. But not late enough.

As I closed on the mangroves, the water was so shallow that I got to my knees and attempted to crawl the last few yards before slipping into the trees. I had landed on an oyster bar, though, shells like razors. My shoes could survive them, my hands and knees couldn't.

As I got to my feet, I took another look. Vladimir wasn't far behind. But I also saw that, finally, the gunman was on the dock, and he had spotted me.

No doubt about it, because I saw the man straighten with surprise. Then, suddenly, a spotlight blinded me. I became a solitary figure on an empty stage—not an intimidating figure, I guessed, with my bleeding forehead, my bleeding hands; a cartoon figure wearing khaki BUDS swim shorts and black T-shirt.

Next, the flashlight found Vladimir, who was getting to his knees, dead left arm at his side—and that's the last I saw of the man for many busy seconds because the gunman started shooting, rapid-fire. Judging from the number of rounds that kicked water nearby or sizzled near my ears, the gunman was targeting me, not Vladimir.

The man continued firing as I ducked limbs and hurdled roots into the mangrove thicket, then dived to my belly into sulfur-scented muck. One of the rounds made a bumblebee *buzzzzzzz* as it passed near my head—the distinctive sound of a slug whirling asymmetrically after nicking a leaf or twig.

It was impossible to continue running, though. Red mangrove trees grow as thick as reeds on rubbery, knee-high roots—prop roots that provide oxygen to submerged tendrils. Even by daylight, and not under fire, traveling through mangrove swamp is slow going. It combines gymnastics with bulldozer determination.

On my belly, I snaked my way deeper into the trees when the gunman began to space his shots. As I did, I became aware of a sustained and rhythmic splashing from the shallows to my right. Not loud, but steady. It told me that Vladimir wasn't dead. He had managed to get to his feet and was skirting the oyster bar, trying to put the line of trees between himself and the dock.

Apparently, the bodyguard succeeded because soon the firing stopped.

I stood . . . listened for a moment . . . then I angled toward what I hoped was an intersection point. If the gunman was determined to kill us both—and that seemed apparent—he would abandon the dock and wait for us on the shoreward rim of the mangroves.

Exit the trees and we'd be easy targets.

I admired the bodyguard's tenacity, but his life meant no more to me than my life meant to him. He had information, though, and I wanted it. I wanted to intercept him before he cleared the trees and took a fatal round.

After two minutes had passed, I knew that the gunman hadn't stopped firing just to reload. He was changing positions. As I lifted myself over a root, I checked the tree canopy. Yes, he was on the move. I could gauge his progress by the changing angle of his flashlight. Occasionally, a streak of red laser painted the treetops, too.

As anticipated, the gunman circled to the shoreward edge of the swamp to wait for us. When the beam of the flashlight blinked off, and after a couple more minutes of silence, I knew he was in position. Probably a comfortable place with cover nearby. For once, the man had done something smart. If he'd risked venturing into the mangroves after us, I might get an opportunity to jump him and use my knife.

I hoped it would happen. With all the noise Vladimir was making, it might. The night was a chorus of summer sounds—insects, faraway thunder, restless birds—but nothing so loud as the wounded bodyguard entering the mangroves off to my right.

I winced at every sound, but I knew he couldn't help it. He was a big guy, with a bad arm, and he'd lost a lot of blood. Judging from what I heard, he propelled himself steadily from branch to branch, stumbling occasionally, stopping often to gulp air.

I've spent more time in mangrove swamps than most, but I made my share of noise, too. Impossible not to. I stepped on dead limbs. I leaned too much weight on more than one rotting tree trunk that snapped. And each time I gave my position away, I paused, expecting to hear shots.

But the gunman had become patient. Or he had run out of ammunition . . . or had abandoned the hunt entirely—a possibility that I entertained only because it gave me hope.

Finally, the moving tree canopy ahead told me that Vladimir was close. I knelt and waited, mosquitoes creating a whining veil around my head.

The sound of the man bulling his way through the underbrush was so loud, I probably could have yelled his name and it would have made no difference. Instead, when he was close enough, I stood, placed my hand on his good shoulder and whispered, "Get down."

It startled him. Then, relieved, he knelt on one knee in the muck, breathing hard.

"I'm surprised you're still alive," I whispered.

The bodyguard replied, "I am more surprised—you make so damn much noise!"

Maybe he was attempting humor again. I stopped wondering about it when the man suddenly turned his head and vomited.

6

Vladimir told me, "Is real name. Not Vladimir Putin, of course. But what matters my name if bleed to death?"

I hadn't asked the man's name. I had asked about the poison gas. A bomb was troubling enough, if it existed, but gas could kill everyone and everything on the island. Where had he gotten his information?

Either Vladimir didn't want to tell me or his brain was muddled from shock.

Now, sitting up, he pulled a plastic bottle from his waist pack. "Need water. Feel like shit." He swatted at the haze of mosquitoes descending on us, adding, "I cut his throat for do this to me. Son-bitch!"

Meaning the gunman.

I knelt, opened the bottle and handed it to him. "You know who he is?"

"Don't know nothing no more. You sure not your longhair friend?" The man's hands were trembling as he tilted the bottle to his lips.

I said, "No. Impossible." Then, looking toward shore, I added, "He's waiting for us to come out of the swamp. He won't risk coming in, and our cover's too thick to waste more ammunition. We can rest here for a little bit, I think."

Vladimir grunted as he leaned his weight against a tree.

"Unless he radioed friends for backup," I whispered. "With one, maybe two more guys, he can seal off our exits. Are these the same people who shot Kazlov?" I thought for a moment. "Do they have radios?"

Vladimir was shaking his head while he emptied the bottle and tossed it aside. "I maybe pass out soon. Lose too much blood."

As I moved to check his wound, he added, "Radio, no. Don't worry about radio. Everything jammed, nothing work. He cannot call—unless they stop jamming."

To confirm it, Vladimir reached into his waist pack and produced a tangle of wires attached to a miniature transceiver. He tapped at the thing, touched a switch, and a tiny green LED light proved the radio was waterproof and still working. After a couple attempts to transmit, though, he pushed the radio into his pack, saying, "Son-bitches. See what I tell you?"

The demonstration was useful and disturbing. An explosion could have knocked out the island's power, but it wouldn't have affected radio communications. Jamming electronics on a small island wasn't difficult, but it required specific technology—and *intent*.

I knew because I've used portable jammers twice while working overseas. The newest generation of jammer is the size of a paperback book. The device I'd used was water-resistant, it had a triad of antennas and it could disrupt multiple wireless frequencies for more than a mile.

If I'd wanted to shoot Kazlov and steal his beluga research, activating a sophisticated jammer would have been a priority. If those were the objectives, however, his enemy had already succeeded, from what Vladimir had told me. So why were people still shooting?

More to the point, why was some persistent, untrained asshole trying to kill us?

Because the makeshift bandage was sticky with blood—and because I wanted the guy to trust me—I had my shirt off and was using my knife to cut a fresh compress. "Maybe it's one of Kazlov's competitors. Steal the man's research, then kill him. What do you think?"

Vladimir didn't reply, and it was too dark to see his reaction.

I tried another angle. "The smart thing for us to do is swim back to the marina. Take cover in one of the boats. He won't expect that. Even if he figures it out, he can't shoot worth a damn. And every move he's made is wrong. Any chance he's one of your people?"

The man made a sound that resembled laughter. "Idiot like him? I would kill him, then fire him."

I had the old bandage off and was rigging the new one with a loop at each end. Add a length of wood for torque and it could be tightened like a tourniquet.

First, though, I packed the wound with crushed mangrove leaves. It couldn't hurt. The leaf fibers might slow the bleeding, and I knew that mangrove bark and extract are used as folk medicine in the jungles of South America. In Colombia, the mountain people make a gargle to treat throat cancer by boiling mangrove bark.

As I worked, I told Vladimir, "He's trying just as hard to kill me as he is you. Damn it, you know more than you're saying."

The man slapped at a mosquito, then looked at his arm. "Why you putting leaves and shit on my wound?"

"Because I'm a goddamn vegetarian—tell me who's shooting at us!"

Vladimir leaned his good shoulder against a tree, silent for several seconds, before he said, "That is problem. I don't know. Is true. First, I think it is you—you and longhair friend's asshole group—who make explosion. Then shoot Mr. Kazlov. Now I am not sure."

I whispered, "That's bullshit and you know it. Why would my own people try to kill me?"

"Is possible! You *know* that bitch woman from hippie group. I see you talking tonight. The men-boys with her, they remind me of—what is word in English? They remind me of small animals with teeth that feed at night. I tell them, 'Get out before Mr. Kazlov come back and see you!' Then bitch *slap* me."

I replied, "I didn't meet those idiots until tonight. And we didn't exactly part on friendly terms."

It was the truth.

"Weasels," Vladimir said. "That is animal. Or it could be . . . *anybody* shooting. Tonight, is true! When power is off, everyone go crazy. Not at first. At first, we all at reception, eating, drinking. Best caviar and vodka in world, Mr. Kazlov serving. Then explosion, and lights go out. People laugh, they make jokes. No big deal, understand?"

I could picture it because I had been in the fishing lodge an hour before the explosion. The lodge had been built in the ornate days of the Rockefellers and industrialist royalty. Polished wood and brass, chandeliers illuminating a formal dining room and bar, men in sports coats, the few women in summer dresses.

On the walls were skin-mounted tarpon—taxidermy masterpieces—and photos of overheated anglers in old-time suits, women in elegant hats, posing by their game-fish trophies. Background music was kept low: swing band classics from the 1940s, which added to the illusion that Vanderbilt Island had stopped in a time warp of its own choosing.

Electrical outages are common on private islands. People in the little dining room and bar handled it calmly—for the first fifteen minutes or so, Vladimir told me.

"But then someone mention their cell phone not working. Everyone check and they begin get nervous because no one has cell phone that working. Restaurant manager try regular phone and that not working, either.

"It was dark in lodge. Not enough candles. And you maybe understand this: Mr. Kazlov's businesspeople are sometimes his business enemies. So people get suspicious. Get scared, I think."

That, at least, made sense. I'd seen the unusual mix of people at the reception. Kazlov's guests had good reasons to be nervous. Along with Vladimir, there were two other bodyguard types in the dining room, both wearing baggy shirts, shirttails out.

It's the way men dress when they are carrying concealed weapons.

As Vladimir talked, I was combining what I remembered and what I had seen with what Kazlov had told me earlier that day. The Russian had rented the entire lodge for the week, which was the same as renting the whole island, since it was the summer off-season.

It was an extravagant gesture for such a small group of guests. Just over a dozen people, not counting the island's small staff, yet the lodge had felt crowded because groups had isolated themselves in cliques. Each clique had staked out its territory, as far from the others as possible—invisible barriers but palpable.

In the formal dining room, the Iranians had a table to themselves, Abdul Armanie and his bodyguard. That was it. Maybe a secretary, too, but I wasn't sure about that.

Armanie had been holding court when I stopped to say hello. His face had a sandstone angularity that dated to the Persian Empire. Heavy black eyebrows, dense mustache and the cold, insolent eyes of a man whose wealth had neutralized most legal boundaries so that he recognized few boundaries of his own.

Armanie had been suspicious of me during the first of two conversations we'd had that afternoon. I'd sat with him on the outdoor patio, near the pool, asking questions about the Caspian's sturgeon population while he drank an espresso and smoked expensive Moldavian cigarettes. His answers were empty and patronizing. The man pretended not to know that I knew the truth about how his organization—and most black marketeers—operated. Harvesting sturgeon roe is illegal, and it can't be done without killing the female. To say the details are unsavory would be an understatement.

Despite his regal gray hair, Darius Talas, from Turkmenia, looked like a man whose body had been assembled from pumpkins. Huge head, swollen belly and a double-sized butt. He sat at a table near the back of the room with one man and two women—neither wearing a burka, so they weren't orthodox Muslim. Not while vacationing in Florida, anyway.

I had spoken with Talas twice that day—the second time when I had surprised him and Armanie arguing about something near the swimming pool. In our first discussion, Talas had shown more interest in what I'd learned from Kazlov than discussing the Caspian Sea. But he had, at least, been charming in the way some fat men are: laughter, and sly references to food and drink and women. When I had entered the dining room, though, stony looks from Talas's bodyguard told me I wasn't welcome, so I didn't bother stopping.

Only Lien Hai Bohai had bothered to stand as I approached his table. The man resembled a Chinese Colonel Sanders, in his white linen suit and billy goat beard, but looked younger for the two women who sat at his side. Maybe his granddaughters or trusted secretaries—or his trusted courtesans. Impossible to know for sure when it comes to aging rich men.

Both women wore sleek silk dresses, and one was a truly stunning beauty. She had implausibly long legs and a world-class body, which I'd confirmed earlier that day when she was at the pool. By candlelight, in the dining room, I had added tannin skin, breasts of marble and Anglo-Malaysian eyes to the list.

Bohai's second escort was also stunning in her way—stunningly plain. Square face framed by black hair; a short, thick body, but a fit-looking woman who had the shoulders of a competitive swimmer. Of the two women, I found her oddly more appealing. More interesting, at least—but then, I prefer female jocks to beauty queens, and I'm always on the hunt for swim partners.

I had been tempted to linger at the table, hoping for an introduction. Instead, I was dismissed by Bohai after only managing eye contact with the tannin-skinned beauty, so I had continued toward the bar to find Tomlinson.

The bar was where the strays gathered. They included a woman restaurateur from nearby Captiva Island and her two lady friends—all late thirties, early forties. Smart, successful and attractive women who radiated a confidence that was spiced with an eagerness to make the most of their bachelorette weekend.

Tomlinson was there, too, but he wasn't sitting with the ladies from Captiva, as expected. He was with his eco-elitist friends, including Densler, the group leader.

It had been my first look at the party crashers, although it had taken me a while to confirm they were on the island without Kazlov's knowledge. Densler was outspoken, loud and a little drunk, which had provided me yet another reason to escape the reception in favor of a solitary night dive. When the lights went out, Tomlinson and his new Third Planet friends had probably still been in the bar.

It was a volatile mix that included a couple of armed bodyguards from three competing organizations, plus an unwelcome group of antagonistic outsiders. The chaos that followed was starting to assume order as Vladimir continued to describe what happened when the power went out and after guests realized their cell phones weren't working.

"That is when people start to get scared," the man told me. "All over lodge, I hear them talking, saying, 'Try reception outside, try near window.' I hear people bang into chairs 'cause not enough candles. Everyone nervous. Then in loud voice, a man—someone in bar, I think—this man, he yell, 'Hey, Internet is out, too! What hell shitty trick is Kazlov playing?' What if emergency? Someone could die."

It was then that a single shot was fired. The shot came from nearby, maybe outside, but more likely from one of the lodge's guest rooms. A pistol, Vladimir told me. Small caliber.

I waited while the bodyguard took several seconds to catch his breath before he added, "That is when whole night go to shit. People start yelling, they go crazy. They panic, they run. How many people left lodge, I don't know. Mr. Kazlov disappear just before hippie group arrive—important business. It take me a while to know he still not return to dining room. That when I go little crazy, too."

Looking at me through shadows, Vladimir sat straighter to make his point. "See why I call it 'crazy'? Power out, phones not working. Of course everyone is afraid. This is not accident. Hear what I say? It is not accident! I should have understood sooner, but . . . but . . ."

Vladimir was beginning to pant, and I noticed he no longer bothered to slap at the horde of mosquitoes—one of the first symptoms of shock in Florida on a summer night. So I torqued the bandage tight, knotted it and helped the man lie down.

I was thinking that someone had gone to a lot of trouble to isolate Vanderbilt Island from the outside world. Was the perpetrator so brilliant that he had anticipated the hysteria he had created? Vladimir had implied as much. Or had he just gotten lucky?

The word "brilliant" didn't fit the gunman who was now getting impatient. I could tell because he was using the flashlight again to search the tree canopy above us. I watched the angle of his light change as he shifted positions. The gunman was coming toward us, I realized.

As I got to my feet, Vladimir said, "Can't move yet. Lose too much blood. I rest, maybe sleep. Then go."

The man was lying on his back, knees drawn up. I knelt and touched my fingers to his neck. His pulse was rapid and weak. He was shivering, too, on a night so warm the air had weight, like steam.

I said, "If you go to sleep, you're not going to wake up."

Vladimir made a vague reply with his hand. "Five minutes," he said. "Too tired. Bring me water. I am very thirsty. Bring doctor, too."

The man was drifting into delirium, so I tried one more time. "How do you know there's a bomb? Someone told you. Goddamn it, there are innocent people in the lodge who have nothing to do with your little war."

The man made a grunting sound of impatience. I had to ask the question again before he finally admitted, "A few minutes after Mr. Kazlov leave party, he send me text. He say someone he know intercept e-mails. There may be device on island that kill everything at midnight—"

I interrupted, "Midnight? You're sure?"

The man nodded. "Information, he say, come from close friend, but not confirmed. This just before jamming start."

"Which friend? The same one who told you Kazlov had been shot?"

"We have many intelligence sources. No need to say name of his friend."

It was someone on the island, apparently, or the man would have no reason to conceal the identify.

I said, "Damn it. Why didn't you tell me this right away?" because it was ten p.m.

Vladimir stirred for a moment and lifted his head to look at me. A moment of clarity, it seemed.

"Does not matter intelligence source. But was your longhair friend who tell me Mr. Kazlov was shot. Why you think I come straight to marina to kill you if you don't tell me where bomb is hidden?"

He said it as if I should have already known.

A moment later, Vladimir held up a warning hand and shook his head—*Enough*—then lay back as if sleeping.

The man was lying on his side in a fetal position when I turned and retraced my path through the mangroves, toward the water. I stayed low, ducking limbs, peeling spiderwebs from my face as the muck, ankle-deep, tried to suction off my shoes. Something the man had said banged around in my head, signaling for special attention. It had to do with isolating people from the outside world.

"This is no accident!" Vladimir had told me, referring to the sudden power outage, then the loss of wireless reception. "I should have understood sooner."

That's when it dawned on me that I should have understood sooner, too. His words had stuck in my subconscious for good reason. A few weeks or so before, I'd discussed this very scenario over beer in my lab back on Sanibel. How would people react if an enemy suddenly jammed public cell phone networks and cut off all Internet service?

"It's inevitable. It'll happen one day. And we should be preparing the same way we plan for a natural disaster. Hurricanes, tornadoes, same thing—only the panic will be ten times worse because the damage will be psychological, and without precedent. It'll be unlike any previous hell storm nightmare our country has ever experienced."

Those were Tomlinson's words, Tomlinson's predictions. I hadn't taken the discussion seriously because it was all hypothetical, plus we had been ping-ponging the idea back and forth for years.

But, now, here we were. And it was real.

Was there a connection?

I didn't like the way my brain was linking events. Didn't like it one damn bit because, in most of the scenarios, Tomlinson provided the only hub in a multi-spoked wheel.

As I waded into the water, like it or not, I no longer felt so certain of my old friend's innocence.

7

On a yellow legal pad, Tomlinson had written *Sudden Internet Isolation Response*, then placed the thing in front of me as I hunkered over the sink in my little laboratory, cleaning an aquarium.

This was almost a month before we'd sailed for Vanderbilt Island, not two weeks before as I'd first thought. I became sure of the timing when I remembered that Tomlinson had received his invitation from Kazlov's staff the next day. It wasn't until a week or so later that we'd even discussed the caviar party at length.

No wonder the details had faded.

As I swam away from the mangroves, where I'd left Vladimir, toward the marina where Tomlinson's sailboat was moored, I replayed the scene in my head, hoping to cull some key bit of data I had forgotten.

I had been wearing elbow-length rubber gloves and a lab mask. On the counter, to my right, was a beaker filled with muriatic acid, and the fumes were getting to me.

"You mind opening those?" I had responded, nodding toward

the windows along the south wall. "There's a fan next to my bed. Maybe put it on the lab cart—you'll have to unlock the wheels first. I'm about to pass out."

The University of Northern Iowa's science department had ordered four dozen spiny sea urchins, an order which I had shipped that afternoon. Because I had done the collecting gradually, over a period of ten days, the acrylic walls of the tank were scarred with calcium buildup. Sea urchins are echinoderms, a family of complex, specialized animals that use thousands of tiny adhesive feet to transport themselves over the bottom. I was guessing the adhesive substance had bonded with calcium carbonate in the water and attached itself in random streaks to the glass.

Tomlinson had nudged the legal pad closer to me, saying, "I'm finally assembling data to write a paper on the damn subject—after all the times we've talked about it, about time, huh? Trouble is, there's no quantitative data available. And the qualitative knowledge base is, like, zero, zilch, *nada*, because it's never happened before—thank this nation's lucky stars."

Over his shoulder, he had added, "Try to come up with a good acronym. Even behavioral scientists go goofy for a sexy acronym—probably because we're too introspective to get reliable hard-ons. Present company excluded, of course."

I didn't bother replying.

"Something spelled close to the word 'serious' because it's, *you know*, a damn serious subject. I'm getting close with Sudden Internet Isolation Response. Just need a couple of more bell ringers. Words that fit without straining—you're familiar with the drill."

I had sniffed, squinted acidic tears from my eyes and looked at the legal pad. Tomlinson's penmanship is unusual. After all the acid *he's* dealt with over the years, you'd expect spidery impressionism. Instead, his writing reminds me of the eloquent calligraphy that I associate with previous centuries—beautifully formed and slanted loops and swirls. Spenserian script, he calls it, and credits his writing hand to a former life in which, he says, he worked as a shipping clerk, eighteenth-century London, on the Thames River.

After he'd left the room, I mumbled the title aloud, then experimented with variations because I couldn't help myself. I'm obsessive, which I have no problem admitting. I'm also a linear thinker who follows avenues of thought as if they were tunnels. By blindsiding me with the problem, Tomlinson had successfully elbowed me into a new tunnel.

As he returned to the lab, and plugged in the fan, I was saying, "Sudden Internet Isolation Response. Uhhh . . . Sudden Isolation *Reaction* . . . After . . . After Undetected Electronic Sabotage? No, that stinks. Sudden Isolation Response to . . . to . . . ?" I looked at him and shrugged. "I've got work to do. Write your own damn paper."

Tomlinson had snapped his fingers, grabbed the legal pad and found his pencil. "How about this?"

I watched him write *Sudden Internet Isolation Response In an Unsuspecting Society.*

"'Unprepared Society' is better," I told him. 'It's stronger than 'Unsuspecting.' More accurate, anyway."

The man thought about it, then nodded as he made the change. "When you're right, you're right. Let's see how it looks on paper: S—I—I—R—I—U—S. Sweet, *hermano*—perfect. *Serious*—" He grinned. "Now I've just got to do the mule work. Write the intro. Put together my materials and methods. I'll have to slip through a few time barriers, take a peek into the future to assemble data. A couple of hash brownies should do the trick. But this'll get me to the starting gate."

Marijuana-laced brownies and time travel—standard equipage

for academic research in Tomlinson World. I knew better than to ask questions.

It kept Tomlinson quiet for all of ten minutes, during which he had found a stool and sat at the stainless steel dissecting table, scribbling, erasing, then scribbling some more. He had stopped only once to go to the galley and grab a fresh quart of beer.

I finished cleaning the tank, and had moved to my desk where there was a file labeled *Mote/Sturgeon Farming/Caviar.* Even though it was four weeks before Kazlov's party, I was already well into my research. In the file were the notes I'd made in Sarasota while touring Mote Marine Lab's aquaculture facility. There were also articles and research papers on sturgeon.

I had been reading an article about the Caspian Sea's black marketeers when Tomlinson returned to the subject of Internet isolation. "Wireless communication is our new tribal lifeline, man. It worries me. Like, *obsessively* worries me. Have you noticed that I rarely carry my cell phone anymore?"

"Maybe they'll start making sarongs with pockets," I had replied. "I don't carry mine unless I'm away from the lab for more than a day. It's like being on a leash."

The man's expression had read *Good!* "But we're the exceptions, *hermano.* The majority of people are so dependent, it makes us vulnerable as an Oklahoma trailer park. Sure, we can survive without cell phones and Internet, but we can no longer *function* without them."

It was an interesting premise. There were Darwinian implications that I would have offered, but Tomlinson had been into the subject, so I let him talk.

"Internet and cell phones have morphed from simple conveniences into human sensory devices. No . . . sensory apparati, because they have unseated our own five senses in importance. As well as our reliance on humans to provide—well, let's face it—actual human contact. Shut down those two electronic senses without warning, man, it'll be like . . . almost like . . ."

I had offered, "Sudden blindness—the psychological response would be similar. Shock, disbelief, denial and then panic. It depends on the person, of course. And how long the system was down. Which is probably an exaggeration, but—"

"That's my point," Tomlinson had interrupted. "No one will know how long the systems will be down. How can we? Combined with a simultaneous power outage and it will be the demon mother of all uncivil chaos. Coast to coast, rumors will spread like butt cheeks at a chili festival. There'll be talk of a terrorist attack. Of government conspiracies. Of the CIA taking control of the White House—not that those bastards aren't above trying. Rumors and disinformation will spread like crabs at low tide, from neighborhood to neighborhood. No . . . I've got that wrong."

As he considered alternatives, Tomlinson had tugged at his hair so hard that, for a moment, I saw the little lightning bolt scar on his temple.

"Nope . . . I was right the first time. Rumors will travel from house to house. Of course they will. But the only real news we'll get will come from fishermen and truckers, because they still communicate by radio. Some of them, at least. It's been a while since I've done any hitchhiking, so I've lost track of my eighteen-wheeler brothers. Do they still use CBs?"

Taking off my lab coat, I had told him, "Truckers might do a better job than newscasters. Less biased, and they probably have better bullshit detectors. But you're getting spooked for no reason. To use a Tomlinson phrase: 'Shallow up, man.'"

My pal had given me an impatient look, meaning the subject was too important for him not to be upset.

I had closed the Mote file and put it away. This was on a Friday afternoon. That morning, I'd had a huge breakfast at the Over Easy Café, just down the road from Dinkin's Bay Marina. The night before, I'd eaten a mammoth piece of Drunken Parrot Carrot Cake at the Rum Bar. Which is why I'd felt as if a slab of lead had been strapped to my butt.

The best way to treat a caloric hangover, I have discovered, is to bludgeon the offender with exercise. That's precisely what I had intended to do: go for a run, then do an hour of serious cross-training—PT, my friends call it.

As I headed out the screen door to change clothes, I had said, "You mind taking your empty beer bottles to the recycle bin? A marine lab isn't supposed to smell like a brewery. Not my lab, anyway. But it does way too often. And don't think I don't know it when you smoke dope in here, too."

Because that sounded harsher than I'd intended, I added, "I'm going to jog Tarpon Bay Road to the Island Inn. Nicky Clements just installed a pull-up bar. Twenty minutes there, and I'll swim the NO WAKE buoys to the West Wind. You could pace me on your bike during the run. I want to keep it under eight-minute miles, then we could meet at West Wind pool later. How's about it?"

Tomlinson had turned and studied me for a moment. "Dude, you are about as ripped as I've ever seen you. Seriously—you've got the veins popping. The whole gaunt predator thing going on. Man, it's like you're getting younger and younger while everyone around you ages."

I had watched his eyes move to the padlocked cabinet where I keep the Schedule III drugs sometimes used in my work. Then I listened to Tomlinson ask, "You got some human growth hormone stashed in there or something? Raw pituitary extract from unborn chimps? I've been wanting to try something like that, but I'm not sure of the side effects, so—"

"You lecturing me on the dangers of drugs," I had interrupted, "carries about as much weight as you preaching the value of sexual fidelity. I'm fit because I work at it seven days a week."

My friend was still eyeing the drug cabinet as he offered, "Then you can afford one day off."

"That's one of the few lies I don't let myself believe. You coming or not?"

Tomlinson had exaggerated my level of fitness, although I *am* in the best shape I've been for many years. I had cut way back on alcohol and carbs—carrot cake the occasional exception—refined my workouts to eliminate injuries and doubled my cardio time on a ball breaker of a machine called a VersaClimber. It meant a lot more surfing and swimming and less joint-jarring sprints on hard sand.

As a result, I'm in better overall shape, but I can no longer talk and run sub-eight-minute miles at the same time. So it wasn't until almost sunset, sitting at the West Wind pool bar, that we had touched on the subject of Internet isolation again. But not for long, because I did most of the talking.

During the mile swim, I had settled into an automaton rhythm—*stroke-stroke-breathe-kick*—that allowed my brain to drift free of the responsibilities associated with survival. It wasn't really freeing, though, because at first I stupidly fixated on personal problems. Nothing serious, but irritating.

My sixteen-year-old son, who lives in Colombia with his regal, bipolar mother, was already being recruited by the Military School of the Americas—Military School of Assassins, as it was known when the institute was based in Panama. That was unsettling in itself, considering my background, but he'd also decided to give up baseball to play *soccer*.

It was a trivial disappointment compared to the problems I'd been having with women.

The previous afternoon, the smart lady biologist I'd been dating, Emily Marston, had asked to have a "serious talk"—among the most chilling phrases in the female vocabulary. She said that our marathon lovemaking was as stimulating as our mutual interests, but, frankly, she'd begun to question my ability to make a lasting commitment.

I had been tempted to point out her concern was based on a flawed premise. I didn't *want* to make a lasting commitment. Not yet, anyway. I was also tempted to mention that she had told me, from the start, that she was too recently divorced to get into a serious relationship. But isn't that what women always say?

"Maybe we should take a month off and think about it," I had suggested. I didn't want to take a month off—we'd been having too much fun—but I was trying to behave like a sensitive, modern male.

Sensitive, modern males are dumbasses, apparently. Five minutes later, Emily Marston, the handsome lady biologist, was out the door, and maybe out of my life.

I had other relationship problems, too.

My workout pal and former lover, Dewey Nye, had decided that she, her new love interest and our toddler daughter were better off living in Belgium, where same-sex marriage is legal. I am all for same-sex marriage—what gives government the right to spare us from our own mistakes or happiness? But Dewey marrying a twenty-two-year-old female golf phenom? And in *Belgium*, for Christ's sake?

Maybe on one distant day, at a soccer match in Brussels, I would get to see my son and daughter again.

As I swam along the beach, though, I'd finally realized I had been swept into negative channels of thought. So I had consciously shifted to an unemotional topic. Tomlinson's theory was fresh in my memory, so I had spent the rest of the swim scanning for Darwinian parallels.

There were many.

Later, sitting at the West Wind pool bar, rehydrating with soda water and lime, I had bounced my conclusions off my pal, who had switched from beer to a Nicaraguan rum, Flor de Caña.

I had told him, "You're right, I've been thinking about it. Our reliance on a tool, any tool, increases our vulnerability as a species."

"Damn right." Tomlinson nodded, as he signaled the bartender for another drink.

"Clothing is a tool. Supermarkets, leakproof roofs, Bic lighters, they're all tool related. Our lives wouldn't be the same without them. But 'reliance' isn't the same as 'dependence.' See what I'm getting at?"

"No," Tomlinson had replied, but he was interested. "Just for the record, I prefer kitchen matches to lighters. Call me old-fashioned. Plus, I like the smell."

"I'm talking about the paper you're writing," I had replied, then explained that "dependence" implied a behavioral shift. "Specialization is a form of adaptation that results in dependence. A specialist species can thrive, but only in its environmental niche. Remove ants from the landscape and an anteater's nose becomes a liability. Does it make sense now?"

Tomlinson was with me again. "The more specialized the tools, the more vulnerable their dependents. Wireless technology—bingo! Doc, you just gave the first line of my introduction."

A few minutes later, sipping my first beer, I had asked the bartender for a piece of paper. Instead, she had given me a cloth napkin, and said, "I was going to trash it, anyway. See the stain?"

I had told Tomlinson, "Use this any way you want," and then concentrated for a couple of minutes as I wrote:

Adaptation funnels some species into ever-narrowing passages of specialization that ensure their success. For a time. In the Darwinian exemplar, specialization is always associated with dependence. Dependence is always associated with risk. There is an implicit fragility, no matter how large and powerful the animal. Specialization can elevate a species to a genetic apex—but the apex inevitably teeters between godliness and the abyss.

"Godliness and the abyss." Tomlinson had repeated the phrase several times, a genial smile on his face. "Your spiritual side is starting to overpower your dark side, Dr. Ford."

I had countered, "I used the word metaphorically, Professor Tomlinson, as you well know."

End of discussion, and we had moved on to more compelling topics—Vision surfboards made by Buddha Bonifay, women and torn rotator cuffs.

It hadn't crossed my mind there was a connection between Tomlinson's Sudden Internet Isolation theory, the party-crashing eco-activists and the events now taking place on Vanderbilt Island. Not until I had listened to Vladimir, anyway.

Now, though, as I swam through darkness toward the marina, I realized the oversight was a gross lapse on my part. In fact, I had received an advance warning, of sorts, from Tomlinson himself. He had referenced the subject obliquely a day or so later, while on a rant about environmentalism and the Caspian Sea.

The linkage was there. I had missed it. But I couldn't be too hard on myself. Not many people would make a connection between hashish brownies, caviar and hijacking an island.

Hash brownies—they were in the paper bag Tomlinson had been holding when he appeared on the stern of *Tiger Lilly*, the floating home of two Dinkin's Bay icons, Rhonda Lister and JoAnn Smallwood. On his face was a tranquil grin and his eyes were glazed. The marina's resident cat, Crunch & Des, was cradled in his free arm.

This was more than a month ago, a Saturday evening, after he had returned from the post office with mail that included his invitation to Vanderbilt Island.

As I'd watched Tomlinson exit the boat, I doubted if he was grinning because he'd just enjoyed the favors of one or both ladies, although it was possible. Anything is possible at Dinkin's Bay, particularly after sunset, when Mack, the owner, locks the parking lot gates, barring prissy, judgmental outsiders from the marina, along with the rest of the world.

As it turned out, though, Tomlinson's grin had more to do with the brownies the ladies had fed him before packing the rest into a to-go bag.

"They made the classic Betty Crocker one-cubed-squared recipe," he had explained, still holding the cat and the paper bag as he followed me down the boardwalk toward my lab.

I'd replied, "Like a mathematical formula, you mean?"

"Even better. A mathematical double entendre. One egg, one great big cube of primo hash resin, one box of brownie mix, baked, then cut into squares. The resin was made with my own brownie-loving hands. You want one?"

Hashish, he meant. Which makes him even more talkative than grass, as he admits. And why I had tuned him out even when he got onto the subject of caviar and Vanderbilt Island, which somehow transitioned into a monologue on yet another environmental group he had joined—Third Planet Peace Force—which was obvious only in hindsight. He hadn't mentioned the group by name. Not even once, until they had appeared at the fishing lodge.

I vaguely remembered him saying that he suspected one of the group's officers was a fan of his writing—Winifred Densler, as it turned out.

"We've been trading rather formal e-mails," he had explained, "but all the evidence is there. There's a lot to learn from a woman's choice of verbs. Freudian stuff, you know? Adverbs, the same thing. Adverbs reveal passion . . . sometimes deep hostility, too. Verbs reveal sexual interest or sexual frustration. Doesn't matter a damn what she's writing about. Modifiers and verbs, man—and don't forget exclamation points and smiley faces. They are the Internet's truest windows to a woman's soul."

The hostility line had stuck with me. Thinking about it now, alone in black water, swimming beneath stars, that phrase—*deep hostility*—suddenly prodded another detail free. Tomlinson, days later, had mentioned he had sent the first few hundred words of his Internet isolation theory to a member of the group—Densler, probably. She had shared it with other key members, and then Tomlinson had given his permission to post it on the organization's private web page. Members' reactions, my pal had told me, had been enthusiastic, but in a way that had struck even him as abnormally angry.

"What bothers me," he had said, "is they seem eager for the Apocalypse. Punish man for all our sins against nature. Me, I'm not into the whole punishment deal. It's bad juju, karmically speaking."

Punish man for our sins against nature.

There! It was the connection I'd been searching for. At the time, it had been a snippet of meaningless conversation. Now, though, Tomlinson's words provided a key part of a disturbing picture.

Possibly.

Verifying that the linkage was real, not fanciful, was so important that I stopped swimming and treaded water for a few seconds to confirm the details in my head.

I could picture Tomlinson following me into the lab and placing Crunch & Des on the dissection table as he told me, "A couple of the members wrote they're all for the Internet crashing. See what I mean? They copied me, of course, and everyone else—members of this group I'm talking about share everything. Very communal in an Internet sort of way, which I find cool."

They share everything—another important point.

Tomlinson had continued, "What they're hoping is, when the Internet finally crashes, it'll give us a taste of what's gonna happen if the industrialized nations don't stop abusing Mother Earth. A microcosmic taste, you know, when the kimchi really hits the fan."

Tomlinson's dreamy idealism can be almost as irritating as his self-righteous certitude, but I hadn't called him on it. I had been busy watching the cat. Tail twitching, Crunch & Des had been eyeing a half dozen fingerling tarpon that I'd recently transferred to a fifty-gallon aquarium near the dissection table. Because I was duplicating a procedure done in the 1930s by biologist Charles M. Breeder, I hadn't covered the tank. Even fingerling tarpon require surface air to survive—which Breeder had proven and the cat now realized.

Crunch & Des was getting ready to attack. I had seen the warning signs before.

Before the cat could pounce, though, I had crossed the room while listening to Tomlinson say, "See why I became a dues-paying member? They're hardasses, man! A group of highly educated, well-informed Greenies who aren't content to sit on their dead butts while the environment collapses around us. You want some examples of how they operate?"

No, I didn't. Which is why I had paid more attention to the cat than to Tomlinson as I returned to my desk. Even so, I remembered the man telling me that the group was made up of true activists, not run-of-the-mill do-gooders and talkers. And they had more than just passion. They had enough financial backing to purchase a commercial trawler in Iran and refit it as a mother ship, from which they launched their fast rigid-hulled inflatable boats onto the Caspian Sea. Members were watermen who knew their way around a wheelhouse. For the past year, Tomlinson had said, they had been manning the trawler with crews of six, systematically harassing sturgeon fishermen at sea and on the docks. Same with the shuttle boats that hauled workers to and from oil rigs in the Caspian.

No . . . I had the wording wrong, probably the result of my own bias. As I continued swimming the last forty yards toward the marina's docks, and *No Más*, I decided Tomlinson had probably said confronting fishermen, not harassing.

He approved, of course.

"How else are you going to deal with international outlaws? My God, look what they're doing to the whales on this planet!"

With a wave of his hand, my strange friend had dismissed all governing bodies—the International Whaling Commission, among them—as if useless, before adding, "If a few tough, smart activists don't organize internationally to stop this rank bullshit, we're going to be the death of our own species—and we'll take a lot of innocent species with us."

I don't have much patience with doomsayers, people who are secretly eager for the Apocalypse to cleanse the Earth of human sloth. Tomlinson knows it, which is probably why he had focused on a subject of mutual interest: whales.

"Just as an example, Doc. What's happening to our sea mammals is a perfect inverse mirror that reflects man's greed, our bloodlust . . . the whole negative karma thing that's going to turn around and bite us on the ass one day.

"It's all about rhythm. Synchronicity is another way of viewing the problem. Crystals, for instance, are repeating three-dimensional realities—but look what happens if *just one* molecule is removed from what's call the 'lattice parameter.' Trust me, *amigo*. I think you know where I'm headed with this."

Nope, not a clue, but I let it go.

Tomlinson had compared the group's efforts with the campaign against the Japanese whaling fleet by another organization, the Sea Shepherd Conservation Society. Over the last several years, Sea Shepherd activists had hurled stink bombs, snared propellers and even collided with opposing vessels in their efforts to disrupt Japan's annual "harvest" of open-ocean whales.

"It's the illegal, cold-blooded murder of a fellow warm-blooded species—it's mammalicide," my pal had said—which also stuck in my memory, because the word "mammalicide" was so unusual. "This is one of those rare cases when a passive response is actually an active form of violence. How? Because it guarantees more bloodshed. That's why I'm helping our environmental warriors in every way I can."

Those weren't Tomlinson's exact words, of course. It was possible he had said, "I'm *backing* our environmental warriors," or that he was "supporting" them—subtle differences, true, but both suggested a more hands-on commitment to . . . to what? Proactive intervention? Or was he tacitly endorsing violence?

Truth was, either one was a possibility, considering Tomlinson's past.

Though few on Sanibel Island would believe it, Tomlinson had spent time in jail because of his associations with radical groups. In South Dakota, he had been arrested at an American Indian Movement rally demanding the release of Leonard Peltier. He had also been a suspect in a terrorist bombing that had killed two people at a San Diego naval base.

But that was many years ago. Had I not been convinced that Tomlinson, while not blameless, wasn't guilty of murder, we certainly wouldn't be friends today. Tomlinson, in truth, wouldn't be alive today—something I knew for certain and he probably suspected.

Was it possible that the guy had turned radical again?

Maybe, I decided. Anyone who lives on the water is an environmentalist by obligation, if not choice. What better cause could there be?

Tomlinson and I seldom agree on anything that has to do with religion, politics or has boundaries that exceed the perimeter of Dinkin's Bay. But he was right about Japan's slaughter of whales. It's illegal and outrageous. Not only does the "fishery" kill more than a thousand whales yearly, the nation shows its contempt for world opinion (and the ocean's resources) by insisting that the butchery is actually a "whale research program."

With a similar research program, the Japanese have destroyed the bull shark population in Lake Nicaragua and continues its assault on a global scale using nets, longlines and factory ships.

Yet, Japan's atrocities are eclipsed by the world's foremost environmental outlaw, China. I had collected some unsavory details while researching one of that country's foremost offenders, Lien Hai Bohai.

China recognizes no international sea boundaries but its own, plus those of countries that have prostituted their futures by selling China all rights to their fisheries. Cuba may be the saddest example—its citizens are legally forbidden from eating shrimp, lobster and pelagic fish caught in their own waters.

Chinese ships catch, kill, process and blast-freeze every living thing in their paths. Floating factories, like the fleet owned by Lien Bohai, destroy a hundred cubic miles of sea bottom daily, fifty-two weeks a year, year after year. The countries of the former Soviet Union do less damage, but only because they have limited resources.

Tomlinson had every reason to support environmental activists in the Caspian Sea. But violence with lethal intent? No . . . I knew the guy too well to believe it. I just couldn't. With him, the lines of morality are often blurry, but no way would he associate with anyone crazy enough to shoot or gas innocent people.

Lien Bohai was a different story. A man who could rationalize a scorched-earth policy at sea was capable of just about anything. The same was true of the Eastern Europeans. Armanie and Darius Talas were Viktor Kazlov's associates, Vladimir had told me, but also his enemies. Any of those men might be behind what was happening tonight, yet my focus kept returning to the members of Third Planet. They had already shown their indifference to the law by trespassing, and only they had been privy to Tomlinson's Internet isolation theory.

As badly as I wanted to dismiss it, though, I couldn't disassociate Tomlinson from what was happening tonight on Vanderbilt Island. Even if he was the unknowing contributor to someone's lunatic plan, the man was too damn perceptive not to suspect he was being used.

As I swam the last few yards to Tomlinson's sailboat, Vladimir's words continued to bang around in my head.

"Your longhair friend told me," he had said, as if I should have already known.

Maybe he was right.

8

I was in the water, hanging off the stern of Tomlinson's boat, when I heard a gunshot from somewhere near the mangroves. Then a second shot.

Vladimir. It was the first explanation that came to mind.

After so much wild gunfire, the two shots, spaced seconds apart, sounded workmanlike and purposeful. They were of similar caliber as the rounds that had chased the bodyguard and me from beneath the dock. A semiautomatic 9mm or something close.

After the second shot, I spun around and took a look. The mangrove point was an elevated darkness backdropped by stars and the silence of empty houses. There was no telltale corona from a flashlight, no streak of a red laser.

Even so, I guessed that Vladimir had been found and executed. Soon, the gunman would be looking for me. Before that happened, I wanted to get what I needed from Tomlinson's boat and be gone.

Because I couldn't risk showing myself on the dock, it took more time than it should have to get aboard.

When it comes to utility, sailboats present too many design challenges to name. High on my list of dislikes is, they are pains in the ass to board from the water. Tomlinson's old Morgan is rigged for single-handed blue-water passages to Key West and the Yucatán. When the skipper of a vessel is often drunk and/or stoned, safety gear must be rigged accordingly.

In the case of *No Más*, it means the deck is fenced with lifeline cables, three high, on thirty-inch stanchions. Less chance of the man tumbling overboard in a heavy sea. So I grabbed the lowest cable, did a pull-up, then slapped a hand around the top cable. I hung there for a moment, then managed to get my left foot through the lifeline gate onto the deck—not easy when you're wearing swim fins.

A minute later, I was aboard, swinging down the companionway into the heat, the darkness and familiar odors of the vessel's cabin. Tomlinson's floating Zendo, his students call the boat. The space smelled of kerosene, teak oil, electronics, sandalwood and the musky odor of marijuana. I reached, closed the hatchway, then pulled the curtains tight before I found a jar of wooden matches above the stove and lit a lamp.

First thing I did was open the icebox and chug a bottle of water. I was trembling from dehydration. I also forced myself to chew a handful of dried apricots even though I wasn't hungry.

With a second bottle of water, I sat for a few seconds at the settee table, then went to the VHF radio mounted above the navigation station and quarter berth. I switched the radio on, reduced squelch, and a familiar warble told me that a jamming device was, indeed, somewhere on the island. Even so, I switched to channel 16 and transmitted a series of Mayday calls, complete with location.

No response.

During my swim, I had also reviewed my options. One option was to cut the lines, fire the sailboat's little Yanmar diesel and attempt to navigate the shallow waters on my own. When *No Más* was out of jamming range, I could try the radio again.

Or . . . I could board the neighboring power vessels, one by one, in the hope their owners had left keys in the ignitions. Because most of the winter residents had pulled their boats, though, there were only a few possibilities. There were two small trawlers, buttoned up tight for the summer. There were two shabby rental boats—one of them an eighteen-foot Boston Whaler—that had probably brought Densler and her group to the island. And there was Viktor Kazlov's black-hulled Dragos Voyager, which was moored off by itself, isolated at the end of the basin. The vessel was sleek as a stiletto, all teak and glass, with a cabin that swept aft toward a massive afterdeck, where there was a swim platform that doubled as a loading elevator. The yacht was still umbilicated to shore power, but its emergency generator had a bad switch, apparently, because it had yet to start itself. The groups from Iran, Turkmenia and China hadn't come by private yacht, so that was it—only a couple of usable boats.

The Whaler was my best possibility, I had already decided—but was there time for me to swim over and take a look?

I checked my watch: 10:30. *Damn.*

Maybe I had time, maybe I didn't. The midnight deadline was unambiguous, if Vladimir was right. He was convinced the danger was real, I didn't doubt that. Someone here, on the island, had intercepted an e-mail, or had been made aware of an e-mail, that contained the threat. The trail of logic told me the person was a reliable source of intelligence, and that Kazlov trusted him.

But who? It had to be one of the man's caviar competitors, but why shield his identify? It was pointless, particularly when it came to an outsider like myself.

There was a more compelling question, though: did such a device exist?

"Everything will die," Vladimir had told me, which, to him, meant a bomb or gas device had been hidden somewhere in or near the fishing lodge. Considering Vladimir's probable background, he had been right to assume an IED—an improvised explosive device—had been planted somewhere where it would do the most damage. The explosion that had knocked out the power had been set by someone savvy enough also to seal off the island with a jamming device. It wasn't much of a stretch to suspect they had also wired explosives or canisters of poison gas to a timed detonator set for midnight.

But what kind of timing device? And had the wiring been exposed to the recent rainstorm? If wet, something homemade might jump ahead an hour or be delayed. Or it might fail to join the polar contacts, which was the best possible outcome—but I couldn't count on that.

The spot where an IED would cause the most casualities was the fishing lodge, which I had known all along.

The lodge. I had to get inside, assess the situation and then do some improvising of my own. The possibility that someone had rigged the building with an explosive was bad enough. But the prospect of poison gas was chilling. Even if they had managed to smuggle a detonator and military-grade C4 into the place, an explosion affected a limited area. The right poison gas, though, could kill everyone and everything on the island.

In that instant, I realized I might have overlooked yet another important subtlety.

"Everything will die," Vladimir had said, not, "*Everyone* will die." The man's English wasn't good—there was no guessing how badly he had mistranslated Kazlov's message. But the bodyguard had repeated the phrase at least twice, so maybe the distinction was important.

Vladimir had been right to assume the worst. So I did the same. I told myself that, at midnight, either lethal gas would be released somewhere on the island or a bomb would detonate somewhere inside the fishing lodge. I had to do whatever was necessary to stop it from happening.

The human brain is a remarkable organ, but it becomes a jumbled mess when responding to danger. The primitive brain takes control of our involuntary systems, oblivious to signals from the highly evolved neocortex. The result is either chaos or catatonic inaction.

In my life, I've dealt with enough risky situations to understand that the brain responds to danger emotionally. It's not until a threat is reduced to some basic linear form that it becomes a solvable problem. The human intellect is fearless—if we ignore the ancient alarms. If we stay calm long enough to access a functional cerebral pathway.

I'm no different than anyone else. I had to think it through. The process took only a few seconds, but the decision provided clarity and the direction I needed.

I turned from the navigation station and went to work.

Because Tomlinson is Tomlinson, there were no firearms aboard, of course. And I am not a gun hobbyist who packs a weapon just for thrills. I own three handguns because my work requires it, but they were all back at my lab, locked safely away, with the state and federal permits that allow me to carry them.

But I had my knife. And I had been trained to make and use unconventional weapons. My main reason for returning to the sailboat, though—aside from trying the VHF—was to retrieve a piece of equipment that would finally give me an advantage over the man, or men, determined to kill me.

By coincidence or good luck, the day before Tomlinson and I had left for the island, a package had arrived from a friend who works for Nivisys Industries, Tempe, Arizona. The company maintains the same low profile as the military and State Department types who are its devoted clientele. It's tough to find information about the products even on the Internet, because if you aren't already familiar with Nivisys, there is probably no reason for you to know that it exists.

The company designs and manufactures some of the world's finest tactical hardware. Esoteric items such as tactical illuminators, laser-aiming systems and superb night vision binoculars and rifle scopes. The company's slogan is Don't Fight Fair, and they take the mission seriously enough to trust operators versed in the craft to test the hell out of their newest creations.

Which is why I had received the package in the first place. And why I wasn't surprised the enclosed note had read simply, "What do you think? Bob Alexander."

Inside was a canvas pouch about the size of a standard flashlight. Inside the pouch was a new-generation TAM-14—a thermal acquisition monocular. Which is tacticalspeak for thermal vision. It is a device that sees what the human eye cannot, day or night, because it is ultrasensitive to heat.

Body heat—its specialty. The unit was unlike any night vision system I had ever used before.

With the TAM, I could track a man by following the warmth of his footprints after he had crossed a stretch of cooling sand. An unwanted visitor's handprints were visible on walls and doors long after he had fled. With this newest generation of optics, I could observe targets through smoke, fog, dense foliage and even walls.

The TAM-14 translated subtle changes in temperature—metal, wood, vegetable or flesh—and sent the information straight to the viewer's eye.

Thermal night vision also recognizes channel markers no matter the weather, so it was ideal for night navigation, which is why I had brought the unit along. And why I had left the TAM stored in a locker beneath *No Más*'s navigation station.

I knelt, retrieved the thermal monocular, tested it to make sure the batteries were fresh and placed it on the settee table. Then I went to work searching the boat for materials necessary to make a weapon.

Or weapons.

Even though it was only ninety minutes until midnight, it would be stupid to venture onto the island unarmed. Or without a plan of attack.

The reason I took the threat of poisonous gas so seriously is because, unlike explosives, poison gas is easily made. Vanderbilt Island had a swimming pool. In the pool pump house, anyone versed in the field could find most of the chemicals required. The one or two missing ingredients would be available in the restaurant kitchen.

Building a detonator and a bomb wasn't out of the question, either. Private islands, just to function, must have well-equipped machine shops and maintenance sheds. All the parts could be found there and assembled in an hour, probably less.

Not that any untrained dweeb could make it happen. It's an urban legend that the average household contains items as lethal as any gun. The fiction is based on Hollywood films and a left-wing manifesto called *The Anarchist Cookbook*. The book, in fact, is as amateurish as anything ever published on the subject and taken seriously only by the dilettante revolutionaries who bought it. And Hollywood filmmakers, of course.

But it can be done.

My knowledge isn't extensive but it's functional. I learned what I know from one of the very few experts in this unusual field. He was a Delta Force specialist assigned to something called "The Funny Platoon" out of Fort Bragg. Not that the man had a bubbly sense of humor—just the opposite. But he knew how to jury-rig weapons, both offensive and defensive. And when it came to psy war ops—psychological warfare—he had accumulated a masterwork of dirty tricks.

Only once did I ever need to create a makeshift explosive while on assignment. It required mixing wood charcoal, potassium nitrate and sulfur with some other common materials, then rigging what's called a pull-loop switch to a battery. Thanks to him, the damn thing worked better than expected, which provided me with confidence now. Not that I intended to build an explosive. If I had to, I could. But I had two very different weapons in mind.

I'd brought a waterproof bag with my scuba gear. I opened the bag and began selecting items from Tomlinson's storage lockers. Among them was a common fungicide, a commercial rust remover, the jar of wooden matches, Ziploc baggies, three glass pickle-type jars, which I had to empty. It was harder to find three glass bottles small enough to fit into the jars, but I finally did. Then I added a box of ammonia inhalers and several replacement wicks for oil lamps. Tomlinson is a hot sauce snob, so I had a sizable selection to choose from. From it, I bagged two bottles of his hottest Amazon Habanero from Colombia.

I added a few other items, too, during my search—including a professional-grade first-aid kit that had been upgraded with painkillers, syringes and sutures for emergencies at sea. Because my BUDS swim shorts had only a small back pocket, I also rummaged around until I found an old photographer's vest that Tomlinson sometimes wears.

As I went through the vest, I wasn't surprised to find a wad of hundred-dollar bills, a big roll of five-hundred-euro bills, three baggies loaded with grass and a sheet of faded Halloween stamps that, I suspected, was a blotter of some kind of hallucinogenic. It seemed likely because there were several missing stamps, all removed in an unsystematic pattern that was telling—and oddly irksome to me.

I expected to find a working battery-operated flashlight and did—one with a corroded switch and another with a bad bulb maybe. The only working lights on the boat, though, were a twelve-volt Q-Beam and a wireless Golight that was mounted atop *No Más*'s cabin—both useless to me.

Something I *didn't* expect to find was Tomlinson's tiny MacBook Air computer, which I'd assumed he had taken to his room at the fishing lodge. The man loved the thing. He carried it everywhere. The computer was forward, in the master stateroom, with enough battery remaining for the screen to flash to life when I bumped the bed. The only reason I saw the open file was because I leaned to confirm there was no wireless signal.

Tomlinson had been watching a video about Third Planet Peace Force. The screen's frozen frame was a close-up of 3P2's Winifred Densler, Tomlinson's irritating new friend.

I checked my watch, then pressed the space bar, anyway. Instantly, the cabin was filled with a chorus of hysterical weeping people as Densler and several others, all kneeling in a forest, caressed and embraced a fallen tree.

Mourning a dead tree? Yep . . . but more than that, too.

"We beg the Earth's forgiveness!" I heard Densler moan toward the sky. "We are the disease—us. The toxic rich. Animal slavers and leeches. A tribe of cancerous pigs who . . ."

I hit the space bar before the woman could finish.

The Toxic Rich, spoken as if capitalized. It was an interesting term, which I had heard Densler use earlier in the evening. Yet, had I not seen similar videos attributed to a group called Earth First, or met the woman, I would have thought it a parody attacking the environmental movement and all the good it has accomplished.

But the video was real. The hysteria and Densler's rage were genuine. Even watching for just a few seconds keyed a visceral alarm inside me.

The evidence against the eco-activists—Tomlinson, too, although I still couldn't let myself believe it—was now even stronger.

9

If I had misjudged Third Planet Peace Force's potential for violence, it wasn't because I found any admirable qualities in the members I'd met earlier that night. I'd disliked them from the start, and the dislike was mutual. Fact was, I'd managed to piss off several people during my short time on the island, but Densler was at the head of the list.

I thought about our first encounter as I returned to the sailboat's galley and placed the empty jars on the counter, then organized the ingredients within easy reach so I could mix them. I had to hurry, but I also had to get the proportions right. They didn't have to be exact, but they had to be pretty damn close.

Tomlinson had been sitting at a table with Densler and a guy named Kahn when I had entered the bar earlier that night. Markus Kahn? I couldn't remember. My pal had been smiling as he waved me over, while his two companions sat grim-faced, irritated by my intrusion.

In my experience, there have been a few rare occasions when I knew within seconds of meeting a person that I would trust him with my life or that I should avoid him for life. Densler registered a polar negative on the scale.

The woman had confirmed my first impression by talking loud enough for everyone in the room to hear as she told me that, as officers of Third Planet, she and Markus Kahn had started a special branch unit called Huso Pelagius Patronus International.

Scribbling on a bar napkin, Tomlinson had translated the Latin as I took my seat: Defenders of the Sturgeon.

Trying to be cordial, I'd responded, "Well, if there's one fish in the world that needs protecting, it's the beluga."

Even so, I had given my friend an impatient look. What were anti-caviar crusaders doing at a reception featuring twenty-some different types of caviar now being served from iced tureens?

In reply, I had grabbed the pen and scribbled a note of my own: *They're trouble. You're worse.*

Which had caused Tomlinson, who looked Bogart-like in his tropical tuxedo, to nod in cheerful agreement. But he had also flashed me a private look that was more serious. It's the way close friends communicate, of course. I had seen the look before, yet the meanings varied. Tomlinson was warning me about something—in hindsight, warning me that Densler and her group were party crashers and looking for trouble. He was telling me to pay attention, stay on my toes.

I hadn't been there long enough to figure out the truth, so I interpreted a different meaning. More commonly, it is his way of notifying me that he isn't as drunk as he seems. That he is playing his stoned-hipster role for a reason. Tomlinson is a character, yes, but he can also slip into a Tomlinson *caricature* when it suits his needs—something that few of our neighbors at Dinkin's Bay suspect because it's so damn hard to tell the difference.

My instinctive wariness of Densler was more deserved than I'd realized. That was true of Markus Kahn as well.

Kahn was mid-twenties, average height and slim—not lean. There's a difference. He had the soft look of a shut-in or a clerk at an all-night college library, despite his disheveled red hair and surfer's tan.

Third Planet members patrolled the Caspian Sea by boat, Tomlinson had told me.

Thinking about it now, Kahn's behavior had signaled several danger signs. The most obvious: he had isolated himself from our table by burying his face in an iPad video game, which he played obsessively. Not unusual, maybe, for a twenty-some-year-old tech nerd—but at a caviar reception?

When I snuck a look at the iPad, Kahn shielded the screen, but not before I saw the game he was playing. He was immersed in a murderous virtual world, firing weapons at an enemy who spilled realistic blood and guts. It was one of those electronic vortex fantasies that I'd read about but, of course, had never tried. The game rewarded wistful killers with vicarious thrills—all from the safety of their own imaginations.

Kahn also checked and rechecked his watch, which seemed more sinister now than it did then. Had he been thinking about a detonator positioned to take out the island's power?

Sometimes he looked up from his iPad long enough to make eye contact with a guy standing near the door—a kindred video game wizard, from the way the guy hunched over the screen of his cell phone. Tall man, late twenties, his gaunt face an illustration of queasy contempt whenever he focused on someone who was eating caviar.

Like Kahn, he had worn a black crewneck shirt with the yellow Third Planet logo on the pocket: the Earth shielded by a death's-head skull. The logo was similar to the one used by the Sea Shepherds.

Densler had struck me as easier to read, but that was another misjudgment. She was long-legged and aloof in designer jeans and a baggy peasant's blouse. Lots of beads and crystals and bracelets, and a bright green ribbon in her honey brown hair. I was greeted with an aggressive handshake and withering eye contact. Jaundiced by my first impression, I guessed she was one of those women who despised her own wealthy antecedents but wouldn't have forfeited the perks she'd inherited for anything in the world.

After a few more minutes, I came to the conclusion that Densler was a type. She was an in-your-face crusader, so convinced of her righteousness that it forbade rational discussion and excused her own rude behavior.

In Densler's mind, anyway.

My opinion of the woman would change as the night progressed—and not for the better.

"Have you met the millionaire Nazi who's paying for all this?" Densler asked Tomlinson, as she worked on her second vodka and rocks. "I haven't yet. I hear that he's tall and good-looking—not that I care."

Tomlinson read the woman's denial accurately, I think, because he replied, "Viktor's about my height, looks like a movie star and is very smooth. I think you two might hit it off—in a dominatrix-dominator sort of way."

Densler tried too hard to appear offended, saying, "Hah! I can't wait to talk to him with our video cameras going. Viktor Kazlov might pretend he's interested in saving the beluga, but that's bullshit. He's only interested in getting a bigger share of the caviar market than his gangster friends. And *them*, my God, they're three of the world's biggest eco-criminals."

The woman, at least, had done her homework on Kazlov, Armanie, Talas and Bohai. Then she revealed her organization's motives by saying, "For years, we've been trying to get those four in the same room so we can confront them. The Toxic Rich, if ever the term applied. Now here we are, finally, all in the same place."

The woman made a face and then amended. "If Kazlov ever *shows up*, anyway."

From the first, I'd suspected the group was on the island without permission, but now it was confirmed. I should have left, but Densler was so neurotic and venomous that I stayed for the same clinical reasons I would have stayed to observe scorpions fighting or a rabid raccoon. Of course, Tomlinson was happy to play along because the woman was physically attractive, which even I had to admit. But it was in a counterculture Barbie doll sort of way. So the two of them chatted for a while, growing more comfortable as they realized they shared similar politics.

Then Tomlinson's stock rocketed when the woman pretended not to know my friend had authored the cult bestseller *One Fathom Above Sea Level*. Densler had read it many times—loved the insights, the spiritual truths, which caused her to admit, "I feel like we're both old souls. Two spirits who haven't seen each other in a thousand years."

When the old-soul boat bum and I exchanged looks, his adolescent grin read *Guess who's getting lucky tonight!* The enthusiasm was genuine, but I knew that it was also part of his stoned-hipster act.

I had planned to get the man alone later and find out if he'd known in advance about Third Planet's intrusion. Until then, though, I decided to just sit there, keep my mouth shut and listen.

Unfortunately, that's not the way the night worked out.

Half a vodka later, Densler was feeling comfortable enough to slap the table and explain, "The Russian wouldn't give us permission to monitor his little caviar lovefest. So what did you expect us to do? Sit back and do nothing while they cut up the Caspian Sea like a goddamn pie?"

The woman was an interesting example of passive-aggressive disorder, but it wasn't reason enough to sit with her. Now my goofball pal, by inviting me to the table, had made us both guilty through association. Finally, I was perturbed enough to ask him, "Did you know these people were going to show up? When Kazlov finds out, he'll call the police, then probably throw us off the island, too. I wouldn't blame him."

Tomlinson shook his head and kept his voice low. "Viktor walked out about twenty minutes ago. They got here just after he left."

Densler ignored us as she surveyed the room, "Judging from his oil gangster buddies, I expected Kazlov to be another overweight, rich slob. Oil—that's all this country cares about. That's probably why the feds gave Kazlov the permits he needed to experiment on Gulf sturgeon. Has anyone even bothered to ask *how* he got the permits?"

I wasn't going to share what I knew, but *I* had bothered to ask. I was interested because I knew enough about the procedures to understand that the paperwork had to have been a nightmare. In that way, at least, Kazlov and I had found some common ground during our short talk that afternoon.

When it comes to an endangered species, the federal and international governing agencies are multilayered, inflexible and complex. To do it properly, Kazlov would have had to file applications with the Convention on International Trade in Endangered Species—CITES—the U.S. departments of Agriculture and Wildlife, as well as the Florida Department of Agriculture, none of which are known for having a devil-may-care attitude toward their repetitive forms and pointless details.

Kazlov, though, had found a "hobbyist" loophole that, in fact, I have used myself when collecting specimens. The gap in the regulations was created for aquarists, amateur herpetologists and other hobbyists whose interests in rare animals and plants is on a scale so minuscule that it's considered benign. So Kazlov had used it to his benefit to continue his research and to keep fish for display. Who is to say a tropical hobbyist must chose a two-inch angelfish for his aquarium rather than a hundred-pound Gulf sturgeon?

"A stack of papers *this* high," Kazlov had told me in his heavy accent, holding his hand at eye level. "This is how many forms they tell me we must complete. And why? To move, only for a few days, two sturgeon from our aquaculture facility in the Yucatán. Fish that were very common here only sixty years ago!"

I doubted Kazlov's claim that the sturgeon he had brought to Vanderbilt Island possessed exactly the same DNA as native Gulf sturgeon, but I wasn't going to share that information with the Third Planet people, either.

Densler went on: "Big oil, big business and our own corrupt federal government: a perfect combination. Kazlov paid off someone. Wild sturgeon in pens—it makes me want to vomit! It's as bad as that freak show across the bay—the gambling casino with the trained dolphins. It's the fish that should be set free and these fat fucks who should be locked up."

Markus Kahn, lost in his video game, looked up and said, "Maybe it'll happen," then gave Densler a warning glare. The woman was talking too much, and Kahn didn't like it.

But Densler wasn't done. Her attention swung to me for the first and only time. "I find it strange that someone like T"—she motioned toward Tomlinson—"a spiritually grounded person, would hang out with someone like you."

I looked at Tomlinson as I replied, "Maybe a little too strange, as of tonight."

Densler took that as an affront because she then asked, "Are you actually a marine biologist?"

I nodded.

"Then I'm curious. Are you the sort of biologist who sells his expert opinion to the highest bidder like most in your field? Or are you a legitimate scientist? I've met very few of those."

I said, "I'm surprised you've met even one."

I glanced at the door, wondering, *Where the hell is Kazlov?* I'd had enough.

Because one of us would soon be leaving, I turned my chair to face her. "Do you know why I'm surprised? Because we avoid people like you."

The woman's face began to color as I continued, "We don't waste time on phony conservationists. Or the frauds who condemn research that doesn't mesh with their own biases. Or that won't scare their members into donating more money. Those are the same groups who damage the movement's integrity by manipulating data to fit their own agendas—or by pulling ridiculous publicity stunts to grab headlines. PETA is the saddest example of a group that discredits its own cause. Why would a legitimate biologist waste his time?"

Kahn slid his iPad onto the table as if to challenge me. He had dull green eyes, his expression intense either because of what I'd said or because he was still fired up by the violent virtual world he had just exited.

Consciously or unconsciously, Densler picked up a fork and gripped it like a knife as she leaned toward me. "If you're talking about Third Planet, you don't have the brains to understand what we do. You're just another oversized fascist who thinks *man* is somehow the goddamn king of this planet."

I was replying "I didn't mention your organization's name, you made the association—" when Tomlinson interceded by thrusting his arms over the table to separate us, then made a calming motion with his hands.

Trying to lighten the mood, he said, "Winnie, don't take it personally. Dr. Ford usually makes up for his lack of social skills by keeping his mouth shut. At least you got him to open up a little, which says a lot about your passion."

Densler glowered at me as she warned Tomlinson, "I hate the name Winnie. Just because I liked your little book doesn't mean you can call me Winnie. No one knows me well enough."

Just then, Kahn leaned over and whispered something in the woman's ear. It might have been something threatening, because Densler's face suddenly paled and she retreated into the silence of a fresh vodka.

My eyes moved from Densler to Kahn to the guy standing near the door, aware that all three had just been reunited by some unspoken motive—or fear. It was then that I got a look at the two additional members of the group. I saw them through the bar's main window: men, late twenties, identical twins, judging from their girlish blond hair and chubby faces. They were visible for only a few seconds, walking north toward the marina, one of them carrying a brightly colored computer bag. The Third Planet member standing at the door nodded to them as they passed, his face expressionless. Then he caught Kahn's eye and nodded again.

At the time, I perceived nothing sinister in the exchange. Densler, Kahn—the entire group—struck me as trivial people whose egos hungered for a celebrity status that their small talents could not earn. They were unhappy people—as the Michael Moores of the world invariably are—and sitting among them had caused me to feel a shabbiness that didn't match my mood.

What was to be gained by watching the inevitable confrontation when Kazlov reappeared and ordered them off the island? There would be shouting, threats and more pious spouting of the Third Planet party line.

It was a waste of time. I scooted my chair away from the table and stood there, waiting for Tomlinson.

Finally, my pal noticed I was standing. When he got up, I shook hands as if we were strangers, saying, "Nice meeting you, Professor Tomlinson. Hope I didn't spoil your evening."

Tomlinson replied, "Then we must have a serious talk about it later, Dr. Ford. Around midnight, possibly?" which was all he could tell me before slipping back into his stoned-hipster disguise. "We'll smoke a joint. Get crazy."

Now, as I sat aboard *No Más*, measuring out liquids, pouring small amounts into jars, the man's reference to midnight had far more significance. And he had no doubt sent other cloaked messages as well. But if Tomlinson had sensed danger, why hadn't he taken me aside and warned me? It would have been easy enough to excuse himself from the table for a few minutes or he could have followed me to the marina.

The answer was, he *would* have warned me if he'd anticipated real trouble. Particularly if he'd known that people might be shot and killed.

There was another, disturbing possibility, though: what if Tomlinson *had* warned me and I'd somehow missed it?

What if? It is among the most popular games played by our species. The wistful scenarios form our favorite fictions—happy endings that give us hope or burden us with guilt and regret.

I played the game as I finished mixing liquids, and screwed the lids tight on the jars. What if Kahn and Densler, and fellow members of 3P2, were behind this insanity? It meant that I had misread them badly—even after seeing so damn many red flags. But who in their right mind would suspect a group of highly educated people—however abrasive and neurotic—of being violent sociopaths?

That's another popular fiction: the belief that mass murderers behave differently than the rest of us. Some expert, some perceptive neighbor, should have recognized the killer's aberrant behavior and stopped him in advance of his bloody deed. Right?

The question is motivated by our deepest fears and our most optimistic hopes: they are different from us, right? They must be different from us. Right?

A single mocking word blurs the demarcation but also addresses both poles of the question, our hopes and our fears.

The double-edged answer is, *Right.*

10

Before exiting the cabin of Tomlinson's boat, I gathered my gear, extinguished the lamp and ducked outside onto the afterdeck. The thermal monocular clipped onto a headband, which took only a few seconds to adjust. Soon I was using the TAM-14 to search for body heat, near and far, and also trying to mesh my experience in the bar with the disturbing video I'd just seen.

Usually, a lapse in concentration is also a lapse in judgment. Maybe that's why I didn't spot the man who was watching me through a rifle scope, although he would make his presence known soon enough.

To my right, mangroves were a reef of gray trees, leaves still aglow, warm from the afternoon sun. Among the limbs were sporadic coals of fluorescence—roosting birds. If Vladimir had been executed, his body, even if he was dead, should have produced a heat signature, too. But I found none.

Surprising. It was unlikely anyone would have moved a man his size—not from swamp that dense. But I also knew that deciphering the subtleties of thermal imaging takes time. I'd had the unit only a couple of days, so I might be misreading what I was seeing.

Atop the TAM-14 unit were a series of pressure switches. I touched magnification as I scanned the mangroves again, then turned my attention to the island.

That's when I spotted the guy who came way too close to killing me a few seconds later.

More than a hundred yards away, a lone figure was standing in the shadows of a ficus tree. A man, as evidenced by the absence of breast tissue. A dot of oscillating heat told me he was smoking a cigarette. He was on the north end of Vanderbilt Island where, I had been told, the Iranian, Abdul Armanie, had rented a large house.

I panned the monocular to the south.

Darius Talas, from Turkmenia, had taken a beach house near the southernmost point, at the end of a walkway that islanders called the Pink Path. Because of a few scattered cottages near the marina, though, Talas's portion of the island was screened from my view.

The same was true of the fishing lodge. It was mid-island, built upon the highest remnants of the shell pyramid. As I adjusted the monocular's focus, though, I realized that my view wasn't entirely blocked. I could see a wedge of balcony on the building's fourth floor, where an American flag stirred in the night breeze.

The porch was empty. But a heated corona within told me that someone had lit an oil lamp or candle.

My main concern wasn't the lone figure standing beneath the ficus tree. It was the trigger-happy gunman who'd shot Vladimir and had tried to kill me. Using the monocular, I searched for the guy, panning from one end of the marina to the other.

Near a maintenance shed, and beneath a wooden water cistern, families of four-legged creatures foraged. They looked like furry balls of light—raccoons. Atop a roof gable, a glowing statue pivoted its black eyes toward me—a great horned owl.

No human beings, though, that I could see, aside from the man in the far distance, now lighting another cigarette.

As I searched the area—no doubt because I was on the stern of Tomlinson's boat—I suddenly realized that I had overlooked another method of signaling for help. Possibly a workable method. The device was staring me right in the face, literally. Secured next to the sailboat's helm was a U-shaped flotation ring, on a hundred feet of line. It was a man-overboard harness, designed for throwing.

In one of the pockets was a waterproof electronic beacon called an EPIRB. Activate the beacon and it would transmit emergency GPS coordinates, and a unique serial number to satellites in space. The satellites then beamed the information to the nearest U.S. Coast Guard stations so that rescue choppers and boats could be launched.

The portable jammers I had used were calibrated to interrupt all but the very highest and lowest radio frequencies. Maybe the EPIRB was immune.

Without further thought, I pulled the beacon's emergency ring . . . which also activated a blinding strobe light, as I should have anticipated.

Damn it!

In a rush, I used my hands to try to muffle the light. Impossible. So I gathered the harness, rope and all, and tossed the whole mess overboard. Seconds later, someone smacked the hull of Tomlinson's sailboat so hard with a sledgehammer, I felt the fiberglass tremble beneath me.

That's what it sounded like, anyway.

For an instant, I was stunned, even though I knew what had happened. It was a gunshot, and the simultaneous impact of a slug hitting the cabin bulkhead behind me. A rifle, probably. Something heavy caliber, and the shooter was using a scope. Unlike the trigger-happy gunman, it was doubtful that he would miss again.

No Más was moored with her transom to the dock. I had thrown the EPIRB strobe off the starboard side, where the light blazed once every second.

Without hesitating, I tumbled over the port side, holding fins and waterproof pack to my chest. As I crashed through the water's surface, I was imaging the man I had seen beneath the ficus tree toss his cigarette away and shoulder a rifle. The angle seemed right. From the north end of the island, a shooter had a clear view of the marina. And the distance wasn't a challenge if he was using a scope.

It was a close call, but I had learned something. The Iranians were housed on the north end. Talas, the Turkmenian, was housed on the southern tip. Suddenly, I was less suspicious of Tomlinson's eco-activist friends. Members of Third Planet Peace Force—even if they were a bunch of pissed-off neurotics—weren't the type to use sniper rifles.

Abdul Armanie, though, had a bodyguard with him, presumably a well-trained man. And Armanie himself was a cutthroat businessman who sometimes used Islam and the Koran to justify his methods—particularly when dealing with non-Muslims. That's why he preferred to go by his last name only when doing business in the United States.

In the bar, Densler, Kahn and I had butted heads, true. But, as I was already aware, they weren't the only enemies I had made during my short time on Vanderbilt Island. The Iranian was furious at me, too. Possibly angry enough to kill me, if he got the chance. It was because, earlier that afternoon, I had embarrassed the man badly—Armanie and Talas both, in fact. I had done it knowingly, intentionally, and then had laughed in his face.

Abdul Rahman Armanie, as I already knew, was not the sort to allow a slight to go unpunished.

When Tomlinson and I arrived on Vanderbilt Island, I'd had no intentions of alienating almost everyone I met—but that's what happened. Which is unusual for me. I'm generally a quiet, private guy who, long ago, learned that a man can't learn anything while his mouth is open.

Even so, people are chemical-electrical beings, and sometimes our polarity swings inexplicably to the negative, inviting all kinds of trouble. In the space of a few hours, I'd invited more than my share by opening my mouth too much and too often.

It happens. In my case, though, there was a purpose. When it comes to the wealthy Eastern Europeans, behaving like an asshole is sometimes the only way to force information out of them.

That morning, I had introduced myself to Darius Talas first, then, an hour later, to Armanie, as a marine biologist who was working on sturgeon aquaculture with Mote Marine. My slanted honesty hadn't been well received, so I'd been forced to reply to indignant accusations. No, I hadn't lied to get an invitation to the caviar forum. Yes, I was a primary investor in two flourishing restaurants, as the forum's rules required. But my primary interests were fish, in general, and sturgeon in particular. All true, of course.

So far, so good.

After getting that settled, my questions had been straightforward enough. They reflected my honest interest in the Caspian Sea's declining sturgeon population. Even so, neither man was willing to talk about how he acquired the caviar his company sold discreetly through an international network of distributors, some of them "legitimate," others gray market wholesalers.

No problem. I already knew too much about both men to expect honest answers. So I had parted from each of them on cool but civil terms. Later that afternoon, though, everything changed.

I had gone out to explore, got lucky and found both men at a table next to the pool, so I had taken a seat before they could protest. Talas and Armanie had been arguing about something, judging from Iranian's expression and Talas's flushed pumpkin-sized face. So I had put an end to the uneasy silence and attempted to ingratiate myself by saying, "The three of us need to get something straight. I'm not a federal agent, I'm a biologist. There's no reason we can't talk openly. Maybe we have more in common than you realize."

Armanie had looked at his watch and asked Talas, "What time is Kazlov serving hors d'oeuvres tonight? Knowing him, it will be potato vodka and that disgusting caviar he's pedaling. Awful peasant-raised shit, have you tried it?"

I had taken that as my opening to say, "Caviar and aquaculture—what a coincidence. Those are the very things I'd like to talk about. For instance, Kazlov's hybrid sturgeon idea—the idea has merit, I think. But, before I can decide, I need to understand what's going on in the Caspian region. Has the fishery gotten as bad as some say?"

Silence—that was my reply. Which I had interrupted by waving to a waiter and ordering a Diet Coke before I pressed ahead, saying, "A good place to start would be to explain how your fishermen get around the ban on catching beluga. Why's it so easy? I'd rather hear the truth from experts—men like yourselves—than get secondhand information. And it's all confidential, of course."

The way Talas had chuckled and demurred reminded me of a Muslim Pillsbury Doughboy. Armanie had smirked and shrugged, like the condescending prick he is, and asked me, "Do you know who killed the cow to make the shoes you're wearing? It is a ridiculous question for a man who claims to be a biologist—but perhaps that delightful dolphin show we attended pays staff with bogus dolphin doctorate titles."

The man had a gift for cutting insults, but I didn't mind. Armanie and Talas were confirming what I already knew about them. And I knew far more than they suspected through my intel sources in Colorado and Maryland. Both men were smart, unscrupulous and rich—very different in terms of style and behavior, but they were also both killers if business required it.

The background summaries I'd reviewed before leaving Sanibel hadn't come right out and said that it was true. But the insinuation was there, between the lines, along with a lot more:

Talas and Armanie each claimed to be "conventional modern" Muslims, yet they also tacitly endorsed fundamentalist causes with their checkbooks. Both had gotten rich piping fossil fuels out of the Caspian Sea, which is the Earth's third-largest reservoir of oil and natural gas.

Talas was a shareholder in Turkmenia's largest petroleum company. Armanie was one of five in a consortium that managed seventeen oil rigs off the Iranian port of Neka. Black market caviar was a lucrative enterprise for both men—fifty million euros a year was a conservative estimate, according to profile summaries I'd received. But oil was their primary source of wealth. Which suggested that if Talas or Armanie wanted Kazlov dead, it had more to do with fossil fuel than a dinosaurian fish.

It was more than just a theory. There was something else I had learned from my sources: the three men despised one another. The reasons weren't given, of course. No way for anyone to know them all. Kazlov's, Talas's and Armanie's families had been competitors for decades, so they had probably all been scarred by past dealings. And some wounds never heal.

But if Kazlov truly had made a breakthrough discovery regarding caviar, Armanie and Talas had more battle scars coming. There were several reasons, but one was that the news would invite international attention to the Caspian Sea and its dwindling beluga population. That's the last thing two men who profited from caviar and oil wanted.

Oil companies in the region despise media attention because they don't want the world to know the truth about the Caspian. The truth is that it has become an environmental cesspool since the collapse of the Soviet Union in 1991. No longer is the oil industry governed or policed. Soviet regulations were never strict by Western standards, but now there are none. None that are enforced, anyway.

The same is true of the sturgeon fishery, which is why the venerated wild beluga is being slaughtered into extinction.

While the five bordering nations squabble about territorial rights and whether the Caspian legally is a sea or the world's largest fresh water lake, a Wild West mentality controls the region. International petroleum companies are rushing to capitalize on a rare opportunity to pump millions of barrels of oil without the expense of minimizing or even monitoring pollution.

With the same hyenalike fervor, international caviar procurers are looting the Caspian fishery because they know better than anyone that, soon, the last mature female beluga will be netted and that will be the end.

Armanie and Talas were burning both ends of the Caspian Sea candle and profiting hugely. I didn't blame them for making a profit. I'm a realist. It's what businesspeople do. But I found their methods contemptible and their superior attitudes galling.

Which is why when Armanie goaded me by saying my questions

were ridiculous, I smiled and gave him a pointed look that read *Anytime, anyplace—asshole.*

That's when the real trouble between us started.

The man was unused to being challenged by inferiors, so it turned into a stare-down. After he finally contrived a way out by lighting a cigarette, I said, "If you won't talk to me about it, maybe you'll let me tell you what I already know. You can fill in the blanks, if you want, or tell me where I'm wrong."

"Dr. Ford, you remind me of one of those stubborn detectives in an American film." Talas laughed, jowls shaking. In my mind, the Pillsbury Doughboy instantly became Sydney Greenstreet in *Casablanca.*

Talas pretended to be interested. Armanie glowered, smoked and checked his wristwatch. It took me about five minutes to tell two of the world's most ruthless suppliers of black market caviar how their organizations worked.

I began by asking, "How many fishermen along the Caspian coast do you employ? Six or seven hundred? No—let's count Kazlov's organization, too. So we can double that. Together, your organizations probably own about fifty percent of the international market, which means you sell how much illegal caviar annually? A hundred and fifty metric tons at least, from what I've read."

I paused long enough for Talas to nod, as if impressed with his own success, before continuing.

"You sell the product on the gray market to five-star restaurants, exporters, whoever will buy it. Your wholesale price is around eight hundred U.S. dollars a pound, right? So eight hundred dollars multiplied by one metric ton—which is what? Around twenty-two hundred pounds? That comes to about"—I let the men watch me struggle with the math—"just under two million dollars per ton. Multiply that by a hundred and fifty tons annually and"—I looked to check their facial reactions—"and we're talking a whole bunch of money. Three hundred million gross. At least a hundred million net. Am I right?"

From the flicker of a smile that appeared on Armanie's face, I knew that I had underestimated the figure.

That was okay. I was getting to him, and we both knew it. It gave me the confidence to attempt to trap the men into telling me the truth about why they'd come to Vanderbilt Island—a trap I began to bait by saying, "But neither one of you is going to be in the caviar business for much longer—unless Kazlov's hybrid sturgeon becomes a reality. If you don't know why, I'll be happy to explain."

Armanie exhaled smoke and said, "This is something I'm going to complain to Viktor about. More visits to the casino, fewer fraud biologists. And after we were guaranteed privacy."

"But I'm enjoying myself!" Talas responded, smiling at me—but his eyes had an empty look, as if I were a corpse who refused to be silent. "I don't believe I've ever heard so many outrageous inaccuracies come from one man's mouth."

I replied, "I take that as a compliment. Apparently, my information is better than expected. Mind if I continue?"

Talas listened while Armanie made a show of turning to face the swimming pool. I could hardly blame him when I saw why. I got my first look at the woman I would see later, sitting in the dining room with Lien Bohai. The one with the exotic face and Anglo-Malaysian eyes. She wore a burnt orange bikini and was lowering herself into the pool. The water must have been cool because the woman paused at rib level while her breasts acclimated—a hypnotic few seconds. Then I watched her remove an ivory quillet, then a comb from the top of her head, before submerging in a swirl of Polynesian hair.

The visual impact was such that I managed only a vague recollection of her stunningly plain counterpart, the square-faced woman with the swimmer's shoulders.

Talas, the fat man, was watching, too, because he said to Armanie, "Have you spoken to her this trip? She really is quite beautiful. And what a magnificent body! Do you think she'd agree to drinks after dinner?"

In an insinuating tone, the Iranian replied, "I think you'd have to ask Viktor's permission. I saw them walking last night and then they snuck off together this morning. I'm sure he can provide her answer—and her price."

At the time, the remark seemed only rude. Later, when I saw the woman sitting with the Chinese mega-millionaire Lien Bohai, it would acquire a sharper edge.

After I turned away from the pool, it took me a moment to collect myself, but I finally refocused and told the two caviar kings why they would soon be out of the caviar business. First, though, I told them how they did what they did. Some of it was an educated guess, most was not.

The fishermen they hired—and paid next to nothing—avoided detection by laying their nets after dark. Miles of nets pulled by boats working in packs. For hours, they would drag their web into slow circles that trapped every living, swimming thing. Then hydraulic derricks would haul the nets and dump the catch in a thrashing, suffocating heap onto the deck.

There are seventy-some species of fish that live in the Caspian Sea, including six species of sturgeon. But only three of those species provide salable eggs for caviar, so everything else would be left to die while the profitable fish were culled. Twenty years ago, the fishermen might have caught a thousand sturgeon in a two-hour drag. Today, a hundred was a more likely number.

Of those hundred fish, fewer then ten would be the valuable beluga. Two other species, the osetra and sevruga, which are more common, but still endangered, would also be kept.

Because it takes fifteen to twenty-five years before a female sturgeon can produce eggs, only one of those ten beluga would be large enough to be considered mature—a fish between three hundred and three thousand pounds. Smaller, mature osetra and sevruga sturgeon would add another twenty fish to the pile. These fish would all be clubbed unconscious and dragged, tail first, into aerated tanks. Smaller fish would be kicked overboard or killed for meat.

At the docks, while the sturgeon were still alive, underlings hired by Talas and Armanie would then stun the fish a second time with a blow to the head. Why? Because it's impossible to do surgery on a conscious fish that's three times the size of the men handling it. And surgery was the *next* step. The only way poachers can find out if a sturgeon is male or female is to make a precise abdominal incision that exposes the fish's reproductive organs.

Males would be hauled away to die and dumped later—the carcasses were incriminating. Gravid females would also be left to die but only after their ovaries had been slit, the valuable egg sacs removed whole, and immediately iced—all while the fish was semiconscious. Studies are as varied as the definitions of "pain," but the consensus is that fish don't feel pain as it is experienced by primates. A fish's existence is brainstem dominated, not cerebrally dominated, but a sturgeon's *behavioral* response to such a procedure would cause even me to wince and I'm not known for my sensitivity.

Nor were Armanie and Talas, judging from their yawning indifference to what I had just described.

"This year, your fishermen will catch about half as many mature sturgeon as they caught last year," I continued. "That's the way it's been going for the last decade, right? It's because you're killing the brood stock. The golden geese. And that's why you'll be out of the caviar business soon. Even if someone very smart, like Viktor Kazlov, develops a beluga hybrid, you'll still be out of the business because the Caspian Sea is so polluted, a restocking program isn't likely."

Both men were listening, although Armanie had pretended to be preoccupied. It got to him, though, when I mentioned Kazlov's intelligence. I saw him react. It gave me additional confidence. Mentioning a hybrid beluga was proving an effective bait for the trap I soon hoped to spring.

"Admit it," I had pressed. "Kazlov is a brilliant man—if he really has found a way to produce beluga-quality eggs from a sturgeon with different DNA. My guess is, you're worried about the media attention he'll bring to your operations in the Caspian. Or you're jealous."

That did it. Armanie couldn't help himself. "Do you realize how ridiculously stupid you sound?" he said, keeping his voice low as he turned to face me across the table. "Kazlov is an uneducated farmer turned gangster. It's the specialists he's hired who have the brains—not *him*. Even so, only a fool would believe they would waste their time creating a hybrid from a beluga sturgeon and your disgusting Gulf sturgeon. And if they have, so what!"

I looked into the man's eyes, trying not to show how eager I was to hear what came next. "You lost me," I lied. "Gulf sturgeon tolerate warm water a lot better than the beluga. They mature faster, too. Isn't that Kazlov's real plan? To start a company that operates outdoor sturgeon farms throughout the tropics? He already owns an aquaculture facility in the Yucatán. They can produce caviar year-round. His investors will get rich. In fact"—I lowered my voice as if sharing a confidence—"I'm thinking of investing a few thousand dollars myself."

Talas managed to say, "A few thousand! Such a risky sum!" before his jowls began to shake again, laughing.

I replied, "To me, it's a lot of money. But if things go as Viktor predicts, who knows? The three of us might do some business down the road."

The look Armanie gave me was memorable because his contempt was multilayered. I was a naïve American hick. Not only was I uniformed, I had no money—which meant I was powerless, and so useless to him.

"You call yourself a biologist?" he said, staring at me, shaking his head. "You actually have a college degree? Then how can you possibly not know that what Kazlov is *supposedly* proposing is impossible."

"A hybrid fish?" I replied as if confused. "New hybrids are being developed every day."

"You idiot," Armanie had laughed. "Even now you don't understand. Here"—the man had put his elbows on the table and leaned toward me—"let me make it simple enough even for you to comprehend. The DNA of a beluga sturgeon simply cannot be disguised. Do you know why?"

Yes, but I let the man talk.

"Because the DNA of every commercial fish in the world is cataloged in an international data bank. Which means there is no possible way that beluga DNA would go undetected. Do you hear me? It's *impossible*."

Armanie, very pleased with himself, paused to light another cigarette. "Your own country wouldn't issue permits to raise such a fish, let alone the international governing bodies. The Convention on Trade in Endangered Species—have you even heard of the organization?"

I had filled out enough CITES forms to wallpaper my lab. The man sat back and chuckled. "No competent professional would waste his time listening to Kazlov's claims about a hybrid fish. Certainly not from two such very different animals. Which, I suppose, explains why you're so enthralled with the idea . . . *Doctor* Ford."

Good. It wasn't much of a trap, but Armanie had finally stepped into it with both feet.

My expression blank, I slammed the trap shut by asking, "Then what are you two men doing here?"

It had taken a few moments, but the fat man, and then Armanie, finally realized what had just happened. Abruptly, Talas stopped laughing. Armanie fumbled for his cigarettes, maybe hoping I'd give him time to think by talking.

I didn't. Not for several seconds, anyway, while I sat back and savored their befuddled reactions. Finally, I herded them deeper into a corner, saying, "You're experts in the field. Yet here you are—at the invitation of an uneducated gangster. If disguising DNA is impossible, then why waste your time and money by coming to Florida? It makes no sense—unless you're here for a *different* reason."

I pretended to be interested while I listened to Talas attempt to explain his presence by praising Vanderbilt Island as a beautiful vacation spot. Then referred to his other business interests in Florida, as Armanie nodded his agreement.

To convey my skepticism, I gave it several more seconds of silence, as if thinking it through. "Sorry, guys. I don't buy it. I don't think you flew halfway around the world for a vacation. It has to be something else." I leaned forward. "A genetically modified beluga, maybe?"

The Iranian wasn't convincing when he responded, "A *what*?"

"We call it a G-M-O," I replied with exaggerated patience. "A genetically modified organism. Imagine a beluga that matures in five years instead of twenty. Or how about a procedure that causes sturgeon to produce preovulated eggs regularly? You know, before the chorion perforates—the skin of the egg. Imagine a female sturgeon that produces eggs two or three times a year without having to be killed. Like milk cows on a dairy farm."

It had been Jim Michaels's analogy, not mine, but the reaction it produced in the black marketeers was beyond anything I had hoped. It revealed the truth, and the truth was in Talas's feigned confusion.

"Why, the idea's ridiculous. That has been proven too many times!"

The truth was in Abdul Armanie's eyes, too, as he glared at me through a veil of smoke and replied, "A fascinating fairy tale. Let me know how the story ends."

"You'll be the first to know," I answered, smiling because I had guessed right. I felt sure of it as I studied the men's faces, yet it was still a shocking truth to process: Viktor Kazlov, and his researchers, had succeeded. They had apparently discovered one of the holy grails of caviar production. At least, that's what the Russian had claimed privately to his three wealthiest competitors, I guessed.

Later, over the course of the afternoon, the broader implications would crystallize in my mind. If true, it meant that Kazlov's caviar weekend, and his claims about altering beluga DNA, were all camouflage. They had been contrived to cloak some kind of business deal taking place between four outlaw organizations. Not just any business deal. It had to be an *illegal* business deal, with a billion-dollar potential. The Russian wouldn't have bothered staging such an elaborate ruse unless big money was involved—and unless he had something important to hide. Meeting his competitors in the United States, out in the open, on a well-known private island, fit one of the maxims of professionals who specialize in deceit: *If you want to guard a secret, put it in a book.*

Vanderbilt Island was the book. The secret was that Kazlov was about to revolutionize the caviar industry with a genetically modified beluga.

When I heard the bullet slam the hull of Tomlinson's sailboat, the memory of Armanie's reaction that afternoon flashed instantly to mind. The man's face . . . his black eyes . . . the way he had glared at me when he'd realized I had tricked him into revealing the truth. Until then, he and Talas had considered me a powerless gnat. But then the gnat had bitten them on the ass and made them look like fools.

Armanie would hate me for it. He would kill me, if he ever got the chance.

Maybe he had already tried. Just now. Using a rifle and scope.

11

After tumbling off Tomlinson's sailboat, I sculled water long enough to get my fins on over my running shoes, then I set off on my back, kicking hard. I couldn't risk looking for the keys to Third Planet's rental boats now. It was time to run. So that's what I did—swam for my life.

When I had put several boats, and a lot of darkness between myself and that damn relentless strobe light, I slowed enough to check my watch—11:15 p.m.—then turned onto my stomach and angled toward mid-island.

Soon, I could see the roof of the fishing lodge backdropped by stars. Framing the building were groves of coconut palms that sagged, frond-heavy, hinged to their own shadows. Overhead, a satellite traced the boundaries of ozone and outer space with a fragile silver thread. As I watched, an owl probed the darkness, its *whoo-whoo*ing an ancient, resonate sound on an island that has been inhabited since the days of the pharaohs.

I wasn't wearing my dive mask. Instead, I'd positioned the thermal monocular over my left eye, mounted on a headband. Through it, I scanned the shoreline, but also occasionally turned to check the marina. The EPIRB strobe was still pinging away as it drifted with the tide, but the man who'd fired the shot had yet to appear.

I was surprised. If Abdul Armanie, or his bodyguard, wanted me dead, why didn't he check to see if he'd scored a hit? It gave the impression the shooter couldn't leave his post . . . or that he was afraid to venture away from his little piece of the island. Which caused me to doubt that Armanie had pulled the trigger himself. The man didn't take orders, he gave orders. After the meltdown we'd had, he would have made sure I was dead *if* he thought he could get away with it. The Iranian was no fool.

Mostly, my attention was focused on the fishing lodge and the area around it. There, I saw something of concern. On the fourth-floor porch, near the flag, outside the room where I'd seen a candle flickering, was a man, standing guard. He was carrying what might have been a rifle or a semiautomatic pistol on a folding stock. The glow of the weapon's barrel was pale in comparison to the heat of the man's hands, yet it told me the weapon had been fired recently.

Presumably, Tomlinson was still in the lodge. The fact that he had not come looking for me proved he was, at the very least, preoccupied with something important—or, more likely, being held hostage, which was tough for me to admit or even think about. The same with the few employees who'd been working in the lodge, and the three businesswomen from nearby Captiva Island. I didn't know them well, but well enough to know they were respected and successful ladies who didn't deserve to be terrorized by some asshole with a personal agenda.

As I scanned various windows in the lodge, I pictured my pal with his hands tied, his mouth taped—which would have been the only way to shut the guy up, of course. Not that I empathized with the kidnappers. It was simply a fact.

It worried me. Tomlinson doesn't handle violence well—not that anyone who suffers pain, or inflicts pain, can walk away unscarred. But I'd seen him survive enough nasty encounters to know that violence stays in his system long after the physical scars have healed. Violence affects him like a slow poison. It rattles his confidence and mocks his conviction that we exist in an equitable universe where events happen for a reason. Which is nonsense, of course. But it is, at least, good-natured nonsense, and anchors the very core of the man's personality and his sense of self.

Hostages or not, whoever was behind this madness couldn't expect to hold the island long. A service boat would arrive at the Vanderbilt Island docks at a little after sunrise to bring staff and maintenance workers. Every day, seven days a week, that's the way the island functioned. Word would then get out—something that would happen much sooner, if I stayed calm, and methodically took the kidnappers apart.

My mind was wandering, I realized. I rolled onto my back and treaded water as I told myself *Concentrate, damn it!* Then I began swimming, my eyes fixed on the fishing lodge.

Using the thermal monocular, I found the porch once again and took a closer look at the flag. The breeze had died. In Florida, in June, night air has the density of warm lacquer. It sticks to the skin as it forms an invisible bubble at treetop level, sealing sky from earth. On a night like this, poisonous gas would hang close to the ground. It would disperse slowly, like steam after a summer rain, drifting among orchids, Spanish moss and palms. It would follow the contours of landscaped lawns, beneath houses built on stilts, and ascend in tendrils of mist through floors.

Not good.

I checked my watch again: fifty-five minutes until midnight. Flattening myself in the water, I began to kick with longer, stronger fin strokes.

Soon, I was close enough to shore to smell the humic mix of earth and salt water. Then my feet touched bottom, and I used the night vision system to search the island before taking a first step.

Off to my right, something big slashed the water's surface. It caused me to jump, then freeze where I stood. Vladimir had been right about sharks, although he didn't realize it. The brackish waters of Florida's Gulf Coast are the breeding and feeding ground of many species of sharks—the bull shark among the most common.

Most sharks don't faze me. When a bull shark is in the area, though, I give it my full attention. A male bull is supercharged by testes that provide it with more testosterone than any animal on Earth. Which makes it among the most aggressive and dangerous predators on Earth.

In the Florida backcountry, June is peak season for big bulls—some of them the size of Cessnas. And night was their favorite time to hunt. Which is why I stood motionless, watching a sector of black water where the fish had hit.

When the fish slammed the surface again, though, I relaxed. It was an oversized snook, judging from the suctioning *fuuuWHOP* as it inhaled bait. The snook is an ascendant predatory, a marvel of adaptation and design, but it's a finicky eater, and mammals aren't on its list. I rotated my neck to relax the muscles in my shoulders and turned my attention to the island.

Ahead, at the fishing lodge, the guard was still keeping watch from the fourth-floor balcony. For a moment, he appeared to be staring in my direction. Even from a hundred yards, I could see the cooler scaffolding of the man's skull beneath glowing white skin. He stared in my direction for so long that I began to worry that he, too, was wearing night vision and had spotted me.

It gave me reason to hurry as I removed my swim fins and tossed them toward shore.

But then the guard turned, in no apparent rush . . . rolled his shoulders as if bored . . . then leaned his weapon against the railing before disappearing inside. Headed for the bathroom, probably, and would be back soon.

I took a deep breath, relaxed a little, then panned to the floors beneath the balcony. The place was dark except for the bottom windows, which showed pale light. Candles or oil lamps. No one moving inside that I could see, though. Or was there . . . ?

Squatting low in the water, I fiddled with the TAM-14's focus rings and pressure switches. It wasn't until I had dimmed the internal lighting system, which improved contrast, that I realized I was doing a poor job of interpreting perfectly good data.

There were five or six people, maybe more, clustered in a room on the bottom floor. They weren't near a window. I could see their heat signatures through the walls. The images were not detailed. More like ghostly figures, their body heat diffused by wood and insulation. When the images moved, they dragged a vaporous, glowing veil behind them.

I checked the next two floors and found four people gathered in a single room. Island staff members, possibly, trying to hide from the violence. The fourth floor, though, appeared to be empty, which was unexpected, because the guard had not reappeared on the balcony.

Where the hell had he gone?

I blinked my eyes and adjusted the focus.

Damn it.

The guard's rifle had disappeared, too!

I crouched low, my head pivoting, as I tucked the waterproof bag under my arm like a football. If the guy had spotted me, it meant that he was wearing night vision. Nothing else could explain it. It meant that I was standing in plain view, an easy target. I had to move.

So I ran—partly out of panic, but also because I had no better choice. I made way too much noise, carrying my clanking bag, knees high, kicking water, fighting for balance in ankle-deep muck, but it didn't matter. In my mind, I imagined the guard shouldering his rifle from a new position. I felt the sting of crosshairs on my chest as the man steadied himself. I anticipated the impact of a slug I would never hear fired if I didn't find cover before the guard touched his finger to the trigger.

But I did hear the shot. The rifle made a pneumatic *THWAP* from the distance, which scared me so badly it caused my knees to buckle. I stumbled, got a hand on the ground as I regained my balance, and then I continued running, hunched low.

I was thinking, *A silencer.* Like Vladimir's pistol, the weapon was fitted with a sound suppressor, *and* the shooter was using some type of night vision system. The realization had all kinds of bad implications. If the man was professionally armed, he was probably well trained. If he was well trained, he wouldn't miss twice.

Ahead was an ornate cottage that had been converted into a VIP retreat. I had seen the place earlier in the day. The structure was a rectangle of yellow pine beneath a tin roof, with a private courtyard that contained a patio and dip pool, all walled with tropical adobe. Elegant Old Florida architecture for old-money guests—and it was empty, judging from the dark windows.

Separating us, though, was an elevated plateau, smooth as a golf green. It was a croquet court. Winter residents of Vanderbilt Island were big on croquet. They hosted international tournaments. They drank gin fizzes in the shade of a huge banyan tree and ate canapés during breaks.

The last thing I wanted was to cross an open area while a marksman dialed in the distance with a night vision scope. So I angled toward the tree.

Banyan trees are unusual. They expand in circumference as they grow. Overhead limbs drop air roots to support their own weight so that, after half a century, the trees resemble the schematic of a circus tent that contains a maze of poles.

The banyan tree—if I could put it between me and the fishing lodge, it would screen me from sight when I crossed the croquet court. So that's where I headed, running hard.

The finesse worked, because I dived and rolled behind the trunk of the tree without another shot fired. Or . . . maybe the guard believed he'd wounded me when I'd stumbled and now he was on his way to finish the job.

A disturbing possibility.

I got to my knees and peeked around a buttressed root to look. No sign of the guard, although I could still see the heat signatures of people clustered on the first floor of the lodge—inside the dining room, I guessed. I waited and watched for a full minute. It wasn't enough time to be sure the gunman wouldn't appear, but it's all that I could allow.

On hands and knees, pulling the waterproof bag with me, I crossed to the opposite side of the banyan tree. Roots suspended from limbs overhead were spaced like bars in a giant jail cell door. It was exactly the kind of cover I wanted. If someone was searching for me with conventional night vision, it was unlikely I'd be spotted.

The veil of roots extended for ten yards from the trunk of the tree, which is where I stopped and tried to figure out what to do next. Was it smarter to approach the lodge from the side and work my way around to the front? Or should I just sprint toward the entranceway and use the veranda as cover until I was sure the guard wasn't still looking for me?

The fastest, cleanest approach was best, I decided. First, though, I wanted to have a weapon in hand, ready to use. I opened the bag. I had wrapped each of the three jars in towels and added electrical tape to secure them. Because I knew the jars would be banged and jostled during the swim, it had been too dangerous to add the necessary chemical catalyst while still aboard *No Más*.

I did it now. I removed three medicine-sized glass bottles, checked again to confirm they were empty, then lined them up next to the much larger jars.

The container of matches, three small Ziploc bags and a pair of Tabasco-sized bottles came out last.

It was dark, and I had to guess at the proportions. Thermal imaging is great for finding people but useless when mixing chemicals at night. I knew that if I screwed up, if I slopped one liquid into another, I would activate the damn stuff. If that happened, I'd not only be incapacitated, I might tip off my location to the bad guys inside.

Finally, when I'd gotten the last lid onto the last jar, I relaxed a little and spent a few seconds looking at the stars. It was a symbolic pause, more than anything. I felt calm, my hands weren't shaking. True, the jars were filled with a volatile mixture that might interact unexpectedly. Same if I dropped a jar while sprinting toward the veranda. But that was okay. I'd done my work methodically, unemotionally. Strangely, that has always been enough for me—whatever the outcome.

Only a few items remained in the waterproof bag, so I closed it and pushed it closer to the tree. I needed Tomlinson's photographer's vest, though. I put it on and carefully placed a jar in each side pocket, then zipped the vest closed. The vest had a big back pocket, too, into which I slid the first-aid kit. There was no guessing the kind of injuries I might have to deal with once inside the lodge.

Getting to my feet, I cupped the third jar in my right hand and found the dive knife with my left. If I could get close enough, I would shatter the dining-room window with the knife, then lob one or two jars inside, depending on what I saw.

The third jar contained a different combination of chemicals, which I didn't plan on using unless my life—or the life of someone else—was on the line and I had no choice. It was most volatile of the three by far, and I paused for a moment, thinking it might be safer to carry the thing in a vest pocket. No . . . If the guard reappeared, I had to able to throw the thing without hesitating.

I was ready. Just as I was about to sprint toward the porch, though, an unexpected sound caused me to hesitate. It was a distant mewing that ascended, then descended. I might have assumed it was a cat, but there was a pleading quality that caused me to worry it might be a child.

I hadn't seen any children in the fishing lodge. Because it was low season, there were no property owners on the island and only a handful of staffers who arrived and left daily on a service boat. The four people I'd seen hiding on the third floor should have accounted for the few who, normally, would have left late after the bar had closed. But maybe employees were using staff housing because they'd brought their young sons or daughters along. It was an unsettling thought.

I turned and listened. The sound seemed to be coming from the courtyard of the VIP cottage or maybe from inside the cottage itself. Yes, it was a person, not an animal. But maybe not a child. A woman, possibly.

Because no lights were showing in the windows of the cottage,

I hadn't bothered to check it carefully using the thermal monocular. Now I did.

I had been wrong about the place being empty. Through the thin pine walls, I could see the glow of a human figure. A woman . . . definitely a woman, judging from the heat signature of her breasts. She was standing near a second person, who was lying on what was probably a bed. Nearby two candles burned, invisible from outside.

The details sharpened as I adjusted lighting and contrast and confirmed they were alone in the cottage. But then the details became unimportant when the woman's mewing turned into a muffled cry, her words indistinct but decipherable:

Breathe for me! Damn you, breathe!

By the time the woman said it a second time, I was already up and running toward the cottage.

12

As I slipped into the courtyard, I somehow managed to bang the gate against the Mexican adobe wall. When I did, sounds coming from inside the cottage stopped. Using the TAM-14, I watched the woman stand straight, as if listening, then hurry to the other side of the room, where another candle flickered.

So much for the element of surprise.

I took a quick look to confirm I wasn't being followed, then I tested the door. It was locked, as expected. Twice, I knocked: two sharp raps. Then I raised my voice to call, "My name's Ford. Do you need help?"

No response. I didn't blame the woman for not answering after so much gunfire, but I wasn't leaving until I found out why she had been imploring someone to *Please breathe!*

I backed away from the door as I slipped out of the photographer's vest. I couldn't risk breaking the jars I was carrying, so I wasted another few seconds while I carefully placed the vest on a ledge next to the dip pool. Then, gripping my dive knife, I kicked the door so hard it shattered off its hinges.

It wasn't a clean break, though, because a chain lock held it suspended, still blocking the entrance. My attempt at surprise had turned into a debacle—a fact made all too clear when a shadowed figure appeared in the doorway, pointing something at me.

"Who are you? Go away!" A woman's voice.

Inside, candles threw enough light for me to recognize the woman I'd seen earlier at Lien Bohai's table. Not the stunning beauty with the Anglo-Malaysian eyes. It was the stunningly plain woman whom I'd found appealing because of her swimmer's muscles and solid look.

In her hand was a black semiauto pistol. The Tritium night sights atop the slide reflected cat's-eye dots on the woman's forehead that implied proficiency. In the weapon, for certain. Maybe in the woman, too, although I wasn't convinced.

I held my hands up, palms out, to reassure her, as I said, "My name's Ford. I saw you earlier tonight. In the dining room, remember? I'm not going to hurt you."

The woman tried to sound unruffled as she responded, "Quite right, you won't! You're leaving. Right now." Then used the pistol to motion toward the courtyard gate.

"It's not safe out there," I said, trying to buy time.

"It's not safe *here* since you broke down the bloody door." She indicated the gate once again. "Please leave *now.* I'm . . . I'm busy!" Then surprised me by turning and rushing inside, calling, "I'll shoot you if you come in. I mean it!" her tough-guy calm unraveling under the pressure of some emergency.

I leaned and peeked around the doorframe. Two candles burned in the room, invisible from the outside because cardboard was taped over the windows. I watched the woman rush to a couch where a man lay motionless. She was still wearing the shiny silk dress, which told me that she had been dealing with the emergency for a while. Instantly, I turned, grabbed the photographer's vest and rushed back to the door.

"I have a first-aid kit," I called. "And I know CPR. I'm coming in." Without waiting for a response, I ducked under the door into the room.

The woman was hunched over the man, doing chest compressions, using both hands, dropping her weight onto him. The unconscious man was Lien Bohai.

"What happened? Was he shot?"

Not looking up, she asked, "Why are you doing this? I told you to get out."

I said, "At least let me try to help," as I placed the first-aid kit on the couch, then touched my fingers to Bohai's throat. No pulse. Bohai's skin was blue from cyanosis and much too cool on this hot night. He was dead or soon would be, but the woman couldn't allow herself to believe it, that was my guess. So I played along because I needed that damn pistol.

"How long's he been out?"

The woman made a sound of irritation but finally said, "The first time he stopped breathing was half an hour ago. I got him going again, he seemed to be coming out of it. But then he stopped again. Maybe longer than half an hour, I don't know. Then, just a couple minutes ago, he started coming around, but then I think he vomited and choked."

There was a hint of Brit in her accent that gave even graphic words a formal quality. No, not British . . . Singapore or Hong Kong, was more likely for a twenty-some-year-old Chinese woman.

I said, "You've been doing CPR the whole time? Mouth-to-mouth and—"

"Of course!"

I knelt beside the couch, tilted Bohai's head sideways, then used two fingers to probe inside his mouth, searching for a blockage. The woman had correctly guessed the problem.

I scooped out what I could to clear an airway while opening the first-aid kit with my free hand. Tomlinson hadn't packed the thing in an orderly way, of course, but it was well equipped. I found a plastic, flexible oropharyngeal airway tube, depressed Bohai's tongue with crossed fingers and pushed the device into his mouth upside down.

The woman watched me, her expression illustrating distrust. "Do you know what you're doing? That looks wrong."

I replied, "Speed up your compressions. I was taught at least a hundred a minute."

The airway tube was giving me trouble. I've got big hands and there wasn't much room to work. After I'd turned the tube a hundred and eighty degrees, I wiggled it around and applied more pressure than I expected to be necessary. Finally, it slid past the man's soft palate, down into his epiglottis.

"Watch his chest," I said. "Tell me if his lungs inflate. I've never done this before—not on a real person, anyway."

I had to remove my thermal vision headgear before I pinched nostrils closed, covered Bohai's mouth with mine and exhaled two long, slow breaths.

"Yes . . . he's getting air," the woman said, continuing to work on his chest. "Good. Thank you."

For the first time, we made eye contact. I watched her expression change from distrust to suspicion as she looked at me. "What happened to your face? You're all cut up, you're bleeding. And that thing you were wearing on your head"—she studied me more closely—"it's a night vision system, isn't it? I've used night vision goggles before. It's not the sort of item an average person owns, now is it?" After a thoughtful pause, she added, "Who are *you*?"

Interesting. The misplaced inflection suggested that the woman, in fact, already knew who I was but was trying hard not to reveal the truth—possibly because the truth was dangerous. There was something else: she was familiar with tactical night vision. Why?

I turned away without responding. In my head, I was counting the compressions—*thirteen, fourteen, fifteen*—then I filled Bohai's lungs with another long breath.

"Was he shot?" I asked again. The man was shirtless, as thin and pale as a withered mushroom. There was a swollen knot on his head but no sign of blood on his chest or white linen slacks.

The woman shook her head in reply, then glanced at the pistol next to her feet as if calculating how quickly she could get to it. "Are you armed? Tell me the truth."

I said, "No."

"You weren't in the lodge when the power went out?"

"I was at the marina."

"There was a gunshot. Are you sure you don't have a gun?"

I replied, "Now I think your compressions are too fast. I don't see any bullet wound."

"No, there's not. Someone said it was Viktor Kazlov. But I'm not certain."

I asked, "Nobody else? When the lights first went out, I mean."

The woman's reply was punctuated by her metronome compressions to Lien Bohai's chest. "I don't know because there was so much noise and confusion. Everything happened so fast. People panicked when we heard the shot. It was dark, just a few candles. People started pushing, a table was knocked over." She paused, brushed a strand of hair away from her eyes, then resumed her work.

"Somehow, we were separated. A tall American in a white tuxedo helped me. He was very kind. I don't know why, but I stayed calm thanks to him. But . . . but then the wind blew out most of the candles, and we were separated, too."

"Tomlinson," I said. "That's his name. He's a friend of mine." In my mind, the compressions were ticking away—*thirteen, fourteen, fifteen*—and I breathed for Bohai once more.

The woman appeared unconvinced that the kind man in the tuxedo would befriend someone like me. It was in her expression. Even so, she nodded at Bohai and explained, "He's so frail, I think he was possibly trampled. I found him lying inside the door of the lodge. He was groggy, confused. Then, as I was helping him here, back to our cottage, I think he had a heart attack. He grabbed his chest and said he had terrible pain in his left arm. I received first-aid training when I was in the army. It had to be a heart attack, I think."

The People's Liberation Army of China—the world's largest standing army. For Chinese males, service is compulsory. Women who volunteer are usually commissioned as officers—often into the medical corps, but the very smartest are snapped up by the Chinese intelligence agencies. It would explain the woman's familiarity with night vision. Semiautomatic pistols, too.

If true, she was the perfect employee for an international predator like Lien Bohai. And she might also be the first to learn, through intelligence sources, that she was on an island where an IED would soon be detonated.

I couldn't keep my eyes off my watch as we continued CPR. It was like a magnet. I checked it for the third time since I'd entered the room—11:30 p.m.—and asked her if she'd heard anything about hidden explosives or gas, and told her what Kazlov had said.

She didn't respond, just looked at Bohai, straightened for a moment, her expression weary, then resumed the chest compressions but with less intensity. "He's dead, isn't he?"

I sidestepped the question by asking, "Do you work for Mr. Bohai? Or related—his granddaughter?"

"Both. I'm his daughter and I'm on his staff. I have a degree in aquaculture, but I also do all of my father's"—the woman caught herself, hesitated, then became more cautious—"I'm like a personal assistant. Private matters that he trusts to no one else. At least"—she stared down into the man's face—"that's what I did before we came to this bloody island."

I exhaled another long breath into Bohai's lungs before saying, "He's your father."

"I just said so."

"Okay, then we can't give up yet. There's one more thing I can try to bring him back. Keep doing the compressions. I'll tell you when to stop." I wanted to delay an emotional meltdown for as long as possible, but the enormity of the daughter's loss was bound to hit her soon.

On the other hand, maybe I was worried for no reason. Judging from what the woman said next, I had overestimated the paternal bond. As I was rummaging through the first-aid kit, she spoke to herself, not to me, saying, "I knew he was dead. But I couldn't let myself give up. He despised a quitter—weakness of any kind, and . . . and he was not a patient man. Quite the opposite. Nor very kind."

She paused before saying the next words, as if testing her own courage. "Dead. My father's *dead*. How strange to stand so close to him, to actually say it out loud, and not feel terrified."

Terrified of her own father? The articulate, evasive man I had spoken with that afternoon hadn't struck me as terrifying, only selfish, manipulative and sinister. But who would know better than Bohai's own daughter?

I felt the woman's eyes on me when she asked again, "He *is* dead, isn't he?"

I replied, "There's still a chance. I need you to stay strong, understand? Your father's not the only one who needs help tonight." Then, noticing the mess that coated my fingers, I said, "Take this little bottle of Betadine. Squirt it on my hands, your father's chest, then get back to your compressions. Hurry. I'll give him another couple of breaths while you do it."

In the kit were needles, syringes and an ampule of epinephrine, which is usually used to treat allergic reactions. Bee stings and ant bites are common in Florida, and people die every year from the shock of the acidic venom. I always keep a few EpiPens on the boat because one quick injection can save the life of an otherwise healthy person. But epinephrine is also sometimes used to jump-start a dead heart.

I found the longest needle in the kit, loaded it with the drug and was tapping air bubbles to the top of the syringe as I positioned myself over the man. "You can stop the compressions now. I'll let you know when I'm done."

The woman's reaction was unexpected. "I'm not a child. Is that adrenaline?"

I nodded. "Same thing."

"Then he'll need air immediately, if it works. If it does, I'll do the breathing while you monitor his heartbeat." An instant later, she surprised me by ordering, "And please stop looking at your watch. There is no bomb, Dr. Ford!"

I had my fingers on the man's chest, feeling for a rib slot near the left nipple. I looked up long enough to say, *"What?"* but then refocused and speared the needle deep into what I hoped was the right ventricle of Bohai's heart.

"There is no bomb," the woman repeated as I pressed the plunger with my thumb. "No canisters of poisonous gas. If people on this island die tonight, it will be from gunshot wounds."

"How do you know this?"

"You have to trust me. My father was very demanding when it came to security—and to investigating his business associates."

"That's not good enough."

The woman was six inches shorter than me, but the look in her eyes was solid, imperturbable. "There are dangerous men on this island who despise one another. And they've panicked because they all assume they're under attack. Nobody's safe tonight. But if someone had planned mass murder such as you describe—my father's staff would have found out enough beforehand to make them suspicious. And we would have canceled the trip."

Bohai's security staff, I guessed, was a large, well-organized group—and unless I missed my bet, they took orders from his daughter. The probability gave the woman some credibility but also made it more likely that she was the one who had intercepted the threatening e-mail. In fact, it suggested that she had hacked the e-mail accounts of Bohai's enemies prior to their arrival as well as the accounts of *everyone* on the island, mine included. A big job, but doable for someone like her.

Because China restricts Internet access to its population, its surveillance agencies have to stay a step ahead of new Internet technology. If I was right about the woman's service in the Chinese military, there were obvious implications about her own role in tonight's events.

Not that I expected Bohai's daughter to admit anything. People in the intelligence community don't share information without receiving something in return. It becomes habit. Like diplomats, they send vague messages. They hide truth between the lines.

I withdrew the needle, capped it and swabbed a pinprick of blood with an alcohol pad. I started to say, "You're leaving something out—" but then stopped as Bohai's body spasmed beneath my hands. I leaned my ear to his chest. "We've got a pulse. Give him some air."

The startled expression on the woman's face was a mix of disappointment and hope as she spun to resume mouth-to-mouth. Whatever emotion dominated, the hope didn't last long.

As I listened, the old man's heart thumped a few times . . . stopped . . . spasmed again, then vanished into the silence of Bohai's final exhalation. I tried a few rib-cracking compressions, but it was pointless.

I put my hand on the woman's shoulder and gently pulled her mouth away from her father's lips. "You can stop now. You did everything you could." I turned Bohai's daughter so that she faced me. "I know it's hard—no matter how you felt about him. Look at me. *Look* at me. Tell me your name."

"Are you sure he's gone?" She sounded dazed. "I want to be absolutely certain before we give up."

"I should know your name. You knew mine from the start, didn't you?"

"Yes . . . Dr. Marion Ford. A man with an unusual past."

I let that go. "And yours?"

"Umeko. In China, the surname is always given first, so it would be Lien Umeko, if I'd stuck with the old ways."

"Nice name. Is that what your friends call you?" I was looking at the pistol on the floor, wondering how she would react if picked it up.

"In Chinese, it means 'plum blossom,' which doesn't translate well. So, legally, I'm Umeko Tao-Lien. Back in Singapore where I live, anyway. In Beijing, it's different because Lien is about as common as Smith in the U.S."

I gave her a reassuring pat and stepped away, looking around the room for the Betadine and a towel. I wanted to rinse my mouth out, too. The stink of death was on my lips. But my attention never wandered far from the pistol. When the woman stepped away from her father's body, I would slip the thing into my pocket like it was no big deal, then sprint straight to the fishing lodge.

I said, "Umeko, I need your help. Someone activated a jamming device—there's no outside communication. Are you aware of that? These people know what they're doing and they're serious. Kazlov's bodyguard was shot tonight. And at least two people tried to kill me. How can you be so sure someone didn't plant an IED?"

"If such a device existed—or if there was even a possibility—I would have been notified," she replied, some spirit returning to her voice.

"By whom? Kazlov didn't hear about it until a few hours ago."

"A company that doesn't have its own intelligence branch is a company run by fools. Our people in Beijing would have contacted me or my father or . . . or one of us."

I nodded at the dead man. "Maybe they did warn him."

The woman's head tilted toward the floor, thinking about it before she looked up at me. "Who told Viktor about an intercepted e-mail?"

I was picturing the stunning beauty I'd seen at Bohai's table earlier, then replaying Armanie's venomous reference about seeing Kazlov with her and the woman's price. "I don't know. Kazlov's bodyguard wouldn't tell me. I figured there was a reason. Wouldn't you?"

Once again, her chin dipped as she considered the possibilities, but then she settled it with a firm shake of her head. "No. I was in the lodge with my father all evening. Our sources would have sent a message to his cell phone or they would have contacted me. I'm sure of it."

"Where's his cell phone? Let's check and make sure."

"He must have lost his phone in the lodge when he fell. It wasn't in his jacket or pants. But it doesn't matter because—"

"It matters to me. My best friend's probably in the lodge and three women I know. And probably the restaurant staff, too."

Umeko waited patiently for me to finish before saying, "Because you've helped me, I'll help put you at ease by telling you something I shouldn't. No one is monitoring the communications on this island more closely than my father's"—Umeko caught herself as she turned to look at the man's corpse—"more closely than our people in Beijing and Singapore. If they contacted my father with information, they would have sent the same message to me, too. And they didn't."

"They could have messaged your father just as the jammer was being activated. It's possible."

"Dr. Ford, you are worrying needlessly. But if you feel so strongly, go to the fishing lodge. I'm not stopping you."

No, she wasn't. But I needed that damn pistol. I could feel the seconds ticking away, which is why I found the woman's certainty so irritating. To shake her, I said, "Then you already know about the five activists who showed up without an invitation?"

Instead, I was the one taken aback. "Yes, of course. Your information is wrong, though. There are seven members here, not five."

Seven? Tomlinson made six—who was the other member? But I didn't doubt the woman. She'd known that Third Planet had planned to crash the party, which connoted their prior e-mails had been reviewed and dismissed as harmless.

Impressive. The information diluted some of my anxiety about an IED, yet I wasn't fully convinced. Vladimir had been so damn sure! Then Umeko caused me to wince when, almost as an afterthought, she knelt and picked up the handgun. From the way she carried it—index finger along the barrel—it was obvious she knew how to use it.

I tried another approach. "What about the woman at your table tonight? Is she your sister? If you're wrong, she and a lot of others are in danger. Maybe she knows if your father was contacted."

Umeko's sarcastic laughter was unexpected. "That's *exactly* what I should do. Go and find her. You're talking about one of the richest woman in all of China. Possibly the entire world. Do you realize that? As of tonight, it's true."

I said, "I don't get it. Why would your sister inherit more than you?"

Umeko ignored the question by replying, "Excuse me, this dress is filthy," and walked toward what was probably a bedroom, carrying the gun. She paused only to take one of the candles. I didn't know what to do. Was she going to slip out a window? Or slam the bedroom door and lock it?

No, because a moment later Bohai's daughter raised her voice so I could hear. "Sakura is much too beautiful to be my sister. The parts of her that are real, anyway. She's my stepmother."

The woman with the Anglo-Malaysian eyes, I realized.

"Not many men make that mistake, even though we're the same age. I guess I should be flattered. And maybe I shall be—but later. Right now, I feel numb."

I was wondering if Umeko knew that her stepmother had been spending private time with Kazlov. But asking her now had the flavor of cruelty, so I raised my voice to ask, "Did she ever carry your father's phone? Some wives do."

"You have a very orderly mind, Dr. Ford. I admire that. You're thinking that Viktor's bodyguard would have a reason to conceal Sakura's name if she'd supplied Viktor with information. Particularly a secret transmission intended for her husband. I don't like the woman. No—I despise the woman. But my father would have never trusted her with his phone or anything else of importance. Once again, I'm afraid you're worrying needlessly."

I had turned my attention to Lien Bohai's body as she spoke, suddenly aware of a detail I had missed earlier. Or . . . maybe a detail that hadn't appeared until now. On the man's rib cage, beneath the left nipple and several inches from where I'd injected the epinephrine, was a thread of blood. Fresh blood, it looked like, brief drainage from an unseen wound. I couldn't figure it out. I cleaned my glasses, grabbed the lone candle and took a closer look as Umeko continued talking.

"In Chinese, 'sakura' means 'wild cherry blossom.' My father believed it a sign of great fortune that his beautiful new bride, and his unattractive daughter, were both named for flowers. I thought I would never understand the stupidity of men, but now I do. Rich men marry their mistresses because they have so much in common. They are both ruthless and both are whores."

Umeko reappeared, wearing slacks, running shoes and a baggy colorless blouse, the pistol in her right hand. Eyes avoiding her father's corpse, she began opening drawers, looking for something. She appeared to be in a hurry.

"Where's his shirt?" I asked.

The woman was preoccupied. She opened one last drawer and then turned her attention to a leather suitcase, probably her father's.

"I can't stay here tonight. Not with . . . with his body in the same house. You're right, though, when you say it's dangerous to go outside. Would you be willing to help me move his body to the courtyard?"

Behind the couch, I had spotted Bohai's dinner jacket. I retrieved it, then held up the man's white dress shirt. After inspecting it for a moment, I asked, "Did you notice this bloodstain? It's dried blood. Not much. It would be easy to miss."

Umeko looked up from the suitcase and shook her head. "He hit his forehead when he fell, I think. Maybe it came from there."

"No. It came from the left side of his rib cage"—I used a finger to point—"from what looks like a small hole. A puncture wound the size of a needle. Or an ice pick. When I injected the adrenaline, the pressure must have reopened the wound for a second or two."

A few seconds later, I was holding the shirt close to a candle. "There's a tiny little hole, too. It's tough to see because of the bloodstain. But it's there."

I was picturing Sakura, the exquisite beauty, in the swimming pool, reaching to untether her hair, as I watched the stepdaughter's expression. "Umeko, do you understand what I'm telling you?"

"No, I don't. He had a heart attack. I was with him when it happened."

"You're wrong. I think your father was murdered. The blood, and a puncture wound in his chest that matches the hole in this shirt. I can't explain it any other way. When the lights went out, I think someone stuck him and kept going. The police can help us figure out later who did it."

The expression of shock on Umeko's face was real. She seemed more overwhelmed by this than the fact that her father was dead. I turned toward the door. "Listen. We have to deal with what's happening now. I've still got about twenty-five minutes, and there could be a dozen people in that building. Why take the chance?"

The woman's thoughts had turned inward, as if reconsidering. My guess was, she was going over the night's events, trying to remember if Sakura had left the dining room long enough to be alone with Viktor Kazlov or had an opportunity to pocket Bohai's phone. But then my attention shifted abruptly to a distinctive sound from outside. A metallic sound that found its way through the broken doorway: the clack of a rifle bolt, then footsteps.

"What's wrong?" she whispered. "Do you hear something?"

I held a finger to my lips, nodded and pointed to the door as I moved to her side. "Give me the pistol."

Umeko pushed my arm away, shaking her head. "Is someone coming?"

"Give me the pistol. A guy took a shot at me ten minutes ago. I think he's still after me."

The woman snapped, "And you led him *here*!" but then softened and said, "I'm sorry. You didn't deserve that."

"I'm familiar with weapons," I told her. "If you know anything about me, you know it's true."

As I watched the doorway, I felt a flicker of hope as her resolve appeared to waver. But then Umeko made a sound of exasperation and confessed, "The bloody gun's not loaded. That's what I was looking for. It's Father's pistol and he always hides the magazines when he's not carrying the thing."

I hurried to blow out the candles, then took the woman's arm. "Is there a back door to this place?"

Yes, there was. When I opened it, though, a man blinded me with a tactical light that was clamped to the underside of a pistol. A moment later, behind us, someone else suddenly kicked the broken door off its chain.

As I tried to shield my eyes, the man gave a simian howl that transitioned into panic when he saw what Umeko was still carrying in her hand. "Drop the goddamn gun!" he screamed. "Do it *now*!"

The voice was manic fueled, an octave higher but recognizable. It was Markus Kahn.

The video game wizard, apparently, was now lost in a new vortex. It was the fantasy that he had turned pro.

13

Before Kahn nearly maimed us all by taking a jar from my vest and shaking it, he painted Lien Bohai's corpse with the gun-mounted flashlight and said to his partner, "Damn it! Wish I'd found him first."

The old man was lucky to die a natural death, Kahn meant. He was a nervous, sullen introvert unused to bragging or making threats, which added to the impression he was trying hard to be something he was not. But being in the presence of an actual corpse had energized him in some strange way and he couldn't hide his excitement. Death. It was right there, within arm's reach. And real. Not like on a video screen.

"One of the Big Four is definitely DOA," he said through a black ski mask as if transmitting on a radio. "One down, three to go."

The theatrics struck me as bizarre until I realized both men wore pin-sized cameras strapped to their heads. They were recording it all on their cell phones.

Talas, Armanie, Bohai and Kazlov were the Big Four, of course.

Kahn was talkative, frenetic, like he was amped up on Adderall. More surprisingly, he seemed eager to impress me.

I didn't tell Kahn that videoing their "assault" was adolescent, pretentious and tasteless. What I did tell him was that some sort of device might be detonated at midnight, which meant that he might have less than twenty minutes to live unless they stopped playing games and did something about it.

As I studied the reactions of the two men, I saw nothing to indicate they knew anything about a bomb. Just the opposite. The possibility that it was true seemed to scare Kahn, although he forced brittle laughter. He was visibly agitated as he panned his gun-mounted flashlight around the room, then stopped when it was pointed at Umeko's face.

"Do you know anything about this bomb bullshit?"

"I wouldn't be on the island if I believed it," the woman replied, staying cool.

"She doesn't know that for sure." I interrupted. It was 11:42 p.m., and I wasn't going to stand here listening to any more talk. To the woman I said, "Tell them the truth. You're not a hundred percent sure."

Umeko said to Kahn, "You're blinding me with that light. Do you mind?" then took a moment to rub her eyes. "There is a small possibility that Dr. Ford is right. But it's unlikely."

Kahn scratched at the ski mask, muttering, "The caviar leeches, they're all rich. They've got no reason to do something so crazy. And nobody in our group has anything like that planned. So it's bullshit. Don't you think, Trapper?"

His partner was even jumpier than Kahn. "Yeah, Rez. Sure," he said. "Rez"—Kahn's nickname. But Trapper sounded worried. He was the skinny guy I'd seen earlier in the fishing lodge, standing at the door, playing with his cell phone. Neither of them were actors and their reactions convinced me they didn't know a damn thing about a bomb threat. It meshed with the probability that his group's e-mails had been monitored by Umeko and her people. But if Lien Bohai's intelligence team was so good, why were these two jerks running around with weapons, wearing masks and holding us at gunpoint?

Kahn put the light on me. "You trying to scare us? Because it's not going to work."

I said, "Why not evacuate the lodge, just to be on the safe side? If there's even that small possibility—"

He snapped, "Kiss my ass!" then gestured toward the dead man. "People like him are bloodsuckers who get what they deserve. Besides, after what happens to the world tonight"—nervous laughter again—"who really gives a damn?"

He meant something a lot bigger than a bomb, apparently, and it was spooky the way he said it. Then it got spookier when Kahn stared at the old man's body, then leveled his pistol at Umeko.

"How many humpback whales you think your boss killed? How many dolphins you think he caught and sold to freak shows like that hotel across the bay?"

I saw Kahn's index finger move from the trigger guard to the trigger and I stepped closer to Umeko. "Take it easy. She worked for the guy, that's all. She was Bohai's aquaculture expert, for Christ's sake. She hates the factory ships as much as any of us. She wanted to take his company in a different direction."

The woman pulled her arm free as if to say she didn't need my help. I liked that. It asserted her independence. The move also confirmed she was smart enough to understand why I had lied and cool enough to play whatever role was required. I was trying to steer Kahn away from the fact that Umeko was Bohai's daughter. He was already eager to pull the trigger. Why give him a powerful reason to do it?

Kahn stopped blinding Umeko by lowering the pistol to her chest. But he wasn't done with her. "You live in China? I've read that Bohai owns a huge mansion on the sea. I bet you live in the same house."

Umeko replied, "I live in Singapore because that's where most of my research is done. I commute to Beijing when needed. Check my passport. Or my driver's license—it's in my purse. My name's Umeko Tao-Lien and I was born in Singapore."

Very smooth. She had added another tier to my lie and then distanced herself from her father by offering proof of her legal name.

Kahn, though, seemed determined to make his bones, and I got a tight feeling in my stomach when he turned to me and said, "You don't think I can do it, do you?"

Pull the trigger, he meant.

I shrugged. "Of course you can—if you had a reason. But you don't. Even if you did, it would be smarter to evacuate the lodge first." My watch read 11:50 p.m.

"Don't be so goddamn sure, man!"

Weird, but for the first time I got the impression *he* didn't believe he could do it—a lot of men can't—and now he was wrestling with his own doubt. But why did my opinion matter? I hadn't exactly hit it off with him and Densler earlier.

The guy was irrational, but irrational people can be manipulated. "What's the difference between killing a whale and an innocent woman? You approve of that?" Touching my head to remind Kahn the camera was getting all this, I added, "It's cold-blooded murder. The same with the people you're putting at risk by not evacuating the goddamn fishing lodge!"

I raised my voice to make the point because it was 11:51.

"This woman works for one of the world's most ruthless eco-criminals," Kahn argued, oblivious. "You expect me to actually believe she disapproved? That's like Göring saying he disapproved of Hitler. What do you think, Trap?"

Kahn's partner was behind us, exiting the bedroom, already pawing through what was probably Umeko's purse. Like Kahn, he had added a black ski mask and mini-camera to his ensemble of jeans and black crewneck with the Third Planet Peace Force skull in yellow.

Unlike Kahn, he was carrying a scoped rifle and wearing what looked like Soviet surplus night vision monocular. Mounted on the barrel of the rifle was a homemade sound suppressor—the sort of thing amateur anarchists learn to make when they're not building homemade bombs. The equipment was cheap, like the semiauto pistol Kahn was holding.

The man had probably been the guard on the balcony. He had come damn close to killing me.

As my watch's sweep hand raced toward midnight, I didn't trust myself to look at the man because I wanted to slap the rifle from his hands and snap his neck. But I didn't linger on the fantasy because I, too, was beginning to panic.

I took a step toward Kahn and watched him recoil as if I'd raised my hand to slap him. "No closer! I'm warning you!"

I told him, "I'm walking out that door. I have seven minutes to evacuate that building."

Because Kahn had the pistol aimed at my head, I had to screen my eyes from the flashlight as I brushed past him, ignoring his threats to shoot if I took one more step. As I neared the couch where the old Chinese man lay, I thought I was in the clear. But then Umeko's scream and a simultaneous gunshot spun me around and I dropped to the floor.

Umeko was yelling, "You shot him! You animal! Why did you shoot him?" as she started toward me, but Kahn grabbed her from behind.

I'd felt nothing. No impact, no jarring pain. For a moment, I assigned it to the inevitable shock of being shot. Finally, though, I realized what had happened. Kahn had put a bullet through Lien Bohai's thigh and was now wrapping an arm around Umeko's throat out of panic or rage, I didn't know.

My chest was thudding, and I felt an esophageal burn that signaled nausea. But it was Markus Kahn who sounded giddy when he said, "*I did it.* Shot the old bloodsucker. First time, and hardly aimed.

"Ford, if you . . . If you . . ." The man was hyperventilating, so he had to pause to gulp a breath. "If you screw with me, I'll waste you, and this bitch, too! Think I'm scared to shoot now?"

Behind him, Trapper sounded awestruck but a little nauseated himself, saying, "Look at the damn chunk you blew out of his leg. Jesus, really . . . mangled. How . . . how's it feel?"

Kahn laughed, "You've got a gun, old lady, try it yourself!" his manner suddenly arrogant as if he'd shot many corpses in his time.

I was furious as I got to my feet. "You're not shooting him again, dumbass, because he's . . ."—I stopped myself to think what argument could possibly have any effect on him—". . . because the round could go through a wall and kill someone else—or ricochet and kill you. Only amateurs take stupid risks."

For some reason, Kahn said to his partner, "See? This guy might be able to teach us something."

The endorsement didn't raise my spirits. It was two minutes until midnight, which meant it was too late to stop whatever happened next. Even so, I said, "We've got to get to the lodge."

Kahn was grinning, but the skin around his raccoon eyes looked waxen like he was feeling queasy, too. He still couldn't keep his eyes off the body. "Christ, not more of your bomb bullshit. It's already after twelve, isn't it?"

Trapper said, "One minute thirty seconds to go. I've got the G-Shock atomic watch—exact time anywhere in the world. It's what a lot of the SEAL guys use."

For the next ninety seconds, the four of us stood in the heat of summer candlelight and the stink of death as Trapper counted down. I didn't realize I'd been holding my breath until Trapper got to the final seconds: ". . . seven . . . six . . five . . . four . . . three . . . two . . ."

Nothing happened. For the next sixty seconds, then two minutes, then five minutes, I continued to wait for the first whiff of chlorine gas, or the delayed ignition of a faulty wiring device, as the two activists began to make sarcastic jokes.

By 12:15 a.m., I decided that whatever was going to happen wasn't going to happen—not now, anyway. Kazlov *had* received a warning about a device that would kill everything on the island. I believed it because I'd witnessed Vladimir's reaction—the man had been scared shitless.

I had a bad feeling I had missed something somewhere. But I didn't have time to dwell on it, I had to move on. Markus Kahn's first taste of violence had made him eager for more, and Umeko Tao-Lien would die in the same room as her father unless I did something to stop Kahn.

I focused on Kahn, gauging his moves. Judging from his behavior, he wanted to shoot Umeko for no other reason than to prove he had the balls to do it. Judging from his physiology—twitching cheeks and rapid breathing—he *would* shoot her the instant he summoned the nerve.

I knew that I had to make a move and do it fast.

They had taken my knife, along with the makeshift weapons in my vest. With men like this, though, I didn't need a weapon. They were both sloppy pretenders. They had already given me a couple of clean openings—opportunities I didn't risk because the woman would have been caught in the cross fire.

As Trapper used a flashlight to go through the woman's billfold, I dropped my glasses while cleaning them, kicked them accidentally, which moved me two steps closer to Kahn.

Umeko noticed. It was in the way she lifted her hand, for an instant, as if to stop me. Kahn didn't, so I gained another half step when I turned to watch Trapper.

I wasn't worried about a rifle. Not in such close quarters—especially when Trapper, the fool, knelt and wedged the rifle between his legs as he tossed credit cards and some bills onto the floor. I could have knocked the man on his skinny ass before he had time to get the weapon to his shoulder.

Kahn was the one I needed to deal with. If I could get to him before he turned the pistol from Umeko to me, I might be able to snap his elbow before he got off a round, then strip the gun from his hand and shoot Trapper in the thigh or the kneecap—I didn't want to kill the guy. Then, depending on Kahn's reaction, I would disable him temporarily or long-term. His call.

I needed a distraction, so I stared at Umeko until we established eye contact. Her face was orchid white in the flashlight's glare. She was trembling, but still composed enough to acknowledge me with a nod, but then shook her head as if telling me *Don't try it.*

The response was confusing. Did she really understand what I was trying to communicate?

Yes. The woman verified it by saying to Trapper, "In my billfold, there's a hidden compartment behind the driver's license. You want proof I hate what Lien Bohai stood for? You'll find it there."

Trapper tossed a couple of more credit cards onto the tile, then used the flashlight to take a close look at something.

After a few seconds, his tone changed. "Hey, Rez! This woman's in the Chinese Army! Here's her ID card, the hologram and everything. And she's in uniform!"

Umeko and I exchanged a quick look as Trapper addressed her directly. "What's your rank? If our parents hadn't made us go to fucking college, we'd both be Special Forces now. Wouldn't we, Rez?"

Kahn interrupted, saying Umeko's military service didn't prove she hadn't profited from Lien Bohai's factory ships. Which caused the men to bicker briefly until Umeko cut them off, saying, "That's not what I wanted you to see. There's another card in there. Same compartment."

"Jesus Christ," Trapper whispered when he had the card in his hand. "You're not going to believe this shit, man! Take a look! She's one of us! A 3P2 member, dues all paid and everything."

I was thinking, *The seventh member,* while Kahn crossed the room to look.

Umeko's tone became confessional as she told the men she had to keep the card hidden because Lien Bohai, or anyone else in the company, would have turned her in to the Chinese government for belonging to a subversive organization. For the same reason, she used a separate personal computer when logging onto the web page or chat rooms. And only in Singapore. Never China.

"That wouldn't have been the worst of it," she added, then nodded toward the old man's body. "He was a dictator, very cruel. I'd have been beaten—or jailed. It wouldn't have been the first time he did it to an employee. You have no idea the amount of power he had in China."

I watched Kahn accept the card from Trapper. He inspected it closely as if he didn't want to be convinced. Finally, though, he used the pistol to summon the woman closer.

What happened next was bizarre. Kahn gave Umeko a quick, impersonal kiss on the cheek, then backed away as if human contact was unsavory. "If this thing's real, you're my double S, like it or not. Symbiotic sister. But you better not be bullshitting us."

Umeko deflected it. "I follow your posts in the chat room—I see you almost every night when I'm home. I'm Dragonfly."

Trapper said, "I've seen the name, man! I shit you not."

Umeko continued to manipulate them like the pro she obviously was. "I've wondered what you looked like in person. On the web page, there's a photo of you on an assault boat. It was posted about a year ago, when you started operations on the Caspian Sea. You and someone with the screen name Genesis, I think. But the picture's blurry and shot from too far away."

Trapper asked Umeko, "A short little chubby guy, right? That's one of the Neinabor twins! Genesis and Exodus, though they only use those names online. With us they're just Geness and Odus. Their parents were Jesus freaks who lived in the desert in a bus or van or something. So they're into the whole biblical thing, which is how they knew the Internet would crash tonight."

I was giving the man my full attention now, thinking, *They predicted it?*

"Not the only ones," Kahn said, irritated. "I saw it coming, too. Everyone gives them the credit, but all they really do is just whine and bicker."

Trapper said, "Not since the power went out. The way they took charge—you've got to admit it—like they knew exactly what to do. Serious badasses all of a sudden. I bet they've already scored a couple of kills. Odus can be a mean little bastard."

Kahn was getting pissed off. "Give me a break! Two core gamers who still carry Super Mario bags from sixth grade and talk to dead people? Last year, I dropped Geness's PlayStation in the toilet and he started *crying*. Yeah, badass nutcases."

I was remembering the colorful computer bag I'd seen earlier, as Trapper explained to Umeko, "They used to be triplets. One of them died, but they still talk to him. You know, like their brother's in the same *room*. That's what he means about them being weird. Smart, but, yeah, seriously out there."

Kahn was done with the subject, his attention still on Umeko. "Having a membership card doesn't prove anything. Any leech can go to our web page and do that."

Umeko Tao-Lien looked right at him. "Two years ago, I joined Third Planet Peace Force. Out of guilt, I guess. It made me sick what Bohai's fishing fleet was doing. I felt like I was taking blood money."

As the woman spoke, I studied her face. For an intense instant, just an instant, our eyes linked to reassure me she was playing a role.

"I'm not wealthy. But I still donate a thousand Singapore dollars every year to Third Planet, which is quite a lot in U.S. dollars. For a single woman who lives alone . . . ?" The daughter of one of the wealthiest men in China ended the sentence with a shrug.

Kahn was now going through the photographer's vest, and the rest of my gear, as he warned Umeko, "We have more than a thousand members and we know we've been infiltrated. Don't get cocky. You're not in the clear yet."

Umeko felt cocky enough to tell Kahn, "Dr. Ford has a head injury. It needs to be cleaned and dressed. Would you allow me to use the first-aid kit?"

Kahn's odd behavior toward me was suddenly explained when he reached for the kit and replied, "You mean *Commander* Ford, don't you?" Then, with a piercing look, he said to me, "I've bet you've really seen some shit, huh? T told me you're, like, one of the biggest special ops guys in the world. Which is what makes this so cool. *I'm* the dude who finally took you down!"

I was about to ask *Who's T?* but figured it out on my own. Tomlinson had been talking about me again.

Kahn explained, "If Winified hadn't made me read T's book, I wouldn't have believed him. Big nerdy-looking guy—she was right about that. Which is sort of cool, too."

Umeko was listening as she scrubbed my forehead with Betadine, then applied salve. I had the impression she already knew the answer when she asked, "Is T the member who posted his theory about mass panic and the Internet? There was an acronym . . ."

"Sudden Internet Isolation and Retaliation," Kahn interrupted, getting it all wrong. "It's what happens when the Earth has had enough of our poisonous bullshit. As of tonight, it'll be months before the Internet is working again. Same with the electrical grids. And T's the one who saw it coming, man. Like he made it happen. 'Plasmic visualization,' he calls this weird gift he has for influencing future events." Which is when Kahn removed one of the jars from my vest, opened it, sniffed, then looked at me, his expression asking *What is this crap?*

Trapper was taking a roll of tape from his pocket, preparing to tape our hands, I guessed, as he told Kahn, "I keep thinking maybe it's just this island. Power goes out here, it doesn't mean the whole system's down. Maybe in a couple of redneck Florida counties but not the entire country. The twins could be wrong about that."

"Bullshit," Kahn said, capping the jar, "I knew it was going to happen before T's first post. Long before those weirdos had a damn clue. So maybe I've got the same gift—plasmic visualization." The man smiled, pleased by the idea, but then got serious again.

"The world is coming to its miserable end, people. Do you have any idea how lucky we are to be on an island, safe from all craziness out there?"

Coming from someone like Kahn, it would have been hilarious if the man hadn't been sincere. He *wanted* it to be true, just as Tomlinson had said. I was thinking, *Virtual world psychosis,* as he added, "It's like being in a space capsule and landing on a new planet where no one is prepared for survival but us."

Umeko was done cleaning my cuts, and I began repacking the first-aid kit as an excuse to ignore the man. Kahn didn't like that. He began shaking the jar again, demanding a reaction, the smaller bottle inside clanking against glass.

"Don't do that," I told him.

"Why? What's in it? It smells like shit."

"It's supposed to," I lied. "Someone took a shot at me from the lodge. I thought there might be hostages, so I made three homemade stink grenades to clear everyone out of the building. Because of the bomb."

"That goddamn bomb again," Kahn laughed but checked his watch. "The bullshit story you invented to scare us? It's almost twelve-thirty. Admit you were lying."

"If I didn't think the threat was real, I wouldn't have improvised chemical weapons."

Kahn looked at the jar in his hand, surprised I'd applied those words to a stink bomb. "Chemical weapons," he said finally. "Yeah . . . I guess it fits." Maybe he was impressed, but then downplayed it, saying, "Cool. Unconventional weaponry, that's the future. We have to use what we can until the last alpha warrior, in the last enemy tribe, is dead. How many times have we talked about this, Trapper?"

The enemy warrior being me, I guessed. It was in Kahn's tone and the way he challenged me by deciding to shake the jar again. Fortunately, though, the man lost interest when his flashlight discovered the TAM-14 unit lying near the couch. The way he rushed to claim the thing reminded me of a kid lunging for a toy on Christmas Day.

Amphetamines or crystal meth? I was wondering. What was the drug of choice for male children whose manhood was trapped in a computer-simulated world?

"Tape his hands," Kahn told Trapper as he looked at the unit. "No . . . wait. Have Dragonfly tape his hands first. Then *you* tape him from his elbows down to his wrists. I'll check it all when you're done."

Adjusting the monocular's headband, Kahn taunted me by telling his partner, "If he really is some special ops hotshot, like T claims, he's got to be, you know, *really* dangerous. And we want to impress him, right?"

14

When I asked Kahn, "Do you still have a guard posted on the balcony?" I was trying to establish myself in the hierarchy of our little group and also account for the only members of Third Planet I hadn't met.

The Neinabor twins—the physical description matched the two chubby blond men I'd seen earlier, right down to the child's computer bag. They had driven their van all the way from California only to be transformed when the shooting started.

"Suddenly, they're serious badasses," Trapper had said.

What worried me was that an abrupt transformation was possible. Fear is an unpredictable catalyst but always powerful. Some people cower, a few snap. Overwhelming fear can turn a timid man into a mad-dog killer. The effect might be greater on twins—or triplets—because it could mushroom exponentially, ping-ponging between them as their panic escalated.

So far, I hadn't been convinced that Kahn and his partner were capable of murder. The same might not be true of the Neinabors.

Trapper had said they sometimes spoke to the dead triplet as if he were in the same room, a disturbing fact in itself.

I wanted to hear more. My guess was, one of the Neinabors was the rapid-fire bungler who'd surprised Viktor and me at the dock. Bungler or not, he wasn't afraid to pull the trigger. I also still didn't know who was being held captive in the lodge. If one or both of the twins was guarding them—and still had some ammunition left—there might be carnage awaiting us.

Ammunition, I'd been thinking about that. From all the gunfire I'd heard, everyone of the island had to be running low even if they'd equipped themselves for mass murder.

Kahn wasn't very talkative, though, because we'd heard two more distant gunshots when we were about halfway between the cottage and the lodge. The shots had scared him so badly that he and Trapper had dived for cover behind the banyan tree. Almost as an afterthought, they had ordered Umeko and me to drop to the ground, too.

Once again, I asked Kahn if a guard had been posted. "I need to know details if I'm going to help you get back to the lodge without your asses being shot off. Play tough guy, though, and I think we're all in serious trouble."

If Kahn believed I was a "gnarly special ops expert," I was going to play the role to my advantage.

Lying in prone position, pistol ready, the man was studying the open area ahead. "Those shots sounded pretty close," he replied. "They sound close to you? Christ, there could be a sniper out there right now, waiting for us to make a move."

I was lying on my side, Trapper slightly behind me, Kahn to my right, the woman to my left. I whispered, "I think you might be right. Out of the corner of my eye, I saw something. A person, I think, just after the shots were fired."

"*Where?* How far was he?"

Scanning the patio near the swimming pool, then a cove formed by oak trees and Spanish moss, I replied, "If I was the guy, I'd wait until we were halfway across the clearing, then shoot the lead man. Which is you, Rez. Then pick off the rest of us when we panic."

Kahn slapped the ground with his hand. "Shit, he's right."

I told him, "There's a ledge below that tree that drops down four or five feet to the beach. Maybe he's wearing night vision, too. He could have seen us, and slid behind the ledge until he has a clean shot." A moment later, I added, "Is one of the Neinabor twins tall and lean? If not, it could be Armanie's bodyguard."

Trapper whispered, "He's lying, right? He just trying to scare us again."

"Did you get a look at Armanie's security guy?" I asked. "The caviar people recruit from the Russian Special Forces. Spetz GRU, maybe you've heard of it. Their insignia is an owl because they supposedly learn how to see in the dark."

Kahn thought about that for a few seconds, his paranoia growing. "Shit, I knew we shouldn't have left the goddamn cottage!"

I added some drama by turning my head, then examining the front entrance beyond the porch as if gauging the odds of us making it before the shooter opened fire.

Kahn asked me, "What are you thinking?"

"I'm thinking you'd better give me some information or we're screwed. How many people are inside, and what about the guard? I need to know before I can offer advice."

The man was suddenly so eager to answer, he ran his words together. "Three women, I don't know their names . . . local women, rich bitches, you know the type. Then there's Winifred. That's it. So what do you think we should do? Head back to the cottage?"

I said, "What happened to the restaurant staff? There was a bartender and at least three servers. Where'd they go?" They were probably still hiding on the third floor, but I wanted to find out if Kahn knew they were there.

"Dude, I have no idea! Everyone panicked and ran. There could be people hidden in some of the rooms, who knows? It was pretty crazy for a while after the lights went out."

Only three hostages, not counting Densler and Tomlinson? It took some effort not to show my surprise. "Are they tied and gagged?"

Kahn was close to emotional overload. "Why the hell would we *bother*? No one in their right mind would leave that place with all that shooting. That's why I posted Trapper on a balcony to stand guard. *Damn it!*"—he slapped the ground again—"When Winified said they wouldn't let us come to this caviar deal, I should have figured out it was reverse psychology. The same with that dolphin place. Someone *knew* we'd come—it's a goddamn plot."

I whispered, "You planned on attacking the casino, too?"

"No! Just confront them and get it on video. Hell, we didn't plan on attacking this place, either. It . . . things just snowballed when everyone panicked. I should have known we were being set up. Ever since we started hassling their fishing boats, they've been plotting ways to get rid of us. You have no idea how many enemies we've made."

I couldn't pretend to take the man seriously, so I chose to fan his paranoia. "It's dangerous to screw with power."

"*Exactly* what I'm saying. First, they knock out the Internet, then they arrest all the activists during the chaos. Shit, it could even be the Illuminati. They've been manipulating governments for five hundred years. Look on the back of a dollar bill—the pyramid and all-seeing eye."

I was thinking, *He's reciting the synopsis of a video game.*

Kahn gestured with his head to indicate Umeko. "Remember

her saying how much power the old Chinese guy had? He was probably one of them." Then Kahn asked Trapper, "Did you notice what kind of ring the old man was wearing? Shit, I should have checked."

No, I decided, Kahn wasn't reciting. He believed what he was saying, which was eerie. Maybe he sensed my uneasiness because he became even more determined to convince me.

"Don't you get it? The caviar guys, they're part of an international society. Like the Mafia, only they keep it quiet. Sooner or later, they'll have to attack the lodge because that's where the goddamn food is. It could be weeks before the mainland gets power again. And who cares about a few people stranded on an island?"

From four miles away, I was looking at the concrete glow of Bare Key Casino reflecting off the stars, and wondering, *How can anyone be so oblivious?* I felt like head-butting the guy, then strangling him with my legs.

I stayed calm, though, and played along, "Everyone will be out of food and water in a few days? That settles it, then. We've got to get inside that lodge. Cut our hands free, we can move faster and quieter. What happens when a women trips but can't use her hands? She screams. She'd give away our position. After that, we take off for the *back* of the lodge, everyone at the same time. Doing the unexpected is the best way to deal with the unexpected."

I struggled to my knees and turned my back to Trapper. "My arms are numb, cut the damn tape. And don't get too attached to that knife—it's mine."

Kahn was suggestible, but he had his limits. "Okay, okay . . . cut Dragonfly free, yeah—but not him! We've got enough to worry about without Ford trying to jump us."

I said, "If you want my help, you will. How long you think that sniper's going to wait?"

Kahn replied, "Nope. No way," sounding like a petulant child.

My fingers were cramping, mosquitoes were like cobwebs on my face and I was out of patience. "For all you know, the shots we just heard was the Neinabors killing a couple of unarmed people. All because you went off, left them unprotected, while you tried to take down a sick old man. For once, show some balls."

As Trapper freed Umeko's hands, maybe he sensed the power shifting because he told me, "We haven't seen the twins for, like, almost an hour. You're right about those two. They grabbed their guns, went out the door, and that's when the fireworks really started."

"Did one of the weapons have a red laser sight?"

I wasn't sure if Trapper nodded or not. "Maybe. They're the ones who found the guns, so they got first choice."

I couldn't believe what I'd just heard. "Found guns *where*?"

"When the Internet crashed, they said it was the sign they were waiting for. From the Bible, you know? So they went floor to floor, ripping everything apart, and found this little closet where someone had hidden weapons. This rifle"—Trapper held it for me to see—"three pistols and three boxes of ammunition."

I said, "In a *fishing* lodge?" then dragged my left foot under me because, in that instant, I realized what was going on. The Neinabor twins had orchestrated the entire hijacking. They hadn't *found* weapons. They had *brought* weapons to Florida in their van—probably along with a homemade bomb, or bombs, plus a portable radio jammer.

I'd been right about Kahn and Trapper—they didn't know a damn thing. Kahn had been telling the truth when he said events had snowballed when everyone panicked. The Neinabors had kept the plan a secret because they wanted to convince their Third Planet friends that Armageddon had arrived. "They're very smart," Trapper had told us—and also so mentally unstable that they conversed with a dead brother.

Kahn, getting angry now, said, "You still don't get it, do you? These guns really are a sign, man. The End Times, it's more than just bullshit prophecy. The Earth is always renewing herself. Hurricanes, tornadoes—but now the real shitstorm is here. You don't think she knows how to protect herself?"

"Shut up," I told him.

"What?"

"You heard me." I got another foot under me and stood. "I'm going inside. Maybe Tomlinson and I—if he's still alive—can think of a way to convince the caviar people you idiots started shooting because you panicked. In the morning, though, it's going to be a lot harder to explain to the police, Coast Guard, ATF and everyone else who shows up."

Kahn hissed, "Get down!" motioning toward the darkness. "You trying to get us all killed?"

I was staring at Kahn. He looked like a frat boy dressed for Halloween, with his ski mask and pistol. He wasn't going to shoot anyone. I walked toward Umeko. "Maybe you should stay with these two. If there's any more shooting, you can at least count on them to find a place to hide."

The woman was shaking her head before I finished the sentence, stood, brushed her hands on her slacks, told me, "Let's go, we'd better hurry."

We did.

Ignoring Kahn's threats, we ran across the croquet court to the lodge, where I followed Umeko into the main room. There, instead of waiting for her to finish untangling the tape that bound my elbows and wrists, I yelled, "Tomlinson! Get your ass in here!" because I was furious.

We didn't have to wait long. We heard footsteps, then a short man, pudgy but not obese, dragged Tomlinson into the room, left hand knotted in his long hair, right hand holding a pistol that cast a familiar red dot on my friend's throat.

Sounding disgusted with himself, Tomlinson told me, "I picked up on the vibe too late, Doc. Sorry, man. Thought I could warn you later, but the whole mess just spun out of control."

Tomlinson's hands were bound behind his back, his left eye was swollen closed and there was blood around his mouth. But he still managed to force a fake smile as his eyes warned me *He's insane. Be careful—he'll kill us all.*

No, Tomlinson was warning me about *both* Neinabors. Because just then the second brother appeared, a half-moon grin on his face, head bouncing to the heavy metal cadence of his earbuds.

With a wave of his pistol, he ordered us into the next room.

15

Because he was listening to his iPod, the twin doing most of the talking yelled when he spoke as if everyone in the room was deafened by the music reverberating through his skull. He yelled at Umeko now, saying, "Which one you want me to offer up first? It doesn't matter to me. The blood's on your hands. Hey, Geness, what's Abraham say?"

Offer. A euphemism for "murder," but with religious overtones because Odus Neinabor was swinging his pistol at the women who had come to Vanderbilt Island for a girls' weekend but had stumbled into a nightmare. And Abraham—that must be the dead triplet. Did that mean that Odus could not speak to him directly, only Geness? Interesting.

The twins must have returned to the lodge soon after Kahn and Trapper had left, from what I saw. It would have taken them at least half an hour to do all that they had done. And they'd done a lot—some of it absurd, all of it cruel. The way they were treating the three most harmless people in the room was an example.

The women were still in their tropical party dresses, like three wilting bouquets sitting with their backs to the wall, their faces clown-streaked with eyeliner because they had been crying. The abuse had been going on for a while. The twins had wired the ladies' hands behind their backs, then tossed their designer shoes into a pile in the middle of the room as if in preface to playing some weird party game.

I knew one of the women by name, Sharon Farwell. She was a successful restaurateur, an over-forty beauty who was business hardened but now displayed symptoms of shock because of what was happening. Her eyes had brightened when I entered the room. But then when she saw that my arms were taped behind me, her chin sank toward the floor.

Pitiless. That described what the twins had done. There was no way the women, or anyone, could have anticipated such crazed behavior.

Odus was Exodus, a mean little bastard, according to Trapper. But the quiet one, Geness—Genesis—was the more dangerous of the two, in my estimation, because I'd be willing to bet he used the dead triplet, Abraham, to manipulate brotherly decisions and as a scapegoat for their viciousness.

Genesis and Exodus, two biblical names given by nomadic hipsters whose sons had lived a caravan life in the desert. The names had no sinister overtones so fit the twins perfectly—two brothers who were benign in appearance, even comical, which effectively disguised the truth that they were both dangerous.

I've encountered killers, both amateurs and methodical pros, but there were only three true sociopaths among them. One was a brain-damaged mercenary who became infamous in Central America for hunting only at night, like a werewolf, then burning his victims alive.

The man, known as *Incendiario* to the peasants of the Maya

Mountains, was Praxcedes Lourdes. He had a grotesque physical presence that warned of the danger he represented. In a lesser way, the other two sociopaths were physically repugnant as well—a freak with an Oedipus fixation and a necromancer witch who believed she was a succubus.

Geness and Odus Neinabor, though, could have been the chubby, wholesome sidekicks in a TV sitcom. They were plump, rosy-cheeked, with wide mouths and weak jaws. Both had feminine qualities: balding, shoulder-length blond hair, breast tissue that bounced beneath their black crewnecks when they walked, delicate, stubby fingers.

Odus was the talkative one, Geness, the introvert—normal for identical twins, normal in appearance. Normal in every way but for their behavior, and the wild glassy eyes that shielded them from reality rather than connecting them.

Insulation and isolation—true sociopaths construct barriers as complex as any maze. Like the heavy-metal music that thrummed from Odus's earbuds, loud enough to resonate through his eye sockets. Like the dead brother who spoke through Geness's mouth.

Aberrant behavior can be ascribed to many factors. What is impossible to explain, though, is the pleasure that sociopaths derive from inflicting pain on others. It is, in my experience, the defining behavioral deformity that links mutants with their monstrous behavior. I had met three sociopaths in my life. Now, though, I could count five. Odus and Geness, who took visible pleasure when they inflicted pain on people. Especially the three attractive middle-aged women from nearby Captiva Island.

No one bullies with more ravenous expertise than those who have been bullied, and it was sickening to watch. Soon, it would be impossible. Arms taped behind me or not, I would have to do something. Tomlinson, standing on the other side of the room, was reaching his breaking point, too. I could tell by the way he closed his eyes, seeking some inner peace that was impossible to access, and so began banging the back of his head against the wall.

"Leave them alone!" he yelled finally. "If you want to hurt someone, try me!"

Which got Odus's attention but only caused him to grin before he looked at Umeko and me and yelled, "If you two don't do what we say, they'll all die!"

Do what? If the lunatics had some plan that included Umeko and me, they hadn't said a goddamn word about it.

Behind us, Geness was thinking the same thing because he surprised everyone by speaking for the first time, saying too softly for his brother to hear, "Odus. You didn't tell the slavers what we want them to do. Odus? *Exodus!*"

Odus responded with a confused expression that asked *Huh?*

Geness raised his voice above a whisper, "Your iPod. Turn down your iPod." Then he repeated what he'd said. "Once the things understand, you can kill one. But until then—"

Nodding, Odus finished his brother's sentence, saying, "Until then, it makes no sense. Okay, okay, but here's the deal, Geness"—the twin's face reddened—"I want to shoot one of them *now*, goddamn it! I'm sick of waiting!"

Geness had his eyes closed, which could be something he did when communicating with the dead triplet, or pretended to communicate—no telling what was happening inside his head—then he translated in a voice that was flat, emotionless. "It is not time yet, Exodus. Later, shoot the blond thing. But not now."

The blond thing was Sharon Farwell, who turned to me, eyes pinched. I winked, trying to reassure her, which is when the front door of the lodge opened and Kahn and Trapper came charging in, ripping their ski masks off before greeting the Neinabor twins. I expected locker-room laughter and high fives, but Geness retreated instantly into some silent sphere while his brother became guarded but willing to do the talking. It was repellent to watch, a reunion of misfits, but I took in every nuance as they exchanged information.

When Kahn told the twins that Bohai had been shot, he did it in a way that insinuated he and Trapper had killed the man, then flashed Umeko and me a look, warning us not to contradict him.

A minute later, Kahn ordered Trapper to the balcony to stand guard, then I listened to Odus Neinabor describe how he had attacked two men at the marina, saying, "I hit one of them for sure. Maybe both. I think they were Kazlov's men—maybe Kazlov himself, I don't know. I hope so, because Geness took a shot at that Russian leech when the power first went out but missed. Didn't you, Geness?"

Geness didn't bother to respond because his brother was already explaining, "It's so dark out there, man, it was hard to score—even with my laser sights. I caught these two guys at the dock and they were, like, firing back two rounds every time I pulled the trigger. But finally, I took my time and—*WHAP!*—one of them went down in the water. After that, though, they snuck off into this sort of swampy place, probably hoping to ambush me. Like I'm *stupid* or something."

I'd learned something. Despite the lie that Vladimir and I had returned fire, it confirmed who had attacked us, and also provided a couple of surprises. Kazlov *hadn't* been shot during the first minutes of the power outage? I looked at Tomlinson, who shook his head in reply, which seemed to be good news, until I realized he might have been telling me *No, the twin didn't miss.*

Either way, the news wasn't as bad as it could have been. After all that gunfire, Third Planet members could boast of shooting only one, possibly two people—both Russians. And Odus hadn't finished the bodyguard with two shots, as I'd guessed, or he would be bragging about it now.

The bloodbath I'd feared had yet to happen. Maybe there was still a way to turn the night around.

As I listened, though, my optimism faded. I became convinced of one key dynamic: the Neinabor twins actually were insane. Maybe temporarily because of whatever drugs they were on—something potent enough to cause hand tremors and a diaphoretic sweat that made their baby-pink faces glisten like boiled hams.

More likely, though, the brothers had repressed so much rage for so many years that some fragile thread had finally snapped. Now a pair of monsters had been set free into a virtual world of their own making and they'd brought the ghost of their dead brother to guide them. These two were the type who strapped on bandoliers and trotted down high school corridors shooting at their classmates.

As Third Planet members traded stories and bragged, they all also confirmed their cowardice. Odus told Kahn that he'd scouted Talas's end of the island, but the gunfire was "wicked." Kahn lied and said the same was true of the north end of the island, and that he and Trapper had decided Lien Bohai's corpse was proof they'd taken enough chances for one night.

"I shot him—hit him the first time," Kahn told the room.

To me, the men were only proving the obvious: they wanted to believe they were gunfighters but knew secretly they were incapable of taking the risks that shooting an armed enemy required. If the twins had a plan that included Umeko or me, my guess was that their own cowardice was the source of the plan's creation.

I also began to suspect that the Neinabor twins had another hostage, maybe more, who they'd isolated in a nearby room. Odus was making veiled references to his "private trophy room."

If there was another hostage, I hoped it was Vladimir. Irrational, maybe, but that's the way I felt. He had tried to kill me, true, but the man had proven his toughness and professionalism when we were on the run. And he was certainly more admirable than the man-child who had shot him. But the prospect that Vladimir had been allowed to live was unlikely because the twins were so eager to prove themselves killers.

I held on to the possibility, though, until Densler stumbled in from the dining room so drunk that she slurred her words when she complained, "The man just pissed his pants, for God's sake! You expect me to clean it up?"

A few minutes later, I found out the truth when Geness shoved and prodded me down a hallway to the manager's office, then nudged open the door.

Inside, a gigantically fat man dwarfed the swivel chair in which he had been bound and gagged. When he recognized me, his facial expression changed in a way that reminded me of the hope I'd seen in Sharon Farwell's eyes.

Cowards or not, the Neinabor twins had somehow managed to take down another one of the Big Four.

I was in Odus's trophy room. The trophy was Darius Talas.

Stashed beneath a desk, I also noticed, was a red-and-green computer bag, the first three letters of Super Mario visible.

I was impressed by how remarkably calm the fat man remained as he listened to Odus argue with Kahn, the twin red-faced and screaming, "It's our plan, he's our hostage! So just keep your mouth shut and let me dictate the goddamn letter!"

From the doorway, behind me, Geness spoke for only the second time that night, which caused the room to go silent. "We don't listen to you anymore," he said to Kahn. "We're too strong for you now."

Kahn and Geness glared at each other through the candlelight. It took several seconds of silence before the twin's craziness won out; a silence dominated by his lingering certainty and metronomic way of speaking. It was the voice of someone who hears voices and records them with the indifference of a computer chip or an android. There was no fakery or theatrics, which was unsettling in itself, but it was Geness's confidence that, at once, was repellent and chilling. Finally, it was confirmed that the chubby blond twins—once the butt of Kahn's jokes—were now in charge.

Talas, who'd been gulping water since his gag had been removed, understood the significance because he attempted to undermine the twins' power by saying, "I will do whatever your organization asks of me, of course. And I believe Mr. Armanie will be cooperative. We only want what's best for the Caspian Sea. But for one person to dictate the demands as the voice of an entire organization"—the fat man shrugged as if the unfairness was obvious—"well, I don't think it will be as convincing. You are, after all, asking Mr. Armanie to entrust his life to the integrity of your organization."

I watched Kahn's nostrils flair, aware of Talas's obvious attempt to manipulate. But he also realized that Talas was trying to help him stay in power, so he said to Odus, "Why not let Winifred decide? She's chairperson. I mean, I hate this fat leech as much as you do, but he's got a good—"

"I'm dictating the goddamn letter!" Odus yelled, still staring at Kahn while his head bobbed to the rhythm of his earbuds.

The two activists continued to argue, volleying threats and insults, until Geness, still in the doorway, said, "No more talking. It's settled."

And it was.

Although composed, Talas looked pathetic, with his glistening jowls and his urine-stained slacks. The twins made him nervous, and Geness scared him. It was in his Sydney Greenstreet chuckle that dismissed the brothers as children but also conceded their new power. So, when Kahn and Odus stopped arguing, Talas took a pen in his sausage fingers and did what he was told. He squared a sheet of Vanderbilt Lodge stationery in front of him and said, "I'm at your service. What do you wish me to write?" A moment later, though, he sealed Kahn's demotion by ordering him to bring him more light.

Odus, whose mood seesawed between rage and euphoria, was too combustible to dictate anything. He began badly, saying, "Okay, get this down, the exact words. 'This is to inform Abdul Armanie, the, uhhh . . . the Iranian douche bag *criminal*! . . . that his criminal friend, uhhh . . .' What's your freaking first name, you fat leech . . . ?" Which is when Geness proved who was really in control by taking over, telling his brother, "Abraham says I should do it."

Invoking the name of the dead triplet got instant results. The twins changed places, and soon Geness was instructing Talas, "I want you to write in English. Nothing else, understand?"

"Whatever you say, of course," Talas replied, "but it might make Armanie suspicious because—"

"No, it won't," Geness said and, with no change in facial expression, hammered his fist against the back of Talas's head. The twins were barely five and a half feet tall, but they were a chunky one-seventy, one-eighty. The shock wave rippled through the fat man's neck to his cheeks and caused his eyes to spark with anger—a spark that Talas managed to hide as Geness continued talking as if nothing had happened. "You're lying," he said. "Today, at the pool, I heard you both talking in English. You'd better not lie to us again. Understand?"

Talas nodded, showing no emotion—the response of a powerful man who was patient enough to wait for his revenge.

Then Geness began to dictate, saying, " 'My dear Abdul . . .' No . . . wait. 'My *respected* associate, Armanie,' " which frightened me as much as anything the Neinabors had done so far. It proved that Geness, at least, was not only perceptive, he was shrewd and calculating. Armanie never used his first name and he had no friends. Geness understood that to begin the letter any other way would warn Armanie that he was being lured into a trap.

That's what the letter was: a personal invitation to Armanie, and his bodyguard, to come to the lodge, unarmed, and meet with Talas.

"To discuss what?" Darius Talas asked, touching the pen to his silver mustache.

The twins nodded at each other before Geness said, "To talk about a computer hard drive that was taken from Viktor Kazlov's boat today. And about a thousand baby sturgeon that will die soon when the boat's batteries go dead."

Fingerling sturgeon?

Talas was nodding as Odus yelled, "Hurry up, lard ass! After this, you're writing a letter to Kazlov. He's the criminal who brought all those innocent fish. We've got to make goddamn sure he doesn't miss the boat."

Miss the boat?

Was he speaking figuratively? I wondered about it as my eyes moved from Talas, who was giving Geness a sharp look, to Kahn, whose face showed surprise, then skepticism. Maybe the twins were lying or maybe they'd actually stolen the hard drive. Either way, it was news to Kahn. Probably news to their drunken chairwoman, too, but Tomlinson didn't appear surprised. He was looking at me with his wise old eyes as if to confirm it was all true.

Talas hunched over the desk, the pen a rhythmic instrument in his hand, as he added a few sentences, then asked, "And what about

Mr. Lien Bohai? If we're meeting, shouldn't we invite our Chinese colleague? Asians aren't particularly emotional but they are easily slighted."

For an uneasy moment, I was afraid Talas was going to mention Bohai's young wife and daughter, too. But Kahn jumped in and tried to regain respect by saying, "The old man's dead. I shot him myself. Bohai didn't cooperate with us and that's what happens. We've got his assistant in the dining room right now."

Once again, I felt a building tension as Talas reflected on what he'd just heard. "Bohai's *assistant*, you say?"

"A woman named Umeko. *What?* I thought you TRs knew everything about each other." Kahn was searching the fat man's face, suddenly suspicious.

Talas was still giving it some thought but then defused it all, saying, "TRs?"

"Yeah, it means 'assholes'—asshole."

The fat man nodded. "I think you're talking about one of Bohai's *concubines*. Forgive me for laughing, but Lien always travels with at least two women. No idea how he introduces them to outsiders. But let's just say they aren't paid to sit at a desk and read reports—old men have their needs, too, you know. On every trip, there's always one woman who's quite beautiful and another who is . . . well, presumably, she is quite skilled at—"

Geness, becoming impatient, interrupted him, saying, "No more of your filthy sex talk. Write the exact same letter to Kazlov. No tricks—hurry up!"

When Talas had finished, both twins looked the letters over before Odus said, "Okay, now put them in envelopes and write each leech's name on the front. Like, we want it to look official. Then we've got a serious question for you."

Geness Neinabor nodded, already looking at me. "Tell us what you know about this dude, Ford." As Geness stared, his eyes sparked, then oscillated with twin images of the candle flame twitching and flaring on the desk nearby.

Talas swiveled the chair around. He said, "Dr. Ford, you mean," then threw his hands up to protect himself as the twin used the pistol this time to hit him. The muzzle caught Talas on the side of the head, which caused a rivulet of blood to race down the fat man's cheek.

"Ford. Plain Ford," Geness said, enjoying himself. "The days of rich men using titles is over. Vanity is the vexation of all liars." Then his eyes swung to Odus before he nodded at Tomlinson, who was standing near the window.

Odus took over. "Ford's friend is a traitor, a Judas. Our brother, Abraham, figured it out. See that black eye he's got? Our brother insisted, so Geness used his fists. We're going to execute him later."

Odus was smirking at Tomlinson as he continued, "But right now, here's our problem: we don't know if the asswipe traitor told us the truth about Ford. The asswipe claims Ford's like this military special agent who could, you know, tell us how to take down this island. You with me so far?"

Talas nodded quickly as he explored the side of his face with massive fingers.

"Of course, this was *before* we figured out the freaky-freak guy is a traitor. Plus, my brothers and I didn't have one bit of trouble taking down this island all by ourselves, did we?" The twin aimed a cutting look at Kahn before he went on. "Now, though, there might be a job Ford can help us with. So what do *you* know about him?"

Talas produced a monogrammed handkerchief from his pocket and concealed his anger with a glowering silence as he dabbed at the blood on his face. Finally, he said, "You are looking for someone to deliver these letters, I take it? And, perhaps, kill Armanie and

Kazlov—as they read the letters, perhaps? That's the only reason I can think of why a skilled military person would be of use to you. Which means he would have to kill their bodyguards, too, of course. Which won't be easy, you need to realize. Kazlov's man especially. He's captained Viktor's various yachts over the years and he's very devoted."

The fat man was talking about Vladimir.

The twins used their eyes to communicate before Odus said, "We never thought of making him shoot the caviar slavers, too. But it's an interesting idea—"

"It's a bad idea," Geness interrupted without inflection.

Odus said, "Yeah, a shitty idea. Ford wasn't sent here to judge anyone. My brothers and me, we're the judges."

"And executioners," Geness prompted.

"*And* executioners. We know why we were sent here. All we want from you, leech, is tell us what you know. You think Ford can get these letters to Armanie and Kazlov without getting killed?"

Talas was giving it some thought as Odus kept talking but not so loud now. "We're sending someone with him, too, 'cause at least one person has to make it back here to let us know they're coming. And we only have"—the twin checked his watch, which caused him to lose his temper again—"*Shit!* We've got only two hours! They'll have to bust their asses to do it, considering no one knows where your *goddamn parasite friends are hiding*!"

It had to be close to one in the morning. I was wondering why the twins wanted Kazlov and Armanie in the lodge before three, as Odus calmed down a little before he said, "At least one person needs to have some experience at this sort of stuff. You heard all the guns banging away out there." He glanced at Kahn. "Unless Rez and Trapper want to volunteer and prove they're not a couple of pussies."

That got him laughing, and it started Geness laughing, and then they both lost it in a two-minute laughing jag that bordered on hysteria. Finally, as Odus regained control, his laughter assumed a childlike quality that was perplexing. I glanced at Tomlinson, who was shaking his head, a sad look on his face, which is when I realized that the twin was weeping now, on an emotional descent.

"Don't be ashamed," Geness said, getting impatient, "it's nothing to be ashamed of," but made no effort to place a hand on his brother's shoulder.

"Can't help myself," Odus bawled. "Don't know why . . . I was thinking about those poor fish in the boat . . . and those beautiful dolphins."

It didn't surprise me the group had planned to target the casino resort as well, even though Talas was right. It had no association with Vanderbilt Island. But to lapse into hysteria because of dolphins he'd never seen, at a place he'd never visited?

The spectacle was so disturbing that I turned away only to discover that Talas was looking me over, still undecided about how he was going to respond to the twins' questions about me.

The fat man had the black eyes of a crow, a bird that preys on weakness and manufactured opportunities. In the last few minutes, I'd come to respect Talas's intellect and his character more than I'd thought possible. But he was in a tenuous position if the twins insisted that he share information about me. By virtue of being sane, if nothing else, the Turkmenian and I had a reason to help each other. He had already attempted to shield Umeko and Lien Bohai's wife from discovery. If he contrived to advance his own cause, though, by helping me, the twins might punish him for trying to manipulate them.

I was wondering how Talas was going to play it.

He played it two ways, as it turned out. The man played it smart for Talas and dangerous for me.

More dangerous for the twins, though, if they dismissed Talas's assessment as a lie or, better yet, as transparent reverse psychology. That's exactly what Talas attempted to do, I realized, because he told the Neinabors everything he knew about me—which wasn't much.

But the little he knew was true.

16

Darius Talas folded the bloody handkerchief until he'd created a clean square. Now he pressed it to his head and said to the twins, "If my sources are right about this man, I could be arrested for what I'm about to tell you. Or assassinated. Would you mind clearing the room so we can speak in private?"

Odus's head was bobbing, his face still pink from crying, but he managed to grin at Geness, his giddy expression asking his brother *Isn't this cool?*

Geness was showing some interest, too, giving me a look of assessment as his brother asked Talas, "You're kidding. Ford is really that heavy a dude?"

Talas appeared mountainous as he turned in the swivel chair. "I can only assume it's true, and I'm not in the habit of taking chances, not when it comes to the international intelligence community. Please, I must insist."

The fat man motioned toward Tomlinson without bothering to look at him. "Ask the long-haired gentleman to leave. And your other colleague. And, of course, Ford. He can't be in the room if you expect me to speak frankly."

Geness was observing the man, possibly interpreting his theatrics as weakness. Or maybe it had nothing to do with his brother telling Talas, "Okay. Everyone but Ford goes. Him, we want to watch how he reacts."

The fat man mumbled something about "a compromising position," but Geness was already signaling Odus, who took charge by grabbing Tomlinson's arm and yanking him toward the door. Then to Kahn he said, "You heard my brother. Get out!"

Kahn was indignant. He reminded them they were symbiotic brothers, members of 3P2, but then he stopped talking when he noticed Geness's glassy stare and left. When the door was closed, Talas became the convivial fat man again, an experienced negotiator who shared confidences as if they were gifts when in fact they were concealed loans that might pay him interest down the road.

To the twins he said, "Your colleague who just left is a truly despicable little brat. Never trust him."

Odus liked that, but Geness remained expressionless as he replied, "Abraham says the more time you take, the better chance you'll think of a believable lie."

Talas appeared chastened but still managed to chuckle, "Yes, let's stick to business. Time is money. Okay, then"—he looked at me and allowed his smile to vanish. "There is an American agent—a specialist with unusual skills—whose existence isn't questioned but whose identity has never been confirmed. Not positively, anyway, although the Russians and the Muslim countries have been trying to do so for several years." Talas maintained eye contact as he nodded. "Some believe this is the man."

"Him?" Odus, enjoying himself now, wanted to believe it but had to ask.

"He is a thoroughly treacherous person, by all reports. And my sources of information are among the best in the world—members of the former Soviet KGB. You're familiar with the organization?"

"We have degrees in engineering and philosophy," Geness said, but even he wore a mild smile now, a man whose only experience with political intrigue had come from computer chips and Bible tales.

"Then you understand why I asked that the room be cleared. Okay, then! I'll give you an example: last night, in a private meeting, I heard Viktor Kazlov tell his bodyguard that if anything happened to him that he should find this man and kill him immediately. 'Don't bother asking questions, just shoot the biologist'—those were Viktor's words, or something similar."

I was wondering if that was true as Talas tilted a bottle of water to his mouth, then emptied it with a series of reptilian constrictions that proved he had an Adam's apple.

"He is a professional assassin," Talas continued. "In Eastern Europe alone, it's said that he's responsible for the execution of at least three men—all innocent Muslims, by the way. In Cuba, one man that I've heard of. In Southeast Asia and Africa? Impossible to say.

"The KGB's only interest in that sort of information would be to add data to create a clearer picture of the doctor's tactics. His *modus operandi*, one might say. Or to eliminate him as a suspect in some earlier assassination."

For the first time, Talas spoke directly to me, saying, "'Interstice timeline.' Isn't that what the intelligence community calls it? A way to connect victims of execution with their probable assassins. Another way to put it, I suppose, is that it's a way to graph a man's sins by charting his travels."

Odus said to Geness, "Interstice timeline. That is *so* sick. Like intersection points, right?"

Geness's expression remained blank as I told him, "I don't know where Talas came up with his story but it's fiction. We had an argument this afternoon about his people poaching fish in the Caspian Sea. That's why he's trying to get me killed. And he's a Muslim, so what's he care about one more infidel? You're a philosophy major, you understand what I'm saying."

Talas made a show of remaining aloof. "Few Muslims are cold-blooded killers. Sadly, the same can't be said for this man. Tie him up and lock him in a closet, that's my best advice to you. If you entrust him with these letters, you are risking—"

"This is complete bullshit," I cut in. "You want the truth, I'll tell you the truth. I'm a marine biologist, plain and simple. For the last ten minutes, I've been thinking more about what's happening to the sturgeon on Kazlov's boat. How do you know there are a thousand? That many fingerling sturgeon, in an area that small, someone needs to get down there and get the generator going. The damn thing should have started automatically when the power went out. The filters have to be changed, the water, too. Depending on their size, they might need fresh water, not salt water. I'm not going to risk my life to find Talas's caviar buddies, but I can help save those fish once it's safe to go out."

I was noticing that Geness rarely blinked. It added an opaque quality to his eyes, as if they were covered by grape skins. Sounding interested, he said to me, "The Judas didn't say you're an assassin."

"Yeah," his brother said. "He told us you're a tactical expert. Like a secret agent or something. This was before we figured out he's a Judas."

"Maybe he wanted to impress you by making me sound important," I countered. "Or save his own butt by turning the dogs loose on me."

Geness appeared amused as his brother said, "That's a shitty thing to say about a friend."

I had already projected how it must feel to be the Neinabors—the butt of jokes, small, soft and emotionally fragile, raised as outsiders by religious nomads. To be taken seriously by the insane, you must insert yourself into their world, which is why I replied, "You ever have a friend who didn't stab you in the back? It happens all the time."

Geness's response was an involuntary nod, and I saw a look go between him and Odus. Then the two got back to the business of how to add Armanie and Kazlov to the list of people they would soon murder.

A few minutes later, I noticed that Talas was trying to engage me with his eyes, possibly to warn me I was making a mistake by denying his story. To ignore him, I stared at my sodden running shoes rather than risk any sign of collusion.

Odus was saying, "So who we going to send with this guy, if we choose him? One of the women?"

"Did Abraham say anything about the Chinese girl? Maybe Rez and Trapper didn't tell you, but they checked her billfold and she's a member of 3P2! Plus, they found a military—"

To silence the man, I took a long step toward Geness, so close the guy thrust his pistol at me in surprise, then used his left hand to shove me away.

"Don't do that," he said, startled. "I didn't give you permission to move."

I told him, "I've got to piss so bad, I can't hold it anymore. Whatever you decide, make up your damn mind."

A risky finesse, but it was enough to shut up Odus and maybe convince Geness that what Talas was saying was true. Biologists weren't expected to be aggressive.

"Get away from my brother," Odus yelled, pushing his way toward me. Before he got close, though, I told him, "If you slap me, you're not going to like what happens next."

It stopped the twin in his tracks, and then Geness helped my cause by saying to his brother, "A marine biologist," as if sharing an inside joke.

"Yeah," Odus said, catching on. "*Yeah.* For a big, goofy-looking nerd, he's kind of a hardass."

That was it. Geness had made his decision, I could read it in his face. They had only one other decision to make—who to send along. Geness expedited the process by warning me, "Abraham says to shoot someone every fifteen minutes until our delivery boy gets back. Motivation, he says. What do you think of that?"

I was looking at a wedge of red-and-green computer bag beneath the desk, thinking, *If they have another bomb, why would he bother killing people one at a time?* Which was reassuring until I remember that the insane are logical only when it serves their irrational objectives.

"Abraham won't spend the rest of his life in prison," I replied. "You will. That's what I think."

Odus was shouting, "Hey, don't be a smartass!" but went silent when his brother, still calm, said, "No, you're missing my point. Who do we shoot first? It's a sacrificial offering, you know." The twin studied me for a moment. "Do you read the Bible?"

"No."

"You should. It would help you understand. Proverbs says, 'God will despoil the lives of those who despoil the Earth. For there is no sin graver than to befoul the Earth, so they *must* be sacrificed.' Understand now?"

I replied, "Those women have nothing to do with any of this. They own a few restaurants, so they came here to have some fun. That's all—"

Odus cut in, shouting, "Shut up. They came here wearing dead animals on their feet!" Then he offered a quote to Geness. "The Earth mourns and withers, and its defilers shall be scorched until none are left. Isaiah, right?"

I was picturing women's leather shoes tossed into a pile in the middle of the room as Geness said, "What I'm telling you is, someone has to be sacrificed. If it was your decision, who would be first?"

Without hesitating, I nodded at Talas. "Sacrifice him."

Geness was actually smiling as he shook his head. "Uh-uh. Mr. Blimpie needs to stay alive for our party. Who next?"

"Tomlinson," I replied with a hint of bitterness—enough, hopefully, to influence the next decision.

Maybe so, because Geness began nodding, pleased with the way he had handled things, as his brother said, "Because your old friend snitched on you, huh?"

Snitched? The Neinabor twins had never escaped childhood.

I refused to discuss the subject with a shake of my head.

"That's what happened, he snitched." Odus nodded to himself. "Say, how do you get into the spy business, anyway? We've heard the CIA recruits people when they're still in college. We'd be good at it, you know. *Seriously.* I even called their headquarters a couple of times but no one called back. My brother and me, we've got master's degrees, so it's not like we aren't qualified."

I pretended to be surprised by the CIA's disinterest because I wanted to confirm something Geness had said earlier. "In philosophy?"

"Western religion and mechanical engineering. We graduated in half the time it took most of the rich asswipe leeches at USC. Straight 4.0s, but the CIA didn't give a shit. And we sent, like, ten e-mails, remember, Geness?"

He turned back to me, "How many people have you executed?

Honestly. We don't believe in hell—not that brimstone shit, anyway. But anyone with brains knows the Revelation of Saint John is coming true. So . . . so, what we're wondering—"

"The thing won't understand because he doesn't read the Bible," Geness reminded him.

Odus's face reddened, and he yelled, "I know that! Stop treating me like I'm fucking stupid!" Then, in a calmer voice, he said to me, "When the Rapture comes, do you think we'll be judged like some random ghetto murderers? It's got to be different for environmental warriors, right? God protects the Earth by helping us, right?"

I nodded because that's what the twins wanted me to do, but I was thinking, *They're delusional, they're volatile, and someone's going to die.*

"In the Hebrew texts," Geness was explaining, "the Latin *homicidium* has a totally different meaning than the Latin for 'warrior' or even 'assassin,' which is *caedis*. For my brothers and me, our bodies reuniting with the Earth as vapor and salt water—that's the ultimate Rapture."

Odus took over, saying, "The whole judgment thing would worry anybody. I mean, maybe Moses gave us the *Thou shalt not kill* commandment first for a reason. Not that we're scared. But you're the first person we've met who's actually done it. You know, *kill* someone. Understand what we're getting at?"

Yes, and the implications as well. The twins saw themselves as martyr warriors. They were willing to die for their cause but were unwilling to suffer the consequences.

There was also something else I now suspected: they had made a suicide pact. The two of them planned to die in a cloud of vapor and salt water, along with their enemies.

That's when I knew for sure what was going to happen. Umeko had been wrong about the bomb. There *was* an explosive somewhere on the island. That's why the twins had demanded that Kazlov and

Armanie be returned to the lodge before three a.m. The explanation was obvious—so obvious now I felt like a fool for not figuring it out earlier. The twins had built their bombs at *home* in California. The detonator clocks were still on Pacific time.

Suddenly, it was all too clear. Two mechanical engineers would have no problem rigging a clock or wireless detonator—both, probably, if they were smart, so one system could override the other. And they *were* smart. Getting their hands on military-grade explosives would be a bigger challenge, but mixing a low-grade explosive was easy. The only difference was that potency—the speed of deflagration—and stability were reduced.

The homemade variety was combustible, more sensitive to static electricity and friction. But that wouldn't bother a couple of martyrs. They could vaporize themselves by pushing a remote button or let a ticking clock make the decision for them.

Chasing midnight. I'd been doing it for the last two hours, but now the danger was confirmed. With great effort, I managed not to look at the Super Mario bag stashed beneath the desk.

"What's the problem, Ford? The idea of being judged worry you, too?"

Apparently, I hadn't heard Odus's question the first time because he sounded irritated. Then he said again, "Tell the truth: how many men have you killed? Or maybe Mr. Blimpie is lying about that, too."

I let them watch me give the question serious thought. I wanted to give it enough time to confirm that such a number existed before appearing to give in. Finally, I told Geness, "All right. I'll do it."

"Really?" Odus sounded excited.

I replied, "I meant I'll deliver your letters. If Armanie and Kazlov are still on the island, I'll find them. If I get lucky, I'll bring them back in person. You can't ask for more than that. But there are a couple of conditions."

Geness was already shaking his head as he used both hands to level the pistol at me. "No conditions."

"Then why should I help you?" I asked, looking down at him over the barrel of the gun.

Geness moved his index finger to the trigger and tilted the pistol a few degrees to the left, maybe something he'd seen in a movie. "No conditions."

I sensed that the quiet twin wanted to impress me. No, I *hoped* it was true because I was too scared to believe anything else. If so, I had crossed the boundary into Geness's irrational world. No longer was I a piece of human furniture. I had been integrated into a plotline in his video fantasy as well as his biblical delusions. I couldn't be certain, though. The crazy ones are easily misread.

"You know, if you really want to do this right, there's a lot I can teach you and your brother, if you're willing to listen. First thing is, your assets aren't going to put their butts on the line unless you offer them something in return. There are always conditions, that's part of the business. And there's never a reason to waste an asset unless you profit in some way. Who knows what they will do for you down the road? Think it over. But if you decide to shoot, get it right the first time. That's the second lesson."

To make my point, I turned my back to the pistol and stood straight—a cleaner target.

I felt oddly calm. There is no predicting what sociopaths will do from minute to minute, but they are reliable narcissists when it comes to manipulating events in their delusional world—a world I'd just done my best to enter. The twins had a plan, and I was betting they wouldn't spoil the game by killing their new playmate now. If I was wrong, it didn't matter. They would kill me, anyway.

I waited for a tense several seconds before Geness finally said, "Abraham says he's right."

Odus pulled out one earbud, then the other. He was nodding and sounded a little breathless. "I know. He just told me the same thing. Or you'd shoot him. Abraham knows you would, too. But it would be dumb before we have all the caviar leeches on board."

I was thinking, *Another boating metaphor,* as Odus asked me, "What conditions? We're not giving you a gun, if that's what you're thinking."

I faced Geness. "I want at least one hour before you shoot those women or anyone else. Not even Tomlinson. That's the first condition. And I need some equipment. Kahn took a thermal night vision unit I brought and I want it back. A flashlight, too. And my knife—you've got nothing to worry about with all your guns."

I had used Tomlinson's name as a final manipulative nudge because that's who I wanted them to send with me.

Odus was still yapping, asking me about the thermal night vision unit, but then Geness silenced him by closing his eyes to confer with Abraham.

Odus said, "Oh," as if apologizing. Then: "Ask him about that other thing, too."

Other thing? I wondered what he meant.

Geness stood for a full minute as we waited; a morning silence of wakeful birds, summer insects and the sounds of an old house as its foundation settles another microinch into the earth.

Finally, he nodded at his twin and said, "Tell him what our brother said."

Odus was ready with the instructions, which was spooky. "Okay, here's the deal. Screw the knife, you're not getting it back. And not a whole hour. Thirty minutes: that's what we'll give you. Which means"—he glanced at his wrist—"which means we sacrifice the first one at quarter to two. One of the women. I'll shoot her in the back of the—"

"The blonde," Geness corrected.

"Yeah, the blonde. The woman who's still sort of attractive, Ford seems to like her. Or the woman who's probably a traitor, anyway."

Sharon Farwell or Umeko, he meant.

"So, we kill your lady friend at one forty-five. The second, she'll die at two. And if you're not back here by two-thirty, we'll shoot everyone we don't need for our special party. Got it? *Everyone.* We want those caviar slavers here no later than two forty-five!"

I nodded, but it wasn't until I replied, "Yes, I understand," that Geness responded with disgusting hypocrisy by bowing his head. "We should pray now. Abraham has a special orison he would like to share."

Orison? I didn't know what that meant and didn't much care, as I endured another silence in which the fat man's labored breathing weighted the air with his death, my own death and all things human and inevitable.

Geness spoke: "Open the door. We'll cut Ford's hands free later. He and his Judas friend are delivering the letters."

I said, *"Tomlinson?"* as if surprised, but didn't give it too much. Then closed the deal by saying, "I don't care who you send with me, but I need to use a bathroom *right now.*"

As I turned to go, Talas caught my eye and acknowledged me with the slightest of nods. His expression read *Well played.*

There was something else I saw in the fat man's eyes for the first time: Darius Talas, the international black marketeer, was terrified.

17

When Geness Neinabor escorted Tomlinson and me out the front doors of the fishing lodge, I thought he would stop and watch from the safety of the porch as we turned north into the summer darkness. Geness was delusional, a frightened adolescent who was trapped in the brain of a deranged man, and he was also a coward.

Wrong. Instead, he followed us into the shadows, staying thirty yards behind. Did he think we were going to jump aboard *No Más* and sail to safety?

Damn it. It was more than a minor irritant because I hadn't intended on turning north toward Armanie's rental house. What I wanted to do was retrieve my jury-rigged weapons, then rush back to the lodge, somehow snatch that little backpack, then force an evacuation. There was no guarantee the explosive was in the bag, but it seemed likely considering the twins' childlike quirks.

No, the window of opportunity was narrowing. Tomlinson and I had only thirty minutes—*supposedly*—before they shot Sharon. Why the Neinabors would execute a woman before vaporizing themselves and everyone else required no explanation because they were insane. Yet, to me, the reasons were apparent: they wanted to savor the experience of killing and it was also a way to manipulate me.

I wasn't going to allow them to do either. Evacuate the fishing lodge, that was still my objective. Tossing a couple of jars into the dining room might do the job. If I got lucky, the armed members of the group might be incapacitated long enough for Tomlinson and me to take their weapons.

It was a long shot but a possibility. Even if we didn't disarm everyone, capturing one gun would be enough to secure the VIP cottage after we'd moved Umeko, Talas and the three women from Captiva safely inside. Possibly some of the island staff members, too, if they were willing to trust us. Dealing with Armanie and trying to find Kazlov could wait. Sunlight was the surest cure for nighttime panic.

My plan, though, was already coming apart. It couldn't work. Not with one of the crazy Neinabors following us with a gun pointed at our backs. Come to think of it, maybe that was the point.

When Geness was still tailing us after a hundred yards, Tomlinson stopped, nudged me and whispered, "Please tell me you have some kind of plan." Tomlinson, wearing a T-shirt and dress slacks now, sounded frantic.

It was only our second opportunity to exchange a word since he had told me that Kazlov had been shot but still managed to escape from the lodge. Now I shook my head and touched a finger to my lips. "Where'd you put the letters?"

Tomlinson touched the back of his pants. "Got 'em."

"How drunk are you? Tell the truth."

The man shook his head, meaning, *I'm not,* then looked to confirm that Geness had ducked into the shadows. "I had no idea they had something like this planned. I don't think Winifred and the others knew, either. You believe me, don't you?"

I nodded because it was true, as I used the TAM to check behind us. Geness was hunched down, waiting, forty yards away.

"The only reason I told them about you was because I thought it might help. You know, keep you alive because you're an expert, someone they'd respect. Those guys, they're stuck in this weird video game Special Forces mind sphere. So I played into the whole superhero psyche thing. The vibe was right, plus I thought it was pretty smart."

"I'm still thinking of ways to thank you," I said, trying to shake blood into my fingertips.

We were on a shell walkway that transected the island north and south—the Pink Path, locals called it—and had stopped near a house that was shuttered tight for the summer. Silhouetted orchids clung to trees, their limbs interlacing overhead with vines and climbing cercus cacti, all punctuated by the white starbursts of night-blooming flowers.

Tomlinson whispered, "Hey—why not just talk to the little weirdo?" then cupped his hands around his mouth, ready to summon Neinabor. Before my pal got a word out, though, I grabbed him and pulled him close enough to say, "Maybe I don't have your attention yet. I told you to be quiet."

"But, Doc—"

"*Listen* to me. You're good at a lot of things, but this is the sort of thing *I'm* good at. At least one person died tonight, thanks to your Internet chaos theory. Are you aware of that? Check your mood ring. Which is darker, your karma or your conscience?"

It was too harsh, I knew it, but I was mad, and so I turned to glance at Geness rather than watch Tomlinson sag under the weight of the bad news.

"Then Kahn wasn't lying about Mr. Bohai?"

"Someone stuck a needle in his heart, but it wasn't Kahn. Maybe one of the twins. I think they're capable of anything. But it might be unrelated to what your new symbiotic brothers have going. And Kazlov's bodyguard was shot, too. He's probably dead, I'm not sure. Did you see where Kazlov was hit?"

Tomlinson whispered, "In the leg, he could still walk," then made a groaning noise. "My God—I'm a menace to myself and everyone who knows me. I'd rather die than cause pain. Shit the bed, *hermano*, this really sucks."

"Take it easy." I grabbed one of Tomlinson's bony shoulders, but it didn't stop him from talking.

"Doc, if I'd met those twins before tonight, I swear to God, I would have known. I would have found a way to stop it. They're both insane—I could *smell* the craziness before they walked into the room. But they do know their Bible, I'll say that much for them."

"Commendable," I said. "Keep walking. Let's see what he does." I gave the man a push.

"You have a plan, right? Please tell me there's something we can do to—"

"Close your hole, for starters. Get moving."

I wanted to think, not talk. In the field, the first rule of engagement is: *Keep the plan simple, stupid.* But that rule is always trumped by the second rule: *Nothing EVER goes as planned.*

Losers bitch about the unexpected, winners grab it by the throat. They improvise, they retool and then use the unforeseen like a club. Geness's decision to follow us, I decided, might give me a chance to ambush him and take his weapon.

I gave Tomlinson another nudge, then passed him, walking fast toward Armanie's end of the island. When I had rounded a bend, I stopped, motioned for Tomlinson to keep going and adjusted the TAM-14 over my eye. Geness was still with us, but he, too, had stopped, which surprised me. I was hidden. How did he know?

I soon saw the answer. The twin had brought along the night vision scope that Trapper had been using. It meant the shadows were no longer useful as ambush cover. I'd have to find a better place to hide—bushes or a doorway or a ledge. More difficult but doable.

I had turned to catch up with Tomlinson when Geness surprised me by calling softly, "Ford? *Wait.*"

I turned to listen.

"There's something you should know. Are you ready?"

What now? "Sure," I said. "What is it?"

"Abraham changed his mind."

I felt a physical, chemical chill that sparked down my spinal column.

I waited for several more seconds, aware that Geness wanted to enjoy my discomfort, before he said, "Abraham told Odus to shoot the blond woman if he hears a gunshot. He said you'd probably try something stupid and cause me to fire—like I almost did just now. I think I'm going to do that, shoot a round at the ground so he kills the woman. How would you like that?"

"No. *Wait.*" I had been crouched low. Now I stood, stepped up onto the path and walked in plain view toward the twin. As I got closer, I didn't need night vision to see that Geness was behind a tree, aiming the pistol at me, so I shoved the thermal monocular into my waistband.

"Stop right there or I'll pull the trigger—and it won't be at the ground."

The man was afraid of me, I realized. It was a source of perverse satisfaction that *I* could enjoy, but only for an instant. I told him, "If you follow us and Armanie sees that you're armed, he'll shoot you. Then he'll shoot us. Your letters won't be delivered. Is that what you want? Is that what Abraham wants?"

The laughter that boiled out from behind the tree was as startling as the change in Geness's voice when he replied, "'The Lord will bring about for Abraham what He has promised him!' What do you think about that, Ford?"

For a moment, I wondered if there were two people hiding there. The voice had a gravely, whiskey-scarred tonality that sounded nothing like Geness's flat monotone. I hesitated, but then continued walking toward him. "Tomlinson was impressed by your knowledge of the Bible. We were just talking about that."

From the shadows, I heard: "'My lips will not speak wickedness, and my tongue will not utter deceit!' Hah! The Book of Job—which you'll never get to read if you lie to me one more time."

A moment later, I heard: "You don't get the picture, do you? Geness might be afraid of you, but I'm not. To fear men is to make man your idol. Why would I be afraid of something that's an abomination on Earth?"

A body length from the tree, I stopped and held my hands palms out so the twin could see they were empty. "Do you want me to deliver the invitations or not? That's what your brother wants me to do. Didn't Abraham tell you that—"

The voice interrupted, "I *am* Abraham, you dumb fucker!"

The pistol revealed another inch of itself from the shadows, an insane man's eyes above it. I took a step backward, an instinctive response.

"Scared?" I heard laughter. "You should be terrified. Because I can blow your heart open, if I want. Then my idiot brother shoots the blond hag like I ordered him to do. One shot, two kills."

I could feel my pulse thudding in my jugular, a series of rapid warning taps that told me to run. But where? The only escape, I decided, was to try to reenter this lunatic's brain, which required a very risky bluff.

"You asked about the Rapture," I said. "You and your brothers wanted to find out if killers will be judged like murderers. I can give you the answer."

The offer was unexpected, judging from the long pause. "Liar! You don't know the first thing about God or His Word."

"You've never broken the first commandment," I replied, then gave it a few beats before adding. "I don't have to memorize a psalm to know what it's like to feel damned for the rest of your life."

"I guess I should be heartbroken—if I gave a shit about your eternal soul. But I don't."

I raised my voice a little. "I'm talking about you if you pull that trigger." Guessing there was a biblical quote that condemned or forgave almost every behavior, I added, "You already know the verse that applies. What is it?"

I was giving the twin a chance to show off again. Hopefully, some fitting Scripture would pop into his brain because I certainly didn't have anything ready. Instead of him replying, though, the lunatic's eyes retreated into the shadows. After several seconds of silence, Geness's soft voice took over, saying, "Tell me. I'd like to know the answer. Abraham says it's okay for me to ask."

I had to clear my throat before I could speak. "When I come back with Armanie and Kazlov, I'll tell you. Not now. But until you hear the truth from someone who knows—*really* knows—you're risking more than you realize."

What was at risk, I had no idea, and I was worried I'd pushed the gambit too far—I'm no actor. But Geness took it seriously because he replied, "Why should I believe you?"

I told him the first thing that came to mind. "Put it this way:

there's a reason I don't read the Bible. You've got thirty minutes to think about that. Then I'll tell you."

Before the man could respond, I pivoted and walked away, then sprinted to catch up with Tomlinson after I got around the bend, the percussion of my shoes as loud as the gunshot I anticipated with each stride.

It didn't happen.

Something else that didn't happen: I didn't find Tomlinson.

I hunted around for a minute or two, called his name, but the thermal monocular confirmed that my pal's heat signature was long gone. Motivated by guilt, probably, or noble intentions, I guessed that he had decided to deliver the letters without me.

So now I had a tough decision to make: retrieve my homemade weapons and return to the lodge? Or find Tomlinson?

I went after my friend. There was no guarantee that Geness had stopped following me, and I still had a chunk of time before the deadline.

Using the TAM, it didn't take me long to pick up the glowing remnants of footprints. I'd been right. Tomlinson had continued north, where Armanie and his armed bodyguard were waiting.

Viktor Kazlov was waiting, too, as it turned out.

18

The house Abdul Armanie had rented was isolated on the northern tip of the island, a ponderous structure of pilings and gray wood that appeared larger, more formidable, because it shouldered a nightscape of stars and clouds that strobed with silent lightning.

There was no guard on the porch, as anticipated. And no sign of Tomlinson, which was unsettling. Could he possibly have been accepted into the house so quickly?

Yes. From forty yards away, I stopped and used thermal vision. Inside the foyer, near the door, were three people. Details were fogged by siding and drywall, but the heat signature showed all men, one of them Tomlinson, because Armanie had arrived with only his bodyguard. The numbers added up.

Plus, Tomlinson's scraggily shoulder-length hair had come loose from its ponytail and it set him apart from the other two men.

How the hell had he talked his way in so fast? Or maybe I was misreading the situation. Armanie and the bodyguard could have *forced* Tomlinson into the house. They might be pointing a gun at him right now.

I didn't like the odds. As I jogged toward a gazebo that fronted the house, I was thinking, *Just one gunshot and an innocent woman dies.*

It could happen. I believed what Geness Neinabor had told me. If Armanie or the guard fired a shot or pulled a trigger accidentally, Sharon Farwell would be killed. "Sacrificed," if you inhabited the brains of the twins—or were inhabited by some bipolar monster who provided an alibi for murder. Unless . . . unless Geness had taken my warning to heart about not killing until he had heard my "truth." It was a long shot, of course, but everything was a long shot now.

The possibility was maddening because it was beyond my control and forced me to be doubly cautious as I neared the house. Even if Tomlinson had been invited inside, I couldn't risk startling Armanie. The man hated me. He might fire a warning shot or even shoot to kill. If that happened, Sharon would die seconds later.

The shell path ended near the ruins of what might have been a boathouse. There were pilings and a cement stanchion. As I ducked behind it, I heard a night bird's warning cry. From atop a piling, a gargoyle shape dropped toward the water, then struggled to flight—a cormorant. I watched the bird angle starward, wings creaking, then I turned and used thermal vision to check the path behind me.

So far, I'd seen no sign of Geness. Maybe he was tailing me from the distance or maybe he had returned to the lodge to wait. If my lie had caused him to turn back, great. If it had fired any moral uncertainties in his brain, better yet, but I doubted it. If the twin had gone to the fishing lodge, it was to score his first kill when, and if, Tomlinson and I failed to return on time.

The luminous numerals of my Chronofighter told me that Sharon Farwell had only twenty-two minutes to live.

In a rush, I turned my attention to the house. I lifted the monocular to my eye and saw the three men moving toward an open doorway. A moment later, they disappeared into another room, shielded by walls from the TAM-14's heat sensors.

Damn it.

I told myself to stay calm. I had to choose my next move carefully. Was it smarter for me to stay where I was? Maybe Tomlinson would hand Armanie the letter and get the hell out. If that happened, it would take us only a few minutes to retrieve my homemade weapons. A couple of minutes later, we'd be in position outside the fishing lodge. If I could force the hijackers to evacuate and somehow find and disarm the explosive, maybe we'd make it through the night with only three casualties.

As good as that sounded, I was reluctant to wait. I decided to get a look at the house from a different angle. If I could see what was going on inside, it might help me make a more informed decision. I checked behind me one last time, then ran.

Ahead and to my left, a hedge of hibiscus traced the property line. Beyond it, near the pool, was a rock privacy wall too thick to reveal a heat signature if someone was hidden behind it. It was a chance I had to take. Beyond that, I could see the marina docks and the vague silhouettes of Kazlov's black-hulled yacht and *No Más*. Not so many minutes earlier, a man with a rifle had been standing near the privacy wall, smoking a cigarette, and he had fired a rifle at me.

Once again, I wondered how Tomlinson had gotten in the house so quickly. And why had the guard left his post to join his boss and Tomlinson inside?

I was still sorting through explanations as I jogged along the hedge, past the wall. That's when the answer hit me with all the subtlety of a sledge. Yes, the bodyguard had abandoned his position—but only for a few minutes. He had slipped into the shadows to urinate, which was apparent because the man was still struggling with his zipper when I rounded the corner and we almost collided.

Startled, the bodyguard hollered something in Russian as I spun away from his shoulder and went stumbling past him. I had almost regained my balance when my foot hit something—a tree root, possibly—which caused the thermal vision unit to go flying before I landed hard in a patch of oversized whelk shells.

Had the man not been so surprised, he might have taken his time and done it right. He could have backed away several yards, then taken aim with the rifle that was slung beneath his arm. Instead, he bellowed something guttural, lunged at me with the butt of the rifle and tried to hammer my head into the ground.

I got my hands up too late, I knew it, and swung my face away from the shattering impact. But the guard's momentum, or the darkness, caused him to miss, and the rifle butt crushed a shell next to my ear. The crunch of calcium carbonate has a bonelike resonance. It was a chilling sound to hear so near my head and a sobering reminder that I would need reconstructive surgery, or a hearse, if I didn't get my ass in gear and take my attacker to the ground.

I was ready an instant later when the bodyguard stabbed the rifle at me again. Hands up, I had my right leg fully extended, my left knee close to my chest. As the man leaned, I knocked the gun butt away while my legs went to work. I hooked my right foot behind the guard's ankle and yanked it toward me as I kicked him thigh-high with my left foot. Kicked him so hard that his knee flexed backward on its own hinges and he screamed. As he fell, I maintained control of his leg, my right foot behind his ankle, left foot on his thigh. I used them to apply more pressure, and steer him away so he didn't land on me.

That should have been enough, but Armanie's bodyguard wasn't convinced. He had dropped the rifle when he fell but managed to grab the thing just as I got my hands on it. The man was on his back, his knee was a grotesque mess and the pain had to be excruciating. Even so, he wrestled the weapon away by rolling toward me, which was unexpected, then battled to get his finger on the trigger. Pull the trigger and the round would either graze my leg or cut a trench beneath me. Either way, the bullet would kill Sharon Farwell.

I slapped my hands over his and bent his index finger back until he yelped. Just before his knuckle joint snapped, he released the weapon, then tried to use his free arm to slam an elbow into my face. I tucked my chin fast enough so that the blow glanced off my forehead, but the impact still caused a dizzying sensation behind my eyes as if an ammonia capsule had burst. If I caught another elbow, it might be enough to put me out, so I got an arm over the man's shoulder and pulled myself onto his back.

Keeping one hand over the trigger guard, I said into his ear. "Stop fighting! Stop, and I won't hurt you."

The bodyguard replied by trying to buck free of my weight, which was futile. From atop his back, I was in a position to control his hands, his legs and the rifle, too. That would soon give me several endgame options—none of them pleasant for Armanie's man. Even if he had been the one who'd shot at me while I was on Tomlinson's boat, there was nothing to be gained by crippling him further. I wanted to subdue the guy so I could get moving, not incapacitate him for life. And I also wanted a question answered—*Who was the third man inside Armanie's house?*—because the numbers no longer tallied.

Even so, the bodyguard didn't stop struggling until I threaded my ankles around his damaged knee and levered his leg upward, which caused him to cry out, "Enough! Is breaking my spine—please!"

I rocked back to reduce the pressure on his knee. At the same instant, I snared the rifle from beneath his belly and got my first good look at the thing. Even though it was dark and we were in the shadows of a gumbo-limbo tree, I recognized the weapon. It was a shortened carbine version of some kind of sniper rifle, judging from the scope; a precision shooting instrument. There was no way to be sure how close the slug had come to hitting me, but it had slammed into the sailboat's cabin more than a foot from my head. How had a trained bodyguard missed a man-sized target only a hundred yards away?

I pressed the rifle's magazine release, ejected the chambered round, then placed the weapon nearby before cradling the man's throat in my hands. As I applied pressure to his jugular vein, I whispered, "You shot at me tonight and missed intentionally. Why?"

When he refused to answer with a shake of his head, I stopped the flow of blood to his brain until he tapped my arm frantically, telling me he'd had enough.

"You were on sailboat?" he croaked after taking several breaths. "Abdul say kill you, but why go to prison for murder? So I missed. Abdul is lying bitch, don't care nothing what happens to me. He tells me I'm fired, I tell him, 'Lying bitch, I quit.'" Then the bodyguard grunted and said, "My leg . . . my leg is broken. Need doctor—son-bitch hurts!"

I released the guard's throat and reduced the pressure on his back by getting to my knees. "Did you see a man with long hair go into the house? Maybe five minutes ago, he just got here."

The bodyguard shook his head—*No*—and said, "Need ice for leg. Drugs for pain—son-bitch, this is bad! Don't tell Abdul, maybe he kill me and blame you to police. He most total lying bitch ever. Seen him kill two men, always blame someone else."

It was useful information, but I didn't have time to pursue it. I swung off the bodyguard and checked his feet because I needed something to restrain the guy. He was wearing running shoes, which was good enough. As I removed his shoelaces, I said, "There's another man inside with your boss. Who is it?"

"You have pills?"

"I'll give you an injection for the pain. But later."

The man swore softly in Russian as he rolled onto his side and explored his shattered knee with his hand. I was about to repeat my question when he said, "Mr. Kazlov is in house. Soon after lights go out, he escape from lodge. He show up asking for help because he afraid they find him on his boat. The hippies, they shoot him, but not too bad. Shoot him in ass, lots of blood, though. Too much blood, I think. Abdul think that very funny. But tell him, 'Sure, come in, I protect you from crazy hippies.' The woman bring him."

Geness Neinabor *hadn't* missed, apparently. I had the shoelaces out and was deciding whether to trust the bodyguard or tie his hands as a precaution. I could guess who the woman was but I asked, anyway.

The injured man told me, "Beautiful Chinese girl, she married to Mr. Bohai. Girl with big"—the bodyguard held a cupped hand to his chest to illustrate breasts—"and long hair. Not very good wife, that woman, because sometimes she in Abdul's bed. Many times with Mr. Kazlov, too, I think. Every meeting with Mr. Bohai, those two fight over who be with her when old man sleeping."

I nodded and knelt to retrieve the rifle and magazine. I hadn't seen Bohai's young wife through the thermal monocular. She would have been unmistakable because the guard had described her physical attributes accurately, which meant she had been in another room. Otherwise, the tally was right. Three men: Armanie, Kazlov and Tomlinson, although it seemed odd that Kazlov was still on his feet after being shot.

I checked the shadows around our perimeter, still wary of Geness Neinabor, and asked, "Did your boss care enough about Bohai's wife to kill the old man?"

"Old Mr. Bohai was shot tonight?" The bodyguard's surprise sounded genuine. "Abdul, he maybe kill because he hate, but not because he love. Mr. Kazlov, though, I think he care for the bad woman. His boat captain, we good friends, and he tell me Mr. Kazlov will do any stupid thing for that bitch."

"Vladimir?"

"We serve Russian Army together. You know Vladie? When we have enough money, we open a restaurant maybe. Hell with this shit, working for crazy assholes."

My respect for Russians, already considerable, was growing by the minute. I thought for a moment, then stuffed the shoelaces in my back pocket. "There's a chair by the pool, I'll help you. But I want your word you won't try something stupid. Any other weapons on you?"

The bodyguard shook his head but I frisked him anyway as he asked, "What means, 'want word'?"

I stood and showed him a switchblade knife, plus a full magazine of .308 cartridges, I'd just found in the cargo pocket of his slacks. "It means don't lie to me again. Or I'll tie your hands, leave you out here all night. No pain pills, no doctor. Understand?"

In the man's pockets, I'd also found a surgical glove stuffed with several more gloves—standard equipment for a professional who might be required to kill without leaving fingerprints. Because I had no idea of what I might be forced to do before the night was over, I snapped on a pair of elastic gloves, then jammed another pair into my pocket.

One arm around my shoulder, I helped the bodyguard hobble toward the pool thirty yards away. It was slow going, which was exasperating because it was 1:30 a.m., only fifteen minutes before the twins executed Sharon. When I realized the time, I dumped the guy over my shoulder and carried him fireman style.

I'd give it five more minutes, I decided. I couldn't risk waiting any longer to return to the lodge—no matter what.

As I placed the man on a wooden pool lounger, I noticed a balloon of candlelight crossing an upstairs window. Taking a couple of steps back to get a better angle, I got a quick look at Armanie, then possibly Tomlinson and maybe a third person, too, although I couldn't be sure because the candle vanished into another room.

I told the man, "I don't want to hear a sound out of you," then rushed to grab the rifle before using the TAM to search the upstairs of the house.

Nothing.

I changed angles, checked again, then ran to the side of the house, where I got lucky. There were two, maybe three people in a corner room, their body heat no longer shielded by multiple walls. The details were blurred, their facial features impossible to distinguish, but they were all flat-chested, so Bohai's wife wasn't among them. Two of the men resembled luminous apparitions, auras glazed with phosphorus. The third man was more difficult to decipher because he remained partially screened by what might have been a wall-mounted television.

Could I be certain one of the men was Tomlinson? I adjusted the monocular's brightness and contrast, then methodically interpreted the data it provided. The heat variations were subtle, the unit's learning curve slow, but I was catching on.

Yes, Tomlinson had entered the room, sandwiched by two men.

It was confirmed by a web of hair that collected warmth from my friend's face and shoulders. I also suspected that he was in trouble. I knew it for sure when, a moment later, I watched him thrust out both arms and crouch into what I would have described as a shooter's position were it anyone but Tomlinson. Yet, he'd reacted so aggressively, I couldn't explain the movement any other way.

I took several steps backward to get an unrestricted view as I experimented with the focus. Was the black geometric in Tomlinson's hands a pistol? It seemed an impossibility, yet the object began to assume shape as heat molecules wicked their way in slow progression from his fingers. A radiating line soon formed that revealed a gun barrel's precision edge. Then a loop of warming metal appeared that could only be a trigger guard.

When I saw the trigger guard, I knew it was true. Tomlinson had a gun and he was using it to threaten either Abdul Armanie or Viktor Kazlov. Armanie probably, because the host would have entered the room first.

How the hell had Tomlinson gotten his hands on a weapon? Not that there was much chance of him actually using the thing. The man was an apostle of nonviolence; a peacenik who refused to even touch a firearm. The incongruity caused me to lower the thermal monocular and blink my mind clear.

When I looked again, though, I no longer doubted what I was seeing. Tomlinson was still in a shooting stance as if moments from pulling the trigger. He had stopped three paces away from a shorter, thicker man. It definitely wasn't Kazlov. Kazlov was as tall as Tomlinson and almost as lean. Plus, the Russian had taken a bullet in the buttocks and was bleeding badly, according to the bodyguard. He wouldn't have stood so erect and unflinching while a gun was aimed at his chest.

Yes, it was Armanie. Tomlinson had the man cornered and was ready to shoot.

This *couldn't* be happening.

If it did happen, though, I knew there wasn't a damn thing in the world I could do to stop it.

19

I felt a morbid sense of the inevitable as I watched Tomlinson hold Armanie at gunpoint, and doubly helpless because Kazlov, who was just as dangerous, stood within easy striking distance only a few yards away.

I had to do something, so I reacted without thinking. I swung the monocular away from my eye, unslung the rifle I was carrying and snapped it to my shoulder. For an absurd moment, I couldn't figure out why I couldn't decipher details through the scope. Before I bothered checking the lens caps, though, I understood the problem.

Idiot.

Problem was, I'd forgotten the obvious: a conventional rifle scope doesn't read heat signatures through wooden siding. I could guess where my target was standing—a viable option if everyone in the room was a threat. But I couldn't open fire with Tomlinson in there. In fact, I couldn't risk squeezing the trigger no matter what happened.

One gunshot and Sharon Farwell dies.

I considered sprinting to the front of the house and kicking in the door. From what I'd just witnessed, though, the scene upstairs was degrading by microseconds, not minutes. No . . . I didn't have time. For now, all I could do was watch the drama play out, then try to provide backup. I thumbed the rifle's safety and ran to look through a nearby window. A membrane of light showed through the curtains, and I hoped it would provide a cleaner view of what was happening. If Tomlinson pulled the trigger, if anyone fired a shot, I wanted to be in position to take out one or both of the black marketeers. There was no helping Sharon if a shot was fired, but I might still be able to save my friend.

The window was useless, though, so I changed positions. As I moved, I heard voices from inside the house for the first time. Angry voices suddenly loud enough to pierce the walls. I couldn't distinguish words, but the escalating volume had the flavor of an argument.

I positioned the thermal unit flush over my eye and took a quick look. In the last thirty seconds, the scene had changed in subtle, dangerous ways.

I could see that Tomlinson, gun in hand, had backed Armanie to the wall. The Iranian had his fingers laced behind his head as if he'd just been taken prisoner. Thermal optics add an X-ray starkness when imaging the human body, so the skeletal framework of Armanie's teeth and jaws scissored with every word as the two men argued. Kazlov was still behind Tomlinson, his face only partially screened. Now, though, he had a shoulder braced against the doorway, probably because his wound had made him too weak to stand.

Good. It made the Russian less of a threat. But where the hell was Bohai's wife while all of this was going on? Sakura, that was her name. English translation: "wild cherry blossom." A benign name for a seditious beauty who'd maintained ongoing affairs with her husband's rivals. Both of her lovers appeared to be in trouble, so where was their mistress now?

Hiding, I hoped. But that seemed out of character for the opportunist that Umeko had described. "Rich men marry their mistresses because they have so much in common," she had told me. "They are both ruthless and both are whores."

Bitter words from the bitter daughter of a man who had been murdered tonight. Yet, I couldn't fault Umeko's assessment after what I had just learned about the woman.

I was thinking, *Maybe Sakura's hiding for a reason,* which caused a fresh suspicion to bloom in my brain: if Tomlinson saved himself by shooting Armanie or Kazlov—unlikely in itself—Sakura might be waiting for him somewhere outside the room. The woman had already proven she was ruthless. Maybe she had already proven that she could kill. If Sakura wanted revenge, Tomlinson would be a helpless target.

Instantly, I regretted the seconds I had just wasted by observing, doing nothing. Before sprinting toward the front entrance, though, I took one last look at what was happening upstairs—which is when, abruptly, everything vanished from my mind because of what I saw.

I watched Tomlinson turn to say something to Kazlov . . . watched my friend slowly pivot and refocus on Armanie . . . Then, without additional warning, I watched the pistol buck in Tomlinson's hands as he fired twice, the slugs hammering the Iranian against the wall, then dragging him downward with inexorable weight.

I was still yelling *"No-o-o-o-o!"* as the gunshots careened off the clouds toward the fishing lodge, leaving in their wake a funerary silence of startled birds, of indifferent stars. In that silence, the response I anticipated slowed the seconds. It taunted me with images of Sharon's face as a bipolar monster chastened her with Scripture, then pressed a gun to her head.

To my right, from the pool area, I heard the bodyguard holler, "What is happening? Who did you shoot?"

It was a senseless question because the gunshots had come from inside. The man was on his feet, struggling to walk, as I ran past him. "Stay where you are! Warn me if anyone comes down that path!"

When I reached the entrance of the house, I checked the rifle to confirm a round was chambered, then tested the door. It wasn't locked. Through a fogged windowpane, a lone candle shadowed the foyer and great room. They appeared empty, so I swung the door wide, then gave it a beat before stepping inside. The space smelled of cigarette smoke, varnish, synthetic fabric . . . Then I got the first acrid whiff of saltpeter, the principal ingredient in gunpowder.

The twins had refused to give me a flashlight, so I had to deal with the Cyclops limitations of the TAM. I took a second to scan the area, the rifle's bore pivoting in perfect sync with my eyes as I crossed the room to the stairway. From above, I could hear the thudding footsteps of someone running, then a rumble of hushed voices. Words were indecipherable, but it was Tomlinson's voice; purposeful, as if trying to pacify . . . then a woman's voice garbled by her weeping. A moment after their voices went silent, I heard the snare beat of someone running again, then a door slam.

The stairway was a helix of varnished wood and brass. I charged up the steps, two at a time, rifle at waist level because the scope made the weapon useless at close range. My vision was tunneled by the thermal monocular, which transformed this strange night into a surreal dream. Walls, the darkened light fixtures, all radiated an eerie fungal hue; the heat signature of my own hands was neon bright, so piercing that I kept my eyes straight ahead.

At the top of the stairs, my ears tried to pinpoint where I'd heard the voices. To my right was a double doorway where heated palpitations told me a candle was burning. Was it the room where Armanie had been shot? I sniffed the air. An odor of freshly sheared copper and patchouli confirmed that it was.

As I moved toward the opening, Tomlinson suddenly appeared, his feverish black eye glowing brighter than the rest of his skeletal face. When he realized who I was, he tried to hug me out of relief, but I pushed him away.

"What the hell just happened? Are you okay?" I tilted the thermal unit upward and blinked as my eyes adjusted

In the candlelight, my pal's face was a tormented likeness of the Shroud of Turin. His wrists had been taped in front of him, and he still held the pistol in both hands. Fighting panic, he told me, "We're almost out of time, Doc! We've got to get back to the lodge. I feel like I'm drowning in blood—I've got to do something right for a change!"

I pulled the man out of my way and stepped through the doorway, rifle ready. Less than a minute before, I had seen a mirror image of this room from outside. It was a master bedroom: tile, imitation wood, ceiling fans and a flat-screen TV mounted on the wall opposite the bed.

Abdul Armanie was on the floor near the seaward window. He lay motionless, wide-eyed, face frozen in eternal surprise, his body as misshapen as a rag doll that had been thrown against the wall by a temperamental child. His formal dress shirt was a blotter of red where two dark holes, spaced a foot apart, pinned him to the tile.

"He's dead," Tomlinson said over my shoulder, voice soft, talking too fast. "There was nothing I could do."

I was thinking, *After you pulled the trigger, you mean?* Instead I asked, "Does anyone else in the house have a gun? Where's Kazlov?"

"He's in the next room. He bled to death."

"Died just now?" That struck me as implausible. The Russian had been on his feet only minutes before.

"Ten seconds ago, an hour ago. It's all a blur, man."

I didn't react. There wasn't time. We had only ten minutes to get back to the lodge before they shot Sharon—if she wasn't already dead.

With gloved hands, I took the pistol from Tomlinson as I heard a door open, then close somewhere down the hallway. I had to move my friend out of the way again to take a look. It was Bohai's widow, Sakura. She appeared to be deep in thought, standing motionless outside the room where presumably the Russian had just died. As I wiped Tomlinson's prints off the pistol, I noted that she had changed from her silk dress into sweatpants and a T-shirt that was baggy at the waist but skintight over her breasts. Kazlov's clothing, probably. They were about the same height.

Tomlinson was staring at the woman, too, as he whispered, "Before the lights went out, she and Kazlov snuck off to a guest room or something. One of the twins shot him when he came out to check on the power. I helped them get out of the lodge before those little freaks got another chance. But I didn't know they came here."

I checked the pistol's magazine, tucked the weapon into my waistband, then used the switchblade to cut Tomlinson's hands free.

"Doc, we've got to hurry. I delivered their damn invitations, what more can we do?"

Now Sakura was trying to light a candle as she walked toward us, so I kept my voice low. "Did you leave footprints?" I used my head to motion to the pool of blood. "Did she see you shoot Armanie?"

The question seemed to confuse the man for an instant or maybe he was already in denial mode. "See *me*—"

Tomlinson stopped in midsentence, and we exchanged looks because he had been interrupted by a distant gunshot. Then we winced in unison at the sound of a second gunshot. To me, it was sickening confirmation that Geness Neinabor hadn't lied about ordering an execution if an unexplained shot was fired.

Tomlinson's face showed bewilderment, then outrage. "You don't think those freaks just shot Sharon, do you? We still have almost ten minutes before they said they would—"

I glanced at Sakura, then pulled the man into the room to silence him. Hands on his shoulders, I shook him and said, "Answer my question. Did she see you kill Armanie?"

Tomlinson's reaction was inexplicable. He looked at me for a long moment, expression unreadable, then said, "I get it. You're worried I'll be arrested for murder."

"That surprises you? I *saw* what happened through the monocular, so spare me the act. Florida still uses the electric chair, pal."

He replied, "Yeah . . . that's true," and turned toward the doorway as if thinking about the woman, then looked at me. Abruptly, his expression changed. "My God . . . you're thinking about killing her if she's a witness—*aren't you*?"

No. It was an option I had considered, true, but not the best option. I shook him again. "Just tell me."

Tomlinson was studying me as if suddenly we were strangers and he was now searching my eyes for something familiar; some kindred linkage that would vanquish the creature he had just glimpsed. "No," he said finally. "She didn't see me shoot Armanie."

"She didn't come in here after she heard the gunshot? I heard you two talking from downstairs. This is serious, old buddy. You only have one chance to get it right."

"I told her to go back in the room, but she didn't see me shoot anyone. I'll swear to that. I would swear on every holy book I've ever read."

I said, "Let's hope it doesn't come to that," then turned to intercept the woman before she could get a look at Armanie's body.

Sakura had gotten the candle burning, one hand cupped around the flame, which created the illusion that her face was floating toward me, skin a shimmering translucence, her dark eyes wide, lips full in exquisite proportion to a body that had evolved to attract the most powerful males of her species. The woman's eyes widened, though, when I stopped her in the hallway, saying, "You shouldn't come in here. It's better if you don't."

As I spoke, I was aware of a phenomenon I've experienced before: a woman's beauty is diminished proportionally as her character flaws are revealed. It's the same with men, of course, but the result is disrespect, not disfigurement, and the truth provides awareness, not an unaccountable sense of loss.

As the woman slowed, then stopped, her beauty vanished, replaced by webs of shadow and the glassine discord of an unshaded candle flame. Sakura looked from me to Tomlinson and asked, "What's he doing here? Who is he?"

"My friend's right," Tomlinson told her as he moved past me into the hall. "Keep out of this room. Lock the doors when we leave and stay with Viktor. Don't let anyone in. Armanie's dead. That was the gunshot you heard."

From Tomlinson's tone, his careful manner, I knew he was trying to send the woman a signal too subtle for me to intercept. But I understood immediately. He had lied to me. Sakura *had* seen him pull the trigger, but he didn't want to put her at risk.

"Dead," she said, unsure how to play it, and I sensed she already knew that her husband was dead, too. It was communicated by her aloofness, the way her attention focused instantly on her own self-interest; a woman alone in the world and suddenly very rich. "But what about Abdul's bodyguard?" she asked. "He was outside, can I let him in?" Then Sakura recognized the rifle I had taken from the man and said, "Oh," as if she'd just made a social blunder.

I took an aggressive step toward her because I wanted the woman's attention long enough to plant a subliminal message of my own. "There are two killers loose on the island. They're twins: blond shoulder-length hair, about five-six, chubby"—I held up the pistol—"and they carry a gun just like this. One of them shot Viktor tonight. You saw the twin shoot him, didn't you?"

The woman's eyes snapped upward, which told me whatever came next was a lie. "Yes," she said. "I . . . I'm sure I did."

I continued, "Your husband might be dead, too. They were after him—doesn't mean they would use the same gun." Sakura was paying close attention as I added, "If they got the chance, they might even stab him—use any weapon handy."

I watched the woman nod as her hand moved automatically to the back of her head where earlier in the swimming pool I'd watched her remove an ivory needle and comb so her hair could spill free.

"They wanted to kill Armanie, too," I told her, then paused before asking, "Did you see a short blond man run down the hall after you heard the gunshot? The bodyguard didn't see anything, so maybe you did."

Sakura was using her eyes, trying to communicate with Tomlinson, but I stopped her by saying, "Think about it. Lock the doors and try to remember what you saw. The police will ask a lot of questions when they get here. You need to have answers."

The woman was assembling details, already putting her story together, because she said, "Identical twins, it's so hard to say. One of them was wearing . . ."

"They're both in baggy khaki shorts and black T-shirts."

Sakura was filing that away as I gave Tomlinson a push. I told him, "Let's go."

20

As we ran toward the fishing lodge, I felt the Gatling gun vibrations of a helicopter through the earth before I heard its engines. But it wasn't until we both saw a searchlight probing the water north of the island that my pal reacted with careful optimism, saying, "The cavalry's coming."

Then he added, "I'm scared, Marion."

I replied, "Finally, we have something in common."

"Not for myself. If they already killed Sharon, do you think they'll stick to the schedule and kill someone else? I feel so shitty about all this because I'm the one who told Sharon about the caviar weekend. I never mentioned it before."

I kept my eyes on the fishing lodge, where a lone window was tinged with light. Of course the twins would execute another person if we didn't make the deadline. I didn't say it, though. Instead, I told Tomlinson, "Stop talking and pick up the pace."

I hadn't mentioned the copter right away because my hopes had plummeted in the few seconds it took for me to understand what was happening. The Coast Guard still had no idea what was taking place on the island. They were searching for the electronic transmitter attached to the life ring I had flung overboard two hours earlier. *No Más*'s EPIRB had drifted free of the island and caught an outgoing tide that streamed toward Big Carlos Pass, five miles away.

"If we can find a good flashlight, we'll signal an SOS," Tomlinson said after I had explained. Then he had to add, "Aren't you the guy who says to always carry a light?"

"That explains the corroded piece of junk I found on your boat," I told him. "Concentrate—we can't afford any more screwups."

Which was true, and my screwups still topped the list. I knew where a very fine palm-sized ASP Triad light was—at the marina, in fifteen feet of water.

There was another frustrating fact, too: the jars of chemicals I had mixed were no longer in the cottage where Kahn had told me to leave them. I had sprinted ahead to check and had just rejoined Tomlinson when we spotted the helicopter's searchlight. So Kahn, or maybe Geness, had grabbed the photographer's vest, afraid I would use the weapons against them.

Now we were only fifty yards from the lodge, close enough for me to slow down and adjust the thermal monocular as I listened to Tomlinson say, "Or maybe the pilot will notice all the lights are out and they'll do a flyover and take a look." He snapped his fingers. "Start a fire. That's what we need to do. A fire would bring them running."

I exhaled in a way that communicated irritation, then knelt to do a quick thermal survey of the fishing lodge. Mosquitoes hovered near my ears, I was sweat soaked from running and my shaky hands were symptomatic of dehydration as I mounted the monocular over my eye. The first spot I checked was the fourth-floor balcony. If Trapper, the Third Planet lookout, was still at his post, he'd have a clear shot at us as we approached the porch.

It was a good thing I looked. Trapper was there. Instead of a rifle, though, he was holding binoculars to his face. It took me a moment to figure out that he had spotted the helicopter and was watching it continue its low-level search. Judging from the man's antsy movements, he was scared. He didn't know I had released an emergency transmitter, so he assumed the Coast Guard helicopter was coming after him and his gang.

Good. The Neinabor twins were sociopaths, but Kahn, Trapper and Densler were nothing but egocentric screwups with terrible judgment. Cowards, too, so the helicopter might scare them into surrendering before anyone else was killed.

Yeah . . . Trapper was spooked, because now, as I watched, he was yelling something through the open doorway, yelling loud enough for me to hear but not understand.

"He's warning them," Tomlinson said softly. "He thinks the cops are coming. Let's hope the Diablo twins panic and run like hell."

As he said it, I watched Trapper kneel, get his rifle and disappear into the room in a rush to get downstairs.

I asked, "How much time do we have?"

"Six minutes. But it's not like we synchronized our watches."

"I want to be sure of what we're walking into. Give me another minute, then I'll get into position. You understand what you're supposed to do, right?"

Tomlinson said, "Simple. I call the twins outside and you try to take them from behind. And you're not going to use the gun unless you have to. You promised."

I hadn't promised Tomlinson anything, and I was tempted to point out that, accident or not, he had forfeited the right to lecture me on the bad karma consequences of violence.

I replied, "Yep, very simple—unless they decide to shoot before you open your mouth. The important thing is, stop at least ten paces from the porch. That's important. Get too close to the porch, I'll lose sight of you from the side of the house. Got that?"

"What if the twins don't come out? Or won't open the door?"

"We'll have to play it by ear—but *do not* get any closer than about ten yards from that porch or I can't protect you." The man was thinking about it as I asked, "Are you sure you're okay with standing out there in the open? I can try to pick them off from a side window before they realize what's happening."

"Nope, absolutely not. We've got to put a stop to this existential bullshit. It's all about getting derailed into the wrong dimensions, you know."

Spooked by his own seriousness, maybe, he tried to downplay it by saying he could invoke a trance that would cloak him from bullets, before adding, "If not, I've always wondered what the goat feels like when it's waiting for the lion."

I was searching the third floor, where I had seen what I assumed to be restaurant staff huddled together in a guest room. The room was at the back of the lodge, though, and the TAM's heat sensors failed to pierce the interceding walls.

After a quick sweep of the second floor, I focused on the dining-room area where Sharon and her friends were being held. At first, I was heartened by what I saw: a female shape was walking toward the next room unrestrained. But then I realized it was Winifred Densler when she stopped at the bar and poured what was probably vodka into a glass radiant with heat from her fingers.

Nearby, two males—Kahn and one of the Neinabor twins, gauging from their height—stood talking. Kahn was bouncing something in his left hand with the jauntiness of some speakeasy gangster flipping a coin at a bus stop. I couldn't identify the object. It was an amorphous shape with a rhythmic liquidity that appeared to change in size as it moved.

As I watched, Kahn and Neinabor turned in unison when a third male descended into the room from the stairway. It was Trapper, just arrived from his lookout post, in a hurry to spread the news about the helicopter. He must have been talking loud enough to be heard in the trophy room because the second Neinabor twin soon appeared.

It was Odus, and he was mad about something, as usual. He was easy to identify because of the wild arm gestures as he confronted Kahn, close enough to stand chin to chin if Odus had been six inches taller.

Beside me, Tomlinson whispered, "Are the women okay? What do you see?"

"If any of them were alive when we got here," I told him, "they're safe for now. All four of your symbiotic brothers are in the bar, too busy to shoot anyone. I think they're arguing about the helicopter, what they should do next. Densler's in the bar, too. Drunk and getting drunker."

"Doc, I feel shitty enough without the sarcasm."

The man was right. I'd pushed it too far. "Sorry. That was unfair." I tilted the monocular away from my eye and said, "Let's move while they're arguing. You ready?"

"Ready, willing and unstable."

I collected the rifle and checked the pistol's magazine one last time. It was an expensive piece, a 9mm Smith & Wesson, one round in the chamber, eleven stacked and waiting, ivory grips and a chrome-plated body with lots of complicated engraving. It could have belonged to Kazlov or Armanie—both were garish enough to own such a weapon.

As I levered the hammer back and engaged the safety, I said, "I'm curious. How'd you get this pistol? Your hands were taped, and Armanie's a fairly tough guy. Or was, anyway." I hadn't asked earlier because when police are involved, sometimes the less you know, the better.

Because it was dark, I couldn't tell if Tomlinson was smiling as he replied, "I used my mystic trance of invisibility. Great for women's shower rooms and stealing guns. Tomorrow, at Dinkin's Bay, we'll start your lessons. It takes years to learn."

I said, "Deal," then sprinted toward the side window of the fishing lodge.

21

Sharon Farwell was still alive. So were her friends—the nicest surprise so far in this long, long night.

I had slipped along the edge of the building, through a hedge of jasmine, lifted one eye to the window and there they were. The ladies sat a few yards away against a wall, hands still tied behind them, Sharon in the middle with her exhausted friends resting their heads on her shoulders.

It was a touching scene, but I didn't let my attention linger. Tomlinson was watching me from the shadows, awaiting my signal. It was almost deadline time—and his nerves were too brittle to go for long without communicating. I ducked beneath the window, then stood with my back to the wall so the man could see me. I gave him a thumbs-up, which he might or might not interpret correctly. Next, I held up a fist, which meant *Halt* or *Wait*, depending on the circumstances as my occasional scuba partner knew. After the man replied with a thumbs-up, I returned to the window. I didn't want to move until I'd done my best to fix the positions of everyone in the lodge—most importantly, the Neinabor twins.

Sharon was awake. I watched her try to wiggle her legs into a more comfortable position, then say something to her friends. Yes, they were all alive. It was reason enough to continue with our plan to surprise the twins and disarm them, preferably alive. I had no moral reservations about shooting one or both, but that would guarantee long sessions with police. Worse, it would make headlines. Killing the brothers would put my freedom in jeopardy and compromise my low-profile lifestyle at Dinkin's Bay. The same was now true of Tomlinson, whose guilt was unambiguous if a smart cop took an interest. Terminating the lives of two sociopaths was sensible, in my Darwinian view of the world, but it wasn't practical, considering the risks.

I looked beyond the dining room, through open French doors that revealed a portion of the bar. The first thing I noticed was the incongruity of a photographer's vest, pockets laden, hanging on a hat rack near the door. The irony caused me to smile. Kahn, or the twins, had placed the vest there for safekeeping but in fact might have provided me with an another weapon. But how could I use it?

I let my subconscious consider the options while I shifted my attention to what was going on in the bar.

Densler was there. She had passed out, her upper body sprawled across a table where a stub of candle burned. And I could see one of the twins—Odus, I guessed. He was still arguing with Trapper and Kahn, although they were blocked from my view. I confirmed it by using thermal vision to count the heat signatures on the other side of the wall. Four people in all, which meant that Geness had probably returned to his trophy room, the office where they were holding Darius Talas.

That accounted for all but one person, not counting the employees hiding upstairs. Where was Umeko? I hadn't seen her since we'd left for Armanie's rental house and her absence was disturbing. We'd heard two gunshots, yet the women from Captiva Island were still alive. Who had the twins executed? Talas was a possibility, or maybe the four staff members had been rousted from their hiding place on the third floor. Umeko was a more likely choice, though, because the twins already suspected she was a spy. If Talas had been forced to confess that she was also Lien Bohai's daughter, it would have sealed her fate.

I barely knew Umeko, but I was impressed by her resilience and intellect—a tad intimidated, too. Because it was painful to believe she'd been executed, I considered a more hopeful possibility: Geness Neinabor had fired those shots into the ground to torment me. And also to remind me that he was awaiting the truth about how he and his brothers would be judged. That he believed my fanciful lie would have been amusing if it didn't illustrate how crazy the man actually was. On the other hand, maybe it had awakened Geness's conscience to the possibility that murder was wrong. No . . . that was wishful thinking. Abraham, his alter ego, wouldn't tolerate it.

Thinking about the dead triplet caused me to test the rifle's scope by shouldering the weapon, centering the crosshairs on the photographer's vest, then lowering it to a side pocket that bulged with the weight of one of my homemade weapons.

But which weapon?

There was no way of knowing, that was the problem. One of the jars contained an incendiary mix that required a flame to ignite it. In movies, a bullet might cause a gas tank to explode, but that doesn't work in real life. Only a few paces away, though, the candle sputtered on the table where Densler slept, its flame burrowing its way through the wax.

I thought about it for a moment, then aimed the rifle at Odus Neinabor, taking my time, breathing into my belly, as I steadied the scope's crosshairs so that they segmented the man's temple. My timing was good because, at that instant, the twin checked his watch and yelled to his brother, "Hey, Geness! It's time. Ford's not back yet!" which I heard faintly through the window.

Sadly, Sharon and her friends heard it, too. Their vocal reaction was a garble of panic that ascended into a wail so heartbreaking that I was tempted to shatter the window, shoot Odus and anyone else who threatened the women.

Instead, I turned and signaled Tomlinson to action. Immediately, the man stepped into the open and strode toward the front porch, calling, "I'm back! Stop everything! I found Kazlov, I found Kazlov!" which was exactly as we'd planned.

I spun toward the window and this time aimed the rifle at Neinabor's chest because he was moving and still talking as he pulled his semiauto pistol from his waistband. At this range, the scope was a liability. The rifle was a cut-down knockoff of a Remington 800, but the scope was an expensive Leupold, elevation and windage knobs clearly marked, with a side-mounted parallax adjustment. It was an instrument designed for long-range targets, which is why I couldn't get it focused on Odus, who was less than fifteen yards away.

The Smith & Wesson pistol was in the waistband of my shorts, but the rifle was still a better option. The twin would have been a can't-miss kill at this distance. A target didn't have to be in focus to be obliterated by the weapon's heavy grain bullet, so I had my finger on the trigger, ready to shoot, when the twin heard Tomlinson's voice and stopped. I watched Odus pause, surprised. Then he looked at his pistol as if disappointed and tilted his head to yell, "Hey, Geness! Mr. Freaky-Freak is back!"

It wasn't until Odus turned toward the front door, though, that I moved my finger to the outside of the trigger guard . . . hesitated . . .

then squared the crosshairs on the photographer's vest once again, breathing with purpose because anxiety was creating a growing pressure within me. Where the hell was Geness Neinabor? Certainly he'd heard his brother calling. The guy was wearing a wristwatch, so he knew our deadline had passed. I'd already decided that if Geness didn't appear, our plan was doomed—and so was Odus Neinabor because I would shoot him if he so much as lifted his pistol toward Tomlinson.

Both eyes open, I kept the rifle steady and also watched Odus as he started toward the door, which was on the opposite side of the room. I was still thinking of a way to use the concoctions I'd made if Geness didn't appear. Only one of the jars contained an incendiary. It was a last-ditch offensive weapon that I had made to maim or possibly kill. The other two jars, though, were potent but not lethal. They contained a chemical combination that might be as effective as tear gas—theoretically, anyway.

I was thinking, *If it's the incendiary jar, the spray might reach the candle,* but knew the odds weren't good enough to risk it.

As I waited, Tomlinson was closing on the porch, still summoning attention, calling, "Stop everything, I found Kazlov!" while I sent him a telepathic reminder even though I don't believe telepathy: *No closer than ten paces, damn it!*

At the same moment, Kahn and Trapper appeared from behind the dining-room wall and crossed in front of the scope's crosshairs. Neither man carried a weapon, which suggested that the helicopter's arrival had scared the hell out of them and they were done trying to prove they were killers. Instead, Kahn had something else in his hand. It took me a moment to figure out that it was the same amorphous object I had been unable to identify with thermal vision.

It was the third jar.

Kahn had taken the thing from the photographer's vest and left the other two. Now, as he followed Neinabor toward the door, he continued to bounce it in his hand just as he had in the VIP cottage.

For an instant, I looked away from the scope, toward the bar, where I hoped the second twin would materialize. Geness not only didn't appear, he still hadn't responded to his brother, who was now only a few steps from the entranceway, where, as I had anticipated, he would disappear briefly before exiting the front door. I'd also known that Tomlinson would be unprotected for those very dangerous few seconds it would take the Neinabors to cross the porch—which is why I'd told him to stop where I could keep an eye on him. The risk had seemed manageable, but only because we expected the twins to be together.

The danger wasn't manageable now, though. Geness—and his manic alter ego—could be anywhere, armed with a pistol or a rifle, watching Tomlinson. I decided I had to shift gears and change the momentum because our plan was falling apart.

I glanced to my right and saw Tomlinson stop where he was supposed to stop, ten strides from the porch, hands above his head, in darkness. Then, inexplicably, the man resumed walking toward the lodge and vanished from my view.

What the hell is he thinking?

In a rush, I pressed my eye to the scope and swung the crosshairs toward Odus. I had to shoot him. Killing the man was suddenly my only option—but I was too late. I got just a glimpse of his back before he disappeared into the entranceway, already reaching for the door.

Simultaneously, a spotlight from the second floor came on, and I could only imagine it isolating my pal in glacial light, as a voice boomed, "Where is Ford? He's hiding somewhere. Tell us or I'll shoot you where you stand!"

It was Geness Neinabor's monster voice. Brother Abraham was back.

In one motion, I drew the semiautomatic pistol, took a giant step to the corner of the building and swung the pistol toward the spotlight. Yelling, "Over here—leech!" I fired two rapid shots that caused Geness to drop the light and duck for cover—but not before he'd gotten off two rounds, one of them splintering wood a foot above my head. I took a third shot at the darkened window, aware that Odus had retreated inside and that Tomlinson was on his belly, facedown.

Had he been shot?

No . . . Because when I moved toward him, calling, "Hey! Are you hit?" he jumped to his feet and sprinted toward me, sounding hysterical as he yelled, "He's crazy as ten loons! That midget tried to *shoot* me, the Buddha can kiss my pacifist ass!"

I was already charging toward the side window, the rifle still in my left hand but the pistol ready in case I saw one of the twins coming toward the ladies from Captiva.

Behind me, Tomlinson dived behind the corner of the building, still yelling, "Goddamn bullet came *this* close to my ear."

At the window, I shielded my eyes to look. No sign of the twins, but I could see Kahn standing over shards of broken glass and steaming liquid, a pained expression on his face. Instantly, I perceived what had happened. It was confirmed when the man recoiled from the mess, tried to fan it from his face and then ran toward the bar's back exit.

The gunshots had caused Kahn to drop the jar he'd been toying with.

As I watched, steam emanating from the chemicals began to assemble as an ascending fog. Not quickly, as it was supposed to do, but it was definitely spreading. One jar, though, wouldn't be enough to evacuate the entire lower floor. So I leaned the rifle against the wall, then tapped on the window to prepare Sharon and her friends for what was about to happen. When I had their attention, I used the pistol to shatter the window, ready for the screams of surprise from inside.

"Sharon, it's me, Ford. Your ears, cover your ears. Do it now!"

It took three shots to shatter both jars, spattering glass and liquid across the barroom, then I called to the women, "If your eyes start burning, it's harmless. We'll get you out."

Sharon's cry of relief—"Awwwww, it's Doc!"—followed me as I grabbed Tomlinson's arm and pulled him to his feet.

"You're not hurt?"

Tomlinson was slapping sand off his shirt, his hands, the man's expression a blend of rage and indignation. "*This* goddamn close, I'm telling you. And the lunatic was grinning at me. Like shooting me was fun!"

I told him, "Calm down. I need your help," but he was too mad to listen.

"I saw the freak's eyes when he fired! Yellow goat's eyes—slits like a damn snake—and horns, too! Satan's been after my ass for years, now it's time to turn the tables on that son of a bitch!"

I levered the pistol's safety and slapped the weapon into Tomlinson's hands. "We've got to get in there. Use this to cover my back—only six rounds left. Can you do that?"

The man was saying, "Damn right—" but his words were swallowed by the gasoline *BOOM* of a fireball that shattered windows from inside the bar.

22

I could hear Winifred screaming from inside, so I hollered to Tomlinson, "Get Sharon and take them out the window," then ran into the lodge and turned toward the bar.

Fumes from the incendiary had caused the explosion, but pools of flaming liquid had yet to ignite the wooden floor. There wasn't much smoke, but, as I approached the bar, I slammed into a wall of capsicum gas so potent that it almost knocked me down. Capsicum—the alkaloid that gives chili peppers their heat. It's the key ingredient in tactical tear gas, as well as my homemade version—compliments of Tomlinson's Amazon habanero sauce.

I stopped, cracked the door so I could grab a breath and then crawled into the bar area on my hands and knees to avoid the fumes.

Densler didn't appear badly hurt, but she was in shock. She'd been thrown from her chair and now sat among the flames, knees cradled against her chest, sobbing childlike as she rocked. Her eyes were closed against the searing sting of the gas, but she stirred when she heard me enter.

"Markus . . . is that you? I can't see! Help me, Markus!"

The woman's hair was singed—I could smell the stink—and part of her blouse had been torn away. But her face wasn't blistered, so I doubted the explosion had blinded her, although it was possible.

When I was close enough, I took her wrist and tugged gently. "We have to get out of here, Winifred. Follow me, you'll be okay."

The woman tried to pull away and shrieked when I refused to release her arm. "Who are you? Get away from me!"

I was tempted to do exactly that. To my left, I heard someone running and got a blurry glimpse of Geness Neinabor as he scrambled down the hallway, presumably headed for the rear exit. He carried Trapper's rifle in one hand and used the other to cover his mouth and nose with a towel.

Above me, I could hear people running, too, and the sound of panicked voices. Maybe staff members were reacting to the gunshots and the explosion, but I suspected the capsicum gas was spreading faster than I'd thought. The fishing lodge had been built in the 1800s, so it still had the old floor vents for heating.

"Winifred, listen to me. The place is on fire. It'll burn to the ground if I don't put it out now." I tugged at her wrist once again. "You'll be safe, I promise."

I saw the woman's eyes open into slits, and then close. "My God, it's *you*. Am I dreaming?"

"Come on. Get on your knees. We have to stay low."

"Why are you trying to help me after all those terrible things I said? Is this some kind of trick?" She shuddered and began to cry.

Maybe it was shock, or all that vodka, but the abrasive Ms. Densler was suddenly behaving like a remorseful child.

"We have to go *now*."

"But I can't! My God, I'm blind, I'm telling you! And I can't walk!"

In old films, heroes slap women to save them from their own hysterics. True, the thought of belting Densler had some appeal, but I'm no hero nor can I rationalize any reason to hit a woman. Instead, I pulled my shirt to my mouth before taking a full breath, then I swept her up in my arms. When I squatted to retrieve the rifle, I also noticed the woman's beach bag–sized purse, so I grabbed it, too, then headed for the door. As I passed the opening to the dining room, I saw Tomlinson helping the last of Sharon's friends out the window.

I yelled to him, "The twins went out the back. Keep that pistol handy."

Tomlinson hollered back, "See his horns?" as I shouldered the door open and hustled the woman outside.

Because the lodge was built on the island's highest shell mound, a stone stairway led down to the water, where there was a service dock and a beach. At the entrance to the stairs was a corniced balustrade, hip-high. I sat the woman on the ledge, placed her purse within easy reach, then stripped my shirt off.

"Use this on your eyes. But pat at them, don't wipe That'll just spread the"—I'd almost said "alkaloid"—"it'll spread the chemical that's making your eyes burn."

As Densler took the shirt, I touched a hand to her thigh. "When Tomlinson and I were gone, who did the twins shoot? I heard two shots." I was looking over my shoulder, seeing firelight echo through the broken window as I gauged the speed of the flames.

"I don't know. But you have to promise me you'll tell the police I had nothing to do with this. *None* of this was supposed to happen. It's all because of those crazy Neinabor fuckheads. Do you promise?"

My dislike for the woman had begun to soften, but her self-obsession confirmed my first impression—she was a neurotic ass. I asked her again, "Do you know what they did with Umeko? The Chinese woman."

"I don't know anything. Remember that! That's what you have to tell the police because it's true."

When I failed to respond, Densler cracked one crimson eye, then recoiled, frightened by the expression on my face. "Why are you looking at me like that?"

I was pissed off and it showed. "I'm picturing you handcuffed to some bull dyke at Raiford. Now tell me what the hell they did with Umeko."

The woman sat up straighter. "You don't have to be nasty. She's the one who lied about being that Chinese gangster's daughter."

"What?"

"They found out the truth. So they dragged her down the hall, and that's the last I saw. I told them not to do it—ask anyone."

Because I didn't trust myself to say anything else, I replied, "I'll need that," and yanked my shirt from the woman's hands, then put it on as I jogged toward the flames that were now wicking their way up the window frame.

The woman's indignant voice tracked me. "Don't tell me you're going to go off and leave me! Ford? *Ford!*"

My attention had shifted to Tomlinson, who was calling to me from the shadows near the corner of the building. "You want me to check upstairs?" He had one arm wrapped around Sharon Farwell and another around her friends.

I hollered, "Stay with them," then leaped onto the porch and stepped inside, holding the rifle at waist level.

The place appeared to be empty. The downstairs, anyway. I could smell woodsmoke, which meant the floor had ignited, but that wasn't all bad because heat was now venting the capsicum fumes upward.

For a moment, my eagerness to go after the twins battled my obligation to save people from being trapped in a burning building.

Reason won out, so I found an industrial fire extinguisher behind the bar and emptied it on the flames.

There was another extinguisher on the dining-room wall and I used it, too. Ironically, as I doused the last of the flames, the bar's sprinkler system came on, soaking me and everything else in the room.

My shoes creaking like squeegees, I ran down the hall to the office where I'd last seen Darius Talas.

23

The fat man was still bound to the swivel chair. Dead, I thought at first. His porcine hands resembled inflated gloves because they'd taped his wrists so tightly. He was slumped forward, eyes closed, and his face was a swollen mask of contusions and blood. But I saw one bovine eye open as I approached, and then both eyes opened when he recognized me.

Once again, I was impressed by his composure when he sat up and attempted to smile. "I'm not crying—*someone* set off a tear gas bomb." The man gave it a beat. "When I told them you are a thoroughly dangerous man, Dr. Ford, they should have listened."

I flicked open the switchblade and stepped toward him. "What happened to Bohai's daughter? Everyone else is safe, but I can't find her."

The man sniffed and cleared his throat. "I had to tell them about Umeko, I'm afraid. They planned to kill me, anyway, of course, but I preferred a bullet. So, rather than be beaten to death by a dwarf, I talked. I know it was cowardly. And I liked her father. Old Lien was cold-blooded and deceitful, but he loved women and lived a man's life, I'll give him that."

I said, "Try to tilt your hand back. I don't want to cut you."

As I worked at the tape, Talas said, "I've been sitting here patiently, thinking how best to kill those poisonous little brutes. I have an associate who owns a sausage plant where there is a giant meat grinder. A great big chute like a sliding board and more than big enough for two screaming little pigs. If you'll help me get them aboard one of my oil tankers, I'll pay you enough to last the rest of your life."

I was done with the man's left arm and went to work on the right. "Do you think they shot Umeko? I heard two shots."

He shook his head. "The girl was locked in here with me at the time. I thought they'd forgotten about us but just minutes ago the craziest one dragged her out the door—*after* he tried to shoot me. I must admit, I thought my check had been cashed. He put the pistol to my temple and . . . and he . . ." The man took a huge shuddering breath, his chin dropped to his chest, and I realized he'd begun to weep.

I said, "They used enough tape to wrap a mummy. A tribute to your physique, I guess."

Talas's chortle was more like a growl. A moment later, he'd regained control and went on talking as if it had never happened.

"His pistol must have jammed. Over and over, he tried to pull the trigger—the longest few seconds in my life. But he was in a hurry. There wasn't much the poor girl could do, of course. He'd taped her hands and mouth. That was before the nasty beating he gave her. Geness—is that his name?—Geness didn't want to risk being hurt if she fought back."

"Are you sure he wasn't out of ammo, not jammed?" The man was thinking about it as I took a closer look at his face. "Your nose is broken, I think. You'll need X-rays, too."

"I'll have my physician flown in. My guess is that my girth saved me—and not for the first time in my life."

He was explaining why Neinabor had dragged the girl out the door but left him.

"Any idea where he was headed?"

"To Kazlov's boat, I would think. You picked up on the nautical metaphors very quickly. That was my impression, anyway." He turned to look at a bottle of water sitting on the desk. "I'm so thirsty, I thought I would pass out. I sustained myself, though, with thoughts of revenge. Revenge is a powerful survival tool, you know."

I handed the man the bottle, then knelt to cut his legs free.

"Viktor's not going to be happy about all this. If those dwarfs don't end up in a sausage grinder, it'll only be because he hasn't managed to leave the dock yet, taking Lien's sturgeon and wife with him. That's something else I realized as I was sitting here. My Russian colleague contrived the whole affair so he could trade fish for a beautiful woman—*and* put the rest of us at one another's throats. Brilliant plan, actually. I give credit where credit is due."

I said, "Are you sure about that or guessing?"

"There's no other explanation. It's possible Lien had agreed to the deal before he arrived—that *is* conjecture, by the way. He probably has one of China's Evergreen freighters out there in the Gulf right now, rigged to offload the sturgeon and close the deal. Sex and power—the only international currencies that never depreciates. Women have a dollar value, and Viktor pretended Sakura was worth a billion to him. And maybe she was. I know for a fact that Armanie offered Lien several millions, but Viktor was too smitten to be outbid."

I looked to see if Talas was serious. One of his eyes was swollen nearly shut, the other was bloodied, but the man was coherent. He was in pain but still in control. He was telling the truth about Bohai auctioning his wife.

"Poor Lien. The old villain was never bested in a business deal, as far as I know. But when it finally happened, he lost big. Spoils to the winner go, so congratulations to Viktor for pocketing the entire pot."

I tossed a ball of duct tape toward the trash, closed the switchblade, then waited while Talas got to his feet in the slow, experimental way of large men who've lost confidence in their legs. It was almost two a.m.

"I've been wondering about that myself," he said when he saw me look at my watch. "Did the brutes set more explosives? If they snuck one aboard his yacht, too bad for Viktor—and after going to all that trouble to steal a married woman. Is there time to warn him?"

"Kazlov's dead. Armanie, too."

"You're joking." The man spoke the words with an ascending inflection as if he hoped it were true.

"You're not saying . . . you don't mean those inept little idiots killed two of Europe's shrewdest men? But what about their bodyguards? Both officers in Russian Special Forces!"

"I saw the bodies," I replied, which was enough to convince him that the twins had killed both men. I was watching Talas's expression as I added, "What I can't figure out is why they let you live as long as they did."

Talas shrugged, feigning disinterest, and looked away. He was shaken and in pain; an injured man on the verge of nausea, judging from his color, which might have explained his evasiveness. But it didn't mesh with the way he stopped, thought for a moment, then thrust up an index finger as he looked at me, an epiphanic smile on his face. "The fish! I've just had an inspired idea regarding Viktor's sturgeon."

I was looking at the man, weighing the chances that he knew more than he was admitting. "What about them?"

"The authorities don't know about the fingerling beluga. Viktor brought them for Lien to inspect, I suppose, but no one knows that but us. How many did the little brutes say? One thousand, I think."

What came next was outrageous but not out of character.

"Are you a businessman, Dr. Ford?"

I picked up the rifle and checked the safety. "I'm going after Umeko. You'll have to get back to your rental house on your own. Is one of the women there your wife? You need ice and a first-aid kit."

I was referring to the two women I'd seen Talas with at dinner, but it confused him and he had to think about it. "Oh . . . my *wives*, you mean. Don't worry about them, I'll be fine. Wait . . . give me a moment."

Talas lowered his weight into the swivel chair before continuing. "Dr. Ford, you're a proven professional in a competitive trade. I'd like to retain your services with a lump sum offer. Are you interested?"

With a shrug, I consented to listen.

"Here it is, then. Secure Viktor's yacht. Make sure the fish are healthy and well enough to deliver to a vessel I'll have waiting offshore. Do that in the next . . . twenty-four hours and I will pay you one million dollars in the form of a bank draft. Or better yet, I'll have it wired into an account I can have established in the Cayman Islands. Tax-free, in other words."

When I tried to respond, the man silenced me with an index finger. "Hear me out! If you can also manage to subdue those hideous twins and deliver them along with the fish, I will pay you an additional five hundred thousand. *No.* No . . . I will pay you an additional one million dollars and it'll be worth every penny. They must be alive, of course—the brothers. Not necessarily fully functional but conscious at least."

I was smiling because I found the second part of the offer appealing. "You have an oil tanker in the area?"

"My company has a freighter that transited the Panama Canal last week. It's now off Naples, in international waters, awaiting word from me."

In reply to my pointed look, Talas scolded, "Please, Dr. Ford, don't moralize. It's true that I know more about Viktor's correspondence with Bohai than I've admitted. But business is war, you know. No matter how it's wrapped and perfumed, business is war in its most rarefied form. And you certainly understand that winning is the only rule."

I asked him, "How do you think Turkmenia's customs officers will react when they find two kidnapped Americans aboard?"

"With closed eyes and open hands, as always. In other words, I own them. And because our population is largely Muslim, my friend's sausage factory is usually very quiet after dark."

Profit is a repugnant motive for what I do, so freelance work has never been of interest—until meeting Darius Talas. "Know what?" I said. "I'll think about it. If not now, who knows, maybe down the road."

As I headed out the door, Talas was still trying to close the deal. "The numbers are negotiable, of course. You are among the elite in your field and I'm a man who rewards professionalism. So instead of two million, let us say . . ."

I didn't hear the number because my attention swerved to Tomlinson's voice. He was somewhere inside the building, calling, "Doc? Where the hell are you? Someone just started Kazlov's boat!"

24

When Winifred saw me dump the contents of her purse on the ground, she sounded nervous as she asked Tomlinson, "He doesn't believe me? I said I don't have the boat keys and I don't. After he left me with all these goddamn mosquitoes and nothing to drink, why would I let him use the damn thing, anyway?"

Tomlinson replied gently, "For the second time, Winnie, your guys just stole Viktor Kazlov's boat. We think they have Umeko. You don't want anything else bad to happen, do you?"

It was ten after two, and I could only admire my pal's patience. I'd been tempted to throttle the witch when she'd told us she didn't know where the keys were. They weren't in the ignition, we'd already checked.

The purse contained a discouraging pile that would have filled an airplane carry-on. Densler lunged to stop me when I plucked her cell phone from the heap, but Tomlinson got his hands around her waist. "We know the twins are aboard, but where are Markus and

Thomas? We're trying to prevent a disaster, and the cops aren't going to be very happy when they hear you refused to cooperate."

Thomas was Trapper's real name, apparently.

I pocketed Densler's cell phone after checking her recent calls, then began to sort through the stuff, occasionally glancing to my left. Down the mound, through a web of palm trees, Kazlov's dark-hulled Dragos Voyager was still idling out the channel, no lights showing. We had run to the marina immediately but had arrived at the docks minutes after the boat pulled away. Then when Tomlinson had made the mistake of whistling to get our attention, we'd had to dive for cover when Odus's red laser sight began probing for a target.

The vessel was riding much too low in the water. Even from this distance, I could tell by its sluggish progress, the way it wallowed and its mountainous wake cleaved too far aft at a speed so slow. My guess was, the Dragos had almost sunk at the dock and might still be taking on water.

Sharon Farwell, standing between her friends, came to Densler's defense, saying, "She's had a terrible night, can't you go a little easier on her? She never really did anything to help them. Not *really*."

Sliding past Tomlinson, Sharon took Densler by the arm and helped steady her. "Let's go inside and make some coffee, dear. Or maybe a good strong drink. We'll all feel better in the morning."

Touched by the kindness, Densler began bawling again. "I had nothing to do with this, you have to believe me. Markus didn't know what the Neinabors had planned, either—none of us did."

"We believe you, dear, of course we do. We've all been through a lot."

"We got . . . got swept along by their craziness, I guess. The twins were so sure of themselves, it was like . . . like being hypnotized. They made us believe what they believed. That's exactly what happened!

Now, though . . . well, if Markus and Thomas are on that boat, it's because the twins forced them. They had a big argument, plus they'd never leave me behind on purpose."

Kahn and Thomas had apparently tried to mutiny, information that caused Sharon to look at Tomlinson, her expression asking *See how easy it is?*

An impressive woman. But it wasn't important enough to make me pause as I tossed aside combs, a day planner, cigarettes, several bottles of prescription pills, and then, finally, I held up two keys attached to a float.

"Here they are! Let's go."

I was already moving as Tomlinson asked, "Winnie, there are two rental boats. Which one?"

"For Christ's sake," the woman hollered, "it's an old Boston Whaler. Do I have to provide every single little detail?"

Tomlinson is the faster runner, so I handed off the keys as he went flying past. By the time I got to the dock, he was already aboard the little boat, tilting an ancient Mercury outboard into the water. The engine looked too small and old for what I feared we'd have to do: stop a thirty-ton boat that was carrying maybe five people, plus a manifest of fingerling sturgeon, in a hull that was awash with salt water.

Despite all that had happened, the young sturgeon had been on my mind since their existence had been confirmed. I'd tried to convince myself they were just fish and what happened to them was unimportant. After all, trillions of fish died daily, some by my own hand. They are useful animals but little more than a mindless, expendable source of protein encased in scales.

From a cynical overview, that might be true, but not from the microperspective that defined my own life. I hadn't been aboard the yacht nor had anyone shared a description of the fish. No matter.

These weren't ordinary sturgeon—as if there is anything ordinary about that implacable genus. With the exception of one beautiful woman, Viktor Kazlov was nobody's fool. Nor was Lien Bohai. If the Russian had risked transporting a cargo of live sturgeon from Mexico to Florida, it wasn't because he hoped to fool an aquaculture expert like his old rival. Not for long, anyway. The logistics alone were daunting. Kazlov's custom yacht probably had a motion stabilizer for rough seas, but he would have had to install oversized aquarium tanks below deck, plus an oxygen generator and a chiller to maintain water quality for the fish. It would have been a sound investment *only if* he actually had modified a beluga that could produce eggs dependably, profitably, and also thrive in the warmer water of the tropics.

No, the Dragos Voyager wasn't carrying just sturgeon. It was carrying the first generation of the caviar industry's future—and possibly the future of the beluga sturgeon itself.

After I had started the boat's engine and adjusted the thermal monocular over my eye, I said to Tomlinson, "You have Densler's cell phone, right?"

My pal stepped down from the dock, the boat's lines free. "Right here," he said. I could see his swollen eye in the iPhone's glow as he studied the screen. "No signal. But when I get one, she has the Neinabors in her recent calls—that was early yesterday. And a bunch to Markus Kahn. If we called, they'd think it was Winifred."

"The moment you can, try nine-one-one," I told him as I throttled the Whaler onto a laboriously slow plane. "Then call Kahn. Tell him he either helps us or he's going to die."

"You didn't learn anything from the way Sharon handled Winifred?"

As I searched for the first channel marker, I had to raise my voice over the sound of the engine. "On second thought, I'll call him. Tell the nine-one-one operator to contact the Fort Myers Beach Coast Guard. Maybe that helicopter can scare the twins into stopping. Or, at least, be on station to rescue survivors—if there are any survivors." I nodded to the northwest where the chopper, four miles away, was fanning the water with its searchlight.

After that, I stopped talking. The channel was narrow, the boat's steering was sloppy, and just making it out of the basin required my full attention. I hadn't switched on the Whaler's running lights, so I used the neon residual of the thermal unit to check the instrument panel once we were running flat. The boat's top speed was thirty-four hundred rpm—twenty miles an hour at best—and the engine began to cough and sputter when I tried to push it harder. That made us more than twice as fast as the Dragos, but I still made a silent vow to never, ever leave my own boat at home again.

At the entrance to the marina, I made a hard left and picked up a line of navigational markers that were spaced uniformly like fence posts and not much taller. Each was tipped with a reflective red triangle or a green rectangle that gleamed with thermal vision heat like Christmas ornaments. I kept the red markers to my left, or port, side. Stray too far to the left and we'd bounce hard aground in water not deep enough to cover the legs of night herons that spooked to flight as we passed.

To my right, a ridge of limestone tracked a ditch-straight line along the channel from which it had been dredged. If we veered off course, or the steering cable broke, those rocks would kill the boat and maybe us, too.

Tomlinson was aware of the hazards because he said, "I know the twins learned on the Caspian Sea, but they're fools if they think they can run these narrow channels at night without lights."

I hadn't mentioned the cheap Russian night vision that Geness

Neinabor was carrying. The optics were too poor to help much out here. At least, I hoped it was true, which is why I replied, "If they run aground—or I can force them out of the channel—we've got a chance. They're not going to fight, so they'll try to run."

When Tomlinson started to reply, I shushed him with my hand. I needed to think. Ahead, channel markers curved northwest where the night sky was fogged by the lights of Bonita Beach Club condominiums. Ultimately, though, the channel would turn west toward Big Carlos Pass, which was screened from view by the black undulations of mangrove islands. The Neinabor twins, and Kazlov's yacht, had to be somewhere on the other side of those islands.

"What time is it?" I yelled the question because I was frustrated and worried.

"We've got less than forty minutes."

"You have a signal yet?"

Tomlinson cupped the iPhone to his eyes, then said, "A T and T stands for 'abysmal third-rate tele-shit-the-fucking-bed-phone.' Some soup cans and a string would be better."

"But it's not jammed, is that what you're saying?"

Tomlinson shrugged, punched in three numbers, then pantomimed throwing the phone overboard. "I'm telling you, soup cans and a string."

I tapped my fist on the throttle and studied the unmarked water separating us from the last stretch of channel and islands that screened the Dragos from view.

"What are you thinking?" Tomlinson had one hand on the console as if trying to push the boat faster.

"What's the tide doing?"

When he heard that, the man understood exactly what I was thinking because he knows boats and water. "We're three days past the new moon. Low tide's around four a.m. So the sooner we leave the channel, the more water we'll have." He took a look over the side before adding, "Which won't be much."

Leaving the channel was risky and we both knew it. The west coast of Florida is a macrocosm of every leeward island in the subtropic world, just as every bay and sandbar is a microcosm of Florida's Gulf rim. On windward coasts, water drops abruptly into the descending troughs of open ocean. On leeward sides, though, water is shallow and tilts incrementally toward the sea. The bottom possesses the geography of a grass mesa, pocked by limestone implosions, guttered by currents, fissures and the wheel tracks of long-gone vessels that might have made it across the shallows but probably didn't.

Tomlinson asked me, "Have you ever run this flat before?"

Once, but that was years ago, so I shook my head and told him, "Get up on the bow, that'll help," then waited until he had scrambled forward before I turned the wheel, banking us out of the channel and into shallow water.

In my own skiff, I would have felt an instant buoyancy as the hull was lifted by turbulence echoing off the bottom only inches beneath. But my skiff was designed for backcountry passages, the Boston Whaler was not. It is a popular name brand that came into vogue after builders sawed a Whaler in two and discovered both pieces remained afloat. It was an effective PR gimmick for a craft that's built like a truck but also handles like a truck. The eighteen-foot Whaler has the esthetics of a Tupperware dish, with a bow as flat as an ax. Popular or not, it may be the heaviest, wettest, roughest-riding boat in its class, which is why I didn't feel much confidence as I cowboyed the beast across the flat.

From the bow, I heard Tomlinson yell, "It's getting thinner!"

The warning wasn't necessary. I could already feel the motor's skeg banging bottom, which caused the boat to jolt and surge as if the carburetor was sucking water, not gas. We were losing the speed required to maintain plane and I had to do something—either that or circle back to the channel.

I yelled, "Hang on!" then spun the wheel left so the boat heeled on its port chine, a maneuver that angled the propeller away from the bottom. A moment later, I spun the wheel right so that we rode our starboard chine. Zigzagging could help maintain our speed, but it would cost us too much time, so I studied the area ahead, searching for roils or a riverine chop that might signal deeper water.

Instead, I found something almost as good: a Styrofoam buoy that marked the location of a crab trap. In shallow areas, blue crab fishermen often set their traps in a line that follows the deepest water so wire cages won't be exposed at low tide. Unless the trap had been blown astray by a storm, I might find more.

I did. Tomlinson hooted and raised a fist when we raised a second crab buoy, then a third, each trap framed by an oil slick that proved it had been recently baited. One by one, I left the buoys rocking in our wake, as I followed a dozen more, the trapline traveling a scimitar arc that threaded between mangrove islands and would soon intersect with the channel to Vanderbilt Island.

"I got a signal, Doc!" When Tomlinson yelled the news, I made a shushing motion with my hand because, absurdly, I feared that if the twins had run aground they might hear us coming. Which was ridiculous because our outboard was as loud as a machine gun, and Tomlinson, with a finger plugged into an ear, had to yell to be heard by the 911 operator he was now talking to.

The wind sailed snatches of conversation past me, only some of it understood.

"In a boat, ma'am. Yes, a boat . . . Definitely life and death . . . No, I can't stay on the line. The Coast Guard, please . . . Right! And the sheriff's department, marine division . . ."

I tried to piece it together but then stopped because of something I saw a mile ahead: it was Kazlov's yacht. The vessel had a black angularity that set itself apart from the black water and it plowed a silver wake. The yacht had reached the final bend in the channel and was motoring northwest toward Big Carlos Pass, where, beyond, the Gulf of Mexico was a sparkling vacuum of space and Yucatán stars.

I was thinking about the electronics that a yacht of that quality would carry. It would have autopilot and a sophisticated GPS mapping system with all navigable channels precisely located. Use the touch screen to mark a destination and the autopilot would tractor the vessel precisely through every turn. No wonder the Neinabors had been able to negotiate so much shoal water without knocking the bottom out of the boat. Trapper had been right. The twins were smart but probably not savvy enough to realize that an unerring navigation system made their course unerringly predictable.

I looked northwest, toward Big Carlos Pass. Navigation lights that marked the main channel were robotic eyes, red, green and white, that blinked every four seconds. A red light, though, pulsed a two-second rhythm, alerting mariners that the intersection of two channels lay ahead. The yacht's autopilot would steer a rhumb line toward the light because in that triangulated spoil area, as I knew from experience, water outside the channel was only ankle-deep even at mid-tide.

Suddenly, I knew the best way to take the Dragos by surprise.

Careful not to turn so fast I'd throw Tomlinson off the bow, I banked northwest to leapfrog ahead of the yacht, throttle wide open. On my right, the shell pyramids of Mound Key traced a dinosaur's hump on the starscape. Ahead and a few degrees to starboard, Monkey Joe Key was a gray vacancy, trimmed like a hedge. Less than a minute later, when I was sure we were in deeper water, I backed the throttle until the boat began to buck on its own wake, then switched off the ignition and let the boat glide.

In the sudden silence, I could hear the diesel rumble of the Dragos Voyager as it plowed past us only three hundred yards away. The vessel rode at an abnormal angle, bow tilted so high it reminded me of an airplane frozen in takeoff—too much water in the hull.

Tomlinson, still on the phone, made no attempt to hide himself, but I crouched low. At that distance, it was unlikely the twins would see us. But, even if they did, a lone boat had materialized in front of them, not from behind as would be expected of a vessel giving chase.

As she passed, I used thermal vision to scan the yacht, which appeared to be shearing liquid sparks that were forged by engine heat and exhaust. Twice, I clicked the magnification button to zoom in. The flybridge was empty, but I could see two vaporous profiles, maybe three, in the steering room near the helm, images blurred. On the afterdeck were two people, both probably male.

Kahn and Trapper were aboard. Possibly Umeko, too, but I still couldn't be sure there were five people. If I had seen the woman, she was standing, which meant her legs weren't bound.

Good.

Tomlinson, in a normal voice, was just finishing with the 911 operator, saying, "Tell the Coast Guard pilot to steer directly for Big Carlos Pass. We'll flash our running lights." Then he looked at me, asking, "What's the number of the closest marker?"

I focused the monocular, then held a fist away from my face to gauge the distance. "Green marker number nine, maybe a quarter mile northwest."

When Tomlinson was done, I checked the time, then said, "Give me the phone."

It was 2:30 a.m.

25

When Kahn answered, I said, "Don't talk, just listen. You've got thirty minutes to live. Got that? Thirty minutes—unless we get you off that boat. I can help if you cooperate."

It took Kahn a long second to react, but he finally did, saying, "*You?* What do you want?"

"Do the twins think you're talking to Densler? Don't do anything stupid, just answer the question."

He said, "Her picture came up, so, yeah—" then his tone changed when he finally figured out what was happening. "Oh . . . *Winifred*. I understand now. I couldn't, uhh . . . I couldn't hear what you were saying at first."

The man sounded shaky and out of breath, which told me he was scared.

I said, "Is someone holding a gun on you?"

"Uhh . . . no. Geness decided we should take the sturgeon out and release them. So . . . so that's what we're doing. Uhh . . . letting the fish go. Maybe rescue those dolphins, too."

I wondered if Kahn actually believed that.

In the background, Odus was yelling, "How'd the bitch get a call out?" as I asked Kahn, "Is the Chinese woman with you?"

"*Yes* . . . uhh . . . I think it's a good idea myself. About the fish, I mean. But I really can't talk right now, we have to go under a bridge pretty soon."

Holding the phone to my ear, I started the Whaler's engine and took a look. We were only three hundred yards off the vessel's stern quarter, and Big Carlos Pass bridge was still almost two miles away.

At the southern lip of the pass stood the high-rise condos of Bare Key Regency and Casino, the lights an aggressive checkerboard of neon blues and greens. Kahn had just told me they would soon go under the bridge, but it was possible the twins had lied to him. Maybe they actually planned to detonate their bomb near the casino's dolphin pens. If true, it was still possible they could make it by three a.m. because the casino was closer.

Whatever their destination, the yacht would soon have to turn sharply north, a switchback that would cause it to pass within a hundred yards of the Whaler. Because the Dragos was so much heavier, it couldn't have made it across the shallow delta where we now waited. I knew that the autopilot would follow the channel every foot of the way.

I told Kahn, "No matter what the twins say, don't hang up. I'm trying to save your life. Understand?"

"I . . . I'm beginning to."

"Are they running low on ammunition? I need to know."

"They were just saying . . ." The man hesitated. "I heard that, too—just a few minutes ago. I'm hoping it's true."

Kahn had overheard the twins talking, apparently.

"Are they out?"

"No! No . . . uhh, definitely not. Look, Winifred, I don't know how many fish we have."

"Fish" equaled "cartridges." Kahn was trying to help, which told me he definitely wanted off that boat.

I put the Whaler in gear and started idling across the shallows toward the section of channel where the yacht would pass closest. "Can you move freely around the boat?"

"Uhh . . . well, yeah. Not entirely, but pretty much."

What did that mean?

In the background, Odus was now shouting, "I told you to hang up that goddamn thing, asswipe!" which caused Kahn's voice to change when he said, "I wish I could help but I really have to go—"

I cut him off, saying, "*Listen* to me—you're going to die, anyway. Twenty-nine minutes, that's all you have. But it doesn't have to happen."

I could hear Kahn arguing with Odus, telling him Densler was worried, so what was the big deal? Then he said into the phone, "I've got to hang up soon, so make it fast."

Through the monocular, I could see a person scrambling up the ladder from the yacht's afterdeck, as I said, "The Super Mario bag the twins are carrying, I think there's a bomb in it."

Kahn whispered something that sounded like *"Oh my God"* while I continued talking. "It's set to go off at three a.m. But now they can probably detonate the thing with a remote because we're out of jamming range. Which means, anytime they want, that boat will become a fireball. Are you with me so far?"

Kahn made a coughing noise. "I'm sorry to . . . uhh . . . to hear that, Winifred. Yeah, I'm definitely listening."

I wanted to tell him to stop using the woman's name so often—it was a dead giveaway, but I couldn't waste the time. "Get Umeko, get your partner, then think up some excuse to go to the back of the boat. Tell the twins you want to look at the stars or something. Can you do that?"

Voice suddenly louder, Kahn surprised me by saying, "A . . . a meteorite shower, huh? That's pretty cool, Winifred. Yeah, there's a big open deck. Trapper'd probably like to see it, too."

The guy was a terrible actor, but I said, "Good. Okay, don't answer, just listen. In less than two minutes, you're going to hear something hit the hull of your boat. It'll sound like a sledgehammer. The moment you hear it, jump overboard. All three of you. Less than two minutes from now, so you've got to move fast. Make sure Umeko is with you. She has to be with you."

In the background, Odus was now screaming at Kahn, so I raised my voice and kept talking. "Jump overboard, you hear me? Don't hesitate or you're going to die. Swim to the edge of the channel—water's only a foot or two deep there. You'll be able to stand up, so keep your shoes on. A boat will be there a few minutes later. But make sure the girl's with you or we won't stop."

Kahn sounded dazed when he replied, "Are you absolutely sure that's true?"

Phone wedged against my ear, I nudged the throttle forward so the boat would flatten itself in the light chop, a more responsive idle speed. "Your only other option is to throw that backpack overboard. Do you know where it is?" Which is when Kahn made a yelping sound of pain as if he'd been slapped, so I focused the monocular to see what was happening.

A few seconds later, a man appeared at the steering-room door while the autopilot turned the yacht northward as I knew it would. At the same instant, Geness Neinabor's monster voice caused the phone to vibrate against my cheek.

"You neurotic old bitch!" he shouted. "Talk to me, Winnie! It's about time we met."

I put my hand over the mouthpiece, wondering if the man would keep talking if Densler didn't respond. He did.

"If you hadn't passed out, we'd have brought you along. As if God cares about drunken sluts! I can feel you listening, old woman. So listen to this!"

Through the lens, I watched the most dangerous twin step out onto the deck and draw his arm back. By the time he'd launched the phone into the air, I had the bow of the Whaler pointing at the yacht and had picked up the rifle.

"Take the wheel," I said to Tomlinson. "Keep idling toward them, keep the chop off our stern." Then I slid down the bench seat so we could change places before sharing the little bit I'd just learned from Markus Kahn.

When I'd finished, Tomlinson said, "But why the rifle? You're not going to shoot anyone, right? I was pissed off at that lunatic earlier, but I didn't really mean it. I can't take part in killing a person, Marion, I just can't."

I used a look to remind my pal of what had happened at Armanie's house earlier, then removed my glasses so I could use the scope. "We need a diversion so they have time to jump," I explained, fitting my left arm through the rifle's sling. "And maybe scare the twins into switching off that autopilot. If they don't jump, we might have to force that big bastard aground. Which will be tough enough without fighting a robot at the wheel."

"They'll jump," Tomlinson said. "They're idiots if they don't jump. After that, all we have to do is pick them up, right? We're done chasing the Diablo triplets, right?" The man was amped up, jittery, but he was doing okay.

I rested the rifle's forearm on the windshield frame and popped open the scope's lens caps. "We're getting as far from Kazlov's yacht as we can, once they're out of the water. I'd like to save those fish, but it's not worth the risk. Umeko, she's the one I'm worried about.

I think they're watching her a lot closer than the two guys. Or maybe her hands are still tied. Something's wrong, I'm not sure what."

The rifle scope had an illuminator switch, I discovered. When I touched it, the crosshairs became two intersecting filaments, ruby red, that I tried to steady amidships on the yacht's hull less than three hundred yards away, its bow visible as it angled toward us. The optics made the yacht appear ten times larger, but they also magnified the sea conditions as well as the hobbyhorse rocking of the Whaler. I've never been seasick in my life, but I felt mildly dizzy when I looked through the scope for more than a few seconds.

"Don't worry about me trying to snipe one of the twins," I told Tomlinson. "I'll be lucky to hit the damn boat."

The man had no idea what I was talking about, so laughed, "Sure, Annie Oakley, sure," as if I were kidding.

I wasn't.

He was looking over his shoulder to the north. "Oh, man, that *really* sucks. The chopper's moving away from us, not getting closer. Maybe I should try to call the Coast Guard myself."

I got to my feet. "Stand by," I told him because I had switched to thermal vision and could see movement on the yacht. Two people appeared outside the steering-room bulkhead . . . stood there briefly as if looking at the sky . . . then climbed down the ladder to the aft deck.

"Kahn and the other guy are out," I told Tomlinson. "They're both too tall to be Umeko."

"So you can't shoot, right? There's no point in shooting if she's not free. Where's the girl?"

"Stop leaning on the throttle," I told him. "Just keep us flat . . . flat and steady." With my thumb, I disengaged the rifle's safety but continued to watch through the TAM.

The yacht was closing on us at an angle that gave me a better view of the helm area. There was at least one person inside the cabin, maybe two, but the autopilot was still steering the boat because there was no one at the wheel.

Belowdecks, the heat signatures of the diesel engines radiated through the hull, making it impossible to know if anyone was in the forward area where there would be sleeping quarters. The sturgeon were probably stowed aft where I'd seen a cargo elevator, which meant I wanted to hit the vessel somewhere amidships—but there could be sleeping quarters there, too. If I pulled the trigger now, the odds of me hitting the boat were fair, the odds of me hitting an unseen passenger astronomical, but just the thought of it made me cringe.

"Shit," I said. "Where is she?"

Tomlinson told me, "Beta waves can pierce a boat's hull like butter—I've done it before," then began whispering, "Get your butt out of there, lady. Come on out, you little China doll," repeating it over and over as if he were at a racetrack and horses were coming down the stretch. But then he stopped and said, "Doc. About twenty-five minutes. We've only got—"

"Quiet," I told him. A third person had appeared on the upper deck. Not a tall person, so it might have been Umeko, but possibly one of the twins. At that distance, I couldn't differentiate between female and male.

"What's going on? What do you see?"

"Quiet," I said again. "After I fire, get ready to change places fast. I want you down on the deck. Stay low in case we hit something when we cross that flat."

"Bullshit, you're worried the Diablo brothers will start shooting at us."

I *wanted* the twins to take a few wild shots at us—they were low on ammunition—but I didn't respond. The third person had grabbed a handhold and was looking down at the afterdeck as if conversing with Kahn and Trapper. If it was Umeko, her hands weren't tied, which caused me to suspect it was one of the twins. Odus, probably. But then I changed my mind when the third person swung down the ladder, moving fast. Why would Odus leave his brother alone to join two guys who had tormented and bullied him until tonight?

"I think she's out," I said, getting a tight wrap around the leather sling. "I'm not sure, but I think so."

Now Tomlinson was whispering, "Jump and swim, jump and swim, jump and swim your radical asses off."

"Keep us steady," I told him. Bracing my knees against the console, my cheek and left hand pinning the rifle to the windshield, I got ready to fire . . . but then checked the cabin one last time—and was glad I did. Instead of one heat signature near the helm, there were now . . . two? I couldn't be certain, but it looked like one person standing, one sitting. If true, there was no longer a chance of hitting Umeko when my bullet punched through the hull. *If* I hit the boat.

Index finger riding parallel the trigger guard, I put my eye to the scope. Instantly, I was isolated in a tunneled world of amplified light and motion that the luminous crosshairs struggled to convert into quadrants. At first, I couldn't even find the damn yacht, let alone focus on it. But then I realized the vessel's black hull, two hundred yards away, had flooded the lens with a darkness that I wrongly interpreted as water or night sky.

I lifted my head from the lens, blinked the dizziness away, then tried again.

Breath control and focus—components of a clean kill. As the Whaler moved over the bottom, my lungs tried to find the rhythm of our boat's slow-motion greyhounding. I kept the rifle still and allowed each passing wave to drop the scope onto a bow section of the Dragos. The crosshairs would pause momentarily at the yacht's waterline, then rocket skyward again. But the timing was unpredictable. The yacht filled the circumference of my eye, riding and wallowing bow-high while our own boat slapped water, the wind swirling a mix of salt spray and exhaust fumes from behind.

"A little more throttle," I told Tomlinson. "A little more . . . there—*good*."

A scope with a gyro stabilizer is what a shooter would have been issued for an offshore mission like this. But even if I was properly equipped, my confidence would have only been proportional to my skills. I'm an adequate marksman with a long gun but not in the same league with those elite snipers who tune their weapons like instruments, then tap their targets from a mile away.

One thing I can do, though, is pull the trigger when I choose.

When the front of the Whaler lifted toward the stars, I began to exhale evenly, anticipating the inevitable descent. My index finger had found the steel scimitar that linked brain and firing pin, so when the Whaler paused at star level I was already applying a fixed pressure. First, the yacht's flybridge soared into view . . . then an electronic forest of antennas . . . then, in blurry slow motion, the forward windows of the steering room . . . the cabin . . . the starboard rails . . .

That's when I fired—*BOOM*—squeezing the trigger just before the crosshairs touched the yacht's hull. Like a quarterback throwing to a receiver, I'd tried to anticipate where two objects in motion would precisely intersect.

How precisely, though, I didn't have a damn clue.

Immediately, I lowered the TAM-14 over my left eye while, beside me, Tomlinson rubbed at his ears. "Shit-oh-dear, that was loud!"

Not really. At sea, a gunshot rings like a hammer hitting stone but is instantly dispersed, so it doesn't echo in the ears or the conscience. Drowned by the yacht's engines and air-conditioning, it was unlikely the twins had even noticed my muted report.

"You didn't kill anybody, did you?" Tomlinson's head was pivoting from me to the yacht, which was still coming toward us, plowing an eight-foot wake. "You'd tell me if you killed somebody, right?"

I said, "Hang on, I'm trying to see what's happening." Scanning the Dragos, I ejected the brass casing, shucked in a fresh round but didn't lock the bolt because I couldn't look to confirm the safety was engaged.

"Those little pricks, I'll follow them to hell if they've made me a party to murder. Doc, you *would* tell me."

Without turning, I pressed the rifle into his hands. "Hang on to this. You've overestimated my shooting skills, pal, so stop worrying." Then I said, "Hey—you see that?"

Yes, Tomlinson saw it. "Someone turned on the cabin lights!"

A lot more than that was happening. The three people on the yacht's afterdeck were moving erratically, one of them making wild arm gestures before turning and racing up the ladder toward the steering room. When I saw that, I felt a sickening tightness in my gut. It had to be one of the twins.

I banged the console with my fist. "Son of a bitch. I screwed up again."

"What's wrong, man? The lights prove you hit their boat, right? Good shooting!"

"Umeko's still in the cabin. No! Christ, there's only one person in the cabin, not two. I was wrong!"

"She has to be aboard somewhere, we'll go after her. We still have time. Maybe run them aground, like you—"

I put my hand on Tomlinson's arm to quiet him, and said, "Switch spots, I'm taking the wheel."

I was watching a person on the afterdeck—Kahn, probably—climb over the transom, then drop down onto the swim platform. Trapper hesitated for several seconds but then followed.

I told Tomlinson, "Grab something! Stay low," then pushed the throttle forward.

By the time both men had cannonballed into the darkness, we were banging across the shallows on a collision course as the yacht made its final turn toward the bridge . . . or the dolphin pool at the casino.

26

As we closed within fifty yards of the Dragos, the Neinabors still hadn't discovered that Kahn and Trapper were gone nor had they seen us—but they would. It was inevitable. It had been under two minutes since a bullet had slammed into their hull and they would soon recover from their surprise.

As of yet, though, nothing had changed. The yacht hadn't slowed its wallowing pace and it was still on autopilot, although we could look into the lighted cabin and see the brothers standing near the wheel. They were more concerned with the helicopter than some phantom boat. I could tell by the way they paused every few seconds to use binoculars. I also got the impression they were arguing while they studied the boat's electronics, trying to figure out what had made that sledgehammer sound.

It was just a guess. I was too busy steering the Whaler to give them my full attention. And I was also keeping an eye on the progress of Markus Kahn and his partner. It was so dark, the two men were invisible specks, even when I swooped in close enough to yell, "We'll be back!" but their heat signatures confirmed they heard me. They were already standing in knee-deep water, waving their arms and shouting words that faded as we left them behind.

"They're okay!" I told Tomlinson. He was on the bench seat beside me, the rifle in one hand, the other white-knuckled as he clung to the console to keep from bouncing out of his seat. It was because of the yacht's rolling eight-foot wake. The closer we got, the larger the waves.

My friend nodded, but his eyes were locked on the cabin. "I still don't see her. Are you sure she was up there?"

He meant Umeko and he was right: the girl was no longer visible inside the steering room. Maybe the twins had sent her below or told her to lie down—or possibly had done something worse.

I didn't reply. The seconds were ticking away; I felt a palpable pounding inside my head yet I was now wondering about the three a.m. deadline. I had warned Kahn about the twins using a wireless detonator, but the significance of my own words hadn't hit me until now. Maybe because I wanted to believe it, my brain was piecing together evidence that the deadline no longer mattered.

No . . . it was more than just wistful thinking. My suspicions had substance. From the moment I'd realized the twins were carrying a second explosive device, I had believed a mechanical engineer would build a dual triggering system. The importance of redundancy systems is a tenet of the profession. If something happened to the Neinabors, a clock would close the circuit and detonate the explosives at three a.m. If not, they could martyr themselves whenever they wanted.

But did that guarantee the clock could be disengaged?

As I watched one of the twins reaching for the cabin door, I had to admit the truth. Nope. There was no guarantee that I was even right about a dual detonator. Yet if I was wrong, the way the twins were behaving made no sense. With only minutes to live, they wouldn't bother to check on the helicopter—which the second twin was now doing—nor would they care about what had slammed into the boat they'd stolen. A pair of psychotics who wanted to vaporize themselves would be outside on the flybridge, closer to heaven, praying to God for a painless passage.

It turned out, Tomlinson was thinking the same thing. Sort of.

We were approaching the yacht from the aft starboard quarter, close enough now I had to finesse the Whaler through troughs of waves. Make one small mistake, the wake would pitchpole our boat end over end or dump us sideways. Without taking my eyes off the cabin, I leaned and asked, "How much time?" but kept my voice low.

The man checked his Bathys dive watch, then cupped his mouth to talk. "It's not looking good, Doc."

Apparently, he didn't want to scare me by saying.

I insisted by motioning with my hand.

He stood so he didn't have to yell. "About twenty minutes. But I've been watching those two. From the way they're acting, they're more worried about getting caught than dying. I'm starting to think there is no goddamn bomb."

I was putting the TAM and the pistol inside the console as I told him, "Maybe, but we can't risk it. At five till three, we're pulling the plug. No matter what, understand? Keep an eye on the time." Then I banged the locker door closed, saying, *"Grab something,"* and throttled the Whaler up the back of a wave . . . surfed momentarily . . . turned away from the yacht and finally broke through into a starry plateau ahead of the wake. When we were clear, I banked the Whaler to port, running side by side for several seconds, then angled southwest. Now we were on a collision course with the Dragos, heading for cleaner water that glanced off the yacht's hull amidships.

"Damn, man, if they look out the window now, they'll see us!"

Tomlinson was crouched low for balance, looking up at the vessel's glowing superstructure, seeing stainless steel and a wall of maritime glass. Inside the steering room, one of the twins was clearly visible, twelve feet above us, and only twenty yards away.

Then he said, "Doc? *Marion*—Jesus Christ, you're going to ram her!" because we were still greyhounding toward the vessel and would soon T-bone just above the waterline unless I changed course.

The noise of the diesels, of displaced water and of our own engine was so loud, I barely heard him. And I was concentrating too hard to respond or even glance up at the cabin. I'd known that we risked being seen during the brief time our two boats ran side by side. That's why I wanted to shrink the distance so the yacht's own girth would cloak us. It required us to motor so close to the Dragos that I waited until I sensed the flair of the upper deck looming overhead before I turned sharply to starboard.

For a couple of seconds, I continued at high speed, the two vessels running parallel, but then backed the throttle as we neared the yacht's bow. The abrupt deceleration caused the Whaler to rear like a wild horse, but then our hull teetered forward as I experimented with the throttle, trying to match the yacht's speed. I didn't want to pass the boat. I had something else in mind.

Beside me, Tomlinson said something that sounded like *"Wowie-fuckin'-zowieee"* to signal his relief but kept his voice low because we were keeping pace with the yacht, near enough to reach up and grab a railing if one of us was willing to climb onto the Whaler's console and give it a try.

I was willing. In fact, that had been my original hope—to board surreptitiously and take the vessel by surprise and force. It had seemed so unlikely, though, that we could get this close without being seen, I'd abandoned the idea in favor of trying to drive the Dragos aground. But now, here we were.

I gave myself a few seconds to think about it as I battled to hold our boat parallel, which was a job in itself. We were in flat water, ahead of the wake, but the yacht displaced tons of water that boiled from beneath the hull. It created a pressurized ridge that, alternately, tried to fling us away or suck us astern into a whirlpool created by two massive propellers.

Dealing with the twins, however, was a more perilous vortex. Something I hadn't considered earlier was the dangers associated with a wireless detonator. Surprise the twins and they might turn the yacht into an inferno with the touch of a button. That alone was enough to convince me it was safer to attempt to force the yacht aground—not easy but possible.

The Dragos was thirty times heavier than the Whaler, but she was riding bow-high, which meant she was also bow-light. In combat driving courses—I've taken several—operators learn to use their car like a weapon. To pierce a roadblock, you steer for the enemy's rear wheels and transfer the brunt of the impact to their vehicle by continuing to accelerate until you've punched through. The skill is counterintuitive, but I knew from experience that slowing after impact is suicide. That didn't mean you collided with a vehicle—or a boat—at top speed. That, too, was suicidal. It meant you approached at a low speed, *then* accelerated.

Hit the behemoth at the bow at the correct angle, then force myself to use the throttle—do it right and it was possible to turn the vessel enough so that it grounded itself in waist-deep water. Maybe less water, depending on how hard the diesel engines continued tractoring forward. The job would be easier, of course, if the damn steering computer didn't automatically fight me by trying to compensate—which it would—but I was going to by God give it a shot, anyway.

Yes, it was definitely doable. I might have to ram the boat two or three times to knock it off course, but so what? Once the Dragos was grounded, the twins would either detonate their bomb or they would try to escape through the shallows. They were cowards, not fighters, and the rest was up to them. After that, I had zero control, which I understood, but I couldn't just stand by and do nothing while Umeko Tao-Lien died.

I took a quick look around to get my bearings. The channel was wide here, but the autopilot was running precise lines, marker to marker, which put the yacht only a boat length from the shallows on her port side, which faced south. If I was going to ram, now was the time to do it.

As I turned away to create some distance, though, Tomlinson confused me by saying, "Doc . . . hey! She's coming this way." With a glance, I confirmed that he meant the helicopter. But then he said, "Shit! He sees us! Get down!"

Which was nonsensical. The chopper pilot couldn't make out details from four miles away. Even if he did, why should we hide?

When I followed Tomlinson's wide-eyed gaze to the yacht, though, I understood. One of the twins was staring down at us, his face pressed to the window. There was enough peripheral light from the cabin to recognize us, apparently, because he slammed a pistol against the glass, but it wouldn't break. He tried twice more before he shouted something over his shoulder, then disappeared.

"Get down on the deck," I yelled to Tomlinson. I shoved the throttle forward and spun the wheel to the right. "Brace your feet against the casting deck."

"We're ramming her?" The man was smiling for some reason.

"Just do it, damn it!" I was busy watching the yacht over my shoulder, gauging the distance that separated us. Seconds later, I spun the wheel to port, feeling the Whaler sideslip wildly as the engine cavitated. Finally, the starboard chine caught and flattened us. When our propeller found purchase and we began to regain speed, I used the Whaler's bow chock like a rifle sight, holding it steady on the sleek black hull.

Tomlinson, I realized, hadn't budged. "Get your ass on the deck! You'll go overboard when we hit!"

My pal took a look at the helicopter, which had slowed to use its searchlight, then shook his head, now grinning like a madman. "I've always wanted to sink one of those stinkpots, oversized cock prosthetics! No way, man!"

27

Just before our boat gouged a hole in Viktor Kazlov's million-dollar yacht, one of the twins materialized at the foredeck rail, then a spotlight blinded me.

Tomlinson yelled, "That lunatic's shooting at us again!" and tried to hide from the red laser beam by ducking beside the console. His voice was loud over the wind and grinding diesels, but the gunshots touched my ears as distant firecrackers, a series of three, then one more.

Even at close range, the chances of a novice hitting a moving target from a moving platform were negligible, but it was still a tight-sphinctered few seconds. And the timing couldn't have been worse.

During our starboard approach, I had backed the throttle to a moderate speed, just as I'd learned on a Langley driving course. I wanted to hit the yacht at an angle that would cause us to ricochet toward the rear of the vessel, so I could circle away and ram it again. I suspected it would take a couple of tries to knock the beast into the shallows, just as I also knew that if we caromed forward we might be trapped under the yacht's bow, then cut to pieces by the pair of bronze propellers.

When the spotlight blinded me, though, I lost all orientation. But it was too late to stop our momentum, and I had already experienced the skull-jarring effects of a decelerating collision. So I hammered the throttle forward and steered from memory as the Whaler lunged for several yards, then slammed into thirty tons of wood and steel.

I was prepared for the impact but not an implosion of paint and wood—and then a man's howl as one of the Neinabors was catapulted over the railing into the water. Even so, I kept the throttle buried, expecting to be jettisoned away from the vessel at any moment.

It didn't happen.

Not until Tomlinson shouted something and scampered forward, then began pounding at the yacht's hull, did I understand. The Whaler's bow, which was flat as a hatchet, had pierced the yacht's skin between the carlings and had lodged there. Now we were being dragged at an angle that would soon either swamp us or dump us out of the boat.

As the Whaler listed sideways, Tomlinson grabbed the port rail. When I lunged for it, too, my feet went out from under me, which somehow wedged me between the seat and the steering console. It's the only thing that saved me from going into the water. For several seconds, it seemed, I hung there, my ability to move numbed by the debilitating sound of engines, water and splintering wood.

When the brain is overwhelmed by a series of rapid events, it sometimes defaults into a lull of simplified awareness. It was dark, but I was conscious of the vascularity of my own forearm as it strained to hold me. The fumes of a two-cycle outboard are distinctive, a soup of gas and oil, so I knew the engine was still running. That was good. If we had power, we still had options—as long as the prop remained in the water.

I got a hand on the throttle and pulled it into high-speed reverse. Behind me, the outboard bucked and screamed, yet the Whaler's port side continued to ascend at an impossible angle. So I slammed the throttle forward. Maybe a sudden seesaw thrust would do some good.

It did. Instantly, I felt a jolt, accompanied by a wrenching sound of wood being torn from fiberglass. Then the bow of the Whaler dropped several feet and slammed hard on the water, which caused me to lose my grip on the throttle. With no one at the wheel and the engine racing, our boat slammed into the Dragos again, then began a series of smaller collisions as it tracked its way blindly toward the front of the yacht. By the time I was on my feet, we were almost under the vessel's bowsprit and would soon be crushed by the hull and probably suctioned into its propellers.

Tomlinson was on his knees, arms outthrust, trying to fend off as he yelled, "You okay?"

I told him, "Pull your hands in!" while, simultaneously, I grabbed the wheel and slammed the engine into reverse, which spun us toward the rear of the vessel, then safely away.

No . . . not safely because a massive spotlight mounted on the bridge found us, then I heard the keen of displaced air molecules that signals the trajectory of a bullet passing close to the ear. An instant later, the muted reports of a handgun reached me, three . . four . . . five rounds. Instead of slowing to retrieve his brother from the water, the remaining twin was shooting at us while the vessel continued on its robotic course toward the Regency Hotel.

It's Geness, I thought. *Or Odus doesn't know his brother went over.*

Tomlinson also realized we were taking fire because he pressed himself against the casting platform and yelled, "Get us out of here!"

I did. Crouched behind the steering console, I turned north toward the helicopter, hoping it would remind Neinabor that the Coast Guard was after them, too.

The copter was still using its searchlight, now in the area where Trapper and Kahn had jumped, so maybe the men had been found. Even so, the remaining twin got the message. Soon, the spotlight went out, the cabin went dark, so I circled back into the slow lift and fall of the yacht's wake and was soon gaining on it—but not as fast as we should have because the Whaler's deck was awash with water.

I called, "Take the wheel!" but Tomlinson waved me off, saying, "I'll do it!" understanding instantly what needed to be done to drain the boat. He knelt near the outboard, reached into the transom well and unplugged the bottom scupper, which lay below the waterline. Like ramming a car off the road, it was another counterintuitive move—when a vessel's swamped, you *open* the transom to the sea, then accelerate until the propeller wash has suctioned the hull dry.

When the water was gone and we were through the chop, I retrieved the Smith & Wesson, then the TAM unit, from the storage locker. The pistol I wedged between steering console and windshield, then fitted the monocular over my left eye.

"Do you see the twin? We've got to find him!" Tomlinson's head was pivoting as he scanned the water. "Slow down, I can't see a damn thing!"

Yes, I saw the twin—his heat signature, anyway. His head was a lucent white orb thirty yards away and his hands slapped the water like a dog that had never swam before.

Shit.

I yelled, "How much time do we have?" I wanted to continue after the Dragos. Collectively, the Neinabors had just fired ten or twelve rounds at us, so maybe they were out of ammunition.

Tomlinson knew what I had in mind. "We can't go off and leave him, for Christ's sake! Do you think he went under?"

I checked my watch. We had less than fifteen minutes—ten if I stuck to what I'd told Tomlinson about pulling out.

Loud enough for the twin to hear, I said, "All he has to do is swim out of the damn channel! Then he can stand up!"

Tomlinson wouldn't have it. "He can't be far, man, we can't let him drown. Goddamn it, Doc, do you see him or not?"

I veered to the left and backed the throttle until the Whaler dropped off plane. Soon, I could hear Neinabor alternately swearing and screaming for help. He sounded hysterical, yelling, "*Please*, over here! Dying . . . don't let me die!" Then he gagged and began to either choke or sob, I couldn't tell.

When we were a boat length away, I called, "Close your mouth and breathe through your nose." Then I shifted into neutral and swung the stern so it glided toward him.

Before I could get to the twin, though, Tomlinson did something very un-Tomlinson-like. He slipped past the steering console, grabbed Neinabor by the hair and hollered, "You tried to shoot me, you evil little troll! Give me one reason we shouldn't drown your bipolar ass!"

I put my hand on the man's shoulder and said, "I like the way you think, but we don't have time right now. Okay?" Ahead of us, I could see the animate darkness of the yacht only a hundred yards away. The remaining twin was escaping but at slow-motion speed.

My pal held up an index finger, which meant he knew what he was doing. To Neinabor, he said, "You're going to answer our questions. What your brother is doing is wrong and you by God know it!"

The twin nodded eagerly, then grabbed the boat's gunnel when Tomlinson finally released him. When he did, I took Neinabor's wrists with crossed arms and lifted him aboard, which caused his butt to spin toward the boat. He was sitting with his back to me when I asked, "Do you still have the gun?" I was looking to the southeast, where the helicopter had dipped its nose but was still hovering—yes, they had found Kahn and Trapper.

The twin's teeth were chattering out of fear because the night air still radiated midday heat. "No, no gun. I swear. I don't know what happened . . . then Geness left me and . . . and all those sharks—"

Just because he claimed he was Odus didn't guarantee it was true. I cut in, "Stop talking. Just nod or shake your head. Understand?"

No response, which was okay because the twin was thinking about it. I wanted to save time, but it was also an interrogation technique. If allowed to respond silently, subjects will sometimes share secrets they have sworn not to reveal verbally. It provides them a moral loophole.

I tried again. "Is the girl still alive?"

The man nodded—*Yes*—but also began to cry.

I patted the pockets of his soggy shorts, checking for weapons, then returned to the controls, asking, "Is there a bomb aboard?"

Once again, Neinabor nodded, then turned to look at me. "But I didn't want it to do it! All I want is to save those fish, but Abraham doesn't think—" He lost the words and continued bawling.

That was all I needed to know—for now, anyway. I punched the Whaler into gear, telling Tomlinson, "Put him on the seat between us. If he lies even once, or tries to interfere, I'll throw him overboard." Then, because we might need a bad cop, I added, "You saved his ass once. I won't let you save him twice."

I took another look at the chopper—it was still hovering over Kahn and Trapper—then levered the throttle, accelerating toward the Dragos Voyager.

28

The twin we'd rescued actually was Odus Neinabor. I knew from his manic behavior as we questioned him: aggressive and rambling one moment, then wailing a confession the next. Because I'd caught him in an early lie, though, I trusted nothing he said.

We were closing on the yacht fast, the outboard was noisy, so I fed my questions through Tomlinson. When Odus yelled, "Even Abraham wouldn't hit a woman, you asswipe—and he hates the whole worthless race!" I was tempted to lift the guy out of his seat and lob him into our propeller stream.

Darius Talas had had no reason to deceive me when he'd described what Geness had done to Umeko. Geness had tied the woman, which was despicable in itself, but then he'd also assaulted her while she was defenseless.

"I think the twins were afraid she'd fight back," Talas had told me, or something close to that.

Instead of reacting, though, I feigned indifference. We needed a lot of information in a hurry and harsh words or a pointed accusation might catalyze another crying jag. So I listened and concentrated on what was transpiring around us.

A lot was happening fast.

Behind us, the helicopter had finally locked onto our position and was rocketing toward us. It wasn't one of the big Seahawks, a flying platform of electronics. The craft was the smaller medevac variety—an Augusta Stingray, I guessed. So they had probably used search radar or forward-looking infrared to find us. Something else, I suspected: the small search crew had no reason to carry firearms.

But the chopper had definitely received our call for help. We knew because someone aboard the craft had called Densler's cell phone, but Tomlinson hadn't heard the damn thing ringing. Then, when he'd called back, he couldn't be sure how much the crewman had understood because reception was poor and there was a hell of a lot of racket on both ends. Even so, the chopper was three miles away and closing at low level.

Ahead of us, on the yacht, I kept an eye on Geness Neinabor by using my own TAM system. The most dangerous twin had left the steering room, binoculars around his neck, and was watching the chopper descend on him, although our boat would be visible, too. His erratic movements told me he was scared and undecided about what to do next.

He resembled a trapped animal. As if chained to a post, Geness paced the deck, back and forth, indifferent to the autopilot's course, peering out from the sinking boat that had become his cage.

The analogy was disturbing. It caused me to admit I might be wrong in at least one of my assumptions. The twins were cowards, they'd proven it over and over. Which is why I'd been so sure they would either surrender or run once we got them stopped. But trapped animals can't run. So they fight . . . and keep fighting until they escape or they die.

Geness Neinabor, even with all the bullying he'd endured in his life, had never experienced a more suffocating trap than now. The man was armed, he was desperate. There was a very good chance he would fight—or, at the very least, try to take a lot of people with him when died.

The realization caused me to wonder if it might be wiser to back off, apply loose cover and hope the chopper could make contact with the twin by VHF radio. Get a hostage negotiator on the line, maybe, and pipe his voice through the aircraft's booming PA system. As crazy as Geness was, maybe he would believe it was the voice of God.

A nice idea but not practical. Trouble was, it was now ten till three and Odus had told us very little that was useful about their homemade explosive. The bomb did exist and it was aboard the yacht. He and Genesis had made the thing in California, packed it in a waterproof bag, and they had carried it onto the island in a backpack Odus had used since childhood.

"A Super Mario backpack!" he had told us. "My brother and I kicked ass at all the Mario tournaments when the game first came out. Not Mario One—that version sucked. The classic Mario Two, I'm talking about."

We had to have more details, but Odus's self-obsessive rambling was driving me crazy.

I had been standing at the wheel but now sat and put my hand on the twin's shoulder. Not hard, not threatening. I wanted to create a physical connection. Odus shrugged my hand away, though, and snapped, "Hands off! I hate when people touch me!"

I stayed calm, kept my eyes on Geness and decided to use the interrogation strategy that had worked earlier—and also employ a familiar word Odus might find disarming. "I won't ask you to snitch on your brothers. But I want to save those sturgeon, too. So don't talk, just nod—or shake your head. You're not actually *telling* me anything."

Ahead, Genesis was using the binoculars again, focusing on the chopper, as I asked, "The bomb—did you wire it with a redundancy detonator system?"

Odus gave me a sharp look, surprised I understood anything about explosives. It took him a second, then he finally nodded.

That was encouraging.

I asked, "Has the clock detonator been disengaged? It's almost three. Not much time to save those sturgeon—or your brother."

The twin shrugged and spoke. "The dolphin slavers, Abraham hates them, too. So maybe he'll use the"—Odus took a look at the lights of Bare Key Regency, only a mile away, then finished—"Yeah, at the speed we're going, he'll probably use the remote."

Until then, I hadn't noticed the subtle change in course. The yacht's autopilot had turned it a few degrees southwest and it was making for the hotel's marina basin and floating casino. The gambling boat was a carnival of lights—violet, pink, tangerine—a hundred-foot-long party craft that was as garish as a South Beach limousine.

I checked my watch and decided Odus might be wrong about disengaging the clock. Traveling at ten knots, the Dragos would smash into the docks a minute or two before three. It would be close.

I had one more question; a simple question, but an answer would reveal a great deal about the content and potency of what was hidden in that ridiculous bag. Because Geness suddenly disappeared inside the cabin, though, I stood for a moment, but then forced myself to sit and appear unruffled. I said to Odus, "The explosive you made, would it detonate if you threw it into a fire? Shake your head or nod, no need to talk."

The twin's reaction was as unexpected as his answer. He began to cry again as he shook his head—*No*—which was the opposite of what I hoped. Low-grade explosives are ignited by combustion. Commercial-, or military-, grade explosives require a sudden shock, such as a blasting cap.

I didn't have to ask details because Odus was already confessing. "Geness did it! He bought nitrate powder, almost six kilograms. We mixed it into a slurry, with motor oil and a binder—"

I interrupted because I was horrified. "He didn't use RDX powder? Just tell me the truth. Shake your head to confirm he didn't."

I was hoping to hell Odus shook his head because RDX is not only a potent explosive, its fumes produce poisonous gas. If the twins had used six kilograms—about thirteen pounds of the stuff—the residual fumes alone could kill us, everyone in the hotel and even the crew of the chopper that was now closing on us at more than a hundred knots.

Instead of answering, Odus started to say, "We made blasting caps, too—" but I stopped listening because Geness had returned to the railing outside the cabin. We had closed within thirty yards of the vessel's stern, close enough for me to see that he carried a bag in one hand and, in the other hand, a . . . *what*?

I stood and touched the magnification button on the thermal unit, then yelled, "Tomlinson, he's got a rifle!" At the same instant, I saw Geness taunt me with his middle finger, then shoulder the weapon.

It was Trapper's junk rifle, presumably, the one with Russian night vision and a homemade silencer. Junk or not, hitting a moving target is markedly easier when the target is traveling a straight line, directly behind the shooting platform. So I hollered a warning, then turned hard to starboard. Seconds later, rather than risk the yacht's wake again, I turned hard to port while I watched the rifle recoil against Geness's shoulder and heard a faint popping sound.

He wasn't firing at us, I realized. He was trying to hit the helicopter, its searchlight a dazzling starburst two hundred yards off his stern.

I was gauging my next turn as Neinabor worked the bolt and fired again, but this time the report was absorbed by the turbine roar of the helicopter as it rocketed past us, so low I felt the shear off its articulated blades. The chopper tilted bow-high, slowing, then circled back toward the stern of the Dragos. Unaware, apparently, his ship was taking fire, the pilot then settled into a slow observation pursuit a hundred yards behind.

Tomlinson was on his feet, waving his arms at the chopper, yelling, "Get away, get away!" which is why he didn't hear me tell him, "Grab something!" and then almost backpedaled overboard when I turned to starboard, continuing to zigzag behind the Dragos.

Beside me, Odus was disintegrating emotionally. Hands over his ears, he was babbling and sobbing and stomping his feet like a child. Even so, as a precaution, I took the pistol from the console and was sliding it into the waistband of my shorts but then stopped. Geness had placed the rifle on the deck and had picked up the bag. I had assumed the bag contained what little ammunition that remained or even the binoculars. At a distance, it looked half the size of a child's backpack—too small to contain explosives.

Now, though, a chilling suspicion came into my mind, so I used the TAM-14 to check the thing for heat. Commercial explosives require a detonating device that, in turn, requires an energy source, often a six-volt battery. Nitrate powders, whatever the proportion, also radiate heat as the mixture fulminates.

Steering the boat with one hand, I had the other on the TAM's pressure switches, hurrying to adjust contrast and magnification, yet the bag remained a dull entity. No sign of heat or chemical glow. Reassuring, but I still wasn't convinced.

Tomlinson was kneeling on the cooler, facing me. "Here they come," he said, then stood and began waving his arms again, yelling, "He's got a gun, you idiots!"

I glanced over my shoulder to see that the helicopter was now approaching cautiously. Then a woman's voice boomed from the aircraft's PA speakers, "Stop your vessels immediately! This is the United States Coast Guard ordering you to stop! Turn off the engines, let us see your hands. Let us see your hands now!"

My eyes swung to the yacht, expecting to see Geness taking careful aim with the rifle. At this distance, there was a fair chance he'd hit the chopper. But, no, maybe he was finally out of ammunition because he was still clutching the bag. No longer in a panic, either, because he took the time to flip us the bird once again.

Was he grinning at me?

I increased magnification. Yes, it wasn't my imagination. Through thermal vision, the man's teeth were clenched in a skeletal grin, then his mandible bones opened wide as if howling—and that's when he swung the bag in a lazy loop off the stern into the water.

I grabbed Tomlinson's shoulder and pulled as I shouted, "Get down!" then buried my weight on the throttle. We had already crossed the Dragos's stern, and its wake lay ahead in cresting, rolling peaks. Normally, I would have slowed and dealt with each wave individually, accelerating up the backside, then slowing before our bow buried itself in the next.

Not now. I ran the boat wide open, and I didn't look back, either, because I didn't want to witness what happened next. I knew what was in that Super Mario bag just as I also knew that Geness would wait until the helicopter was over the thing—and he was safely out of range—before pressing the remote detonator.

The first wave launched us skyward and we ski jumped onto the next wave, the weight of the Whaler crushing through the breaker yet the cresting face nearly flipped us end over end. I steered to the right, trying a surfer's cutback, and reduced throttle until I felt our speed sync with the velocity of the wave. When the comber had jettisoned us into the next wave, I angled left, toward the yacht, and rode the trough until I saw an opening and finally punched through the last breaker, ski jumping again into flat water.

Odus had bounced out of his seat and lay in a fetal position, helpless as a rag doll, bawling on the deck. Tomlinson had battled his way aft and now sat beside me, his body turned toward the helicopter. I don't know if he realized that Geness had set a trap for the helicopter or not, but the man's eyes were opened wide enough to reflect the glare of the fireball before I heard the explosion.

I tried to yell a warning but the sonic pressure sucked the air out of me. Then a wall of heat consumed us and seemed to slingshot our boat forward before releasing us finally into the benign warmth of a June morning.

"Jesus Christ, she's going down!"

In the shock of those microseconds, I couldn't be sure if it was Tomlinson's voice that had yelled those words or my own. No . . . it was Tomlinson, because my first reaction was to look at the yacht, which I expected to be sinking.

It wasn't. The vessel was listing dangerously to starboard but the autopilot continued to steer it inexorably toward the lights of the casino and the dolphin pens that lay somewhere beyond.

Feeling nauseated, I forced myself to look behind us, where the copter's fuselage was spinning on the axis of its own propeller, descending like a bird with a broken wing, yet it still somehow managed to stay aloft.

"No! She's going to make it!" Tomlinson's voice again. "She'll make the beach!"

I wasn't so sure. For the next seconds, I watched, transfixed, as the chopper autorotated downward but also westward, where, half a mile away, a shoal of curving sand glistened. Without realizing it, I had already turned toward the crash site and was gaining speed when the pilot somehow levitated the craft over the last hundred yards of water, avoided the bridge, then augered the fuselage onto the sand so hard I heard the impact from five hundred yards away. Instantly, the aircraft's doors opened, but the crew remained inside while the pilot powered down, running lights still strobing.

The procedural deliberateness told me they probably weren't hurt.

Tomlinson was grinning as he combed nervous fingers through his hair. "A magic pilot, brother! She made it, they're okay!"

I was smiling, too, because of the helicopter, but also because I realized we had survived the explosion's shock wave, which meant the fumes weren't poisonous. Finally, I'd gotten my answer—the bomb hadn't been made of RDX powder.

But then my mood changed when Odus Neinabor, on his knees, peering at the downed aircraft, said, "I wish those asswipes woulda crashed and burned to death. Woulda served them right for trying to stop my brothers."

Touching the throttle, I turned sharply toward the Dragos, then lowered my voice to tell Tomlinson, "He'll be so busy watching the chopper, he won't see us if we pull alongside."

I meant Geness.

"Christ, Doc, you're not going to ram her again. I mean, it was exciting and all, but—"

"I'm getting off," I told him. "You're taking the wheel. And if that little son of a bitch even tries to touch that"—I nodded toward the rifle lying at our feet—"you push him overboard. Promise me. You've got to swear you'll do it."

When my friend didn't respond instantly, I knelt, picked up the rifle and tossed it over the side.

I wasn't smiling anymore.

29

The Dragos Voyager was only six hundred yards from the Regency Hotel marina when I finally steered the Whaler into position along the yacht's starboard side where, earlier, we had punched a hole in its glistening skin. Now, though, the hole had disappeared beneath the waterline, which told me the vessel was sinking fast.

There was another indicator she was going down: the vessel was heeling to starboard, and two scuppers forward of the midship line were jettisoning leakage with the force of fire hoses. Tomlinson noticed, too, as he got ready to take the wheel. It told us the yacht's multiple bilge pumps were fighting a losing battle, and that water had now risen near the forward cabin. Until that moment, I hadn't given the welfare of the sturgeon much thought, despite what I'd told Odus. Now I did.

The word "fingerling" is an inexact term when applied to fish, but the age of Kazlov's sturgeon—if they were still alive—was suddenly important. Sturgeon are an anadromous species, which means that, at a certain stage, they migrate to sea when not spawning. For many sturgeon, the transitional age is two years or older. Until then, their physiology requires fresh water. If the Russian truly had transported finger-length beluga to Florida, the flooding salt water would probably kill the fish even if I managed to take control of the yacht.

"It's two minutes until three," Tomlinson reminded me as we changed places. Apparently, he, too, was worried there might be another explosive aboard the vessel. It wouldn't be the first time Odus had lied to us.

I nodded, but then gestured toward the hotel, where we could see the miniature silhouettes of late-night stragglers and what were probably maintenance staff on the casino boat's upper deck. We didn't have time to stand off and wait for the deadline to pass, I was telling him. If I was going to surprise Geness, I had to act now.

Odus, sitting in front of the steering console, had slipped into catatonia, or so I believed. And he remained motionless when I hurried onto the Whaler's casting platform and motioned to Tomlinson to swing us closer . . . closer . . . until the two vessels were nearly bumping, our speeds in sync, traveling at less than ten knots.

From experience, I knew how difficult it was to keep the boat in position while also contending with wind and volatile updrafts of displaced water. Tomlinson couldn't hold us there long, so I didn't hesitate when the yacht's safety railing descended within reach. Almost within reaching distance, anyway, because at the last instant I had to jump and grab the lowest rail with my right hand, which kicked the bow of the Whaler out from under me.

It was then that Odus sprung into action. As I hung there, fighting to pull myself up, a pair of hands grabbed me around the waist. Then I felt the full weight of the little man as he wrapped his legs around mine. Odus buried his fingernails into my belly and began screaming, "Don't let me go! I can't swim! You know I can't swim!"

My first thought was, *The little bastard's going to shake the pistol free,* because I'd stuffed the weapon into the back of my shorts. There, even if it was dislodged, my underwear would catch it like a safety net—not an ideal place to carry a pistol that has a round chambered yet it was the only place that would leave my hands free.

With a glance, I saw that Tomlinson was helpless. If he abandoned the wheel to grab the twin, the outboard's propeller would automatically kick the boat into a sharp left turn. If that happened, he not only couldn't pull Odus off me, he'd probably be flung overboard.

I don't know what my pal did after that because I had to muster every bit of strength to steady myself and fill my lungs with air. Then, with the twin still screaming, I attempted an impossible one-handed pull-up. Most days of my life, I do pull-ups. Thirty-three without stopping is my personal best, and I commonly do two hundred in descending sets, starting at twenty. But I've never successfully used only one arm—not backhanded, anyway. I didn't succeed this time, either, but I did manage to lift us enough to get my left hand on the boat's deck, then hung there for a moment, aware that Odus was now screaming, "Shoot him, Genesis! Help me, then shoot this fucker!"

Above us, I sensed rather than saw the cabin lights click on. Then I heard the sizzle of a halogen spotlight, which gave me the adrenaline charge necessary to ladder my left hand onto the railing, which was beginning to buckle beneath our weight. After another moment's rest, I kicked free of Odus's legs and got an ankle hooked around a stanchion.

I don't know what the man expected when he jumped on my back to stop me. Because he was a poor swimmer, maybe he assumed I would put his welfare ahead of my own objective or even pity him—an assumption that a sociopath, secure in his preeminence, might make.

If so, Odus had badly confused Tomlinson's kindheartedness with my chillier attitude toward moral cripples, obnoxious assholes and other conveyors of dead-end genetics.

When my leg was around the stanchion, I grabbed Odus's wrist with my left hand and said, "Hands off! *Remember?*" which he didn't hear because he was still hollering for his brother. Even when I levered his hands apart, he continued to cling to my left side. As if on a trapeze, Odus's face then swung into view, his mouth wide in a sustained howl, his eyes venomous, and that's where I hit him with the back of my hand—on the forehead, between the eyes. He screamed a last profanity as he fell, and the only reason I bothered to watch him hit the water was because I feared he would land on Tomlinson.

He didn't.

Seconds later, I was on the foredeck of the yacht, gun in hand, and immediately rolled behind a bow-mounted dinghy to hide from the halogen glare. Because of all the noise Odus had made, I wasn't surprised when I took a peek to see Geness aiming the rifle at me from inside the steering room. The man was so short, he'd had to settle himself into a captain's chair to get an elevated view.

I ducked, not expecting him to fire, but he did. The rifle made a muted *TWHAP*ing sound because of the silencer, and also because Geness had stupidly tried to shoot through the forward window. The Dragos was an oceangoing yacht, which meant all ports were sealed with marine-grade acrylic or tempered glass nearly an inch thick. Even if he'd had me in his sights, the slug would have been knocked askew.

I crawled to the stern of the dinghy, which was attached to a stainless davit cable, before risking another look. The bullet had blown a hole in the window, but the glass hadn't shattered. As Geness shucked another round, he was screaming something at me, but his words were indecipherable in the din of wind and rumbling diesels. I was ready to duck once again, even before he shouldered the rifle, but then I stopped and stood my ground. It was because I saw the man's expression change as he struggled to close the bolt.

This time, I heard Geness when he bellowed, "Why are you *doing this*?"

The twin wasn't screaming at me. He was yelling at God or the rifle, and I knew why. On some rifles the bolt won't close when the magazine is empty. It's a safety feature, particularly on military weapons, that tells the shooter it's time to reload. In a firefight, no matter how experienced the operator, counting rounds is difficult, often impossible.

Kahn had overheard the twins say they were low on ammunition. Finally, finally, it was true—or appeared to be.

But I wasn't going to bet my life on it or Umeko's life—if she was still alive. It was too late in the game to take stupid chances. So, cautiously, I began to move toward the port side of the cabin, which rode at an elevated angle because the vessel was listing, my pistol in both hands as I sighted over the barrel.

Twice, I yell the man's name—"Geness!"—because I wanted his full attention. If he realized that I, too, would have to fire through a wall of glass, he might go on the offensive instead of sitting there like a madman, pounding at the rifle, oblivious to the reason the bolt wouldn't close.

It was too much to hope, though, because Geness was the shrewd one. He was the homicidal one in whose head the monster triplet, Abraham, lived.

When I was midway along the cabin, where the deck was only a meter wide, the monster reappeared. Geness stared at me a moment, his eyes narrowing as if he finally realized my disadvantage. Then, in a rush, he tossed the rifle aside and lunged for the controls, turning to leer at me as he disengaged the autopilot and spun the wheel hard to port.

It wasn't just the torque of the engines that nearly threw me overboard. It was the collective mass of water belowdecks that slammed against the hull and heeled the boat so precariously that when my feet slid under the safety railing the rush of passing salt water tried to wrench me into the sea.

Geness didn't expect the boat to respond that way. He *couldn't* have anticipated what would happen or he wouldn't have done it no matter how desperate he was to buck free of me. When the mass of water shifted, the dual propellers, even though spinning in opposition, locked the rudders into a grinding turn. The turn slowed our speed and caused the bow to nosedive when the weight of water then suddenly flooded toward the front of the boat.

Our sudden dive was like impacting a wall. Once again, I would have been vaulted overboard had my legs and arms not been wrapped around the railing. For long seconds, I held myself there, pleased I'd managed to hang on to the pistol while also dreading Geness's next turn. If he swung hard to starboard, that would be the end of the Dragos because we would capsize. Probably the end of us, too.

It didn't happen.

When the yacht continued its grinding turn to port, I disentangled myself from the rail and crawled on hands and knees toward the cabin's aft bulkhead. There, above me, was the stainless handhold that Odus had grabbed earlier before scrambling down the ladder to join Kahn and Trapper. I used it to get to my feet and took a few seconds to steady my breathing. I also scanned the water for Tomlinson in the Boston Whaler.

No sign of him. A mile away, though, on Big Carlos Pass Bridge, emergency vehicles were already gathering, their lightbars strobing blue and red. Below and to my right was the yacht's afterdeck. It was an expanse of teak that was end-capped by hydraulics and corrugated metal—a cargo elevator when the sliding deck was retracted. Kazlov had built a yacht that fit the needs of a womanizer who was also a smuggler and black marketeer. His genetically modified sturgeon would be somewhere below that deck; tanks probably secured on metal tracks to facilitate loading. But it was something I couldn't think about now.

I took a last look for Tomlinson—still no sign—then made sure the Smith & Wesson's safety was off before sliding along the bulkhead toward a bank of windows. My eyes locked themselves to the pistol barrel, which scanned the flybridge above, then swung to look inside the lighted cabin.

Geness was there. He was sitting beneath a bank of instruments, in a detritus of glass and shattered electronics. His head was down, and he was rocking as he clutched his shoulder, which suggested he'd been injured when the bow had impacted.

I was done making assumptions, though. The deck was bucking as the yacht continued to turn, so my feet gauged the sea's rhythm while I studied the cabin, looking for a solid place to brace myself once I was inside. When I was ready, I threw open the door, pistol at shoulder level, and charged straight to a mahogany rail that separated the steering room from the salon.

It wasn't until I spoke, though, that Geness bothered to look up, his eyes weirdly pearlescent in the muted light, when I yelled, "Where's the girl? Tell me where she is!"

In reply, I heard: "Fuck you! Where's my brother? Tell me how you killed my brother, then maybe we'll discuss the bitch."

It was the whiskey voice of the dead triplet, but I was in no mood to tolerate evasions ascribed to the man's alter ego. I waited for the boat to lift and yaw, then went up two steps to the helm and kicked the rifle out of his reach.

As I did, I heard: "'There are eunuchs born from their mother's womb, or whose testicles have been crushed! But they may not be admitted to the community of the Lord'—Book of Matthew. I'm talking about my brother, asswipe!"

I stood over the man, sighting down the barrel at his forehead. "Move! I want to see what's under you!" He was sitting at an odd angle, maybe shielding something with his thigh. "Do it *now*."

Geness was bleeding from the side of his head, a rivulet of blood that made his face more grotesque when he grinned at me and said, "What are you worried about? A guilty conscience? Here's what you don't understand—I *hope* Exodus is dead. Know why? I'll tell you—"

"Shut up!" I yelled, then glanced to make sure we weren't on a collision course with something, which was the opening Geness was waiting for, apparently. When my eyes strayed, the man rolled and came up with a pistol in his good hand. Loaded or empty, I didn't know—and it didn't matter, because I was on him before he could get his finger on the trigger.

"You're hurting me! I think my collarbone's broken . . . why are you hurting me?"

The monster was gone and Geness had returned, his voice whiny, frail. It took only seconds to wrestle the weapon away, then turn the man on his stomach, hands behind his back.

He continued to plead and complain even when I stood, popped the magazine from his pistol—empty—then checked the chamber—also empty. He'd been using a 9mm Ruger, an inexpensive weapon but dependable. Seeing the gun gave me an idea, but it was something I would take care of later. First, I had to get the yacht under control.

I rushed to the helm, and then slowly . . . slowly backed both throttles, feeling the hull wallow beneath us as the water we were carrying rolled forward. When the Dragos had settled itself, I shifted the diesels into neutral.

Overhead were rows of toggle switches and circuit breakers. According to the amperage gauges, the electrical system was down, which meant the emergency generators had taken over—something they hadn't done while the vessel was moored. *Why?*

I thought about it as I worked at the controls, only vaguely aware of Geness's nonstop babbling. But then I heard:

"Abraham was going to tell you a secret he's never told anyone. Ever. Except our mother, of course. I think it's because you were willing to share your secret with me. Let me sit up, I'll tell you. My goddamn shoulder's broken."

Even if I hadn't forgotten my promise, there was no purpose in continuing the deception, so I ignored him and focused on what I was doing. The sooner I got the boat stabilized, the sooner I could go in search of Umeko.

Now, as I checked the sonar for water depth, the little man was telling me, "I'm not Genesis. Not really. Abraham suffocated me when the triplets were five. Which, of course, *you know* made his mother feel guilty—because he'd swallowed some of her LSD. That's why she gave Abraham my name, so his soul would be resurrected. *Now* will you let me sit up? My fucking shoulder hurts!"

If the man was trying to manipulate me, it wasn't going to work. If he was confessing, he was speaking to a person who neither believed nor had an interest.

In a dunnage cabinet, I found a ten-foot piece of line. I used it to tie his wrists, which I then clove-hitched to his ankles. Only when I was sure the knots were secure did I turn and run to search the lower decks, indifferent to Abraham's shrieks of pain.

30

Finally, I discovered what had happened to Vladimir, Kazlov's bodyguard. Like a wounded animal returning to its den, he had somehow managed to crawl aboard the Dragos, down the companionway to the crew quarters, then into the little cabin that had been his home.

The twins had surprised him there.

Because emergency generators had taken control, the lighting on the lower deck had been automatically dimmed. Even so, I could see that Vladimir had been shot at least four times—once, maybe twice in the head. Not much of a challenge because the Neinabors had taped his hands behind his back, unmoved by the man's crippled arm.

If I had felt even a hint of remorse about tying Abraham, I no longer did.

Shell casings still seesawed on the deck, echoing the movement of the waves, as I noted family photos, a shot of Kazlov and Vladimir grinning at the camera, and a couple of framed military decorations.

Something else I found, when I lifted the man's arm, puzzled by all the blood—my Randall knife. The twins had added to their fun by stabbing him. The scabbard I found nearby on the deck.

I didn't linger. I hurried out the door, pausing only to retrieve the last pair of surgical gloves from my pocket. Fingerprints on the two semiauto pistols were a concern.

I dreaded what I expected to find as I went through the vessel, throwing open doors, calling the woman's name. That's why I hesitated before checking what I guessed to be the guest quarters. Even though the cabin was near the middle of the vessel, water was already sloshing at my ankles, which made it more difficult to force the door open. Finally, I did, though—and there she was.

I called, "Umeko! Are you okay?" not expecting the body that lay curled on the floor to move. But the woman *did* move. As I stood blinking in the doorway, she responded by lifting her head in surprise, then made eager cooing sounds through the tape that covered her mouth.

I knelt, lifted her onto the bed, and soon she was sitting up, rubbing her wrists, dazed but trying to make sense of it all, saying, "I thought you would be dead. I thought they'd killed everyone but me. And he was *going* to shoot me! He had a gun to my head—but then the boat hit something, and he ran out the door!"

She was talking about Abraham or Odus, I couldn't be sure, and about what had happened after I'd put a rifle round into the yacht's hull.

"The explosion—I thought I was dreaming but I wasn't, was I? You were right about a bomb all along. Lying here, I figured out Sakura must have taken Father's phone when our people tried to warn us—"

"We'll talk later," I said, trying to calm her, although she was right. Somehow, Lien Bohai's intel network had found out too late about the twins. Sakura had to have texted the information to Kazlov, her not-so-secret lover, to whom she had recently been sold. That's why Vladimir—ever loyal—had refused to tell me his boss's informant.

I gave Umeko's shoulder a squeeze and stood. "Stay here. It'll take you a while to get your balance. I'll be right back."

"No!" The woman grabbed my arm and tried to stand but then sat heavily on the bed. It was only then that I noticed her left eye was swollen almost closed and her lips were bruised.

I put my hands on her shoulders and felt her body convulse, but she still did not give in. "Sit here for just two minutes. You'll be safe—I promise. There's something I've got to check."

What I wanted to see was the cargo area and the engine room—and not just because I was curious about the fate of Viktor's sturgeon. What the lunatic Neinabors had failed to consider when they'd decided to "free" the casino's dolphins was that the yacht would poison Estero Bay if it crashed into the docks and flooded. I didn't know how many thousands of pounds of fuel the vessel still carried, but I wasn't going to add to this nightmare by letting the goddamn boat sink.

When I forced open the engine-room hatch, though, one look told me there was nothing I could do to prevent the vessel from going down. It also forever changed my opinion of Boston Whalers. Ours handled like a truck, but it was unbeatable when it came to sinking larger boats. The hole we had smashed in the side was bigger than I could have guessed and the inflow was overpowering the pumps. Diesel engines can continue to run underwater—for a short time, at a shallow depth. But a floating object cannot support a weight greater than the volume it displaces, and this boat was slowly being forced to the bottom.

As I jogged toward the cargo area, my brain considered, then discarded, a jumbled list of options. When I stepped into the cargo room, though, my synapses were instantly cleared by what I found inside.

The twins had been wrong when they'd said the yacht carried a thousand fingerling sturgeon. What Kazlov had brought for Lien to inspect were several hundred specimens, most of the fish a pound or more in weight, from what I saw, which suggested they were mature enough to survive salt water. They were expertly housed in oversized tanks, and in a room outfitted to transport valuable exotics—or a billion dollars' worth of beluga seed stock. It had everything needed: a Multi-Temp water chiller, what looked like a custom SCADA oxygen monitor, an oxygen cone injection system, plus a Bio-Weave emergency backup that was in operation now.

Even so, the young sturgeon bobbed to the surface like corks as I sloshed past, snouts breaching the surface as if starved for air—which they certainly were not.

All of the fish had not survived, of course. Kazlov wouldn't have expected zero casualities. Sturgeon are jumpers—boaters are injured regularly by leaping mature sturgeon—and several had jumped to their deaths. Their bodies now floated around my ankles as I returned to the watertight hatch. Because I am a stickler for cleanliness in my own lab, my mind shifted automatically to how Kazlov would have sluiced the decks clean, had he lived.

Near the door to the cargo room was my answer: a raw-water pumping system that fed a fire engine–sized hose. Above the mount that secured the nozzle were two switches that activated the cargo elevator and the retractable deck above me.

For a moment, I stood there, looking from the switches, to the hose, from the hose, to the switches. For some reason, that unlikely combination dislodged a word from my subconscious: *counterintuitive.*

No . . . it wasn't a word, it was an avenue of thought. It had to do with any contrary action that produced an unlikely result. To transfer energy to an enemy vehicle, you don't slow to lessen the impact, you *accelerate.* When a small boat has flooded, you don't plug the scupper below the waterline, you *open* the scupper, then throw the throttle forward and let the propeller suction drain the hull empty.

In that instant, I knew exactly what I had to do to save the sinking yacht, and maybe even save Viktor Kazlov's valuable sturgeon.

First, I figured out how to unlock the safety shield that guarded the switches to the cargo elevator and the retractable deck. After I had pulled both levers, a clattering bell gave a five-second warning and the roof overhead began ratcheting inboard. As it did, I stared upward as the room became a planetarium, revealing a slow universe of stars. Beneath a third switch, a little brass plate read TRN/DN/UP, so I engaged that lever, too. This time, it sounded like a garbage truck was backing into the area as a four-foot section of transom slid down into the inner hull. Much lower, even another few feet, and the sea would have flooded the area.

That's not what I wanted. But not yet.

Unscrewing the fire hose from its four-inch spigot was more difficult than expected. The brass fitting had corroded, but I found a crowbar. When the hose was free, I spun the valve open so that salt water began jetting into the room at a startling rate. Commercial units can pump four thousand gallons a minute, and Kazlov had equipped his vessel with the best.

When the deck overhead was fully retracted, and with the room flooding around my knees, I wished the fish good luck, then slammed and sealed the watertight hatch behind me.

To rescue a foundering vessel and the fish trapped therein, flooding the cargo area wasn't just an unlikely solution, it was the *only* solution—and it would work, if I made every second count.

Counterintuitive. It was something I didn't have time to explain to Umeko when I grabbed her by the hand and yelled, "Follow me. We've got a lot to do."

31

When I was sure the woman was behind me, I went up the companionway steps two at a time and didn't slow until just before my eyes topped the floor of the salon. My sudden caution was due to a premonition that Abraham Neinabor had freed himself and would use some makeshift weapon to brain me.

Like most premonitions, though, it was groundless. The triplet was tied where I'd left him, but he had managed to roll onto his side. So he was glowering at me as I rushed to the helm, checked the area around us, then the depth sonar, before levering the engines into gear. I wanted the boat moving but was also aware I had to give the cargo room time to fill before increasing speed.

Something I should have intuited but didn't was Umeko's reaction when she entered the cabin and saw the man who had beaten her. I heard her stop at the top of the stairs and then in a whisper say, "You *animal*!"

Instantly, I shifted into neutral and turned around.

Neinabor was staring at the woman, openmouthed. He had interpreted her expression accurately so was hollering, "Keep her away from me! My shoulder's broken, keep that bitch away!" as Umeko walked toward him, eyes glassy, as if in a trance. Before she could get to him, though, I intercepted her and pulled her close.

"You're better than that," I said, lips to her temple.

In my arms, the woman's body was trembling muscle cordage and heat. "You don't understand . . . you don't know what he did to me. What *they* did to me."

"No. But right now, I need your help—again." I pulled her closer. "I do know how strong you are."

"Some of the things . . . what he said to me . . . there was . . . there was no *reason*." She paused, then stiffened. "What happened to the other one? Is he still on the boat—does he have a gun?"

A rhythmic thumping between the shoulders is supposed to comfort even adults. It reminds our subconscious of the womb and our mother's heartbeat. "He's gone," I told her. "You're safe now."

The woman kept her face buried against me. I don't think she trusted herself to look at Neinabor, who lay tied on the deck and was now shouting, "What was I supposed to do? Let you interfere? For once, try to put yourself in my shoes!"

I squeezed the woman tighter when she tried to wrestle away. "*Listen* to me. This boat's sinking. We have to run her aground. Then you have a tough decision to make. The man who helped you tonight when the power went out, the man in the white tuxedo—you said he was very kind. He's waiting for me in a small boat. I've got to get off before police show up. I can explain later but my guess is you know why."

Umeko's face tilted upward, her fixation on Neinabor suddenly broken. "Tomlinson?"

I nodded.

"I want to go with you. Don't leave me with him, you can't."

She pulled away and looked around the room, accessing the situation, maybe, but definitely back in control.

I waved her toward the helm. "Come on. I'll show you what we have to do."

The yacht had drifted southeast, still in the channel, bow turned so that we faced the casino boat, its lights a violet smear on the water. A few degrees to the right was the bridge. I slid into the captain's chair, put the boat in gear, but continued to scan the windows until I saw what I'd been hoping to see: the faint sheen of an outboard's wake and then the storkish silhouette of Tomlinson. He was standing at the Whaler's console, applying loose cover only a few boat lengths away.

I flicked my running lights in acknowledgment. He waved—but his body language lacked energy. It wasn't difficult to guess the reason. If Odus Neinabor was aboard, he wasn't standing.

I said nothing to Umeko, though. Instead, I touched my finger to the screen of the GPS and explained, "Just outside the channel, the water shoals to less than three feet. It's a spoil area created by the dredge. I'm going to build up some speed and run us aground. I'll warn you just before we hit. I want you on the deck with your feet braced against a forward bulkhead. Got that?"

The woman nodded while, behind us, Abraham hollered, "Hey—what about *me*?"

I was pleased she didn't bother to turn. It demonstrated a stubborn refusal to be bullied that told me Umeko was going to be okay. It might take weeks, or months or even years. But she would make it.

I nudged the throttles forward—*tap-tap-tap*—and felt the yacht's front end lift . . . and continue to lift as water poured toward the stern. When the hull had settled, I tapped the throttles again, and the bow lifted enough so that, through the pilot window, it looked like we were motoring into a haze of stars and distant lightning.

Umeko turned toward me, startled. "We *are* sinking."

"Yeah—but not in deep water. I want the hull so flooded the next high tide won't set it adrift. Even then, with diesels this size, we should be able to plow until it's shallow enough I can step off and walk to Tomlinson's boat. A tug can drag her off later when the damage is fixed."

From her expression, I knew she was deciding whether to stay and deal with the police or leave with me. I tapped the throttles again, alert for the slow, gelatinous response that would tell me the hull couldn't float any more weight.

It was time.

I told the lady, "Go to the salon, look out the back window and tell me what you see. Then grab something and hang on tight."

Above me was a bank of toggle switches that controlled the outboard lights. When the woman was braced against the aft bulkhead, peering out, I illuminated the deck with spotlights, then pressed the throttles forward another two inches. Beneath us, the roaring torque of the diesels caused the hull to shudder, the windows to vibrate, as we gained speed, bow lifting. For a spooky moment, I thought the yacht was going to tumble over backward like a rearing horse.

Standing to keep my balance, I hollered, "What's happening back there?"

I'm not a particularly sensitive person, but I did feel an emotional jolt when Umeko made a whooping sound of surprise, then called, "There's water pouring out of the back of the boat, a waterfall almost. And, Doc . . . Doc! There are fish . . . I'm *serious*. Like they're swimming downstream—I can see their tails moving. Dozens . . . no . . . there are *hundreds* of . . . my God . . ."

I could feel the woman's eyes on my back as she turned to look at me. "Those are sturgeon! You're releasing Viktor Kazlov's hybrid sturgeon!"

No . . . actually, they were her sturgeon. But that could wait.

Because I whispered, she didn't hear me when I replied, "Please don't tell the Florida FWC." A moment later, though, I made sure she heard my warning call to get down on the deck because we had left the channel and were headed for the shoals.

I killed our lights, then began to throttle down slowly . . . slowly. I didn't bother to watch the sonar because I knew how abruptly the depth would change. The first jolt of our propellers touching bottom would tell me what to do. Seconds later, when it happened—*THUD-THUD*—I pulled the throttles back to dead idle . . . waited for our wake to balloon beneath us . . . then jammed the throttles forward full bore, feeling the hull lift as it slammed aground, then continued, careening wildly to starboard, hearing the friction scream of metal on metal as the diesels tractored us another twenty yards, gradually slowing, then teetering to a stop.

When the yacht had settled immobile, angled steep as an incline, I switched off the engines and flicked on the cabin light. The silence was so abrupt that I felt the sensation of air molecules around my ears communicating the heat of the engines, Abraham Neinabor's groans and the outboard clatter of Tomlinson in the Whaler approaching off our stern.

Then Umeko's voice: "Are you okay, Doc? My God, we hit hard." She was on her feet, experimenting with her balance on the sloping deck.

I had wedged both pistols and my Randall knife between the cushions of the chair. After I retrieved them, and as I unloaded the Smith & Wesson, I told her, "If you're staying here, we need to talk. But not in front of—" I gestured toward the triplet.

Before she could respond, I stopped her, saying, "Give it some thought before you decide." Then I knelt and cut Neinabor's hands and ankles free.

He didn't expect that. It scared him and also made him suspicious. Then he was even more frightened when he saw that I was holding the Ruger in my right hand, the Smith in my left. Not aiming, just letting them rest in my hands.

"Hey! Don't do anything crazy—don't shoot me." The man began crabbing away as I stood over him. "I won't tell the police what you did to my brother. I . . . I promise."

"Tell them everything," I said. "I hope you do. If you want to give me credit for releasing all those sturgeon—*alive*—that's great."

Because Neinabor actually was intelligent, he was confused for only a moment. "Really. You got them out of those tanks? But when? How? I mean . . . that's what I was doing—trying to save animals those leeches have been destroying before it's too late."

Aware that Umeko was trying not to notice I wore surgical gloves, I knelt, now holding both weapons by the barrel. "Go below and check for yourself."

The twin's crazy eyes were desperate for the refuge of a new fantasy—or a different form of martyrdom—but he wasn't convinced. "You're letting me go? I don't get it."

I spun the Ruger, then the Smith, within the triplet's reach and told him, "If it makes you feel safer, take these with you."

Meaning the gun that Tomlinson had used to kill Abdul Armanie and the gun that had probably put an end to Vladimir's life.

When Umeko and I were outside, wading through knee-deep water toward the Whaler and home, I didn't explain to her why I had left a homicidal maniac with empty pistols—even though I knew I could trust her. It's because of the way she responded after I warned, "If you leave in the boat with us, it means you'll have to lie to the authorities. Several lies—and convincingly, too."

"Are you kidding?" the Chinese aquaculturist told me, no hint of smile in her voice. "It's what I've been paid to do my entire adult life."

EPILOGUE

It wasn't until weeks later, at South Seas Plantation on Captiva Island, that I finally confirmed the truth about Tomlinson, the unlikely killer. Two hours before the revelation, though, at Dinkin's Bay, I was summarizing for a lady friend something I'd written in my lab journal the previous night:

When people of value tell me they could never live in Florida because they'd miss The Seasons, I point out that the peninsula cycles through solstices and equinoxes in the breadth of a single summer day.

In July, at sunrise, wind off the Tortugas makes landfall with a penetrating March chill. By 2 p.m. the heat is equatorial; nimbus clouds thermal skyward. At late afternoon, the world stills beneath an autumnal overcast. Odors linger, temperature plummets. Then a blizzard of rain booms through the palms; an electric gale that chases the sane indoors to await the drizzling thaw of sunset.

I was explaining this to the lady because we had just escaped a storm after a day on my boat. We'd spent the morning near the Estero River, close enough to Big Carlos Pass to confirm that after three weeks waiting for a full moon the Dragos had finally been plugged and hauled for repairs. No diesel spill reported, which was significant because the media had focused full attention on anything associated with Vanderbilt Island and the murderous events that June night.

That's one reason we didn't stray too close to the shoal where the yacht had been grounded nor the beach where the body of Odus Neinabor had been found. I'm not superstitious, but the maxim about "criminals always returning" was enough to keep me at a distance. Not that I felt any guilt. Abraham Neinabor, under his legal name Genesis, would carry enough of that into the courtroom for both of us. No—all three of us, because I had to include Tomlinson.

I still couldn't get my mind around the fact he had shot Abdul Armanie even though I had *seen* it happen. And the man hadn't said anything to convince me otherwise. Not that I had asked—even discussing the subject was dangerous. The police had their killers—the twins from California—and that was enough.

Another reason we didn't venture closer to the Gulf was that I'd brought along mask and fins. I knew it was unlikely I would find any of Kazlov's sturgeon in the maple red water at the river's mouth. And I didn't. But someday, some fisherman would—and who knew how it would impact the caviar industry twenty or thirty years from now?

Until then, the Florida Department of Law Enforcement had impounded Kazlov's possessions, presumably his computer, hard drives and anything else that might have rendered some clarity to the night in which two eco-fanatics had murdered four people despite the objections of their intended accomplices.

The fate of those accomplices, a jury would also have to decide.

It was a topic that had devoured my time and attention for too long, and I was tired of it. There is nothing like salt water to sluice away the weight of a land-based existence, which is why I had asked the lady to join me on the boat. So we had explored, I had snorkeled, and she had seemed to enjoy her first fly-casting lesson.

Then the storm came. We'd raced its lightning rim back to Dinkin's Bay and the safety of my stilthouse and lab. Up until then, the lady and I had behaved as friends, by mutual agreement. Nothing more. Ever. And we meant it.

Storms, though, *are* transitional. I've never read a research paper on the subject but it is possible the human nervous system can be excited by an ionic pelting of electrons and raindrops. And when your clothes are soaked and you've chugged a glass of beer over ice, one thing certainly can lead to another.

And it did.

Now the lady's bra hung catawampus on my bedpost, each grapefruit-sized cup promising a geography of warmth and weight that my happy hands had liberated—and were *still* exploring. Apparently, though, I'd put our second coupling at risk by opening my damn mouth about why Florida is a great place to live no matter the season.

"You really tell people that, Doc? The thing about the solstices and autumn skies? I've never really thought of you as . . . Well, I'll put it this way—if you have a feminine side, *I've* never seen it."

I replied, "Feminine what?" because my focus was elsewhere, so she had to repeat the question.

After a battle with my conscience, I told her, "Nope. I made it up last night after working late in the lab. Lately, I've become a terrible liar. I hear myself saying things so outrageous it makes me cringe. I think it's the people I hang out with. One person, anyway."

The lady said, "Huh?" and tried to sit up, but I pulled her back. "Not you. Don't worry." Then I disappeared beneath the bedsheet to continue my explorations.

A minute later, though, I realized I hadn't ruined the mood by talking. Physiologies are different, and some of us need more time to recover than others.

I heard: "Ooohh. I'm still sort of, you know . . . sensitive. It's just the way I am after I—*you know*."

I was learning. The lady's "you know" was unlike any in my experience. If there's such a thing as a grand mal seizure with a happy ending, it was this woman's "you know."

So I smiled and said, "I see!" Then told her, "Let's take a break. I've got more caviar, fresh from Mote Marine Labs. And mangoes in the fridge—a ripe Julie and a Nam Doc Mai. Mack and Jeth just made a mango run to Pine Island."

"I like those guys," the lady nodded, reaching for her bra, then hip-canting naked toward the door. "Everyone at the marina is so friendly and . . . *normal*."

I was thinking, *Why disappoint her with the truth?* which is when the day's mood was irrevocably changed.

Outside, I heard *clang-clang*—the ship's bell I'd hung because I'm tired of being surprised by visitors. Then, from the kitchen, I heard the lady say, "Oh no. It's *him* again."

She could have meant any one of the three investigators, from various agencies, who had stopped by almost daily for the last three weeks. So I slipped into khaki shorts, a blue chambray shirt and was still hopping into my boat shoes when I exited to take a look.

I'd thought I was done with their questions. Two investigators had insinuated they were finished—probably exhausted from hearing the same repetitive answers from four primary witnesses: Tomlinson, me, Darius Talas and Umeko Tao-Lien. And an unlikely fifth had, apparently, corroborated some of what we claimed: the billionaire widow, Sakura Lien. Then the woman had vanished at the first opportunity rather than risk more questioning—Switzerland, some said, although I now knew for a fact it was not true.

As Umeko had pointed out, Europe would have been a wiser choice than China, where, tannin beauty or not, Sakura might have been shot or beaten to death for murdering one of the country's most illustrious (and cruelest) businessmen.

When I got to the kitchen, though, I was relieved to discover it wasn't another cop who had clanged the bell.

"Tomlinson," the lady told me as she hurried past to get into her clothes. "Why don't you just adopt him and be done with it?"

"He won't answer to a dog whistle, and they don't make shock collars his size," I replied, not surprised by her attitude. The lady had been smitten by my pal not so long ago. But then he had gotten stoned or drunk, or both, and had slipped his hand down her bikini on the pretense of helping her up onto a surfboard. It was outrageous, she thought, for a guy to hit on a girl his best friend had brought to the beach.

I liked that about her; the memory had spurred my fingers to action when they'd hesitated over her bra snap. Loyalty should not require a shock collar.

It is something I have stopped reminding Tomlinson about. He had remained outside, standing on the boardwalk, waiting for me to appear. Rather than opening the door, though, I called through the screen, *"What now?"*

Instead of answering, he pointed at his watch, then at the setting sun, as if I was late for some appointment. Finally, he yelled, "Later than nine-thirty and we might miss something!"

I thought for a moment and then said, "Damn it," because I'd forgotten that I had agreed to join him on Captiva Island for some mysterious event he had refused to reveal.

Behind me, I felt the woman's fingertips trace the curvature of my spine, from shoulder to buttocks. "Something wrong?" she said into my ear.

I told her what was wrong. Then stood there like the fool I am and watched the lady's smile vanish because I did not invite her along. "It's Tomlinson's deal," I added as if that were explanation enough.

"I see," the lady said, an autumn and vernal chill in her voice. "Well, when you and Huck Finn get off the river, make sure and give me a call."

Then, for the second time in two months, I watched my handsome, curvaceous biologist friend, Emily Marston, march down the stilthouse steps and out of my life.

For three weeks, Tomlinson had barely said a word to me. He had smoked and moped and stewed to salve his scars, the lone exception being the day he had staggered to the beach, whistling Buffett songs, and tried to play grab ass with Emily.

Not that he didn't stop by the lab. On days he didn't disappear in *No Más*, he visited regularly. Which also irritated the lady because he'd dragged his guilt—or whatever the hell was burdening him—inside my home like a silent weight.

On this hot July night, though, he was suddenly chatty for reasons I had yet to discover. And even more irritating than usual. As I drove my pickup west on San-Cap Road, past ball-diamond lights, Bowman's Beach, then over the bridge onto Captiva, he was lecturing me on romance and my romantic failings.

I wasn't in the best of moods to begin with. Now the man risked crossing a dangerous line.

He was telling me, "The reason you choose women schooled in the sciences is because they feel obligated to at least *pretend* sex can be recreational. Like it has no more importance than two primates playing drop the soap. Which can be a healthy attitude, if you actually believe it. But they don't. So they're torn between what they think and what they want to believe—just like you. No wonder your love life is so messed up. You're screwing yourself by screwing *yourself*."

The man paused, looked over his shoulder to check for cops, then popped open a fresh Corona. "See what I'm going for here?"

My truck's an old Chevy, white on turquoise, not built like the trucks of today. My hands were gripping the steering wheel so tightly, I realized, the plastic hoop was bending.

I said, "You're going for another black eye? I'd suggest something I'd enjoy even more, but I don't want to visit you in the hospital another goddamn time and listen to the goddamn nurses tell me how lovable you are while they jockey for the honor of wiping your ass."

That caused the man to tilt his head back and laugh, snort, laugh again, then whack me on the shoulder. "That's so . . . *Fordian*. You can say stuff like that and not even crack a smile—a lot of people wouldn't know you're joking." He cleared his throat. "No, but seriously, Doc. The reason I—"

I interrupted, "Tomlinson, why are we on Captiva? You still haven't told me. Why are we going to South Seas Plantation? And why the hell did you make me bring this?" I picked up the TAM thermal unit and slapped it on the seat beside me. "I gave up a fun night with a smart, fun lady—a lady with *morals*, by the way, which is probably why you don't approve. So, at least have the courtesy to explain why I shouldn't dump your irritating hippie ass at the pool bar right now."

Tomlinson had been looking at the lighted 'TWEEN WATERS INN sign as we passed. "Whoa," he said, turning to face me. "That was eerie. You totally read my mind. At the very moment you said it, I was thinking, 'Pool bar at 'Tweenies. Stop for a beverage on the way home.' Weird, huh?" The man smiled, maybe to let me know he was playing his stoned-hipster role, maybe not.

I pressed, "South Seas Resort is where the Dragon Woman has been hiding out, isn't it? That's why you won't tell me."

It was a question I had never asked even though I suspected that Sakura had spent a night or two aboard *No Más*. The man knew too many details about her testimony for there not to be an intimate connection.

Still smiling, he shook his head, but then the smile faded. "I finally figured out what happened that night. The night the dude from Iran was shot. Armanie."

It had been three weeks, but I still didn't feel confortable discussing the subject in more than a vague way. "Yeah. Someone shot Armanie, then someone lied to protect a woman—a murderess, likely—probably in the hopes you'd get her clothes off down the road."

Slowly, a smile reappeared, but it was his serious smile. "With you, Doc, the fastest way to convince you of the truth is to make all the data available. Let your eyes communicate the results directly to your brain. So that's what we're going to do. Tonight, the Psychiatric Practitioners of Minnesota are having a cocktail party at the pool by the T-dock. It's the first night of their annual convention. Bring this with you"—he tapped the thermal monocular—"and we'll both relive what really happened that night."

"Psychiatrists," I said, trying to understand.

"And behavioral scientists, psychologists. Some of the best in the world. Plus their husbands and wives, of course. Mostly wealthy, not that I would care, normally, but it can be an indicator of clinical success."

"You mean, relive it *clinically*," I said, and was suddenly no longer irked with my old friend. In fact, I was touched because I finally understood what he had in mind. The man felt so ashamed of what he'd done that chaotic night, he wanted me to experience, with a physician's help, what had driven him to pull the trigger.

Tomlinson stared at me for a moment and then started to laugh.

I said, *"What?"* totally confused.

He replied, "You'll see."

The temptation was to boot the man out of the car and call Emily to beg forgiveness. Instead, I concentrated on my driving.

South Seas Plantation, at the northern tip of Captiva Island, is one of Florida's historic treasures. Almost five hundred acres of tropic theater that, over the years, has provided luxuriant solitude to luminaries from around the world. The resort is isolated by water on three sides and a security gate to the south. We were a mile past the gate, almost in sight of the Plantation House and swimming pool cabanas, before Tomlinson got control of himself.

He sat back in his seat and said, "Doc, you are so totally overthinking this! We're not going to a hotshot pool party to be analyzed by a group of"—he stopped to reorganize his thoughts, or to swallow a spasm of laughter, then tried again—"Don't think of it in terms of shrinks from Minneapolis. Keep it basic. Here's the way I filed it when I heard they were meeting: *blond lady doctors with really nice tits*. Simple, see? Real or fake, who cares? It shows their hearts are in the right place. Most of the wives are Scandinavian stock, too, so we're going to see some of the Gopher State's finest." He pointed to a parking area. "I scoped it out last night. From that row of trees, you can see the pool."

Two minutes later, we were standing behind a screen of cabanas and young coconut palms. On the other side, a steel drum band played while forty or fifty people milled around a pool of luminous jade, drinks in hand. Most wore shorts and tropical shirts, but several women were in swimsuits and wraps. And near the pool steps, a covey of five blondes were chatting away waist-deep in water.

"Okay," I said. "Now what?"

Tomlinson pressed the thermal monocular into my hand. "Take a look at the ladies through this."

I couldn't believe what I was hearing. "Are you insane? I'm not some damn Peeping Tom—"

"Doc," my pal said, "I wouldn't ask you to do it if it wasn't important."

I started to argue, but he interrupted, "You were wrong about Sakura staying here—but she did spend two nights on my boat. That's how I figured out why you saw what you saw that night. Until then, I was pretty down, man—*offended*—because you immediately assumed the worst. You've got reasons not to trust me, I admit it, but I still wish—" Instead of finishing, he shrugged, then chewed at a strand of his shoulder-length hair.

Shaking my head, I put the monocular to my eye for a few seconds, then said, "Okay, so what am I supposed to be looking for? Sakura?"

"Take a real look," Tomlinson insisted. "Sakura flew to Spain three days ago, so don't worry about that. Take a *close* look, focus the damn thing, and think about the night you saw me shoot Armanie."

So I used the focus, I fiddled with the contrast, and then, abruptly, my breathing changed because I understood why Tomlinson had brought me here.

To confirm he was right, though, I checked the pool again without the monocular. I saw five women, one with a hibiscus behind her ear, two with particularly gorgeous breasts.

Then I tried the thermal-sensing monocular again and saw *three* women chatting with what now appeared to be two males, thinly built, each with a warming gloss of long hair.

I turned to Tomlinson, who was nodding but appeared a little sad. "Silicone doesn't register a heat signature," I said softly, then cringed at my own obtuseness. "My God—I should have realized. Breast implants! You weren't protecting Sakura because she saw you shoot Armanie. You were protecting her because *she* pulled the trigger! Why didn't you tell me she'd had—"

Tomlinson held up his hand, gazing at all the pretty ladies from Minnesota. "It doesn't matter now, *hermano*. Let's get a drink, pick out a couple of new doctor buddies and take them home to the lab. Maybe after a couple of rums, I'll explain something I know for sure: the Dragon Woman's heart definitely *is not* in the right place."

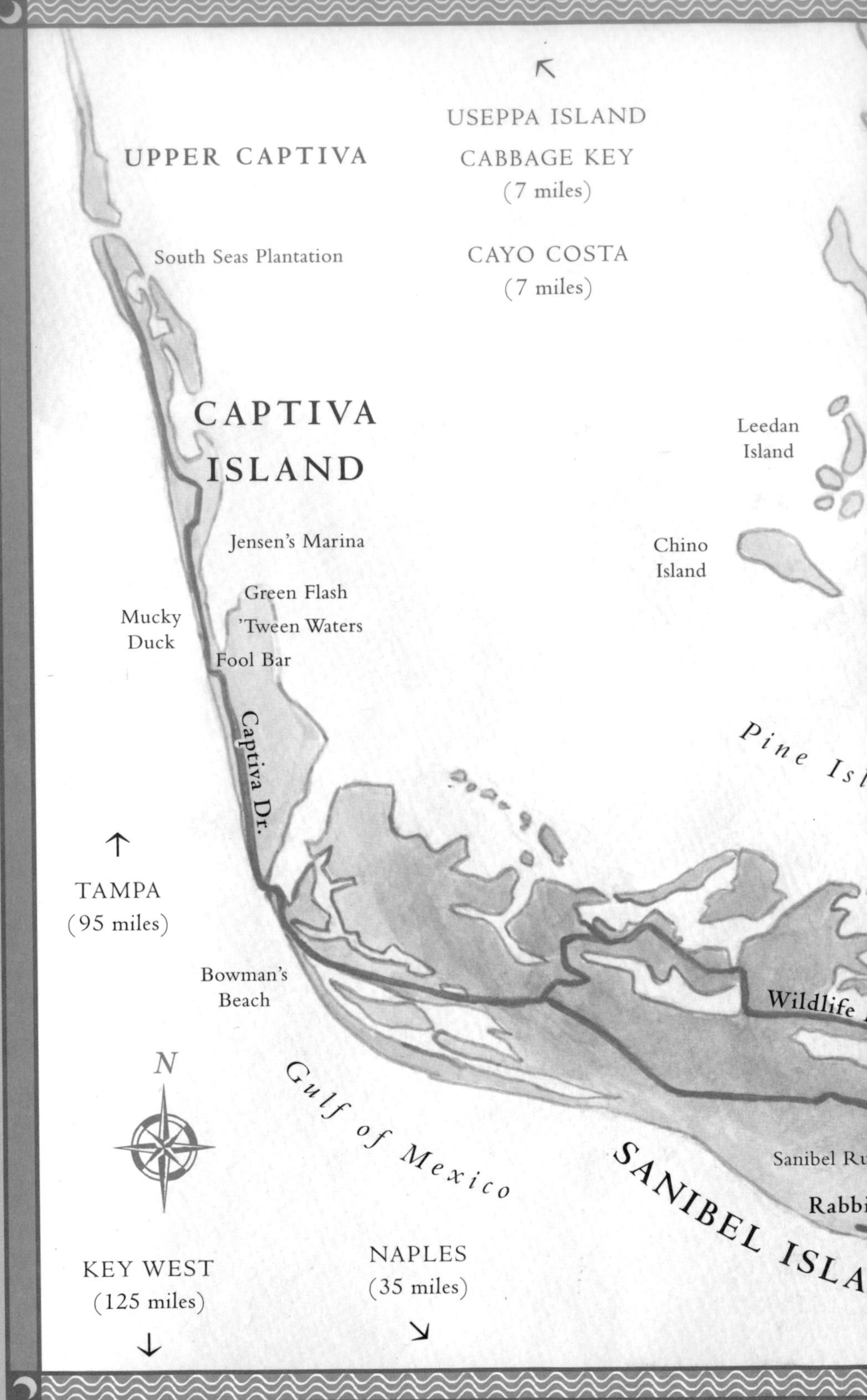
USEPPA ISLAND
UPPER CAPTIVA
CABBAGE KEY
(7 miles)
South Seas Plantation
CAYO COSTA
(7 miles)
CAPTIVA
ISLAND
Leedan
Island
Jensen's Marina
Chino
Island
Green Flash
Mucky
Duck
'Tween Waters
Fool Bar
Captiva Dr.
TAMPA
(95 miles)
Bowman's
Beach
N
Gulf of Mexico
SANIBEL ISLA
KEY WEST
(125 miles)
NAPLES
(35 miles)